knowledge of the child during the past 15 years. This volume lives up to the expectations that many of us have come to have for this annual publication which keeps us abreast of the current analytic thinking."
—A. M. A. JOURNAL OF DISEASES OF CHILDREN

"This annual has an eminent place among psychoanalytic periodicals. Year after year it publishes high-level contributions to psychoanalytic theory and practice. The wide variety of articles in this volume proves that this latest collection of papers maintains, and by its innovations even raises, the previous standards set by this series."—CURRENT MEDICAL DIGEST

"This annual continues to maintain its customary standard of excellence, presenting an epicurean assortment of papers on psychoanalytic theory, research, and application. It is highly recommended for all professionals in the field."—JOURNAL OF CLINICAL AND EXPERIMENTAL PSYCHOPATHOLOGY

"As usual, the high quality of the papers we have learned to expect from *The Psychoanalytic Study of the Child* is maintained in this number. This publication is highly recommended, as are all the previous publication of this Annual."—MENTAL HYGIENE

"Again the editors of this renowned annual publication have compiled a group of outstanding clinical and theoretical papers. This volume presents diverse subject matter applicable to the understanding and the treatment of both children and adults, integrates traditional psychoanalytical concepts with the new contributions of ego psychology, and exemplifies most of its theory with rich clinical material."—YOUR FAMILY

The Psychoanalytic Study
of the Child

VOLUME XVI

The Psychoanalytic Study of the Child

VOLUME XVI

INTERNATIONAL UNIVERSITIES PRESS, INC.

New York   New York

Manufactured in the United States of America

CONTENTS

Contributions to Psychoanalytic Theory

Aspects of Normal and Pathological Development

Clinical Contributions

CONTRIBUTIONS TO PSYCHOANALYTIC THEORY

A STUDY OF THE PSYCHOLOGICAL PROCESSES IN PREGNANCY AND OF THE EARLIEST MOTHER-CHILD RELATIONSHIP

I. Some Propositions and Comments

GRETE L. BIBRING, M.D., THOMAS F. DWYER, M.D.,
DOROTHY S. HUNTINGTON, PH.D., and
ARTHUR F. VALENSTEIN, M.D. (Boston)[1]

In an article titled "Some Considerations of the Psychological Processes in Pregnancy" (G. Bibring, 1959) a historical account was given of the clinical observations and theoretical assumptions which led us to undertake the "Study of Psychological Processes in Pregnancy and of the Earliest Mother-Child Relationship."[2] This research is now approaching its last phase, and a number of reports on different aspects of it are currently in preparation.

The following presentation is not intended to be comprehensive. Its purpose is threefold: (1) to indicate briefly some of the reflections and observations which led to this research on pregnancy; (2) to report some aspects of the research, its main hypothesis and a general outline of its design; (3) to discuss some special ideas and speculations derived both from the actual material and data of this research as well as from certain findings and theoretical considerations gained in our experience with patients in psychoanalysis. Some of these considerations are not an intrinsic part of the main course of our investigation and therefore might not be proven by it directly, or they may concern aspects of our findings for which sufficient data are not yet available. Nonetheless, we decided to present part

1 Psychiatric Service of the Beth Israel Hospital, Boston, and the Department of Psychiatry, Harvard Medical School.

2 Supported by a grant from the Filene Foundation, Boston, and by grant #M-1393, United States Public Health Service, National Institutes of Mental Health.

9

of them in this form because they seem to us of general interest for the psychological understanding of pregnancy and motherhood and a useful introduction to the various other reports which will follow.

One of the teams of our Psychiatric Service in the Beth Israel Hospital, Boston, which is a general hospital, gave us the opportunity of observing and treating patients from the Prenatal Clinic.[3] We became increasingly aware that these women seemed to be, comparatively, more severely disturbed on the average than patients from other clinics of our hospital. However, these patients, in spite of the rather alarming type of interview material, did not show a proportional degree of disturbance in their history preceding the pregnancy. Equally unexpectedly, they often responded favorably and with relative ease to simple—though carefully planned—supportive psychotherapy.

To give one example: A young pregnant woman worked as a volunteer on the obstetrical floor and had to be removed from the service because of what seemed a rather disturbed, and disturbing, behavior. The obstetrical house officers felt concern about her for two reasons: in spite of being reprimanded repeatedly, she intruded into patients' rooms, asking many questions about their pregnancy and delivery experiences and could not be stopped, though the patients often reacted with fatigue and irritation and wanted to be left alone. She furthermore tripped frequently during her work, and fell downstairs once, so that the question was raised by the doctors whether this seemingly intelligent and sensible person might not be either mentally deficient or unbalanced.

The patient, twenty-four years old, married for two years, was an only child. Her mother was a pianist with great ambition, disappointed by her daughter's stubborn refusal to devote herself more to music. Her father was explicitly against his beloved daughter's pregnancy "when she was still so young." The husband, a nice, somewhat immature young man, was more of a partner for sailing, skiing, climbing than for planning a family life with her. They made no preparation for the arrival of the baby, they did not change their sport activities, they even expressed some regret that the costs for the baby might interfere with their plans to buy a motorboat.

[3] The members of this team were Cecil Mushatt, M.D., psychiatrist; Mildred Alexander, M.S.W., social worker; Jeannette G. Friend, Ph.D., psychologist.

It was our impression that nobody in this young woman's family supported her pregnancy and that this motivated her compulsive and uncontrollable search for contact with other pregnant women and young mothers; and it probably also led to her ambivalence against the baby if we consider her accidents and the lack of preparation for the child as expressions of an unconscious rejection.

An understanding, sensitive but not yet highly experienced social worker was assigned to the patient. Her main goal was, at the outset, to convey her interest in the patient's pregnancy and her appreciation of it. When the patient complained about feeling deserted by her skiing husband on week ends, and wondered whether she should not take up playing the piano in order to pass the time better, the social worker quite gently raised the question whether it would not be more worth while and satisfactory for her to prepare for this, her first, child and to permit herself to take it easy instead of concentrating on music—which the patient had rejected before: mainly because it was her mother's occupation and preoccupation. This, one has to agree, is a very simple suggestion, and does not seem to have much to it. (Though in our thinking it represented a "positive attitude of a motherly figure toward the patient's pregnancy," and it attempted to counteract the patient's tendency to succumb to her ambitious mother's pressure for professional achievement.[4]) What puzzled us was the effect of this innocuous intervention—if one can give it this title at all. The patient not only started to plan and to knit for the baby with quite marked enjoyment, but she also succeeded in awakening her husband's interest in her pregnancy and his excitement over becoming a father—though not that of her parents, we have to add—and in a relatively short time these two young people behaved like normal expectant parents. It was further of interest to note that little had been said by the social worker to the patient about our impressions: namely, that to our mind this young woman had been surrounded by figures who were either negative or indifferent toward her pregnancy, that she had helplessly surrendered to their reaction with no resilience or mature attitude of her own, and that she compulsively may have attempted to gain some strength from her contact with other pregnant women. Nor had it been dis-

---

[4] In the terminology of Edward Bibring (1954) and Grete Bibring (1947), the principle applied in this technique pertains to "psychotherapeutic manipulation."

cussed with her that she may have tried to eliminate this undesirable
pregnancy by her repeated accidents. In other words, there was hardly
any direct clarification or interpretation which could have led to
meaningful insight. In spite of this lack of tangible, major psychotherapeutic activity, the patient reacted to the social worker's simple
appreciation of her role as an expectant mother with the deepest
gratitude. She brought her husband along to the Prenatal Clinic,
to meet her friend, the social worker, and could not say enough about
his changed behavior. To us this indicated that she had finally permitted herself to accept the pregnancy and to share this with her
husband in contrast to her former efforts to deny its significance.
We felt puzzled by this case, as by many others who seemed even
much more complicated and more distressed: how did we achieve
so much with so little? We finally arrived at the conclusion that
frequently this picture of serious disturbance in our prenatal cases
reflected not the severity of the neurosis of the individual woman,
but rather something characteristic for pregnancy itself.

We came to regard pregnancy, like puberty or menopause, as a
period of crisis, involving profound endocrine and general somatic
as well as psychological changes. These crises represent important
biological developmental steps and have in common a series of characteristic psychological phenomena. In all three of these periods a
number of new, specific libidinal and adaptive tasks confront the
individual, often diametrically opposed to the central tasks and functions of the preceding phases. All three seem to revive and unsettle
psychological conflicts of earlier developmental periods, requiring
new and different solutions; all three are significant turning points
in the life of the individual, and in all three the mastery of the thus
initiated phase depends on the outcome of this crisis, namely, on the
solution and maturational reorganization of this disequilibrium; i.e.,
adulthood in puberty, aging in menopause, and motherhood in pregnancy. The special nature of such acute disequilibria may also be
responsible for the readiness with which help of an understanding
transference figure is accepted, and for the relative ease with which
stabilization may be achieved through brief psychotherapy in a number of these cases. It is well known among psychoanalysts that adolescents, in spite of what seems an alarming symptomatology, frequently
are more in need of supportive rather than of intensive psycho-

therapy. We have had similar experiences with a number of meno-pausal patients, and we suggest that pregnancy be considered as one among these special conditions. However, we have to add here what is equally well known: these three states of crisis mentioned have still another characteristic feature in common. They also are the testing ground of psychological health and tend to lead under unfavorable inner and outer conditions to neurotic or even psychotic solutions.

In the discussions of developmental crises, Erik Erikson's work (1950, 1953, 1959) stands out as the most important contribution in the field. In full appreciation of this fact, we want to emphasize, though, that puberty, menopause, and pregnancy, as much as they have in common with Erikson's significant principal steps in human growth, at the same time have to be singled out as different. The difference lies in the intense and specific interdependence between the psychological and the biophysiological changes in this group of fundamentally biologically determined maturational crises. It is this factor which adds to the adaptive process the quality of the inevi-table, emphasizing it as the point from which there is no return. Once an adolescent you cannot become a child again; once menopausal you cannot bear children again; and once a mother you cannot be a single unit again. This special point we shall clarify and discuss later on in more detail.

Therese Benedek's (1959) concept of pregnancy as a psychosomatic condition determined by corpus luteum and progesterone and their retentive, oral and regressive psychological counterpart refers directly to this biological substratum. On the other hand, we find in psycho-analytic literature on female sexuality, especially in Helene Deutsch's writings (1944-1945), that implicitly and sometimes explicitly preg-nancy has been considered as a state of crisis, and reference has been made to some of the characteristics which we enumerated above.[5]

Nonetheless, there is a prevalent tendency in most of these dis-cussions to relinquish this position prematurely without pursuing further its implications and to turn to the more customary considera-tions of the pathogenesis of its phenomena. (Exception has to be made for Erikson's contribution which concentrates on the normal developmental aspects implicit in the concept of crisis and growth.)

[5] In the Josiah Macy, Jr. Conference on *Problems of Early Infancy* Transactions of Second Conference 1948, these aspects are especially emphasized.

This difference in emphasis on whether the crisis of pregnancy is basically a normal occurrence and indeed even an essential part of growth, which must precede and prepare maturational integration, or on whether this has to be understood mainly as a disturbance in the neurotic woman, with the implication that the healthy woman does not pass through such a crisis, is of some consequence on several counts, of which we will only mention two. First, it directs our attention toward those conditions which may adversely or beneficially influence the intensity or the resolution of this crisis, be it of a personal, social, or cultural nature; and from it there follows the possibility of considering these factors in our psychological contributions to the comprehensive prenatal care programs. We shall not go further into this aspect beyond referring here to the so-called intervention in the case sketched above and beyond indicating that preventive, psychological management as part of prenatal care may be as essential as it is when dealing with puberty and its turmoil in schools, families, and recreational organizations. A second point in favor of a clearer differentiation between normal and pathological crisis is of significance in the understanding of the early mother-child interaction. The question of early mother-child disturbance has been presented in the article previously mentioned (G. Bibring, 1959) and will be taken up more explicitly by us later. We shall repeat here only the points of special relevance: if we assume that pregnancy involves acutely such profound psychological changes, we may raise the question what effect this could have on the attitude of the mothers toward their infants—especially on that of the primipara who is under the full impact of this new experience. In attempting to answer this question we have to consider whether the reorganization of her psychic equilibrium has not yet taken place adequately in many cases when the woman is confronted with the reality of her newborn and the demands which this reality places on her. This may then be partly responsible for some of the disturbances in the earliest attitudes of the young mother toward her newborn baby and may then lead to the establishment of a vicious cycle of mutually induced sensitive reactions and frustrations, and finally result in the well-known, frequently described, early tensions in this relationship.

Such considerations could be of help in introducing into the study of early childhood development a more general, over-all factor of crisis and maturation in the mother, and thus revise in time the confusing concept of the overwhelming number of rejecting, hostile, and narcissistic mothers which at present is presupposed in many child psychiatric writings in order to explain the multitude of serious developmental and psychosomatic problems of infancy.

Pregnancy regarded as a normal maturational crisis confronts us with a crucial question: if it has so much in common with other states of psychobiological crisis, what then distinguishes it from them, what is psychologically the idiosyncratic task of this and only this maturational step? What is its specific goal, the form and pursuit of which in turn vary from woman to woman, according to her individual personality structure, her special kind and degree of adjustment and conflict solution with which she enters pregnancy, the particular life setting and family constellation in which this event takes place?

We felt that this can be answered best by focusing on the unquestionably pertinent and unprecedented experience of a sexual union that leads to the creation of a new life, a life toward whom an equally unprecedented relationship will be established. In order to reduce these phenomena to their basic elements, we chose to define the developmental process of pregnancy and parenthood in terms of the relationship of the woman to her sexual partner, to her "self," and to the child as it is expressed in the level and distribution of object libido and narcissistic libido. With it we arrived at the following formulation: the biophysiological, developmental process in pregnancy has its significant psychological counterpart and equivalent in the specific sequence and alterations of the woman's object-libidinal and narcissistic positions. An intense object relationship to the sexual partner leads to the event of impregnation, by which a significant representation of the love object becomes part of the self. To accept this intrusion and incorporate it successfully is the first adjustive task of the pregnant woman. Under the impact of the marked physiological and anatomical changes of the first months of pregnancy, the libidinal concentration on the self increases and leads to the integration of, and merging with, this foreign body, turning it into an integral part of herself—until the quickening disrupts this narcissistic process and undeniably introduces the baby as the new object within the self. From here on, to the delivery, the second task of adjustment sets in: within a state of growing self-cathexis, which is due to the pregnant woman's unique situation of extensive body changes and body functions, serving the growth within herself as if it were part of herself, an opposing trend simultaneously develops. This part of herself begins to move on its own, is recognized as the coming baby, begins to be perceived as if it were another object, and thus prepares the woman slowly for the delivery and anatomic separation. This preparedness equals a readiness to establish a relationship to the future offspring, and this in turn represents the new developmental achievement. The relationship, if it fulfills the maturational requirements, will have the distinctive characteristic of a freely changeable fusion—varying in degree and intensity—of narcissistic and object-libidinal strivings, so that the child will always remain part of herself, and at the same time will always have to remain an object that is part of the outside world and part of her sexual mate. The variations in this fusion will depend on the inner and outer life circumstances of the woman, the child, and the husband.

It may be appropriate here to qualify the term narcissism as to the way in which it is applied by us. It is used here in the sense of the "cathexis of the self": i.e., it refers to the distribution of libidinal energy in which the self (or better, self-representation) is the object of the cathexis (Hartmann, 1950).

We emphasize this in order to clarify what we have in mind in the preceding theoretical formulation. It does not suggest that we disregard the aspect of narcissism which relates to the process of withdrawal of cathexis from the outer world into the inner reservoir of energy, thus rendering it available for supporting and sustaining the growth, the changes, and the special body functions of the pregnant woman. (To distinguish between these two different aspects of narcissism we may formulate it best by applying Paul Federn's [1929] terms of medial and reflexive narcissism. Expressed in these terms, we concentrate here on the specific form of "reflexive narcissism" peculiar to the cathexis of self-representation in pregnancy. At the same time we do not want to exclude from the general consideration concerning pregnancy the part that "medial narcissism" plays in conditions of such intensive changes in ego functions.)

However, to restate our position, the special task that has to be solved by pregnancy and by becoming a mother lies within the sphere of distribution and shifts between the cathexis of self-representation and of object-representation.

To say it in other words: any normal girl, though she might have intense wishes for a child and though she might love the man who will be the father of this child, still must make a major developmental move in becoming a mother. This step takes place between her being a single, circumscribed, self-contained organism (though capable of intense closeness in her love relationship) to reproducing herself and her love object in a child who will from then on remain an object outside of herself. And yet a special relationship will be established to this child—different from any other earlier or later. It will persist in the form of a synthesis of her relationship to the child, representing a person in his own right, of her relationship to the child, representing her husband, and last, not least, of her relationship to the child, representing herself.

The most impressive and simplest form in which we heard this stated came from a young primigravida who was one of the members of a group under the leadership of the late Dr. Leo Berman. This girl arrived once belatedly at a group session and still in the doorway began to talk, visibly under inner pressure. What she had to say before she even could sit down was the following: "I was quite excited last night, quite anxious! It suddenly struck me, that I won't be Jeanie much longer, but mother forever and ever after!" She then proceeded in a calmer way to reveal more of her thoughts. She spoke of her relationship to her own mother; how she always wanted and finally succeeded to get away from home, to be independent, and since then had visited mother only rarely. But as she sat there last night and searched her soul, she knew that when something really terrible happened to her, the first thought had been to tell mother. And this was what she felt so deeply would be soon her own indestructible role in the life of a new child, of her own baby.

Considering our preceding formulation further, we became aware of the complexity of the process and of the major areas of potential conflicts it involves. At any point along this line of integration and adjustment, complications may arise: be it from the relation to the husband, or men in general; be it from the modes of receiving, retaining, or releasing which the woman has established as a result of her own infantile development and her leading libidinal positions; be it from the emotional charge of her object relationship which may be prevalently positive or ambivalent or destructively hostile; be it from her relationship to herself as compared or contrasted with that to the external world and its objects. In all these areas the woman will be taxed by the stress of pregnancy, and this in turn will be reflected in the signs of crisis. The solution or partial solution of the different aspects of this stress and the reintegration on a new level toward new experiences represents the maturational step of motherhood and of the attitude toward its functions and toward the child.

To this list of potential areas of complication one more has to be added which has been mentioned so far only indirectly in connection with Jeanie, the girl from the group therapy sessions—though it represents probably the core of the adjustive task underlying all those which have been enumerated, running like a red thread through all of them. This is the gravida's relationship to her own mother, its infantile aspects and its maturational resolution in the daughter's move toward becoming a mother herself (H. Deutsch, 1945, Vol. II, p. 141; Benedek, 1959, p. 730).

Pregnancy seems to affect this relationship in a characteristic way. We find repeatedly, in the spontaneous statements of our patients from the beginning of pregnancy on, remarks which refer to a change which they sense in their reactions toward their mothers. It is as if the attitudes in this relationship established as solutions of childhood experiences are abandoned and replaced by various new forms of identification with their mother. These identifications may first show the scars of the preceding childhood conflicts either by an admixture of remorse and guilt or of ambivalence and resentment. We have, however, reasons to believe that in the case of successful maturation they develop into a conflict-free, useful identification with the mother as the prototype of a parental figure.[6]

With all these considerations in mind, we proceeded to set up an investigation consisting of two parts. The first part centers around the longitudinal study of fifteen primiparae. For this we had developed a systematic and comprehensive set of variables in the course of

[6] This process has been discussed by G. L. Bibring (1954) in connection with problems of transference and countertransference as they appear in the training analysis and in the subsequent clinical work of the young psychoanalyst.

a preliminary pilot study. These variables were chosen in order to provide us with points of reference concerning the psychological structure of each patient with special consideration of those areas in which we could denote the signs of crisis and signs of maturation. This set of variables established a system for recording data, permitting us to explore our material in as much detail as feasible with regard to the questions stated above. We furthermore planned our design so as to permit flexibility in the range and utilization of the data, lest, though the study was mainly based on interviews and psychological tests, it might lose its clinical properties and vitality. Finally, we structured the study to be as exact and explicit as possible, so that the data from different periods of the pregnancy when analyzed and coded should be comparable with each other. This permitted us to ascertain whether there were changes in the psychological condition over time, starting with the beginning of pregnancy and continuing through it to a state of maturation or reorganization on a different level at the time of delivery. The details of this systematic methodology are reported in the companion article in this volume (see pp. 25-44). We therefore shall not elaborate further here on the methods used in this project, their assets and pitfalls, but turn now to some of our findings.

Though the study is not yet completed, our data show that the character of crisis can be established. We find especially in the evaluation carried out shortly after quickening that a variety of meaningful changes became evident, strongly supporting our hypothesis. Only in some individual cases did we find gross symptomatology and mounting anxiety, but as a general finding in all the cases we observed shifts in three main directions: First, an increase of previous signs of conflicts. Secondly, more frequently, we saw clinically and confirmed by psychological tests a regressive shift with the emergence of developmentally earlier patterns of behavior, attitudes, and wishes. There was a marked prevalence of oral, anal, ambivalent or hostile material which often stood out in contrast to what had been noted within the first thirteen weeks, at the time of the initial evaluation; this shift was consistent, regardless of whether the original diagnosis was that of a demanding, dependent personality or of a hysterical or phallic character type—if the use of such inexact, yet commonly applied and succinctly meaningful terms be permitted. Thirdly, women with predominantly compulsive character structure seem to be less prone to these regressive moves. The compulsive personalities frequently showed a different, somewhat less anticipated change, namely, a marked increase in the intensity of the defensive position, making them appear more rational and even better organized and more rigidly entrenched than was the case in the first round. This finding raises some interesting questions—which regrettably exceed the framework of our present discussion.

Though our hypothesis concerning the crisis character of pregnancy is likely to be confirmed by our data, we find ourselves facing certain problems in regard to our assumption concerning maturation. It seems to have been somewhat unrealistic and too theoretical or speculative to expect the phenomenon of maturational integration to manifest itself in a preparedness for delivery,[7] considering that our sample consisted of primigravidae. Although in most of our cases we found signs of resolutions of earlier disturbances which appear to be maturational changes toward the new function of being a parent, the predominant reaction at this period is that of an increased tension or anxiety now specifically related to the oncoming trauma of delivery. Those few women in our sample who insisted on natural childbirth (which is not the usual procedure of this hospital) equally showed signs of unconscious preoccupation with the delivery, though they were of a different, and what seemed intensely gratifying, nature.

As might have been anticipated, consistent with the developmental concept of epigenesis, the crisis inaugurated by and specific to pregnancy does not come to completion at parturition and with the arrival of the baby. The essential maturational changes seem to take place following delivery. The findings that crisis continues, more or less so, beyond parturition offer strong support in favor of the proposition that the frequent problems in the early mother-child relationship are partly due to an as yet incomplete reorganization of the mother's psychic equilibrium at the time of delivery.

The data in our study are not yet sufficiently processed to justify any definite statement at this point concerning the further course of maturation beyond the postpartum period. Speculative but none-

[7] This point was equally emphasized by Dr. Phyllis Greenacre in her discussion of this study presented by Grete L. Bibring to the Western New England Psychoanalytic Society, January 7, 1961.

theless heuristic thinking suggests that maturation may prove to be a slow and persistent process, keeping pace with the child's developmental steps and with the shift of the family structure in the direction of an increasingly independent social unit. Such clinical impressions as we have of those mothers who again became pregnant during the course of this study indicate that maturation is probably markedly accelerated when a second child comes into the family. We may expect that maturation will show a special thrust or regressive reversal, as the case may be, at significant junctures, like illness of the child, his entering school, puberty, etc.; and that it may reach its height when this child in turn becomes a parent himself.

It seems that the event of a daughter's becoming a parent—as it releases her from her infantile bondage to her own mother—also changes the nature of her mother's relationship to her: from a still prevalently mother-child configuration to one between two women as partners and coequals. This, we believe, takes place simultaneously with a partial shift of the grandmother's libidinal investment from the daughter onto the daughter's baby. Possibly the ultimate, post-ambivalent phase of motherhood finds its fullest realization in the grandmother's attitude toward the grandchild (H. Deutsch, Vol. II, p. 486; Abraham, 1925). It is this resolution of ambivalence which may be of help in explaining some of the well-known peculiarities in the attitudes of grandparents, which have received rather insufficient attention in psychoanalytic literature.

We have predominantly described the first main part of our study: the explorations concerning fifteen pregnant women. We have intentionally bypassed at this time applying corollary consideration to the course of the father's attitudes and development toward parenthood. They have many similarities, real and unconsciously determined ones, to those of the mother, but they also, as is to be expected, differ in some important points.

In conclusion, it should be mentioned that an ongoing complementary second project, The Psychoanalytic Study of Pregnant Women,[8] was originated to make possible a more detailed exploration of our main hypotheses regarding crisis and maturation in pregnancy, and of some of the emerging theoretical questions en-

8 Supported by the Foundations' Fund for Research in Psychiatry, Grant #57-155.

countered in testing them. The study through psychoanalysis provides an additional meaningful dimension in depth, both with
respect to data and inferences, beyond what can be reached in the
main research. It furthermore permits the investigation of pertinent
unconscious conflicts in a coherent and concentrated form.[9]

Summary

Pregnancy, like puberty or menopause, is regarded as a period
of crisis involving profound endocrine and general somatic as well
as psychological changes. The crisis of pregnancy is basically a normal occurrence and indeed even an essential part of growth, which
must precede and prepare maturational integration. It varies, individually, however, from woman to woman, according to her personality structure, her special kind and degree of adjustment and
conflict solution with which she enters pregnancy, and the particular
life setting and family constellation in which this event takes place.

An attempt is made to define the developmental process of
pregnancy and motherhood in terms of the relationship of the woman
to her sexual partner, to her "self," and to the child as it is expressed
in the level, distribution, and vicissitudes of object libido and narcissistic libido. The woman moves through a phase of enhanced
narcissism early in the pregnancy, until quickening undeniably
introduces the baby as the new object within the self. The mother's
relationship to her child, if it finally fulfills the maturational
requirements, will have the distinctive characteristics of a freely
changeable fusion—varying in degree and intensity—of narcissistic
and object-libidinal strivings, so that the child will always remain
part of herself, and at the same time will always have to remain an
object that is part of the outside world and part of her sexual mate.

With these considerations in mind, an investigation was set up
which centers around the longitudinal study of fifteen primiparae
admitted consecutively for obstetrical care to the Prenatal Clinic of

---

[9] Some of the problems and findings of the psychoanalytic study have been presented by Grete L. Bibring at the Panel on Research in Psychoanalysis, at the Fall
Meetings of the American Psychoanalytic Association, December, 1960. This material
will be published separately at a later date.

a general hospital. A systematic and comprehensive set of variables was developed to provide points of reference concerning the psychological structure of each patient, with special consideration of those areas in which the signs of crisis and the signs of maturation could be recognized and recorded. In this article the methodology is only briefly described, since the details are reported in the companion article in this volume (see pp. 25-44).

Preliminary findings show that the character of crisis can be established in that a variety of meaningful elements become evident, especially in the evaluation carried out after quickening. Generally the observed changes involve an increase of previous signs of conflict, a regressive shift with the emergence of developmentally earlier patterns of behavior, attitudes, and wishes, or, as in women with predominantly compulsive character structure, a marked increase in the intensity of the defensive positions.

Maturational integration seems to occur later and more gradually than had been expected. The current impression is that crisis inaugurated by and specific to pregnancy continues on after delivery. It appears that maturation evolves slowly, in reciprocity with the child's development and with the growth of the family as an independent social unit. Subsequent pregnancies probably accelerate the maturational process. Speculative consideration was given to the special and relatively unambivalent attitude of the grandparent, as it is derived ultimately from the mature, even though complex, relationship of the parent to the child.

BIBLIOGRAPHY

Abraham, K. (1925), Character-Formation on the Genital Level of the Libido. *Selected Papers on Psycho-Analysis.* London: Hogarth Press, 1927.
Benedek, T. (1959), Sexual Functions in Women and Their Disturbances. In: *American Handbook of Psychiatry*, ed. S. Arieti. New York: Basic Books.
Bibring, E. (1954), Psychoanalysis and the Dynamic Psychotherapies. *J. Am. Psa. Assn.*, II.
Bibring, G. (1947), Psychiatry and Social Work. *J. Soc. Casework*, XXVIII.
—— (1954), The Training Analysis and Its Place in Psychoanalytic Training. *Int. J. Psa.*, IV.
—— (1959), Some Considerations of the Psychological Processes in Pregnancy. *This Annual*, XIV.
Deutsch, H. (1944-1945), *The Psychology of Women*, 2 Vols. New York: Grune & Stratton.

GRETE L. BIBRING ET AL.

Erikson, E. H. (1950), *Childhood and Society*. New York: Norton.
—— (1953), Growth and Crisis of the Healthy Personality. In: *Personality in Nature, Society and Culture*, ed. C. Kluckhohn, H. A. Murray & D. Schneider. New York: Knopf.
—— (1959), Identity and the Life Cycle. *Psychological Issues*, No. 1. New York: International Universities Press.
Federn, P. (1929), Das Ich als Subjekt und Objekt im Narzissmus. *Int. Ztschr. Psa.*, XV.
Hartmann, H. (1950), Comments on the Psychoanalytic Theory of the Ego. *This Annual*, V.

A STUDY OF THE PSYCHOLOGICAL PROCESSES IN PREGNANCY AND OF THE EARLIEST MOTHER-CHILD RELATIONSHIP

II. Methodological Considerations[1]

GRETE L. BIBRING, M.D., THOMAS F. DWYER, M.D.,
DOROTHY S. HUNTINGTON, PH.D., and
ARTHUR F. VALENSTEIN, M.D. (Boston)[2]

The methodology to be presented in this article refers to a study whose theoretical framework stated briefly is: "Pregnancy is a crisis that affects all expectant mothers, no matter what their state of psychic health. Crises, as we see it, are turning points in the life of the individual, leading to acute disequilibria which under favorable conditions result in specific maturational steps toward new functions. We find them as developmental phenomena at points of no return between one phase and the next when decisive changes deprive former central needs and modes of living of their significance,

[1] This study has been supported by a grant from the Filene Foundation, Boston; by grant #M-1393, United States Public Health Service, National Institutes of Mental Health, and by grant #57-155 from the Foundations' Fund for Research in Psychiatry (Psychoanalytic Study of Pregnant Women).

The preparation for, and the carrying out of, the various phases of this research has been done by the following group: Grete L. Bibring, M.D., psychiatrist; Benjamin B. Brussel, M.D., psychiatrist; Thomas F. Dwyer, M.D., psychiatrist; Sophie Glebow, M.S.W., social worker; Norman Goldstein, Ph.D., psychologist; Howard H. Hermann, M.D., psychiatrist in the pilot-study period; Dorothy S. Huntington, Ph.D., psychologist; Bernard Levine, Ph.D., psychologist; Margaret Meiss, Ed.D., psychologist; Barbara C. Mueller, M.D., psychiatrist; Malkah Tolpin Notman, M.D., psychiatrist; Davida Rees, M.D., psychiatrist; John Reichard, M.D., psychiatrist; Joae Graham Selzer, M.D., psychiatrist; S. Norman Sherry, M.D., pediatrician; Arthur Valenstein, M.D., psychiatrist; Olga Wermer, M.D., medical gynecologist.

Appreciation is expressed to Dr. John Benjamin who on several occasions participated in our theoretical and methodological discussions, and gave us as a friend and colleague the benefit of his extensive knowledge and experience.

[2] The Psychiatric Service of the Beth Israel Hospital, Boston, and the Department of Psychiatry, Harvard Medical School.

forcing the acceptance of highly charged new goals and functions. Pregnancy as a major turning point in the life of the woman represents one of these normal crises, especially for the primigravida who faces the impact of this event for the first time. We believe that all women show what looks like remarkable, far-reaching psychological changes while they are pregnant. The outcome of this crisis, then, has profound effects on the early mother-child relationship." These considerations are discussed at length in a previous article (G. Bibring, 1959), and in a companion article in this volume (see pp. 9-24).

Aims of the Research

The broad aim of this research has been the study and understanding of the normal psychological processes of pregnancy. The specific aim has been to elucidate the elements of crisis and maturation in the pregnant woman and to demonstrate how certain of these maturational elements may be influenced by the personality pattern and by different types of medical management. The basic hypothesis of this research is that pregnancy is a maturational crisis. Briefly, the thesis is that the psychological organization the woman has achieved in adulthood must undergo a significant degree of dissolution as a specific response to pregnancy, to allow for a corresponding recomposition to a new position not identical to that previously held. This recomposition is initiated during pregnancy or soon thereafter. A corollary is that the woman during pregnancy and for a period after delivery is undergoing rapid psychological change as compared with other periods of her life.

Examples of some signs of crisis we anticipated finding were loosening of defenses usual for the particular woman, appearance of more primitive content material, and major shifts in significant relations to people and activities. Examples of some of the signs of maturation we expected were changes in self-image, moving toward appropriate identifications, and emotional investment in the child as a separate object.

It is also the aim of this study to derive information about the following related assumptions:

1. Significant anxieties other than those of a neurotic nature are

a characteristic part of pregnancy, that is, certain specific anxieties are inherent in this condition of crisis.

2. Specific social and cultural factors may support or adversely affect the normal psychological processes of pregnancy.

3. Tensions specific to pregnancy that remain unresolved at the time of delivery introduce a disturbing element in the earliest mother-child relationship, tensions to which in turn the infant reacts.

4. Appropriate psychological management by the obstetrician or other person during the prenatal period may serve as a replacement for the tension-reducing supports that are now receding in our culture: the extended family, the Church, and certain traditional beliefs and ritualistic procedures.

Within the framework of our hypotheses, the goals in terms of the over-all areas of investigation are:

1. To delineate a natural history description of pregnancy: a longitudinal study of how fifteen women respond to this experience.

2. To test the working hypotheses, cross case, on crisis and maturation.

3. To test the informal hypotheses about affectivity in pregnancy and delivery, about changes in the body image, and about the nature of fantasies concerning the fetus, and so forth.

4. To use the data to test somewhat less rigorously other hypotheses bearing on such matters as shifts in the gravida's narcissistic balance during periods of stress, the pregnant woman's relationship to her own mother as it is reflected in her relationship to the child, and so forth.

5. To examine the processes whereby the research group reach conclusions on the different variables.

A second study within this program of research is the psychoanalytic investigation of two pregnant women. The psychoanalytic research enriches and complements the larger project, allowing a detailed "microscopic" view of the mechanisms seen at times only in partial and manifest form in our larger sample. Two women will have been seen in psychoanalysis throughout their pregnancies and will have been carried in analysis to its natural completion. The influences on the analyst involved have been kept to a minimum, and the research aspects other than the general knowledge that maturation was under study were purposefully withheld from both analyst and analysand, so as to prejudice the analysis as little as possible.[3] The current goals of the psychoanalytic research are:

1. The study of the processes of pregnancy, specifically the vicissitudes of the woman's relation to her mother as it is reflected in the relationship she then establishes to her child.

2. The study of the validity of the assessment procedures of the over-all, larger research, in comparison with the findings of the psychoanalytic investigation.

Choice of Methods

Given the theoretical issues involved, the choice of method might have ranged from the single case study to the broad survey. The single case method offers many advantages, especially when the tool of psychoanalysis is employed. Nonetheless, under certain circumstances, the knowledge gained through a psychoanalysis as such, however detailed, might be enriched in important ways by systematically bringing in other factors: biological, social, and cultural. Furthermore, psychoanalysis as a research procedure is economic in terms of time or personnel only under rare and favorable conditions. On the other end of the scale from the single case method, the broad survey approach is able to give extensive, but preponderantly descriptive, limited, and sometimes unreliable information about phenomena, dependent on the cooperation of the respondent. Especially important for the present research was a method that would allow us to elicit information actively in specific areas in given time periods.

An appropriate procedure for the study of the psychological processes of pregnancy was designed and developed specifically for this research, using where possible previous work by others (Murray, 1938; O.S.S. Assessment Staff, 1948). It was felt that the design of choice was the small sample method of intensive study of each case, formulated and carried through within the framework of psychoanalytic concepts. This allows for the answering of questions highly pertinent to the research: questions about changes in psychological mechanisms, identification patterns, defenses, superego, and so forth, as well as changes in interactions with significant environmental

---

[3] This part of the project will be presented separately at a later date.

figures, attitudes, and ways of responding. There are disadvantages to this method, as well as advantages, in that data are not obtained on many cases, nor are extremely intensive data gathered. To answer the disadvantage of the lack of detailed information at the unconscious level, a complementary research was originated, the Psychoanalytic Study of Pregnant Women.[4] To answer the disadvantage of lack of extensive information, that is, a large number of cases, it was chosen to know the patients thoroughly and to make the primary focus of the research a longitudinal study of each case rather than cross-case comparisons, although this does enter into account as will be discussed below. Thus, the primary interest was to obtain a longitudinal picture of pregnancy.

The initial task of the research was to translate the theoretical considerations into workable procedures which served the ideas, and to avoid procedures which dictated the types of ideas to be explored. One problem was to define both conceptually and operationally the phenomena of "crisis" and "maturation," and to specify as far as possible the factors governing these phenomena, and how they might change over time. It was decided that a detailed specification of the anticipated characteristics of crisis and maturation would best serve as the framework around which the methodology of the research should be built. This was carried out in conferences over a number of months, in which the research team suggested, both on the basis of material gathered from pilot-study patients, and on the basis of their general clinical experience, a large number of variables that seemed relevant to the research. An attempt was made to strike a balance between the extreme of a rigid statement of expectations which might have limited our knowledge before we were certain about the pertinent variables, and the other extreme of allowing the material to go completely unstructured, and therefore amorphous and difficult to handle.

Since the theoretical considerations were so intimately involved with changes over time, the collection and handling of the data pertinent to the variables were established in such a way that the variables might be studied over a set of time periods. A systematic Outline of Variables was formulated, which will be discussed below.

4 This investigation has been supported by grant #57-155 from the Foundations' Fund for Research in Psychiatry.

˙ It is felt that a sharing of a common theoretical framework and a sufficient consensus involving basic concepts is essential for a research as this. As has been stated, this research has been formulated within the theoretical framework of psychoanalysis. All members of the team, regardless of their professional background, have an understanding of psychoanalytic concepts.

Tools

One of the major areas of necessary emphasis in psychiatric research is that of the methodology employed to implement the investigation. As the first and most basic tool of the research, the Outline of Variables (see Appendix A) was established, that is, a list of categories systematically covering family background, personality development and structure, and current functioning. This set of variables allows for the organizing of a large amount of data around a relatively few significant categories and allows for comparison on each case over time. All of the detailed data from each of the five time periods in which data were collected for each subject are organized and assessed according to this outline for each one of the periods.

In addition to this, a reclassification of defenses was carried out in order to have a baseline from which to work in referring to the defenses the patient is using. The glossary established from it is a comprehensive statement of the organization of the mechanisms of adaptation and defense, with succinct definitions of each of these mechanisms.[5] The glossary has enhanced the comparability of the analyzed data from trimester to trimester during the pregnancy, and the comparison of data from pregnancy to postpartum.

Another set of tools developed was the Pregnancy Sentence Completion Test and the repeat Sentence Completion Test[6] which allow the gathering of material in specific areas that are related directly to the woman's feeling about her own childhood and adolescent development, sexual development, relationship to peers in general, relationship to husband, mother and father, and her attitudes toward

[5] See Appendix B, Glossary of Defenses.
[6] These tests were developed primarily by Dorothy S. Huntington, Ph.D. To be published separately.

pregnancy and the coming child. In addition, there was prepared a set of projective pictures, copyrighted as the Pregnancy Evaluation Test.[7] This set of pictures permits the collection of material which may be compared with the standard Thematic Apperception Test and with the more conscious interview material in terms of attitudes and feelings toward husband, sibling situations, mother and mothering situations, and general attitudes toward the pregnancy. The psychological tests used throughout the pregnancy and during the follow-up period were the Rorschach, the Thematic Apperception Test, the Draw-A-Person Test, the specially designed Sentence Completion Test, and the Pregnancy Evaluation Test.

Also prepared were rating sheets for the obstetricians and detailed outlines[8] for interviews by the psychiatrists seeing the woman and her husband, the social worker, the medical gynecologist, the pediatrician, the psychological test report, and the psychologist doing the infant observation. These outlines were by no means intended to be limiting, but rather were guides for the organization of material to enhance comparability, and guides for areas of concentration according to the main focus of interest of the different professions engaged in the interviewing.

METHODOLOGY

A pilot study was carried out, in which a consecutive sample of fifty-one women coming to the Beth Israel Hospital for their prenatal care were seen. On the basis of the material gathered from this group, the tools of the research (that is, the Outline of Variables, the Pregnancy Sentence Completion Test, the Pregnancy Evaluation Test, the Glossary of Defenses, and the various interview outlines) were refined.

The research sample itself consists of fifteen primigravidae, a consecutive sample of those primigravidae coming to the Prenatal Clinic of the Beth Israel Hospital. The only exclusions from this consecutive sample were unmarried women and these women entering the Clinic after the thirteenth week of their pregnancy. The women concerned were informed at the time of their first prenatal

---

[7] The pictures were drawn by Jean Wechsler Knapp. To be published separately.
[8] Both to be published separately.

visit that they would be part of a Comprehensive Pregnancy Care
Study, and only one patient refused to participate.

Data were obtained by observation, interview, and testing, and
since relatively rapid psychological change was expected to be an
important part of pregnancy, the data were collected from each
subject at five different time periods:

1. First trimester of pregnancy
2. Second trimester, that is, after quickening
3. Third trimester
4. Labor, delivery, and lying-in period
5. Up to at least one year postpartum.

In order to have data gathered in a given area from more than
one point of view, as well as to increase the diversity of areas, the
work was carried out by members of different disciplines: psychiatrists, psychologists, social worker, medical gynecologist, and pediatrician, all of whom were psychiatrically and psychoanalytically
oriented and had personal psychoanalytic experience. The reader is
invited to follow the course of the research as it is schematized in
the accompanying Table 1 (pp. 34-35). It depicts the chronological
sequence of observations and data gathering, and their assessment.

At the time of the first visit, the women were observed by a
psychologist[9] while they were waiting to be called for their obstetric
examination. During this examination, the psychiatrist[10] and the
medical gynecologist[11] who later interviewed them were present as
observers; the social worker[12] also saw each woman for an interview.

In addition to this, at each one of the five time periods noted
above, the woman was seen for a complete psychiatric interview, for
psychological testing[13] (all periods except six weeks postpartum), for
medical gynecologist's interview (prenatal periods) and social service
interview. Each woman was also seen by the social worker at each
one of her regular prenatal visits: monthly until the eighth month
and then weekly thereafter until delivery. In the majority of cases,

9 Margaret Meiss, Ed.D.
10 Benjamin B. Brussel, M.D.
11 Olga Wermer, M.D.
12 Sophie Glebow, M.S.W.
13 Dorothy S. Huntington, Ph.D.

it was possible for a psychiatrist[14] to interview the husband once during the first half of his wife's pregnancy and again during his wife's delivery or lying-in period. In the eighth month, the woman was also interviewed by the pediatrician[15] who later was responsible for well-baby care. The entire labor and delivery were observed by one of three physicians[16] on the team and the woman was interviewed briefly as soon as she was out of anesthesia. The baby was then observed regularly in the nursery by a psychologist[17] and one feeding by the mother each day was observed by a woman psychiatrist.[18]

After leaving the hospital, the mother returned at monthly intervals to the Well-Baby Clinic for further care. During these visits, observations and brief movies were made through a one-way viewing mirror with the knowledge of the mothers. At each well-baby visit the baby was tested developmentally by a psychologist,[19] and the pediatrician not only did a careful physical examination of the child but learned all he could about the baby while giving appropriate pediatric advice. At each one of these visits the social worker had an interview with the mother, and at other intervals home visits were made by her.

ANALYSIS OF THE DATA

Each member of the observing, interviewing and testing group recorded his material immediately after each contact. Subsequently, this mimeographed material was distributed to each member of the research team and the entire group met for a set of *data-assessment conferences* on each time period under study. This group included those who had seen the woman, her husband, and the baby, as well as those who had not.[20] The design entailed the reading of all the material in advance by each person with the exception of the principal investigator, Dr. Grete L. Bibring, who read the material only after hearing the first conference presentation. This was done

[14] John Reichard, M.D.
[15] S. Norman Sherry, M.D.
[16] Benjamin B. Brussel, M.D., Malkah Tolpin Notman, M.D., and Olga Wermer, M.D.
[17] Norman Goldstein, Ph.D.
[18] Barbara C. Mueller, M.D., Davida H. Rees, M.D., and Joae Graham Selzer, M.D.
[19] Norman Goldstein, Ph.D. and Bernard Levine, Ph.D.
[20] Grete L. Bibring, M.D., Thomas F. Dwyer, M.D., and Arthur F. Valenstein, M.D.

Table 1
CHRONOLOGY

	1st Prenatal Visit	Between 1st and 2nd Prenatal Visits		Every Prenatal Visit	Once during pregnancy
1. DIAGNOSIS OF PREGNANCY	Psychologist doing observations in waiting room Social work interview Psychiatrist and medical gynecologist doing observations during obstetric examination	Psychiatric interview Psychological tests Medical gynecologist's interview	Clinical Assessment Conferences and Data-Coding Conferences	Social work interview	Psychiatric interview with husband Home visit by social worker
		Clinical Assessment Conferences and Data-Coding Conferences		Clinical Assessment Conferences and Data-Coding Conferences	

	After feeling life		Immediately prior to delivery		
2. QUICKENING	Psychiatric interview Psychological tests Medical gynecologist's interview		Psychiatric interview Psychological tests Medical gynecologist's interview Pediatrician: 1st contact and informal short interview		
	Clinical Assessment Conferences and Data-Coding Conferences				

	Labor and delivery	Lying-in period				
3. DELIVERY	Psychiatrist or medical gynecologist: observations	Psychiatrist: short visit and interview Pediatrician: visits with mother and examines baby Social work visit and interviews Psychiatrist: doing feeding observation Psychologist: doing infant observation	Clinical Assessment Conferences and Data-Coding Conferences			
	Six weeks Postpartum	Every Well-Baby Visit (monthly)	Six months postpartum and again one year postpartum			Final Clinical Assessment Conferences and Data-Coding Conferences
4. RETURN HOME WITH BABY	Psychiatric interview Social work interview Pediatrician: interview with mother and examination of baby	Pediatrician: interview with mother and examination of baby Social work interview Psychological test of baby Movies taken	Psychiatric interview Social work interview Psychological tests			

in order to encourage the fullest possible expression of impressions from the group at large before the introduction of her own formulations. Conferences on a given case began with each of the members who had seen the patient presenting in turn a report of his interview, test, or observational material for the entire time period under consideration. These presentations served several purposes. As direct verbal reports they enlivened the written record and freshened the recollection of details. In addition, issues that seemed unclear as stated in the written record could usually then be clarified. Precautions were taken to insure that only clarification took place, and not a reinterpretation of the material under question on the basis of new information belonging to a later date. The original written record stood as a fixed point of reference, unchanged by any extemporaneous presentation of the interviewer. This was of value in another sense also, in that the verbal summary could be critically evaluated by drawing upon the written material.

In addition to these spoken presentations from the previously written material, the movies taken in the Well-Baby Clinic were shown just prior to the assessment of the fifth and final time period.

At the conclusion of each set of conferences, one set for every one of the five consecutive time periods, the material had been reformulated into a dynamic representation of the patient for each period under consideration. This had its expression in a summing up by one psychiatrist of the research team's evaluation of the material. This amounted to a detailed, descriptive, and dynamic formulation of t! woman's material for the period under scrutiny. The entire conference group offered collaboration and any minority view was carefully noted and listed under the initials of the person with his reason for a differing conclusion.

Following each set of clinical conferences came the *data-coding conference* where the formulations were specified systematically according to the Outline of Variables. Again, if unanimous agreement on different items was not possible, the minority view was carefully recorded as part of the assessment with the initials of the dissenter and his reasons for a differing judgment. There was distinctly no attempt to force a unanimous agreement, and the members avoided coming to a judgment that "averaged" opposing views.

To summarize, for each woman, there were five sets of data-assessment and data-coding conferences: one for each time period studied. Systematic coding of data according to the previously established Outline of Variables appears to be an important contribution to the methodology of this type of research.

At the close of the data-assessment conference concerned with the interval just preceding delivery, a series of predictions were made, covering behavior during labor and delivery, the lying-in period, going home, attitudes toward feeding, toilet training, masturbation, erotic and aggressive behavior of the child. These predictions were made informally but were carefully recorded, and have served as a stimulating and rewarding part of the research.

The results of the research are being treated in six ways:

1. The integration of findings, that is, a delineation of a natural history description of pregnancy: a longitudinal view of pregnancy and the earliest postpartum period.

2. The establishment of conclusions relating to the over-all goals of the investigation, that is, hypotheses on crisis and maturation, informal hypotheses, and the generating of new hypotheses.

3. The tool analysis by discipline—the psychiatric interviews as such, the psychological tests as such, and so on.

4. The individual variable analysis, that is, what changes are noted in defenses, in narcissistic/object-libidinal balance, superego, and so forth.

5. The relationship-between-variables analysis. This is the complex relationship between sets of variables, as they are modified over time.

6. The revising of the theoretical conceptualizations on normal development, crisis, and maturation.

One goal of the psychoanalytic research, namely, the study of the validity of the assessment procedures of this research, has been set up and is carried out in the following manner: the group that is responsible for the gathering of the data in the larger research also interviewed and tested the woman who was to be analyzed before she started her analysis. This material was then handled in the same way as on the larger research, that is, through assessment conferences and data-coding conferences, arranging the material according to the Outline of Variables. The analyst treating the patient was not informed of the content of this assessment. After the woman's delivery, two research analysts assessed the analytic material according to the same Outline of Variables, which then was compared with the original coding. Only after the completion of the entire analysis did the research analysts and the analyst who had treated the patient join in a common evaluation of the material and in a final coding according to the Outline of Variables. This final coding is being compared point by point to the initial coding done by the original assessment team.

TECHNICAL CONSIDERATIONS

Some of the difficulties and disadvantages of broad survey studies, on the one hand, and of the use of psychoanalytic case material *in toto*, on the other hand, have been mentioned and are well known. It would be a major advantage to workers in the field if it were possible to deal with a far smaller number of particulars than one does in psychoanalysis, and yet to work with a sufficient number to permit meaningful assessments. Limiting a research to a smaller number of particulars may deprive it of reliability in comparison with psychoanalysis by reason of the lack of details in many areas. However, there should be a compensatory gaining of certain other sources of reliability. It seems possible that the methodology of the present study at least moves in the direction of this goal.

The collection of data by a number of different individuals with a common theoretical framework but also with somewhat different outlooks and assigned goals, and by different means (interviews, tests, observations), provides a large number of particulars usefully overlapping in part or in whole with respect to a single area. In the actual clinical setting, there were five different professions and six different personalities interacting with each patient under fairly controlled circumstances. As stated earlier, however, all the people shared a familiarity with psychoanalytic concepts and had a psychoanalytic orientation. All the women were observed, interviewed, or tested by the same psychiatrist, social worker, medical gynecologist, and psychologist. All the women were observed on their first visit in the Prenatal Clinic by the same psychologist and were later in their pregnancies seen by the same pediatrician. There was also a psychiatrist who was available to take over the therapy when necessary, and who shared in the delivery observations with two other medical members of the group. There was a psychiatrist who interviewed the husbands; there were three women psychiatrists who participated in the observation of feedings. Each was assigned in rotation to a particular patient whom she watched with her infant once a day. Beyond this, a psychologist observed the infants. To complete the research group, there were three psychiatrists who never saw the women personally.

This range of observers and situations allowed for a detailed picture of the functioning of the individual patient, in the sense of a concept of triangulation. It is germane in this respect to consider that there was a total of at least twenty-five sessions with each patient between the first prenatal visit and delivery, and at least fifty more between delivery and one-year postpartum. There were a wide variety of observations, interviews, and tests in many situations on each patient. This specifically allowed for the later structuring of each patient in full terms. Both the transference elements and the countertransference elements were carefully taken into account. Since each type of situation was the responsibility of the same person, the differences in material elicited by each of the different research workers formed a significant part of the diagnosis of each patient. In other words, what to expect of each interviewer was known in general, and the patient's idiosyncratic responses could then be judged more accurately. It was possible to obtain the varied responses of the patients to the different interviewers according to their individual personality or their sex. Intentional use of these differences has been made in gaining the widest possible view of the patient.

For example, one woman was extremely depressed and longing for her family when she spoke with the women interviewers but presented herself as well integrated and adequate with the male psychiatrist. Another woman spoke quite freely and openly about sexual material with the male psychiatrist and hid much of this pertinent background, such as having an illegitimate brother, from the women interviewers. A third patient, when talking to an older, more maternal woman, gave a good deal of material indicating withdrawal. This raised the question of a previous schizoid type of adjustment. This same patient was more outgoing, alert, and active with the younger female social worker, relating to her as a sibling figure, casting doubt on the previous impression. A fourth patient told her story in such a way as to make two of the women, both nonmedical figures, the social worker and the psychologist who tested her, suspect that this woman was quite depressed and that her marriage was going very poorly. To the male psychiatrist she presented no difficulty whatsoever and painted a glowing picture of her marriage.

The important issue is that in this research, a large group of people with consistent roles were seeing these women. In the first interviews, a number of things were seen through the eyes of different people that would not have been noticeable if only one person had seen each woman. This led to the impression that under circumstances which limit the number of times that a patient may be seen, there might well be a definite advantage to having the patient seen by more than one interviewer, and this consideration could be of importance to many research projects which may have only a single opportunity for clinical contact. The importance should be stressed also of carrying out interviewing by different disciplines: not that, for instance, four psychiatric interviews would give four times the amount of material, but that observations, interviewing, and testing by four different disciplines may give a more accurate picture in depth of the patient.

It seems possible that the distorting factor, for research, of transference and countertransference reactions may, to a substantial amount, be lessened when the data are collected on one subject by several interviewers and, furthermore, are evaluated by a group according to the effects of the different personalities.

Another consideration that exists in this type of psychological research is the question of how much the procedure influences the subject, and specifically, the question of how much the procedure itself changes the crisis signs which are seen in pregnancy. We are aware of the fact that the presence of the research in this case would influence the phenomena under study. The interviews were research tools, and the contacts in the research were tangible and meaningful to the women even though our intention was to do nothing more than was humanly appropriate. This was an action research, but intervention was intentionally kept to a minimum. Full acknowledgment was made, in evaluating the data, of whatever transference and countertransference attitudes may have existed, and of whatever

assistance may have been given, and its influence on the data collected. These effects are inevitable and possibly not deleterious to
the research, since explicit awareness may be kept of their presence,
degree, and effect. Moreover, in this particular research, in so far as
there was an implicit therapeutic gain for the patient, it would
usually have minimized those findings that verify a hypothesis of
crisis of pregnancy.

The particular group approach used in analyzing the data is
also a methodologic consideration. The research requires that a large
number of particulars (from interviews, tests, observations) come to
the attention of the individuals in the group, and that each individual research member order the particulars hierarchically. By the
nature of these processes, each individual reads somewhat differently,
attends more or less to different particulars, and especially in later
steps of evaluation (all of this before the group discussion) may vary
widely in the routes by which judgment is reached, in the kinds of
judgment reached, and in the certainty in which judgments made
are held. Such variations will be influenced by the nature and
amount of the research worker's professional and personal experience
and by his subjective predilections.

It might be anticipated that the most skillful people within the
group would sharply affect the direction of the discussion. It has
become clear that working together as a group for some time, as was
done on the pilot study, was necessary to arrive at the point where
each person felt free to contribute according to his own skill and
his own professional background. To date, the retrospective review
of conference material shows no convincing evidence for a consistent
swaying of opinion by one "dominant personality" in this particular
group, nor has there been significant evidence of the opposite danger: the substantial fragmentation of the group on the basis of
intrapersonal disruptive processes which would have a deleterious
effect on the achievement of consensus.

Related to the group-conference procedure is the use of the carefully specified Outline of Variables. It should be noted that a conclusion was expected for each variable within the Outline. The
group was "required" by the Outline to give an assessment for each
particular variable; deviance was noted and indicated by individual
initials. This would appear to be one of the major methodologic

points to be made; that is, when obliged to make a decision, because of a prior structured outline, a decision was reached. However, in contrast, when going along on a highly skilled clinical basis and only drawing a summary from a clinical discussion, vagueness may unintentionally enter. In a clinical conference where there is a free expression of judgments which are drawn together in an unstructured fashion, certain areas may be not only left confused, but unintentionally ignored. The use of the Outline of Variables requires an explication of the data which allows for markedly greater comparability over time and with less distortion. It is believed that in research done purely by clinical conference and a reaching of a clinical agreement, it will be found, as has been noted in other researches, that clinical conferences cannot be made as fully valuable or comparable over time. When attempts are made to return to the clinical summaries, often material is either missing or ambiguous, and one may retroactively misconstrue what really had been meant at the earlier time. The outcome is a serious distortion because what has come about, even quite unconsciously, is the application of what has been observed recently to what was known at an earlier time period and the confusion of the two. John Benjamin (1959) has excellently discussed this point in his article on prediction.

A further advantage of the use of the Outline of Variables in coding the collected material is that it permits the discussion of any one particular variable as it appeared at any time during the pregnancy or subsequently, or of any variable such as defenses, for example, as it may have changed over time, or for the purpose of cross-case comparison, without the necessity of returning to the entire body of data. This makes the use of the vast amount of material far more economical and practical from a research point of view.

Another question to be raised relates to the area of changes over time, and the problems encountered during evaluation of the comparison of trimesters. When changes in the women were seen, the question came up of whether these changes were due to the pregnancy or due to having more information about the women. This is a problem that is of interest to a number of other researchers. How much interviewing must be done to carry out a particular study and to provide enough material to make an accurate assessment on the foci of the research is a highly relevant matter. In several of the cases, the major areas of difficulty and the larger trends for the future seemed quite clear in the first assessment conference. In other cases, this was not so, and an accurate picture was not gained until the second or third time period under study. Many factors come into play here: among them, the particular personality structure of the woman, her attitudes to the research and its team, her current environmental circumstances. One may occasionally be seriously misled by the initial impressions, especially if the women are not seen by several interviewers.

Summary

The methods developed and used for a clinical study of the psychological processes in fifteen primigravidae are described and discussed. The subjects were studied from the time of their first prenatal clinic visit, when they were pregnant for twelve weeks or less, to at least one year postpartum. Data were collected from the women and their husbands, and later on the infants, by means of interviews, tests, and observations, by psychiatrists, psychologists, a social worker, a medical gynecologist, and a pediatrician. The recorded data were distributed, read, and assessed in conference by the latter personnel and an additional three psychiatrists who had no direct contact with the subjects. The theoretical framework was psychoanalytic, and all members of the research group had an understanding of psychoanalytic concepts and varying degrees of personal experience with psychoanalysis.

The tools used for the collection of data are described, including some specially devised for this study. The purposeful overlapping of areas of observation by the various interviewers during a given period of time is discussed with reference to a concept of triangulation.

The application of a detailed and systematic outline of variables developed for this study, and the usefulness of this type of outline for a variety of psychological studies is considered.

The gathering of data was concentrated on five time periods: each of the trimesters of pregnancy, the delivery and lying-in period, and the interval thereafter up to at least one year postpartum. During each of these periods, interviews and tests were repeated by the same person. In the fourth and fifth periods, other methods and observers were added: a woman psychiatrist made daily observations of the mother feeding her infant during the lying-in period, the pediatrician did all monthly well-baby examinations, and the psychologist observed and tested the infant.

The assessment of data in conferences was also done separately for each of the five time periods on each subject. The particular usefulness of this procedure and the methods of analyzing and coding the data are discussed.

More broadly, consideration is given to the development of methodologies for dealing with psychological data whose magnitude is substantially less than in the case of an individual psychoanalysis, but substantially more than in the case of broad survey studies. Each of these three methodologic approaches has its own unique potentiality; there is need for further development of methodology appropriate to longitudinal developmental research, as described in this study.

Appendix A

Section One: Information Collected

I. Up to and including first contacts of research team with patient

    A. General data

        1. Social Service Index

        2. Face-sheet Data

          a. Expected date of confinement

          b. Date of marriage

          c. Birthdate and birthplace

          d. Education

          e. Religion and religious history

          f. Siblings

          g. Occupation

          h. Parents' birthplace, religion, and occupation

          i. Husband's birthdate, birthplace, education, religion and religious history, siblings, occupation, and parents' birthplace and occupation

    B. General observations

        1. Physical appearance, physique and clothing

        2. Mood

        3. General behavior or manner of reacting; peculiarities and manner of speech or action

        4. Physical signs of tension: nervousness, wringing hands, perspiration, blushing, other autonomic signs

        5. Medical, endocrine or neurological features

          a. General body habitus, immaturity, infantile elements, etc.

          b. Hair distribution, excess, etc.

          c. Secondary indications characteristic of pregnancy: breast changes, posture, bearing, etc.

---

[1] The Outline of Variables presented here has been revised editorially but not substantively. In the actual research, the older version was used.

6. Reaction of patient to hospital personnel: admitting officer, nurses, obstetrician, observer, psychiatrist, social worker, psychologist, gynecologist, pediatrician
7. Differences in patient's reaction in terms of sex, status, and role of personnel, and time sequence of contacts
8. Reactions of hospital personnel to patient: of admitting officer, nurses, obstetrician, observer, psychiatrist, social worker, psychologist, gynecologist, pediatrician

C. Attitude to clinic setting, personnel, and procedures: past and present attitudes to and relations with social workers, psychiatrists, psychologists, Visiting Nurses' Association, physicians, dieticians, nurses, to hospitals, and this particular hospital, to the medical profession in general, and to specific clinic procedures

D. Past history, to the time of pregnancy
   1. Family constellation
      a. Mother, father, siblings, grandparents, aunts, uncles, etc.
      b. History of these individuals, their relationships to each other, their attitudes to patient (patient's place in family)
      c. Special events within family: losses, gains, traumata, etc.
      d. Economic history of family
      e. Significant medical history of family
         (1) Cancer, cardiac difficulties, allergies, ulcers, etc.
         (2) Mother's and sisters' menstrual history
         (3) Mother's and sisters' pregnancy history
      f. Work history and leisure-time activities
         (1) Father's work history
         (2) Mother's work history
      g. Talents, achievements, and intelligence of family members: patient's relationship to family talents and achievements
   2. Significant nonfamilial figures: teachers, employers, clergy, friends, therapeutic and authoritative figures; patient's attitude toward them
      a. Special relationships: "crushes," identifications, aversions
      b. Losses and gains
      c. Pregnancy and medical history
   3. Personal history
      a. Medical history (illness, accidents, and injuries)

    b. Childhood development

    c. Sex education, circumstances, and by whom

    d. Adolescence

       (1) reactions to breast development

       (2) menstruation: onset and course, physical symptoms

       (3) relation to peers in general, to boys, to girls, to school, authority figures, patient's attitude toward them

       (4) adolescent daydreams

4. Educational and work history, activities, interests, talents

5. Social influences other than family (standards and values: moral, social, aesthetic, intellectual)

    a. Educational

    b. Religious

    c. Ethnic patterns

    d. Economic factors

    e. Special group ethos

    f. Political

6. History of religious beliefs, secular and nonsecular

7. Special events

    a. Traumata

    b. Benevolent factors

E. Marital history up to the time of pregnancy

1. History of relationship to husband, premarital

2. Attitudes toward and expectations of the marriage

3. Sex interests and activities, approach to intercourse, when first intercourse occurred, orgasm, contraceptives, history of conception, etc.

4. Relationship with in-laws

5. Previous marital history, if any, of husband and/or wife; husband's children, if any

6. Occupational history since marriage: household, work (for economic reasons or by preference), other significant activities

F. Present life situation

1. Present family constellation

    a. Wife's family

    b. Husband's family

    c. Couple's relations with each family

2. Present significant nonfamilial figures

3. Setting of pregnancy in terms of emotional, social, and economic environment
   a. Current needs; major economic, social, or marital problems
   b. Anticipated reaction to the pregnancy by husband, parents, others
4. Patient's reaction to pregnancy
   a. When first suspected, why suspected, reaction
   b. Planned pregnancy or accidental: pregnancy desirable at this time or not
   c. Attitude to childbearing; expectations as to discomfort, illness, diet restrictions, anesthesia, delivery, baby
      (1) positive ideas and feelings
      (2) negative reactions, worries, and doubts
   d. Nausea and vomiting, etc., when started, ended, time of day, previous history of nausea and vomiting; in school, under stress, etc.
   e. Fatigue, and sleep habits
   f. Complaints
   g. Any abnormal symptoms
   h. Weight and diet: dietary history, attitudes to food, will dieting be difficult and why; use of alcohol and cigarettes

G. Dreams, fantasies, superstitions and TAT stories

H. Information from husband
   1. Personality evaluation of husband
      a. Personality type, behavior patterns, gross symptomatology, etc.
      b. Problems of dependence, orality, compulsiveness, authoritarianism, passivity, etc.
      c. Relationship to wife and women: identification, competitiveness, fears, feelings of superiority, etc.
      d. Attitude toward sex, menstruation, pregnancy, having a child, children, desired sex of baby, breast feeding, infant care, etc.
      e. Role husband plays in marriage and his expected future role
   2. Emotional relationships in husband's family: relations with mother, father, brothers, sisters; relation with in-laws; husband's view of wife's relation to her mother, father, siblings and other important figures

3. Economic situation: reality and subjective reaction; attitude to wife's working; husband's work history
4. System of values and traditions
    a. Ethnic, religious
    b. Figures of significance in husband's development

II. Changes noted by patient, reported by husband and others
    A. During course of pregnancy
        1. Changes patient feels in herself since pregnancy
        2. Recreation and work since pregnancy (talents, achievements, intelligence)
        3. Preparations for baby
        4. Ideas, fears, and questions about pregnancy and delivery; patient's attitude to family myths, superstitions, and beliefs about pregnancy and delivery
        5. Anticipated feeding of baby
        6. Reaction to quickening
        7. Changes in symptoms
        8. Changes in ideas about pregnancy, delivery, and baby
        9. Changes in relation to husband, family members, in-laws, friends, other figures, research team
        10. Changes in actual life situation, economic, social, marital, etc.
    B. After delivery
        1. Changes in husband's attitude toward pregnancy
        2. Changes in husband's relation to wife before, during, and after pregnancy

Section Two: Assessment of Information

I. Mood and affective state

                   Prepregnant   Since pregnancy   During interview
    A. Anger
    B. Anxiety
    C. Apathy
    D. Apprehension
    E. Bewilderment
    F. Blandness
    G. Brooding
    H. Contemplative
    I. Contentment
    J. Depression
    K. Despair
    L. Detachment

    M. Disgust
    N. Euphoria
    O. Excitement
    P. Exhilaration
    Q. Guilt
    R. Indecisiveness
    S. Irritability
    T. Lability
    U. Optimism
    V. Pessimism
    W. Preoccupation
    X. Sadness
    Y. Shame
    Z. Well-being
  AA. Other

II. Relationships with or attitudes toward, and fantasies about:
    A. Parents and in-laws
    B. Husband
    C. Siblings
    D. Authoritarian figures
    E. Benevolent figures
    F. Men
    G. Women
    H. Sex
    I. Pregnancy
    J. Baby
    K. Children
    L. Animals
    M. Job or profession

III. Characteristic ways of behaving
    A. Overt behavior patterns in areas of family, peers, authority, subordinates, religion, education, social institutions, food, cleanliness, dress, money, sex, etc.

    B. Ways of behaving
      1. Aggressive
      2. Altruistic
      3. Apathetic
      4. "As if"
      5. Autistic-schizoid
      6. Compliant
      7. Compulsive
      8. Confused

9. Critical
10. Delusional
11. Demanding
12. Dependable
13. Dependent
14. Efficient
15. Egoistic
16. Emotional
17. Exhibitionistic
18. Greedy
19. Hypersensitive, paranoid
20. Hysteric, seductive
21. Infantile
22. Ingratiating
23. Inhibited
24. Insecure
25. Intellectual
26. Irresponsible
27. Masochistic
28. Negativistic
29. Outgoing
30. Overindependent
31. Passive
32. Phobic
33. Psychopathic
34. Realistic, flexible, rational
35. Rebellious
36. Reserved
37. Rigid
38. Sadistic
39. Shy
40. Somatizing
41. Stubborn
42. Submissive
43. Superior, pretentious
44. Suspicious, paranoid
45. Trusting
46. Unassuming
47. Uninvolved, aloof
48. Withdrawn

IV. Talents, achievements, and intelligence

A. Conflict-free (relative to degree of freedom from conflict)
B. Conflictual

V. Object-libidinal positions and their gratifications or frustrations (libidinal and aggressive)

    A. Oral
    B. Anal
    C. Phallic
    D. Early genital[2]
    E. Genital
    F. Maternal generative

VI. Character of object relations

    A. Positive, negative, ambivalent
    B. Genuine, pseudo, sham, "as if"[3]
    C. Masochistic, sadistic
    D. Submissive, dominating, rebellious, manipulative, controlling
    E. Passive, active
    F. Dependent, independent
    G. Fragile, durable; sticky, fickle; shallow, deep
    H. Sparse-abundant; relatedness, withdrawal

VII. Level of development reached

    A. Libidinal development
    B. Object relations
        1. Fixation on infantile objects
        2. Mature object choice
    C. Signs of regression from this level

VIII. Narcissistic position

    A. Degree of narcissism
        1. Low
        2. Average
        3. High average
        4. Extreme
        5. Schizoid
    B. Attitude toward self and others
    C. Signs of narcissistic withdrawal
        1. Used defensively

---

[2] The first genital feminine position after the phallic phase is resolved, as an outcome of a positive oedipal period. In normal feminine development, it is the position reached during latency, and endures until puberty introduces both anatomical and instinctual changes leading to a fuller genitality. See Marie Bonaparte's (1953) concept of the masochistic struggle during this early genital period.

[3] See Helene Deutsch (1934).

   2. Not used defensively: evidence of gratification in body-
pregnancy change
      a. Gratified withdrawal
      b. Conflict-free self-fulfillment with objective and sub-
jective signs

IX. Self-image
   A. Body image
   B. Mental image
   C. Patient's self-evaluation of talents, achievements, intelli-
gence, and physical attributes

 X. Identification
   A. With mother, father, siblings, husband, other significant
figures
   B. As an adult, as a child, as a woman, as a man, as a girl, as
a boy, as a mother, as a "little mother," as a father, as a
parent
   C. Quality of identification
      1. Maturational
      2. As conflict solution
         a. Identification with the loved object
         b. Identification with the lost object
         c. Identification with the aggressor
         d. Identification out of guilt

XI. Superego manifestations
   A. Superego identification with early and late figures connected with developmental phases and experiences
   B. Quality of superego
      1. Lenient
      2. Indulgent
      3. Compromising
      4. Defective
      5. Rigid
      6. Punitive
      7. Strong
      8. Strict
      9. Conflicting (multiple identifications)
      10. Other peculiarities (projected blame)
   C. Standards and values: moral, ethical, aesthetic, religious,
social, intellectual; culturally and familially determined
prejudices, superstitions, beliefs, and general attitudes
toward life

XII. Defenses
    A. Type used
        1. Basic (first order)
           a. Acting out
           b. Affectualization
           c. Avoidance
           d. Blocking
           e. Control through thinking
           f. Denial
               (1) Denial by exaggeration
               (2) Denial through fantasy
           g. Desexualization
           h. Detachment
           i. Displacement
           j. Intellectualization
           k. Introjection
           l. Isolation
               (1) Compartmentalization
               (2) Splitting off
           m. Magical thinking
           n. Projection
           o. Rationalization
           p. Reaction formation
           q. Regression
           r. Repression
           s. Restriction of ego function
           t. Somatization
           u. Sublimation
           v. Turning against the self
           w. Undoing
           x. Withdrawal
        2. Complex (second order)
           a. Aestheticism
           b. Altruistic surrender
           c. Asceticism
           d. Clinging to object
           e. Clowning, mocking, and scoffing
           f. Compliance
           g. Controlling
           h. Counterphobia
           i. Depersonalization
           j. Eating and drinking (a form of acting out)
           k. Falling ill

l. Identification
    (1) With the loved object
    (2) With the lost object
    (3) With the aggressor
    (4) Out of guilt
m. Ritualization
    Formalization
n. Sexualization (libidinization)
o. Whistling in the dark
B. Adequacy of defenses
  1. Level of anxiety
  2. Quality of reality testing (disturbance by intensity of anxiety, defenses, etc.)

XIII. Signs of unconscious conflict
A. Symptoms
  1. Psychosomatic symptoms
  2. Psychoneurotic symptoms
  3. Psychotic symptoms
B. Acting out
C. Affects
  1. Anxiety and reflections of anxiety
  2. Depression
  3. Other affects
D. Disturbance in reality sense
  1. Affects
  2. Behavior
  3. Cognition
  4. Orientation: sense of time, space, etc.
E. Rigidity or inadequacy of defenses

XIV. Evaluation of fantasies
A. TAT stories
B. Dreams
C. Superstitions, prejudices, beliefs
D. Personal mythology

XV. Manifestations of transference and countertransference

XVI. Personality diagnosis

Section Three: Signs of Crisis

I. Changes in affective state
A. Subjectively reported feelings (or their equivalents) and contents

      B. Objectively observed expressions of feelings (or their equivalents) and contents

  II. Inconstancy of attitudes or the coexistence of contradictory attitudes in areas of parents and in-laws, husband, siblings, authoritarian figures, benevolent figures, men, women, sex, pregnancy, baby, children, animals, jobs, or professions

  III. Changes in characteristic ways of behaving
      A. Overt behavior patterns in areas of family, peers, authority, subordinates, religion, education, social institutions, food, cleanliness, dress, money, sex, etc.
      B. Ways of behaving (See III, Section Two)

  IV. Changes in use of capacities, intelligence, and talents
      A. Conflict-free (relative to degree of freedom from conflict)
      B. Conflictual

  V. Changes in libidinal and aggressive strivings
      A. Changes in aim, goal, and intensity of instinctual needs; shift in balance of instinctual need: oral, anal, phallic, early genital,[4] late genital
      B. Changes in specificity and quality of object choice
        1. Revival of object loss
        2. Intensification of infantile fixations
        3. Weakening of mature object relations
      C. Altered demands on the environment for protection, support, appreciation, submission, or equivalents and the lability of these demands

  VI. Changes in narcissistic/object-libidinal balance (See VIII, Section Two)

  VII. Changes in self-image
      A. Body image
      B. Mental image
      C. Patient's self-evaluation of talents, achievements, intelligence

  VIII. Loosening of established identification patterns and searching for new patterns (See X, Section Two)

  IX. Changes in superego manifestations
      A. Quality of superego
        1. Lenient
        2. Indulgent

4 See footnote 2, above.

3. Compromising
4. Defective
5. Rigid
6. Punitive
7. Strong
8. Strict
9. Conflicting (multiple identifications)
10. Other peculiarities (projected blame)
  B. Changes in ego ideal
  C. Standards and values: moral, ethical, aesthetic, religious, social, intellectual
  D. Increased or decreased allowance of gratification

X. Acute changes in defenses

  A. Types of defenses (See XII, Section Two)
  B. Adequacy of defenses
    1. Level of anxiety
    2. Quality of reality testing

XI. Intensification of unconscious conflict

  A. Symptom formation
    1. Psychosomatic symptoms
    2. Psychoneurotic symptoms
    3. Psychotic symptoms
  B. Acting out
  C. Affects
    1. Evidence of anxiety and reflections of anxiety
    2. Depression
    3. Other affects
  D. Disturbance in reality sense
    1. Affect.
    2. Behavior
    3. Cognition
    4. Orientation: sense of time, space, etc.
  E. Changes in flexibility or adequacy of defenses

XII. Appearance of more primitive content material, or intensification of defense against this material; content of unconscious fantasies about pregnancy, changes in these fantasies, and reactions to the changes, including TAT stories, dreams, prejudices, superstitions, and beliefs, etc.

XIII. Changes in transference manifestations (attitude toward the help of supportive figures) and in countertransference

Section Four: Signs of Maturation

   I. Resolution of mood disturbances and stabilization of affect
      A. General: appropriateness of affect in various situations and
         toward specific objects, especially toward baby: freedom to
         enjoy and ability to worry
      B. Specific: resolution of mood disturbances occasioned by
         objects, and by events of pregnancy: fetus, delivery, baby,
         husband, body changes, etc.

  II. Fuller utilization of talents, achievements, and intelligence,
      and broadening of area of autonomous functions
      A. General: gain in conflict-free functions
      B. Specific: interests and activities in the baby and in the
         providing, caretaking, nurturing, mothering activities

 III. Changes in libidinal and aggressive strivings consonant with
      the function of wife and mother
      A. General
         1. Changes in aim, object, and/or goal (attaining full
            genital position)
         2. Greater libidinal freedom
         3. Realistic demands on the environment as to herself,
            baby, and husband
         4. Loosening of fixations on infantile objects
      B. Specific
         1. Attitude toward mother: changing from child of
            mother to coequal status as mother
         2. Shifting of family ties with consideration of the cul-
            tural family pattern; relating to the parents, grand-
            parents, in-laws, and siblings in a different, less con-
            flicted way
         3. Signs of libidinal cathexis of child (acceptance of the
            child as part of one's self and an object outside of
            one's self, as part of husband, and as object in its own
            right); the child as a new member of the family

  IV. Changes in narcissistic/object-libidinal balance
      A. General: decrease of conflict between interest in objects
         and interest in self: flexibility in maintaining this balance
      B. Specific: acceptance of role of mother with the attainment
         of a reasonable object/narcissistic interest in the child.
         The successful resolution of the changing narcissistic/
         object-libidinal balance particular to pregnancy ideally

leads ultimately to the attainment of a balanced narcis-
sistic and object-libidinal interest in the child.

V. Changes in self-image

    A. Body image: shift from the libidinal perception of the body as predominantly erotic to appreciation of the body (breasts, uterus, etc.) in its maternal functions and configuration

        Ultimately, in an ideal maturation, this shift subsumes an enlightened maintenance of the valuing of self as the attractive feminine woman, i.e., the Venus role in addition to the Cornelia role, and the attainment of both roles without essential conflict.

    B. Mental image: broadening of the self-image to include maternal patterns; acceptance of more realistic self-image

VI. New identifications appropriate to motherhood; acceptance of the assets and liabilities of these functions with minimal conflict

    Associated with this is the realization and acceptance of one's identity and role in the family and social group as interdependent rather than dependent or independent; as adult rather than child; as woman rather than girl; as mother rather than daughter; as woman rather than man; as wife and mother rather than one or the other.

VII. Changes in superego and ego ideal

    Shift toward greater ego/superego harmony, toward an equilibrium between permissiveness, and demands and requests; a change in ego ideal reflecting the new functions and goals

VIII. Changes in defenses

    A. General

        1. Toward greater adequacy of defenses

        2. Use of more mature defenses (in individual evaluation)

    B. Specific

        1. Shift from projective/introjective mechanisms toward an identification mode of functioning, possibly promoted by a forced recapitulation of modes, as a consequence of the pregnancy experience

        2. Loosening of defenses characteristic for pregenital libidinal positions

            This is based on the assumption that pregnancy, with its characteristic crisis, unsettles and revives repressed infantile fixations and makes them again

available for solution. A reliving of the unresolved conflicts at the different phases of development is stimulated.

IX. Changes in symptoms (psychosomatic, psychoneurotic, psychotic); changes in acting out; disappearance of symptoms relevant to pregnancy

Section Five: Summary

    I. Clinical Impression

   II. Prognosis (predictions)

 III. Management

Section Six: Outline for Final Comparison

    I. Characteristic personality structure, prepregnancy

       A. Psychoneurotic features
          1. Primary (major)
          2. Secondary (minor)
       B. Autonomous areas, areas of specific strengths

   II. Patterns of pregnancy crisis: what was the pattern of crisis: during pregnancy, during delivery, and lying-in period

       A. At what phases and points did crisis make its manifest and/or substantial appearance
       B. Whether warded off or not and until when: factors facilitating or inhibiting the development of normal crisis
       C. The specificity of crisis response for the particular personality structure in question
          1. What does the pregnancy represent for this particular woman
          2. The nature of the relationship of the woman to her own mother—in what way it influences the crisis features
          3. The meaning of delivery to the woman
       D. Whether resolved or not (if so, how?)
       E. Differentiation of crisis signs; normal and neurotic connotations and their combinations
       F. Reality factors which may have had a direct effect upon the course of the crisis of pregnancy: specific environmental problems, economic or social problems, relationship to husband, etc.

III. Patterns of maturation

A. At what stage during the pregnancy or after did maturation begin to occur, what were the signs of maturation evident by the time of delivery and thereafter
B. Type of maturation: proportion and interrelationships of each type
   1. In what way has the maturation fitted within the particular personality structure of the patient
   2. Ego-syntonic type of maturation: extending and adapting within existing ego mechanisms and personality framework
   3. Ego-reorganization type of maturation: the development of new modes, within a reorganized ego structure
C. What interfered with or facilitated the occurrence of maturation: relationship with mother, husband, others, etc.

IV. Mother-child relationship: the meaning of the child to the mother and the interaction of mother's personality and behavior of child

A. Early period: how did crisis signs and maturational elements at time of delivery manifest themselves in the patient's handling of the child during the period of dependency: in feeding, diapering, bathing, etc.
B. Later period (phase of emerging independence, more activity, greater autonomy: eating solids, sleeping through, etc.)
C. Developmental aspects and problems of the child in reciprocity with the personality structure and neurotic trends of the mother: specific difficulties and areas of ease and competence in relation to each developmental phase

V. Factors relating to the ego development of the child: effects of interaction with mother's personality and reality factors on rate and kind of development of child, as seen through developmental testing and observation

VI. Cultural influences affecting the rearing of the child

VII. Prognosis

Appendix B

This glossary is not intended to be a definitive classification of defenses. Defensive activities of the ego include not only specifically describable unconscious mechanisms but also complex unconscious functional responses which are more or less specific and recurrent and yet of a defensive nature. It appears that there is a continuum of defensive measures making up the defensive organization of the ego. The extremes can be readily distinguished from each other, but there is an indeterminate middle range which defies exact specification regarding those defensive functions which justify explicit specification as defense mechanisms, and those more complex measures made up of various combinations and sequence of defense mechanisms and admixtures of other ego functions. However, they are so closely related to those relatively irreducible defense mechanisms as to justify inclusion in a tabulation of defenses.

In recording our defenses, we were constantly aware of the fact that a variety of classificatory problems emerged: for example, basic and complex, pure and composite, including the greater or lesser admixture of instinctual elements, ubiquitous and specifically determined, archaic and mature. This will be elaborated in further publications. At this point we decided to include on an experiential basis in the generally accepted catalogue some defensive measures peculiar to and characteristic for individual patients, and to divide the list in this glossary into two groups:

1. Basic (first order)
2. Complex (second order)

However this might seem arbitrary, the arrangement is a tentative one, not meant to suggest mutual exclusiveness, but only the more or less quality of basic irreducibility, and complex synthesis of various ego-defensive functions. Reserved for future publication must be the problem of classification, the relationship of defenses to

[1] This work was derived primarily by Arthur F. Valenstein, M.D., from unpublished notes and concepts developed by Edward Bibring, M.D. and Arthur F. Valenstein, M.D. It is based in part on Anna Freud's formulations in *The Ego and the Mechanisms of Defense* (1936).

symptom formation, as well as considerations concerning the dual aspect of defenses, namely, the warding off of anxieties in relation to unconscious conflict; and second, the actively autonomous, adaptive function in the service of constructive, maturational, progressive growth and mastery of the drives.

I. Basic (first order)

Acting out
Affectualization
Avoidance
Blocking
Control through thinking
Denial
    1. Denial by exaggeration
    2. Denial through fantasy
Desexualization
Detachment
Displacement
Intellectualization
Introjection
Isolation
    1. Compartmentalization
    2. Splitting off
Magical thinking
Projection
Rationalization
Reaction formation
Regression
Repression
Restriction of ego function
Somatization
Sublimation
Turning against the self
Undoing
Withdrawal

II. Complex (second order)

Aestheticism
Altruistic surrender
Asceticism
Clinging to object
Clowning, mocking, and scoffing
Compliance
Controlling

Counterphobia
Depersonalization
Eating and drinking (a form of acting out)
Falling ill
Identification
   1. With the loved object
   2. With the lost object
   3. With the aggressor
   4. Out of guilt
Ritualization
   Formalization
Sexualization (libidinization)
Whistling in the dark

Acting out: serves as a resistance against conscious recognition of an
impulse. The unconscious fantasy, involving objects, is lived out
impulsively in behavior. Acting out is ego syntonic and involves
more the gratification of the impulse, whether sexual or aggressive, than the prohibition against it, thus differentiating it from
a symptom. Acting out may occur through the omitting or impulsive exaggeration of a normally adjustive, appropriate behavior, or it may be behavior which is contrary to established
modes. Behavior is called acting out if it disrupts social adjustment.

Aestheticism: a shift of interest to the formal, aesthetic value of
objects or experiences, in order to avoid awareness of direct
sensual affects. In this sense it is akin to intellectualization and
may be supported by reaction formation, denial, and splitting
off.

Affectualization: the overemphasis on and the excessive use of the
emotional aspects of issues in order to avoid the rational understanding and appreciation of them. Feeling is unconsciously
intensified for purposes of defense.

Altruistic surrender: a surrender of direct gratification of instinctual
needs in favor of fulfilling the needs of others, with vicarious
satisfaction being gained through identification with the other.

Asceticism: the elimination of directly pleasurable affects attributable
to an experience. Direct satisfaction of biological or sensual
pleasures is not allowed, whereas the gaining of pleasure and
"joy" nonsensually, in the "good" as laid down by one's group,
is countenanced. The moral element is implicit, in setting values
on "high" and "low" pleasures; often the feature of altruism
versus nonaltruism is significant. Asceticism is directly against
all "base" pleasures perceived consciously, and gratification is

derived from the renunciations involved. In brief, asceticism wards off awareness of needs of a physical or sensually pleasurable nature, and may become a habitual defense pattern.

Avoidance: an active turning away from conflict-laden thoughts, objects or experiences.

Blocking: an inhibition, usually temporary in nature, of affects especially, but possibly also thinking and impulses. It is a dynamic defensive process which comes close to repression in its effect. However, it is briefer, often with a dawning awareness of tension, resulting from the holding back of the affect, thought, or impulse to act.

Clinging to object: an exaggerated holding on to objects, in fact or in effect, with reluctance to loosen the tie to or to leave the object.

Clowning, mocking, and scoffing: the excessive or habitual use of wit to lessen anxiety, consequent to the impact of a stressful situation or of disturbing thoughts or affects.

Compliance: avoidance of issues by passive surrender.

Controlling: the excessive attempt to manage and/or regulate events or objects in the environment for defensive purposes and in the interest of minimizing anxiety and solving internal conflicts. It is manifested in various strategies such as interference with suggestions, sabotage, seduction, excessive compliance, etc.

Control through thinking: the use of the thought process in a compelling way to defend against acute emergent anxieties. It is characterized by a need to know all the details, to quite a complete extent. The content of the frightening situation is not primarily drained of anxieties, but through extended anticipatory familiarization with the danger, an attempt is made to prepare oneself and thus lessen the anxiety.

Counterphobia: a specific defense against a phobia through denial by action in the specific area of the phobia.

Denial: Denial accomplishes the negation of awareness in conscious terms of existing perceptions of inner or outer stimuli. Literally seeing but refusing to acknowledge what one sees or hearing and negating what is actually heard are expressions of denial and exemplify the close relationship of denial to sensory experience. It is to be distinguished from avoidance which is manifested, for example, by the actual closing of the eyes or the refusal to look. Denial plays its part as an important defense with respect to experience in the spheres of action, affects, and thought. In contrast to repression, which is immediately concerned with drive discharge, denial is closer to the perceptual system, whether it operates with regard to the external world, the environment, or the internal world, the self. Denial may be made

more effective through exaggeration, negation, fantasy formation, or displacement.

1. *Denial by exaggeration:* a particular and often encountered
    response which exactly exaggerates, often in a carica-
    tured way, the element which is laden with anxiety, to
    the point that it becomes apparently "foolish" and un-
    real.

2. *Denial through fantasy:* denial is sometimes characteristically
    supported by the elaboration of fantasy which supplants
    certain anxiety-laden elements with more reassuring
    considerations. For example, "dreams of glory" may
    supplant and support a denial of either actual ineffec-
    tiveness or helplessness, or a sense of inadequacy.

Depersonalization: a disturbance of self-image and self-function
image, caused by decathexis of the percept of "me-ness," with the
feeling of unreality as a result. Percepts of self and affects seem
unreal as if belonging to someone else; there is a feeling of
estrangement from the self.

Desexualization: a change in the quality of an instinctual impulse
but not its object. It signifies a neutralization of the libidinal
or aggressive cathexis of the object.

Detachment: the withdrawal of a libidinal or aggressive cathexis
from an object. It usually is associated with elements of isolation
and splitting off.

Displacement: as a defense mechanism involves a purposeful unconscious shifting from one object to another in the interest of
solving a conflict. Although the object is changed, the instinctual
nature of the impulse and its aim remain the same.

Eating and drinking: as a defense involves a compelling inclination
to ingest (food, drink, medicine, etc.) for purposes of augment-
ing or maintaining intactness of the self, especially the body
image, and the controlling of the environment. Incorporation
and introjection are subserved.

Falling ill: the habitual use of existent illness which may be over-
emphasized or exaggerated for its evasive and regressive possibilities. Responsibility may be avoided, guilt may be circumvented,
and aggressive and libidinal impulses which are experienced as
dangerous may be warded off. The unconscious exploitation of
illness as a defense is almost certain to be associated with other
mechanisms such as regression and turning active into passive.

Identification: a complex ego function which clearly has its place
among the defenses, but also goes far beyond a purely defensive
activity of the ego. Identification is conceived of as (1) having
a fundamental developmental and adaptive role in the evolution

of personality, and (2) lending itself in various ways and at various levels to the defensive needs of the ego, both in (a) archaic terms (modeled on incorporation and introjection) and (b) the less instinctually oriented functional potentialities of the ego (predominantly ego-imitative and learning activities).

By and large, the employment of identification as a defense brings it closer to the archaic instinctual modes of incorporation or introjection, although there are significant exceptions to this.

Identification achieved through imitative activity, whether conscious or unconscious, accomplishes the modeling of one's own personality in the image of an object, thus insuring that the cathexis of the object representation is not lost. Identification is said to have taken place when the imitation becomes habitual, even in the absence of the object. Identification in this form is pre-eminently developmental and structure building. It differs from incorporation in that destruction of the object is neither implied nor necessary, and instead there is awareness of the object as another person. The achievement of a final identity is the integration of many different identifications and partial identifications.

Identification as an outcome of introjection has much more to do with conflict solving. At least initially, there is involved much more of the instinctual interest in the object, although as a practical outcome it may well have its effect in final character building and adaptation. Identification, whether maturational or a specific defensive activity, can lead to increased adaptation to reality. On the other hand, where the identification is more archaic, relating to qualities of the object construed in more magical and omnipotent terms, the outcome may be ego restrictive, thus hampering adequately resilient functioning of the personality, and leading to subsequent maladjustment.[2]

In so far as identification *as a defense* has much to do with instinctual conflict around important objects, it leads to specifically describable forms of identification, as follows:

1. *Identification with the loved object:* describes that type of identification in which one models one's self according to the characteristics of a significantly loved object, with the goal of establishing a closeness to and *constant presence* of this object. Anxiety consequent to separation, or tension arising out of hostility toward the object, is thus alleviated.

[2] This point was stressed by Dr. Joseph Sandler in the course of an informal discussion with him.

2. *Identification with the lost object:* nullifies or negates a bereavement or loss of a valued object through taking on characteristics of this object. It often appears that this is preponderantly an introjective identification.

3. *Identification with the aggressor:* avoids anxiety through placing the aggression characteristic of a feared object within the self, and thereby under one's own control and available in one's own interest. The aggression is no longer felt as coming from the outside, but is taken into one's self and turned outward on the principle that "attack is the best defense."

4. *Identification out of guilt:* describes that form of self-punishing identification which is attributable to the hostile destructive component of an ambivalent tie to an object. It usually leads to taking over qualities of a self-punitive nature, more on an introjective than an imitative basis. One might in this way establish within one's self a personality trait or symptom characteristic of the object, which in effect represents both the destruction of and the preservation of this object.

Intellectualization: based on thinking as a special and limited variety of doing: the control of affects and impulses through thinking them instead of experiencing them. Intellectualization is a systematic overdoing of thinking, deprived of its affect, in order to defend against anxiety attributable to an unacceptable impulse. It is the thinking process, defensively directed against and replacing emotion and impulse. In that thinking has been in one sense defined as experimental action in small and contained degree, intellectualization restricts the individual to the realm of testing.

Introjection: has as its prototype oral incorporation, which has libidinal as well as significant aggressive components. Introjection is similar to incorporation in that it is also close to the oral part-drive, but it further connotes a specific defense and early ego functioning. Introjection specifies the perceiving and treating of that which is in fact outside as if it were inside one's self. Through introjection, an attempt is made to obliterate the existence of a separation between self and object.

Isolation: the intrapsychic separation of affect from content. Isolation is a *splitting off* process followed by three possibilities: (1) the idea is repressed, (2) the affect is repressed, (3) neither the idea nor the affect is repressed, but once separated the affect is displaced to a different or substitute thought. Isolation refers to "loss" of affect, whereas "emptying of content" refers to "loss" of the idea through repression, suppression, or distraction. *Compartmentalization* is a specialized form of isolation in which there is a keeping apart of sets of ideas or affects one from another.

Magical thinking: the treating of thinking as if it were doing; "thinking or wishing makes it so." In the discrimination of thought and action, reality testing is given up. Magical thinking is used illogically as a way of avoiding danger or fulfilling needs. It comes close to rituals. Animism and superstitions are manifestations of magical thinking.

Projection: the perceiving and treating of certain unacceptable inner impulses and their derivatives as if they were outside the self. The impulses may arise in the id, or activity of the superego may be so reflected, as, for example, in a hallucinated recrimination.

Rationalization: attitudes, beliefs, or behavior which otherwise might be unacceptable may be justified by the incorrect application of a truth, or the invention of a convincing fallacy.

Reaction formation: the management of unacceptable impulses by permitting the expression of the impulse in an exactly antithetical form; in effect the expression of the unacceptable impulse in the negative. Reaction formation may be a temporarily invoked defense mechanism, but on the basis of a persistent instinctual conflict, it may become imbedded in the developing ego structure in the form of a character trait on a relatively permanent level.

Regression: (1) a return to a previous stage of functioning to avoid the anxieties and hostilities involved in later stages; a re-establishment of an earlier stage where conflict is less. As a purposive way of handling a specific conflictual situation, regression is a defense and an ego mechanism. It is a "way out" and, as it were, a flight into earlier modes of adjustment.

(2) A return to earlier points of fixation marking modes of behavior that had been given up. This could well be an outcome of a breakdown of equilibrium at a later phase of development. It implies a conservative biological principle of adjustment, namely: the constant trend to attain instinctual gratification in one way or another and to return always and ever to earlier modes of doing so whenever more specialized and later developed modes fail. In this sense, regression is the outcome of instinctual biological trends.

Repression: repression occupies a central position in the organization of the defensive measures and mechanisms of the ego. In almost every instance of defensive activity, repression plays a part in insuring the effectiveness of the various defenses. Repression is uniquely related to, and predominantly directed against, specific instinctual impulses.

In the historical evolution of the concept of repression, its special role in warding off unacceptable instinctual manifestations was recognized. In this regard, it is to be distinguished from all other defenses in its singular position in rendering these manifestations unconscious in the dynamic, economic, and structural sense. With the introduction of a systematic ego psychology, the concept of repression gained a new significance with regard to its effect on ego functioning. Much of ego function is in itself unconscious, in particular the operation of the entire defensive organization of the ego. Repression is the paramount mechanism through which this unconscious ego state is maintained, and the activity of the various defenses kept at an unconscious level. As an unanswered theoretical problem, there remains the unique relationship of repression to instinctual drive on the one hand, and its dynamic role with regard to the unconscious ego state on the other hand. As a consequence, the concept of repression is in need of fuller clarification, with special regard to its role in the interrelationship of ego and id, and of drive and ego function. It is our impression on the basis of clinical experience that the instinctual element implicit in defensive activity seems to be more emphatically repressed in the sense of unconsciousness [Ucs.] than the ego functional element [Ucs. → Pcs.].

Restriction of ego function: the unconsciously determined limitation or renunciation of specific ego functions, singly or in combination, to avoid anxiety arising out of conflict with instinctual trends, with the superego, or with environmental forces or figures. Restriction of ego function may be relatively benign, involving little interference with over-all ego effectiveness. Often, however, it becomes structuralized in the form of substantial inhibition of ego functioning, sometimes to so pathological an extent as to become symptom. (However, this touches upon the unsettled theoretical issue of the relationship between defense and symptom, and instinctualization of ego function.)

Ritualization: the establishment of a certain order or sameness of things or behavior. The meaning disappears through a repression, but is implicitly in a form or order which has a magical meaning. *Formalization* is a precursor.

Sexualization (libidinization): the endowing of an object or function with sexual significance that it did not have before, or had to a lesser extent, in order to ward off anxieties connected with certain prohibited impulses or reactions. It very often makes its effect known under the impact of displacement.

Somatization: the defensive conversion of psychic derivatives into bodily symptoms.

Sublimation: the gratification of an impulse whose goal is retained but whose aim, or aim and object, is changed from a socially objectionable one to a socially valued one. Libidinal sublimation involves the inhibition of the manifest sexual aspect and thus the renunciation of direct sexual gratification. There are, then, two aspects involved in the complex process of gratification through sublimation: (1) for the sexual drives, a desexualization as far as consciousness is concerned, and (2) the placing of a value judgment: replacing the aim, or aim and object, with something valued by the superego or society. There is a question, not yet answered, of whether a sublimation may be maintained exclusively, or only relatively, as a secondary autonomous function, on the basis of ego gratification. It seems that a sublimation remains supported, however slightly, by the original instinctual impulse, which is still active at an unconscious level.

Turning against the self: the turning back upon the self of an impulse directed against an object. This usually refers to an aggressive impulse, but may also refer to turning of libidinal feelings toward the self rather than toward an object. Turning against the self is displacement onto one's self, but it is that singular displacement of using one's self as the object.

Undoing: balancing or canceling out an unacceptable action, affect, or thought by a subsequent action, affect, or thought in contradictory terms.

Whistling in the dark: contains elements of counterphobia, denial, and reaction formation, and also implies identification with the unafraid one (this could be identification with the aggressor).

Withdrawal: the removal of interest or affect from an object. There are two facets of withdrawal: (1) withdrawal occasioned by anxiety attributable to conflict were the interest to be maintained, and (2) withdrawal initiated by increased narcissistic requirements, as, for example, in times of illness or crisis such as pregnancy, etc.

BIBLIOGRAPHY

Benjamin, J. (1959), Prediction and Psychopathologic Theory. In: *Dynamic Psychopathology in Childhood*, ed. L. Jessner & E. Pavenstedt. New York: Grune & Stratton, pp. 6-77.

Bibring, G. L. (1959), Some Considerations of the Psychological Processes in Pregnancy. *This Annual*, XIV.

Bonaparte, M. (1953), *Female Sexuality*. New York: International Universities Press.

Deutsch, H. (1934), Über einen Typus der Pseudo-Affektivität ("als ob"). *Int. Z. Psa.*, XX.

Freud, A. (1936), *The Ego and the Mechanisms of Defense*. New York: International Universities Press, 1946.

Murray, H. A. (1938), *Explorations in Personality*. New York: Oxford University Press.

O.S.S. Assessment Staff (1948), *Assessment of Men*. New York: Rinehart.

PERCEPTION, REALITY TESTING, AND SYMBOLISM[1]

DAVID L. RUBINFINE, M.D. (New York)

This paper is based on the premise that the term "symbolic process" is a broad one, covering a continuum ranging from symbolic thinking to indirect representation. The hypothesis to be advanced is an attempt to grope toward a structural theory of the formal aspects of true symbol formation and symbolic thinking in the sense used by Jones (1916).[2] As Rapaport (1951b) has observed,

> . . . the interest in the formal characteristics of thought and of their disturbances is currently reawakening. Pre-psychoanalytic psychiatry showed considerable concern for these formal characteristics in disturbances of thought. Freud himself paid much attention to them, yet his work on content was fated to impress psychoanalysts, psychiatrists, and even psychologists, more than did his work on formal characteristics, probably because the former seemed more immediately useful in treating patients. It is clear, however, that the formal characteristics of thought and Freud's contribution to their understanding are shifting closer to the center of attention than ever before.

[1] Read in an abbreviated form in May, 1960 at the Annual Meeting of the American Psychoanalytic Association, as part of the Panel on "The Psychoanalytic Theory of the Symbolic Process."

Many of the ideas that appear in this essay germinated in the fecund atmosphere of a section of the Ernst Kris Study Group. Chaired by Dr. Charles Brenner, this group at the New York Psychoanalytic Institute devoted itself to the study of "Symbolism" and the "Symbolic Process" during the Academic year 1959-1960. I am deeply indebted to this group, and especially to Dr. Brenner, for the very stimulating discussion of these topics.

[2] It is almost axiomatic that all cognitive activity is symbolic in nature (e.g., language). To grapple with problems of symbolism in general would involve an attempt to formulate a general theory of cognitive processes. Rather, in this paper, I shall try to deal with the conditions for the emergence of one realm of symbols: those connected with basic biopsychological motives.

For the development of my theme, I shall assume that indirect representation operates in an ego state characterized by a fully cathected perceptual apparatus, normal waking consciousness, and full self-awareness. Symbol formation, on the other hand, seems to occur when there is a reduction of cathexis of the perceptual apparatus, inadequate investment of the boundary between self and nonself, and a corresponding alteration in consciousness. Of course, there must be transitional phases between these extremes.

In what follows I shall attempt to demonstrate that a sufficiently reduced degree of intake of external sensory stimulation interferes with the perception and testing of reality and is followed by a regressed ego state, including an alteration of consciousness. In this state, boundaries or barriers which differentiate self from nonself become fluid and "imaging" replaces perception. One of the possible issues of this state is the formation of symbols in the psychoanalytic sense.

SENSORY INTAKE AND EGO STRUCTURE

Let us open the argument with a quotation from *The Interpretation of Dreams* (1900), which, I believe, is the best possible introduction to a study of clinical and theoretical aspects of symbolism. Freud discusses, in this passage, some characteristics of the state of consciousness necessary for the pursuit of dream interpretation:

> This involves some psychological preparation of the patient. We must aim at bringing about two changes in him: an increase in the attention he pays to his own psychical perceptions and the elimination of the criticism by which he normally sifts the thoughts that occur to him. In order that he may be able to concentrate his attention on his self-observation it is an advantage for him to lie in a restful attitude and shut his eyes. . . . What is in question, evidently, is the establishment of a psychical state which, in its distribution of psychical energy (that is, of mobile attention), bears some analogy to the state before falling asleep— and no doubt also to hypnosis. As we fall asleep, 'involuntary ideas' emerge, . . . As the involuntary ideas emerge they change into visual and acoustic images . . . [pp. 101-102].

In this passage Freud is mainly concerned with psychic contents and their relationship to censorship. However, his comparison of the ego state to those of falling asleep and hypnosis suggest both structural regression and an alteration of consciousness. To achieve this state, it is noteworthy that an attempt is made to reduce intake of external perceptual stimuli to a minimum. That such states are indeed characterized by structural regression and altered consciousness is attested to by Isakower's work on falling asleep (1938). He describes vividly how cathexis of the "side of the perceptual system which faces outward is relatively depleted, while the side which faces toward the ego is more abundantly cathected . . . there results a regressive diminution of differentiation. . . ."

I shall now cite, as further evidence for the main argument, the experiments reported by Hebb (1949), Bexton et al. (1954), and Lilly (1956). In these experiments, the subjects were exposed to conditions in which most sensory stimuli were screened out by various devices. It is important to note that in these experiments tactile and kinesthetic sensations were minimized as well as stimulation of visual and auditory pathways. After the passage of a variable period of time, certain peculiar spontaneous phenomena began to appear. These were predominantly visual, ranging from geometric patterns to fully formed hallucinations:

> Among our early subjects there were several references, rather puzzling at first, to what one of them called "having a dream while awake." Then one of us while serving as a subject observed the phenomenon and realized its peculiarity and extent. The visual phenomena were actually quite similar to what had been described in mescal intoxication. . . . In general where more "formed" [i.e., more complex] hallucinations occurred they were usually preceded by simpler forms of the phenomenon. Levels of complexity could be differentiated as follows: in the simplest form the visual field with the eyes closed changed from dark to light color; next in complexity were dots of light, lines, or simple geometrical patterns. . . . Still more complex forms consisted of "wallpaper patterns" and isolated figures or objects without background (for instance a row of little yellow men with black caps on and their mouths open. . .). Finally there were integrated scenes (for instance a procession of squirrels with sacks over their shoulders marching "purposefully" across a snow field and out of the "field of vision"; prehistoric animals walking about in a jungle). . . . such scenes frequently included dreamlike distortions with the figures often being described as "like cartoons." . . .

There were also reports of hallucinations involving other senses. One subject could hear the people speaking in his visual hallucinations and another repeatedly heard the playing of a music box. Four subjects described kinesthetic and somasthetic phenomena. One reported seeing a miniature rocket ship discharging pellets that kept striking his arm and one reported reaching out to touch a door knob he saw before him and feeling an electric shock. The other two subjects reported a phenomenon which they found difficult to describe. They said it was as if there were two bodies side by side in the cubicle; in one case the two bodies overlapped partly occupying the same space. . . . In addition, there were reports of feelings of "otherness" and "bodily strangeness" [Bexton et al., 1954].

Lilly (1956) described the changes occurring in his experiments as follows:

. . . one notices that one's thoughts have shifted from a directed type of thinking about problems, to reveries and fantasies of a highly personal and emotionally charged nature. These are too personal to relate publicly, and probably vary greatly from subject to subject. The individual reaction to such fantasy material also probably varies considerably from complete suppression to relaxing and enjoying them. If the tension and the fantasies are withstood, one may experience the furthest stage which we have yet explored: projection of visual imagery. I have seen this once after a two and one half hour period. The black curtain in front of the eyes (such as one "sees" in a dark room with eyes closed) gradually opens out into a three-dimensional, dark, empty space in front of the body. This phenomenon captures one's interest immediately, and one waits to find out what comes out next. Gradually forms of the type sometimes seen in hypnagogic states appear. In this case they were small, strangely shaped objects with self-luminous borders. A tunnel whose inside "space" seemed to be emitting a blue light then appeared straight ahead.

These experiments suggest that ego structures and functions such as defense, perception, reality testing, and consciousness require for their maintenance and stability a continually varied sensory input from the external environment. It is appropriate to note here that both in the passage cited from *The Interpretation of Dreams* and in the experiments of Bexton et al. and Lilly, restriction of muscular action is a significant factor in inducing the altered state. This is clearly true of the induction phase of hypnosis as well (Gill and Brenman, 1959). That such restriction may well play a significant role in bringing about a regressed and altered ego state can be inferred from the importance given to muscular action by Freud in the genesis of the capacity to distinguish external from internal perception, i.e., in reality testing.

> In an earlier passage we ascribed to the still helpless organism a capacity for making a first orientation in the world by means of its perceptions, distinguishing both "external" and "internal" according to their relation to its muscular action. A perception which is made to disappear by an action is recognized as external, as reality; where such an action makes no difference, the perception originates within the subject's own body—it is not real. . . .
> This function of orientating the individual in the world by discrimination between what is internal and what is external must now, after detailed dissection of the mental apparatus, be ascribed to the system *Cs. (Pcpt.)* alone. The *Cs.* must have at its disposal a motor innervation which determines whether the perception can be made to disappear or whether it proves resistant. Reality-testing need be nothing more than this contrivance [Freud, 1917, pp. 232-233].

Thus, when there is an interference with the apparatus for maintaining contact with the external world, and with muscular activity or motility, regression occurs in the state of consciousness, in the capacity to test reality, and in the differentiation of the inner from the outer world. One outcome of these alterations is the appearance of visual imagery.

CONSCIOUSNESS AND REALITY TESTING

It becomes logically necessary at this point to tackle and attempt to formulate some thoughts on the nature of consciousness, attention, and their relationship to perception and reality testing. Freud (1900) first conceived of consciousness as

> . . . *a sense-organ for the perception of physical qualities.* . . . In its mechanical properties we regard this as resembling the perceptual systems *Pcpt.:* . . . susceptible to excitation by qualities but incapable of retaining traces of alterations—that is to say, as

having no memory. The psychical apparatus, which is turned towards the external world with its sense-organ of the *Pcpt.* systems, is itself the external world in relation to the sense-organ of the *Cs.,* . . . Excitatory material flows into the *Cs.* sense-organ from two directions: from the *Pcpt.* system, whose excitation, determined by qualities, is probably submitted to a fresh revision before it becomes a conscious sensation, and from the interior of the apparatus itself, whose quantitative processes are felt qualitatively in the pleasure-unpleasure series when, subject to certain modifications, they make their way to consciousness [pp. 615-616]. Becoming conscious is connected with the application of a particular psychical function, that of attention—a function which . . . is only available in a specific quantity. . . . Under certain conditions a train of thought with a purposive cathexis is capable of attracting the attention of consciousness to itself and in that event, through the agency of consciousness, receives a "hypercathexis" [pp. 593-594].

In a later paper, Freud (1911) wrote of consciousness as follows:

The increased significance of external reality heightened the importance, too, of the sense-organs that are directed towards that external world, and of the *consciousness* attached to them. Consciousness now learned to comprehend sensory qualities in addition to the qualities of pleasure and unpleasure . . . A special function was instituted which had periodically to search the external world, in order that its data might be familiar already if an urgent internal need should arise—the function of *attention*. Its activity meets the sense-impressions half way, instead of awaiting their appearance [p. 220].

It is necessary that we emphasize here the inference that prior to the development of active attention the hypothesized picture of psychic functioning is as follows: if the significant sensory stimuli (presence of the need-satisfying object) do not impinge on the psychic apparatus, hallucinatory wish fulfillment proceeds. In contrast, actively searching the world for the sense impressions by which we register and organize percepts into memorial data, even when drive tension is low or absent, provides for the time when drive tension or need will arise so that the need-satisfying object can be found in reality. You will note here that Freud had apparently anticipated the idea that adequate and varied sensory intake is necessary for the maintenance and nutriment of secondary-process operations and had seen that in the absence of the need-satisfying object, which is the main source of sensory input for the infant, the tendency was toward a topographic regression in which memory traces were cathected to perceptual intensity resulting in visual imagery of a symbolic character. This regression was primarily in the perceptual function but depended also upon the still undeveloped capacity to distinguish between the self and the nonself.[3]

> The activity of this second system, constantly feeling its way, and alternately sending out and withdrawing cathexes, needs on the one hand to have the whole of the material of memory freely at its command [Freud, 1900, p. 599].

We might add here that a command over all sensory data is also necessary. To return to Freud (1900):

> . . . it would be an unnecessary expenditure of energy if it sent out large quantities of cathexis along the various paths of thought and thus caused them to drain away to no useful purpose and diminish the quantity available for altering the external world [p. 599].

Thus, the memory image is no longer cathected to hallucinatory vividness. Instead, delay is introduced and small quantities of cathectic energy are utilized in the thought process so that all memorial and sensory data relating to the need-satisfying object can be organized to facilitate the search for the need-satisfying object in reality. The developing ego organization now controls the attention cathexes and binds them so they can invest only ideas that are central to the reality task at hand, rather than freely displaceable in the framework of drive organization.

> For this purpose the *Pcs.* system needed to have qualities of its own which could attract consciousness; and it seems highly

[3] I am aware that in the infant this hypothesized hallucinatory activity is not regressive—but rather progressive—and that imagery ontogenetically heralds the emergence of thought. Thus deprivation in our genetic model is the stimulus for imagery, the first step toward secondary-process thought. To my mind, this also constitutes an experimental confirmation of the hypothesis of the hallucinatory wish fulfillment as the ontogenetic predecessor of thought.

probable that it obtained them by linking the preconscious processes with the mnemic system of linguistic symbols, a system which
was not without quality. By means of the qualities of that system,
consciousness, which had hitherto been a sense organ for perceptions alone, also became a sense organ for a portion of our
thought-processes. Now, therefore, there are, as it were, *two* sensory surfaces, one directed towards perception and the other
towards the preconscious thought-processes [Freud, 1900, p. 574].

Freud explicitly stated that vivid sensory qualities are furnished
to consciousness by the perceptual apparatus registering data from
the external world. I can only allude here to the function of judgment. I quote from the paper on "Negation" (Freud, 1925):

The decision . . . namely, as to the real existence of something
imagined, . . . is now no longer a question of whether something
perceived . . . shall be taken into the ego or not, but of whether
something which is present in the ego as an image can also be
re-discovered in perception (that is, in reality) . . . the question
is thus one of *external* or *internal* [p. 183].

Before proceeding to further considerations it is worth noting
that when the data of environmental perception are not available,
this decision (i.e., whether something is imaginary or real) by inference becomes impossible and the distinction "I" versus "non-I"
becomes blurred. Since the most primitive antecedent of judgment
is the motor act which makes a percept disappear, and hence identifies it as external, the restriction of motility further reduces the
ability to make this distinction. Actually, the ego function of reality
testing encompasses a variety of aspects: (1) pleasant versus unpleasant; (2) veridical versus imaginary; (3) inner versus outer; (4) purely
memorial versus recoverable in reality. I believe that the material
quoted from Freud vividly illustrates the role of an ongoing and
varied stream of sensory input from the environment as a major
guarantor of the autonomy of the ego from drives. Similarly, the role
of drives in bolstering the ego's autonomy from thralldom to the
environment is clear. I am unable in this context to do more than
mention the momentous consequences of superego formation on
these structures, or, perhaps more broadly, the role of projection–
introjection mechanisms on ego development and on the development of thinking.

From this brief statement it is already evident that consciousness is not a unitary, all-or-none phenomenon, but rather a kind of sense organ with a variety of states of excitation, each of which is characterized by its own type of representation of both inner and external sensory data relayed to it. Each particular state or variety of consciousness (or awareness) has perhaps its own form of registration of percepts, as well as its unique memorial data, recall, thought forms and contents, self-experience (identity), and relationship to external reality. What I mean here is that:

1. The experiences of memory, recall, synthesis, etc., are different in different states of consciousness.
2. Cathectic changes characteristic of various levels of awareness have unique effects on the quality of memorial data, on percepts and their registration, and on learning.

A number of investigators have reported their findings in exploring such states (Silberer, 1909; Varendonck, 1921; Rapaport, 1951a). Rapaport (1951b) has summarized these findings as follows:

1. As one moves on the continuum from waking consciousness to dream consciousness, the ability for reflective awareness decreases. That is, waking consciousness is characterized by the ability to be aware of thought content and by the capacity for being aware of this awareness.

2. The more closely the dream state is approximated, the less is the capacity to exert effort or to will, that is, to regulate the thought processes voluntarily and actively.

3. The form in which intrapsychic and external perceptions are represented is clearly different for each variety of consciousness. Thus, (a) the closer the thought to waking, the more it is verbal; while the closer to dream, the more it is pictorial, that is, characterized by visual imagery. The same holds for internal and external data of perception.

(b) In waking consciousness thought is explicit while in dream forms it is implicit (by this it is meant that there are forms of knowing, not requiring explicit data: thus a patient reports a dream in which "I knew it was your office although it looked different.")

(c) Logic characterizes the formal aspects of waking thought, while in dream thought primary-process mechanisms hold sway.

(d) Changes in cathectic structure underlying the phenomena described in points 1, 2, and 3; e.g., bound and mobile energy distributions, countercathectic organization and drive-restraining structures.

These varieties of awareness are ultimately related to the delay and control of drive-impulse intrusions; that is, the restriction of operation of the pleasure principle so that impersonal registration of percepts and logical secondary processes of thought are possible. This implies also the taming of anxiety so that it operates as a signal. When a drive impulse or affect becomes imperious, it may exclude all cognitive operations except what is relevant to it. This can of course lead to a true reduction of varied intake of external sensory stimuli and thus to a regression in the perceptual function, the sense of own identity, as well as in other ego functions, and to a restriction or alteration of consciousness. Examples of the latter occur in fugue states, amnesias, and so forth (Rapaport, 1957).

Rapaport (1951a) has written of this continuum as follows:

> The gradual development to thought as experimental action from thought by "hallucinatory gratification" reflects the gradual development from monoideic consciousness of drive gratification, to polyideic consciousness of . . . perceived external reality, internal need, and memories of past experiences. This gradual development corresponds to varieties . . . of consciousness in which various balances are struck between perception of internal and external reality, in which internal experience is to various (ever decreasing) degrees experienced as external reality, and in which the differentiation between internal and external perception (thought and perception of reality) are differentiated with increasing clarity. Correspondingly, the thought forms consciously experienced change gradually from pre-logical to logical, from syncretic to abstract, from idiosyncratic to socialized [pp. 41-42].

Let us see if we can apply these concepts in a practical manner to a clinical problem. I shall choose as an example, the forgetting of dreams. Not only do we forget our dreams, but often we have great difficulty relating them. All of us are familiar with the frequently expressed dissatisfaction of patients such as, "I can't quite reproduce it," or, "It was something like this." We are all familiar with the effects of censorship and resistance, but let us for a moment consider the formal aspects of this problem. Is it possibly true that this difficulty arises partly because of the difference in the two states of consciousness that are involved, one of dreaming, the other of waking? Fisher's experiments (1956, 1957) as well as observations in hypnosis seem to bear out the idea that the images characteristic of dreams are better recalled or reproduced in reverie states, that is, in states of consciousness similar to that in which they occurred. Thus, one is left with the possibility of several types of registration, and perhaps several types or kinds of memory organization, each pertinent to its own state of consciousness.

The experiments reported by Fisher (1956, 1957) suggest that his observations of subliminal registration of stimuli may be understood as registrations *not* outside of awareness, as he proposed, but rather as occurring in a simultaneously existing state of awareness differing from waking consciousness and ordinarily masked by the cathectic organization of waking consciousness. In this connection, Klein (1959) reported that when a subject is "encouraged" into a reverie state, increased responsiveness to subliminal registrations results.

Such simultaneously existing states of awareness suggest the possibility that different types of registration also operate simultaneously and that these in turn are more or less loosely organized into clusters or memorial systems—ranging in quality from logical thought in verbal trace form to dreamlike images (see Kris, 1950). Perhaps many stimuli are simultaneously registered on different levels of awareness in such qualitatively unique forms. Each such registration is "recruited" to its own schema.

From such considerations it may be hypothesized that it is not so much a question of the transformation of one form into another (e.g., verbal trace into image), but rather that the state of consciousness prevailing at a given moment favors the emergence into awareness of one form of registration over another.

This would seem to have some pertinence to problems of schizophrenic thought and perceptual disorders. Here the ordinarily stable cathectic and countercathectic energy distributions typical of waking consciousness are disrupted; hence, registrations from all levels, of inner and outer data, achieve perceptual intensity and carry a sense of conviction of their veridicalness. They are organized according to drive schemata. Thus there is a specific disturbance of judgment, clearly based on a failure in capacity to distinguish "inner" from external.

Klein (1959) suggests that there might very well be complex organizations or schemata, each with its own characteristic conscious-ness, degree of self-awareness, distinction of self from nonself, memory registration, type of perception, etc. Thus, there is a reality-oriented schema characterized by waking consciousness which is, for example, prominent in such activities as problem solving. Such apperceptive schemata include states of consciousness, memorial data, and so forth. In this framework, there would be no such thing as "apperceptive insufficiency" but only a hierarchy of apperceptive schemata, each appropriate to certain levels of ego development and ego states. Perhaps the only exception to this rule would be where there is organic damage, and here we should specify what schema has been damaged by the organic involvement. It would be tempting, as an exercise, to carry out a systematic application of this concept, for example, to the varieties of aphasia.

Thus, in recalling a dream in the waking state, it is quite likely that "secondary revisions" are not only part of a disguise or distortion due to censorship, but that this revision is a formal characteristic of the thought of the waking state in which we recall the dream. That is, it may occur at the moment of the attempt at recall or narration.

Symbol Formation

I believe that I can now formulate my central point. Simply stated: what distinguishes symbols and symbol formation from other derivatives of primary-process operation is that the ego state de-scribed above favors the development of imagery, predominantly visual. These images constitute the raw material of symbolism. When subjected to primary process, symbol formation results. When such an image is formed, and represents a percept or memory trace thereof which has a conflicting affective charge (that is, painful and pleasur-able, good and bad) and a strong drive cathexis, there is conflict as to whether to seek out and approach, or to avoid and withdraw. The "signal" thus has opposite connotations. The conflict must revolve around an aspect of a significant object or part of the self. It is this kind of conflict which results via processes of displacement and condensation in the formation of a symbolic representation. The drive aspect of the object or organ is split away by this process and is represented by the symbol whose connection with the object, or self, is no longer in awareness (repressed). This concept stresses the adaptive nature of symbol formation, for at least three adaptive tasks are accomplished:

1. The symbol preserves the relationship to the significant object and hence ensures satisfaction. At the same time the symbol provides a target for displaced discharge of libidinal and aggressive drives.

2. The symbol contributes to a defense against "pain" and anxiety due to libidinal and aggressive drive impulses directed at the object.

3. Even the painful in mental life is preserved, if only indirectly, by a representative. Perhaps this is as much a necessary preliminary to adequate reality testing as is negation.

The reduction of sensory intake from the external world which triggers the regressed ego state and altered state of consciousness may result from severe anxiety or panic, the use of massive denial, doubting, or projection, eruption of a powerful drive impulse, toxic or organic illness, sleep, hypnosis, reverie or hypnagogic states, psychosis, prolonged solitary confinement, etc. The state of relative sensory deprivation that interests us most is of course the analytic situation where transference phenomena strikingly exemplify the regression in the distinction between self and nonself. Thus, we have all had the experience of revival of archaic ego states in our patients, loss of ego boundaries, and perceptual changes such as the emergence of pictorial imaging rather than logical forms of thought. Here, too, I would include the registration outside of waking awareness of trivial events during the analytic hour which then return symbolically in dreams, transient symptom formation, bodily sensations, and so forth.

Let me, at this point, quote from Piaget's work on *Play, Dreams and Imitation in Childhood* (1945, pp. 200-202):

If we consider the mechanism of the formation of the image in the very young child we find a very simple explanation of the anatomical symbol. The semi-consciousness of the dreamer is indeed comparable to the state of complete egocentrism characteristic of the baby's consciousness. In both cases, there is a complete lack of differentiation between the ego and the external world, and assimilation of objects to the activity of the subject. These two aspects of elementary consciousness are interdependent and for the following reason. The ego is unconscious of itself to the extent to which it incorporates external reality since consciousness of the ego is relative to the resistance of objects and of other persons. . . . It follows that all impressions which are internal or related to the body . . . are felt but not connected with the body of the subject, since there is no consciousness of the ego. They therefore become external images. . . . It is extremely difficult to put one's self in the position of a consciousness which is capable of perceiving a bodily impression without being able to connect it to an ego. Observation of a 3 or 4 months old baby, whose hand is being held outside its field of vision, will, however, provide an example of a subject who is very conscious of experiencing a tactile and kinesthetic sensation (since he struggles), but who looks all round him, and not at himself, to find the visual situation corresponding to the impression. The sleeper is in the same situation. The impression he feels, seeks, as it were a visual correspondence, and then, since he can see nothing and is even unaware that he is involved, but is capable of constructing images, he has recourse to any image which offers some point of resemblance.

Thus, it would seem that the ego state described above is the norm for the young child—hence, the by now commonplace observation that symbol formation occurs with such frequency during the early years before refinement, maturation, and consolidation of the perceptual apparatus and function.

This hypothesis also offers a tentative explanation for the observation that so large a proportion of symbols have a bodily significance. Almost all investigators of altered ego states have observed phenomena which suggest that the body image or body ego reverts or regresses to an archaic state (see Isakower, 1938; Gill and Brenman, 1959; etc.). These archaic body states are obviously linked with the bodily sensations of infantile sexuality and involve the pregenital zones as well as the genital organs. As noted before, such sensations in the regressed ego state and altered state of consciousness are apt to be represented as images.

I shall leave aside in this presentation the possible connection of this hypothesis with the "hypnoid state," and with Silberer's (1909) concept of "apperceptive insufficiency" except to note that they can both be reinterpreted in terms of structural regression (see Loewald, 1955; Holzman, 1959).

One further idea suggests itself for discussion: what is the corresponding process when there is a relative reduction of sensory input at the inner perceptual boundary of the ego? (By this I mean when repression occurs). Perhaps the result is a hypercathexis of the external boundary and a resulting search for external stimuli. Is this what Fenichel (1928) would call "the hunger for screen percepts and memories"? If this is a regular and significant component of screen-memory formation, there must be an intimate relationship between the processes involved in the former and those in symbol formation.

SUMMARY

I have attempted, in groping toward a structural theory of true symbol formation, to utilize the well-known clinical observation that there is a kind of continuum of varieties of thought ranging from the strictly ordered thought processes characteristic of problem solving, through daydreams, reveries, hypnagogic states, and dreams. I have assumed that these varieties of thought appear in a corresponding continuum of ego states of an increasingly regressed character, and that, in particular, the regression affects the perceptual function of the ego and the state of consciousness. As there is a regression in the ego state, and in consciousness, there is necessarily a decreasing capacity for active or voluntary attention and a diminution of the boundaries between self and nonself or inner and outer. In this latter state which can be experimentally reproduced by conditions favoring restriction of sensory input, imagery tends to replace perception. In this imagery, drive expresses itself more and more directly, accompanied by a decrease in capacity for secondary-process thinking. The additional operation of defense in this arena and on such raw material produces symbolic forms which are sensorial, and ego alien. These forms take shape from registrations "outside of waking awareness" both of external stimuli and bodily sensations which tend to appear in consciousness as images. This is in contrast to thoughts which appear in consciousness as derivatives or displacement substitutes of drives and which assume a rationalized, verbal trace form and serve as tools for conceptual thinking en route to the discovery of the need-satisfying object in reality. The latter are characteristically abstract, that is, nonsensorial and not affect-laden. Another significant distinction, it seems to me, is that the symbolic form appears to come unbidden and is not understood, that is, it is experienced passively by the ego, while the more rationalized thought forms seem voluntary, understood, and actively evoked by the ego.

In conclusion, where we deal with so-called universal symbols, we are obliged to assume that these are the by-products of regression in self-awareness, body image, and ego feeling—hence, altered states of consciousness, relatively independent of personal significance. They occur, obviously, in individuals with extreme differences and varieties of character structure, defense, and major conflict, and on the pathological side, widely differing neurotic, borderline, and psychotic disease entities.

BIBLIOGRAPHY

Bexton, W. H., Heron, W., & Scott, T. H. (1954), Effects of Decreased Variation in the Sensory Environment. *Canad. J. Psychol.*, VIII.
Fenichel, O. (1928), The Inner Injunction to "Make a Mental Note." In: *The Collected Papers of Otto Fenichel*, I. New York: Norton, 1953.
Fisher, C. (1956), Dreams, Images, and Perception. A Study of Unconscious-Preconscious Relationships. *J. Am. Psa. Assn.*, IV.
—— (1957), A Study of the Preliminary Stages of the Construction of Dreams and Images. *J. Am. Psa. Assn.*, V.
Freud, S. (1900), The Interpretation of Dreams. *Standard Edition*, IV & V. London: Hogarth Press, 1953.
—— (1911), Formulations on the Two Principles of Mental Functioning. *Standard Edition*, XII. London: Hogarth Press, 1958.
—— (1917), A Metapsychological Supplement to the Theory of Dreams. *Standard Edition*, XIV. London: Hogarth Press, 1957.
—— (1925), Negation. *Collected Papers*, V. London: Hogarth Press, 1950.
Gill, M. M. & Brenman, M. (1959), *Hypnosis and Related States*. New York: International Universities Press.
Hebb, D. O., *The Organization of Behavior*. New York: Wiley, 1949.
Holzman, P. S. (1959), A Note on Breuer's Hypnoidal Theory of Neurosis. *Bull. Menninger Clin.*, XXIII.
Isakower, O. (1938), A Contribution to the Pathopsychology of Phenomena Associated with Falling Asleep. *Int. J. Psa.*, XIX.
Jones, E. (1916), The Theory of Symbolism. *Papers on Psycho-Analysis*. Baltimore: Williams & Wilkins, 1938.
Klein, G. S. (1959), Consciousness in Psychoanalytic Theory: Some Implications for Current Research in Perception. *J. Am. Psa. Assn.*, VII.
Kris, E. (1950), On Preconscious Mental Proesses. *Psa. Quart.*, XIX.

Lilly, J. C. (1956). Mental Effects of Reduction of Ordinary Levels of Physical Stimuli on Intact, Healthy Persons. American Psychiatric Association: *Research Techniques in Schizophrenia* [*Psychiatric Research Reports*, V].

Loewald, H. W. (1955), Hypnoid State, Repression, Abreaction, and Recollection. *J. Am. Psa. Assn.*, III.

Piaget, J. (1945), *Play, Dreams and Imitation in Childhood*. New York: Norton, 1951.

Rapaport, D. (1951a), Consciousness: A Psychopathological and Psychodynamic View. In: *Problems of Consciousness*, ed. H. A. Abramson. New York: Josiah Macy, Jr. Foundation.

—— ed. (1951b), *The Organization and Pathology of Thought*. New York: Columbia University Press.

—— (1957), Cognitive Structures. In: *Contemporary Approaches to Cognition. A Symposium*. Cambridge: Harvard University Press.

Silberer, H. (1909), Report on a Method of Eliciting and Observing Certain Symbolic Hallucination Phenomena. In: *Organization and Pathology of Thought*, ed. D. Rapaport. New York: Columbia University Press, 1951.

Varendonck, J. (1921), The Psychology of Daydreams. In: *Organization and Pathology of Thought*, ed. D. Rapaport. New York: Columbia University Press, 1951.

SYNTHESIS AND FRAGMENTATION

ISIDOR SILBERMANN, M.D. (New York)

In this paper I shall attempt to investigate various manifestations of libido and aggression, their continuous interplay, and their roles in the development and pathology of the mind.

It is the goal of Eros, said Freud, to combine living substances and objects into ever larger wholes, and he ascribed the synthetic tendency or function to the sexual strivings, to the libido. This function of synthesis, when active in the ego, binds, unifies and integrates internal and external elements, and combines parts into units (Nunberg, 1930).

In opposition to *synthesis*, there is a tendency to keep parts separated, to prevent their unification and integration, even to detach some parts from existing wholes. This tendency may be conceptualized as *fragmentation*.

These antipodes, synthesis and fragmentation, occur in the id, in the ego, and in the superego. Synthesis and fragmentation are normal functions, essential for the structural and dynamic development of the mind. The former derives its energy from the sexual, the latter from the aggressive drive. A balance between these two drives must prevail to insure the normal functioning of the mind. Prolonged imbalance will cause malfunction and disease.

The equilibrium between libido and aggression is never rigidly stable. It is fluid, always altered, always restored, and generally leaning, it may be assumed, toward fragmentation. This assumption is based on Freud's theory of the origin of the aggressive drive, the microcosmic crystallization of the generic death instinct. The latter, striving for the re-establishment of that absolute equilibrium which existed before life began, holds a preponderant position vis-à-vis the life instinct. Perfect balance can be regained only by the total dissolution of those units which at the beginning of life came into being through the synthesis of disparate elements.

The change from the simple to the complex, from energic nothingness, motionlessness, in short, from death itself, to the dynamic activity of life inevitably creates mounting tensions. Freud assumed that this change was brought about by a force which he called the life instinct. His dualistic drive theory describes the continuous interplay of two vital forces—libido and aggression. These innate and primary, but mutually independent drives—the sexual and aggressive—constitute the powerhouse of all mental activity.

The precarious equilibrium between libido and aggression is contingent upon many factors: upon drive endowment, development, and maturation; upon the drives' quantitative and qualitative differences and their relationships; and of course upon external stimuli as well.

Man has become progressively aware of the forces of nature, their constant and universal motion. Freud, like Einstein, strove for a unified theory of these gigantic forces. Turning his eyes to the microcosm, to life, he considered the basic instincts, the life and death instincts, the *fons et origo* of the sexual and aggressive drives. The two instincts are in opposition; hence their offshoots, the two drives, oppose each other too.

For the purpose of semantic distinction, it might be helpful to assign the term "instincts" to the two basic principles, and the term "drives" to their representatives in the human mind. Therefore, I shall speak of life and death *instincts*, and of sexual and aggressive *drives*.

The life and death instincts are, according to Freud (1920, p. 46), expressions of the "conservative" nature of living substance. Under the eternal and irresistible "compulsion to repeat," they move in opposite directions, the life instinct toward permanence, the death instinct toward ultimate nothingness. From the very beginning of life on earth, both instincts enter into unceasing activity, they battle for supremacy; but in the end death is always the victor.

The two forces, said Freud (1920), are those which seek to lead what is living to death and those which perpetually are attempting and achieving a renewal of life. Since death was first and life came later, everything alive must die; therefore Freud assumed that the death instinct had priority and greater intensity.

Freud's concept of the death instinct as a primary, unyielding, and ceaselessly destructive force has received support and confirmation not only through clinical findings, but also as a result of the observations and deductions made by such biochemists as Oparin (1953), Wald (1955), Mirsky (1955), Fruton (1955), and others.

Life, it has been said, was bound to appear at some time and under certain cosmic conditions, but it could maintain its foothold only by creating larger and ever-enlarging aggregates of the first organic substance brought into existence out of inorganic matter.

Oparin, in his *Origin of Life* (1953), maintains that the normal living cell is a dynamically stable system *as long as* the *constructive* processes predominate over the *destructive*. The latter immediately gain preponderance when the physiochemical organization of the cell is disturbed. Then the protoplasm breaks up, and its components dissolve into its *original substance*.

Wald (1955) paid particular attention to the forces operating *against* life. He assumed that from *the very beginning* there must have been at work a *"fundamental destructive force*, which can be called *spontaneous dissolution* as the counterpart to *spontaneous generation."* Furthermore, the balance between these two factors guarantees life. However, the point of equilibrium "lies far over toward the side of dissolution, which proceeds much more rapidly than spontaneous synthesis." Should failure at some point appear, synthesis comes to a halt; the compound disintegrates and rapidly dies, due to the process which continuously destroys (p. 17).

Thus biology, too, tells us that disintegration and death are ever present; and that the struggle between constructive and destructive forces is waged throughout life, which can exist only as long as the forward-propelling energies outweigh those of dissolution and fragmentation.

Freud made his discovery of the "spontaneous force of dissolution" and "spontaneous generation" long before biology developed these views. Although we are aware that biology and psychology live their lives on different levels, and that the findings of the former must not simply be translated into the latter, it seems worth while to follow the prescription of Freud, Slosson (1919), Niels Bohr (1955), and other scientists, to seek information and look for connections wherever we may find them, and compare results in order to see whether relationships can be established.

True, Freud warns us to be cautious and not to forget that we are dealing only with analogies when we approach biological considerations; yet he stated (1913a, p. 180) ". . . when once the blinkers of partiality and prejudice have been removed, . . . anyone who respects the rule that scientific judgment should not be influenced by emotional attitudes will assign a high degree of biological interest to psycho-analysis." Hartmann (1939) considers biology and psychology as merely two different methods of investigation, using two different sets of concepts for exploration.

The mind is not an independent, ethereal, mystical formation ruled by magic, unrelated to law, and unconnected with matter and the influences of the outside world. It is a functional system of this world, a system which does not exist or operate outside the body and its biological interactions. Hence the question is in order whether or not our mental energies have any relationship to those existing in nature at large. Sherrington (1907) said: "Although there is matter which exists apart from mind, we know of no instance where mind exists apart from matter."

Returning to the basic instincts, the death and life instincts, it is clear that they are eternally active and all-pervading, and that they are forever attempting to achieve their aim, which in each instance is the elimination of the provocative stimulus. Both opposing instincts originate and function in every part, organ, and cell of the human body.

The function of the life instinct is visible to the naked eye, recognizable in the fact of existence, growth, and development. The death instinct, however, operates in deep concealment and silently, in the interior of the living organism, and manifests itself in our slow diurnal dying.

Freud (1930, p. 99) said:

I can remember my own defensive attitude when the idea of an instinct of destruction first made its appearance in psychoanalytical literature and how long it took until I became accessible to it. That others should have shown the same resistance, and still show it, surprises me less. Those who love fairy-tales do not like it when people speak of the innate tendencies in mankind towards aggression, destruction, and, in addition, cruelty.

Flugel (1953) depicted, with sweeping strokes, the ingenious concept of Freud's death instinct when he said: "The concept of the death instinct has a certain awe-inspiring quality, like that of a great natural phenomenon or work of art, the profound implication of which can be dimly felt, though its precise significance, as yet, escapes clear consciousness."

The constancy principle is the expression of the tendency toward a stable and constant balance. Thus the dominating characteristic of mental life is the effort to reduce, to keep constant, or to remove, those tensions that are due to stimuli. This effort is also at the base of the pleasure principle.

Already in his "Project" (1895) Freud considered *inertia* the primary function of the neurosystem. Any change of this inertia due to an increase in the stimulus quantity is experienced as unpleasure, any discharge of it and movement back toward inertia as pleasure.

As man develops, the further he moves away from the state of absolute energic nothingness, which is death, the greater are the tensions. There is not only the all-embracing opposition of the two basic instincts, the life and death instincts, which are the macroscopic version of libido and aggression, but there are the intersystemic and intrasystemic tensions and the tensions resulting from the impact with reality.

A dynamic system is characterized by the flux and impermanence of equilibrium, and by the tendency to re-establish a state of balance. Psychopathology, generally speaking, appears when the effort to re-establish dynamic balance fails. The successful achievement of this dynamic equilibrium through the reduction of tensions is conceptualized as adjustment or adaptation. This principle has been stressed by Plato, Aristotle, and Spinoza, by Freud and his school, by Gestalt psychologists (e.g., Köhler, 1929; Koffka, 1935), and by many others.

Every "task" disturbs balance and increases tension. The completion of tasks re-establishes balance. Tasks not completed leave in their wake tensions which strive for discharge (Zeigarnik, 1927). This fact can be observed, for example, in the role of the day residue in the mechanism of dream formation. The dream is in part a tension-reducing instrument, striving for the re-establishment of emotional balance. As further means of maintaining equilibrium, the ego develops foresight, the ability to anticipate future exigencies, and to prepare new solutions which, carried out without major investment of psychic energy, render unnecessary sudden large expenditures at a later date.

Some habits as well as some mechanisms of defense, at one time adequate, may continue to be used when new solutions, more appropriate to the current situation, would be required. If the old, now inappropriate mechanisms persist, psychological failure may result. These old habits are rigid and stale, and obsessively adhesive. They are uneconomical: being incomplete and inadequate solutions, they are charged with the spark of unrest, and they cry out for further release.

The advance to higher states of development creates increasing demands for increasingly complex solutions and adjustments. If more complex efforts at stabilization fail to produce equilibrium at more advanced levels, attempts will obviously be made to establish balance by more primitive methods, by regressing to lower and more primitive strata, where the reduction of tension is achieved with less difficulty. This point was also stressed by Hughlings Jackson, who spoke of the hierarchy of levels of the mind, and discussed regression as a means of re-establishing equilibrium. Regressions are, according to Freud, expressions of *inertia,* and as such are nurtured by the force opposing propulsion, i.e., by the death instinct.

The proneness to establish equilibrium on primitive levels, by primitive methods, in the hope to achieve more easily a reduction of tension, causes the individual to remain far behind in his mental growth. His is a confusion of past and present, with the resulting false approach to the future. Antiquated wishes, incarcerated in the unconscious, move powerfully into the foreground and demand urgent gratification, as though time and development had stopped. The need for flexible and mature adaptation to changing circumstances is denied. Instead of looking ahead for new solutions, he yields to the rearward force which draws him back to old wishes and fantasies. His tensions are reduced, but so is his functioning.

There are many individual variations in the management of tensions; there are many different methods for the re-establishment

of balance; there are variations of tension tolerance, individual differences in drive endowment and drive development; there are
variations in the defense system permitting or delaying the release
of tension; and there are individual differences in the channels of
discharge and their directions.

However, conflict together with its concomitant tensions is a
sine qua non for the proper development and growth of the mind.
The attempt to prevent conflict and frustration cannot create a
firmer equilibrium. On the contrary, it will adversely affect the
process of adaptation and adjustment.

Of the two basic drives, the sexual drive is the more obvious. It is
clearly visible in the cathexis of the ego, of objects, and of the self,
and in the expressions and distortions of libidinal development.
Man's sexual strivings loudly and urgently demand gratification.

The aggressive drive, on the other hand, is less obvious. It con-
ceals itself more successfully, and the defenses against it are solid
and steadfast—witness its frequent and vigorous denials. Its manifestations can nevertheless be recognized in most normal and pathological phenomena.

We have assumed that the two *instincts* do not have their genesis
in any one part or organ of the body, but that they are all-pervading
and ubiquitous. Similarly, the two *drives* originate everywhere. However, they seem to have assembled in greater concentration at some
points and in some organs, which we have been accustomed to consider their points of origin, as when one is tempted to think of the
sexual glands as the matrix of the libido and of the muscles as the
birthplace of aggression.

Few will dispute the fact that the two basic instincts are separate
and distinct entities. With the assumption that the sexual and aggressive drives are derivatives of these basic instincts, no room remains
for the idea, expounded by Fenichel (1935), Lichtenstein (1935),
Simmel (1944), and others, that libido and aggression are under some
conditions interchangeable.

Just as the two instincts are in constant opposition, so are the
two drives. They move in different directions, and they aim at different goals. The sexual drive aims to bind, to join together, to
attach. The aggressive drive aims to destroy, to disrupt, to disjoin,
to *attack*. For the perpetuation of life, and in order to resist the on-

slaught of aggression, libido must cathect objects in increasing numbers, enlarge its domain, and erect firmer structures.

The aggressive drive strives for the maintenance of the isolated minute fragment, and for the destruction of bonds, thwarting the aims of the constructive and unifying libido. The aggressive drive turns against the cathexes of the sexual drive wherever they occur. For instance, when we speak of the withdrawal of libido from an object, we must ask ourselves what energy has caused this detachment, since by definition libido does not voluntarily abandon a position of attachment. Before libido moves to new positions, it must be freed from its previous position. Such detachment cannot be brought about by libido itself, but only by the disjoining aggressive drive. On the other hand, whenever the latter is concentrated overwhelmingly in the self, the ego directs aggression toward external objects, and thus prevents the destruction of the self. It may be assumed that the outward direction of aggression is in the service of the preservation and the prolongation of life. This is brought about by libido.

Just as the sexual drive is transformed and neutralized, so too is the aggressive drive. Neutralized aggression, as well as neutralized libido, is essential for the proper structuring and functioning of the ego and the superego.

The life instinct is strongest at birth, and reaches its climactic fulfillment when it enables life to re-create itself. The death instinct, on the other hand, gaining momentum with each advancing year, conquering more and more territory, reaches its culmination with death.

Synthesis is nurtured by libido and fragmentation by aggression; therefore we may expect a similar alteration in the configuration of these two functions in time. So it is that with age fragmentation acquires increased momentum as against synthesis.

Since libido and aggression operate in all systems of the mind, we can observe synthesis and fragmentation, though with obviously different *modi operandi,* in the id, ego, and superego. What we have been accustomed to calling the synthetic function is "synthesis at its best," and what we have been accustomed to understanding as fragmentation is fragmentation "at its worst." The functions of synthesis and fragmentation mature with the maturation of the ego.

Whereas the primary process is characterized by a chaotic, wild use of synthesis and fragmentation, the secondary process is characterized by an orderly use of these functions. Synthesis and fragmentation "at their best" in harmonious interplay produce the function of *differentiation*. Through this selectivity, wild synthesis is prevented, the fragments are kept apart until they can be properly aligned, and the ego can sift, select, and arrange as to time, place, sequence, and value.

If synthesis and fragmentation "at their best"—both normal functions of the ego—are in proper equilibrium, mental health results. This in turn depends on the proper neutralization of libido and aggression. If for various reasons, an invasion of the ego by unmodified and untamed drives occurs, the balance between synthesis and fragmentation will be thrown out of alignment. Such an invasion, spearheaded by the aggressive drive, will lead to adverse effects in the total functioning of the ego and thus to psychopathology (fragmentation and synthesis "at their worst").

Fragmentation "at its best" is necessary also for our orientation and concept formation. It cuts off and drives out peripheral perceptions, and keeps them at a point below the threshold of awareness as subliminal values of our perceptual field, cathected with only very small quantities of attention, making it possible for an effective amount of attention to become available for the cathexis of focal points.

Fusion of the two opposing drives is one of the fundamental steps in the development of the mind, and is a product of the binding function of the libido.

Defusion, a product of aggression, comes into play when regression appears. The deeper the regression, the more scattered the defusion, until the opposing forces of libido and aggression have dissolved their unity and stand once more in isolation.

Between the extremes of synthesis and fragmentation "at their best" and synthesis and fragmentation "at their worst," there are disturbances of balance which may be said to be *still within the normal range*. Although they represent deviations from normal equilibrium, they cannot be called truly pathological. They are temporary, and the restoration of the equilibrium is a relatively simple process, as we observe in sleep, dreams, brief intoxications, during fever, and in some women in connection with their menstruation (Silbermann, 1950).

Disturbed equilibrium during sleep is the soil in which dreams grow. Fragmentation here shows its aggressive activity, interfering with order and coherence, and disrupting the secondary process. The primary process moves into the breach, leading to the mingling of divergent elements, which during the day would have been mutually intolerant.

However, these disarranged units will not remain fragmented for long. Their isolated parts, immediately exposed to the synthetic power of the libido, will be conjoined into new groupings which, in accordance with the degree of neutralization, will present different aspects, values, and expressions.

One may schematically describe *normal* balance as that condition in which libido, pitted against aggression, sustains an advantageous position and, always available in more than sufficient amounts, counteracts disturbances caused by the destructive drive. Should the balance change in favor of aggression, temporary or long-lasting disturbance will inevitably result.

Since we assume the forces for the achievement of "normal balance" to be neutralized drives which have lost their id quality, we must also assume that with age, when libido declines, the process of neutralization, deriving its energies from libido, works less effectively, thus permitting the aggressive drive to move into the foreground, where it brings about what we are familiar with as the regression of the aging.

When, however, the function of neutralization continues to sustain itself, as it does in some people even in advanced years, the mind continues to mature and mellow. This phenomenon perhaps explains, in part at any rate, that rare older man, the sage.

In the *pathological* disorders of balance, where the swing from pole to pole is violent, untamed aggression forces libido from its barricades. Libido, similarly untamed, rushes into battle with excesses of its own; and the consequence of this unresolved struggle between unneutralized or insufficiently neutralized aggression and libido is pathology. Synthesis and fragmentation "at their worst" produce mental malformations, disturbances and distortions.

For the purpose of a schematic representation, let us assume

45790

that before life was created there existed free-floating fragments, not yet united into functional units. The creation of physical and mental life depended on the appearance of a binding force which would join the fragments into systems, and keep them in their assigned positions. This unification, we may imagine, would be achieved by "links" charged with libidinal energy. The establishment and the continued existence of synthesized units are threatened by the destructive drive which might cause their fragmentation and ultimate annihilation. In order to repulse the ceaseless assaults of the fragmentizing aggressive force, libido must flow without interruption into these "links," which must be visualized at one and the same time as flexible and resilient, yet firm and resistant.

This flexibility permits the parts to shift freely, within fixed limits, without causing damage to the structure and its internal order. These slight shifts permit the parts and the whole to appear in a variety of colors, forms, and aspects. The elastic quality of the "links" admits the interpolation of new fragments, with links of their own, resulting in new formations, new concepts, and many variations and nuances.

It can now be said that these enlarged units have acquired a new size as well as a new quality. A new structure has been created. There is a constant progression from the fragment to the unit, from the smaller to the larger whole; and the quantitative alteration tends to become a qualitative change as well.

As for the "links" we have been picturing, we must assume that in the state of normal balance their cathexes tend to show an abundance, actually a preponderance, of libido. During the disturbances of balance within the normal range, the "links" are temporarily loosened. This occurs as the result of a reduced flow of libidinal energy accompanied by a simultaneously increased influx of aggression. There seems to exist a reciprocal relationship, the decrease of one generating the increase of the other, and vice versa. The "links," however, are neither damaged nor broken; and they retain enough resilience to tighten up again as soon as an increase in synthetic force appears; and we see the re-establishment of the earlier well-ordered alliance.

Should, however, a large quantity of unneutralized aggression flow into the "links" coinciding with a deficiency in synthetic libidinal force, the "links" will suffer damage and the whole will tend to fall apart. The fragments will break away from each other, bringing injury to the total structure, with possibly far-reaching pathological consequences.

This could be illustrated in the development of the child. At first it is the mouth that is used for grasping and for recognition. Then the little hands touch and handle each object as the child eyes it from all angles, until its various aspects and facets move into a meaningful unit with proper sense, relationship, and place, in an orderly system. The grasp of the tiny fingers has extended to the grasp of the mind. Grasping and recognition are, even in language, synonymous.

In the beginning, he and his mother's breast are his whole world, a limited horizon indeed. Slowly his view enlarges, he sees other parts of her body, still unconnected and isolated, which he touches, but cannot yet grasp. They are still too strange and too vast for his little hands and his little mind.

But all the time the psychic representations of his experience are being deposited. Slowly, building stone is added to building stone, until finally the totality of his mother is completed, a new formation with a new and enlarged meaning, and with new and manifold functions: *mama* (Latin for the giving breast) has become Mama, the giving mother. Thus a new concept has been organized and unified out of the accumulation of separate parts. This child now moves forward again, progressively disjoining himself from his mother who has become part of the external world; while he has grown from a part of her into a new Gestalt, his separate self. More and more objects are cathected, and when synthesis and differentiation unify, discriminate, and systematize isolated experiences and impressions into meaningful units, pictures are transformed into ideas, into ever enlarging conceptual aggregates with ever changing attributes. Through the continuous cathexis of object representations, the function of thinking matures.

The function of differentiation develops slowly, and derives its power and strength from neutralized libido and aggression. It is therefore not surprising that the young child cannot sift and separate opposites, cannot regulate time and place.

In progressive development, the neutralization of a considerable part of the drives takes place. The seeds for the growth of synthesis "at its best" are sown. With its blossoming, the first steps into the world of differentiation and abstraction are made; and the one-dimensional concrete thought processes sprout into multi-dimensional abstract thinking, and the formation of new and expanding concepts.

Before thoughts attain maturation and recognition in the conscious mind they pass through a series of stages. We assume that the first object representations are indefinite and unclear, their images are fused, and they are apt to undergo affective transformation (Schilder, 1920). The connections between the various thought elements necessary for the apperception of the whole concept cannot be given visual expression (Freud, 1900).

Abstract thinking distinguishes the grown, developed personality from the child, the primitive man, the schizophrenic patient. It is the weapon with which barriers are breached, limits erased, and frontiers extended. It is the source of the power that carries man into worlds otherwise untouchable, invisible—in short, into worlds transcending those immediately apprehensible through his senses.

Abstract thinking becomes a mental activity only when an optimal balance between synthesis and fragmentation "at their best" has made possible the highly important function of differentiation.

I shall now discuss synthesis and fragmentation as they appear in the creative activity of the artist and scientist. These functions can be assumed to be *beyond the range of the normal.*

Although the aims of the artist and scientist differ, and their approaches traverse different roads, they resemble each other in the potency of their overcathected "links" which they seem capable of expanding beyond ordinary limits. They possess the motivation and the strength to enlarge the boundaries of their images. They are able to swing freely from the conscious to the preconscious, to the unconscious and back again, and to move in the rarified spheres of great abstraction and profound ideation. These accomplishments the artist and scientist achieve because theirs is the gift of moving fragments about and of rearranging them playfully and at will, as it were, until they have succeeded in creating new images, new contents, and even new functions, which until then had been undreamed of. They are able to separate parts from the whole and focus on each of them with the greatest intensity, cutting off all undesired peripheral stimuli. The fragmented, cut-off perceptions remain in easy reach, always accessible to "the internal eye." This unusual capacity permits the scientist and the artist to use their perceptions as the springboards for the dive into the depths of the mind, without fear of passing the point of no return. Superior synthesis is the conveyor belt that carries back to the creative mind images loaded with the treasures of the unconscious.

The achievements of the scientist and artist are the culminating attainments, on the highest levels of abstraction, of synthesis and fragmentation "at their best" in a balance unattainable by ordinary men.

We shall now attempt to investigate synthesis and fragmentation as they appear in psychopathology. Pathology, in general terms, can be defined as a breakdown of highly differentiated functional systems into less differentiated or even disorganized fragments. The pathological mind shows disorganization and dissolution of units under the impact of pathological fragmentation.

Bleuler (1911) described how the thinking of schizophrenic patients becomes disconnected, how the chain of thought deteriorates and is broken, diverted, resulting in illogical, confused thinking. This fragmented state cannot endure for long. Permanent fragmentation is synonymous with death, for as long as life continues, libido strives for synthesis. Dissolution is thus slowed down and interrupted by synthesis, which rushes into the breach and attempts to force new unifications of the shattered fragments. The process of restitution in psychoses is a frantic attempt to counteract fragmentation by frenzied synthetic maneuvers. Fragments are constantly reunited, without regard to their place and structure. They are drawn together by the need for unification. The result is synthesis "at its worst."

The thinking of such patients, through condensation, displacement, and symbolization, becomes unclear and incoherent. Further deterioration results from the resurgence of affective transformation, with the re-entry of unrefined primitive affectivity with neither modulation nor shading. Thinking becomes overcharged or undercharged with emotions, swinging between extreme aggression and extreme libido, giving rise to ambivalence as well as to emotional emptiness.

The endeavors of schizophrenic patients to collect their thoughts, to realign them, to employ selectivity, to readjust affects and ideas generally fail. In the psychotic patient, due to regression, there is a preponderance of un-neutralized aggression and libido. This causes a disturbance of the function of differentiation. Newly created units are at times torn apart by excessive fragmentation, which in cooperation with synthesis "at its worst" produces pathological monster formations, such as delusions, hallucinations, etc. The body image is disturbed or damaged as is the image of the self, giving rise to feelings of bodily imperfections, or to a feeling of depersonalization, and the like.

There are many more signs of regressive movement, e.g., extreme errors in spelling, or eccentric or disturbed syntax, and particularly changes of the voice which grows either too loud or too monotonous, lacks rhythm and fullness, is uninspired, has no vitality and emotion.

Systematized thoughts and concepts need, for their final formulation, word symbols which are connected by links. When these links are weakened by the influx of unneutralized aggression, fragmentation results. The words themselves, or their emotional content, may be lost. They follow one another in seemingly purposeless pursuit, attracted to each other by the charm of melody and sound or by pictorial similarity, and flow together into senseless sentences.

Here again synthesis "at its worst" binds together these free-floating shadows of words, glues them somehow together, piles them into a disorderly heap, in grammatical disorder, into a word salad. It is uncontrolled aggression which disturbs all means of communication, deters the construction of a Gestalt, and prevents letters, words, and sentences from assuming their proper place in orderly formations, structured with logic and sense. The formation of thoughts in these patients is disturbed, disruptive associations prevail, irrelevant perceptual images intrude, undesirable peripheral stimuli are not excluded, and emotions are not meaningfully connected, controlled, or allocated.

The step-by-step construction of the conceptual world, as noted in the life of the child, may also be observed in patients recovering from coma and in the behavior of schizophrenic patients returning to consciousness from insulin shock (Silbermann, 1940). The shock apparently reduces the ego to an almost primitive level. These patients, very much like infants, move through the range of tactile experience; parts, at first isolated and strange, are gradually synthesized into larger units, until the shattered and fragmented Gestalt of the mind is finally reconstructed. These patients, too, must replace one-dimensional concepts, to which in their illness they have regressed, with multi-dimensional abstract ideas. They must reacquire the sense of time and space which will permit them to put objects into their proper relationships. At first these patients view their fingers, their arms, their legs, as though these body parts were strange objects with no relationship to themselves. Only slowly, with the help of all their sensory organs and reawakened memories, do they rebuild the body image, and the image and the concepts of the outside world.

The following case report illustrates the concept of synthesis and fragmentation, as outlined above. It demonstrates how aggression, untamed and untransformed, and probably also increased in volume, brought about pathological fragmentation and hindered proper integration and synthesis.

An Englishwoman suffering from severe attacks of anxiety was given to explosive outbursts of anger, was unable to concentrate, study, or work, and could not restrain her urge to overeat. Her most outstanding symptom was extreme loneliness, which at times, particularly in the late afternoon, gradually developed into panic. In order to escape her high-pitched, intolerable anxiety, she spent many hours of the day at the movies, devouring large quantities of candy, nuts, cookies, and other delicacies. Mysteries and Wild West films fascinated her, and she identified herself with the screen's victims of violence. On leaving the theater, feelings of guilt, depression, hopelessness, and helplessness again overcame her and threw her into a state of utter despair. After many hours of extreme restlessness and panic she would feel as though she had been defeated in a raging battle. Those "witch hours," as the patient called them, lasted into the evening, and explained her surrender to alcohol, as a means of overcoming her mounting anxiety.

In her extreme loneliness she would cling to anyone near, pleading for support and affection, but always remaining unsatisfied and empty. It was as though storms were about to uproot her shallow

ties and to unbalance her precarious equilibrium which, she believed, could be restored only by a large supply of external warmth.

She felt as though she had to fight for her life against devilish
forces which aimed to destroy everything important and good within
her. After such wild and painful hours, it seemed to her that she
was shattered beyond repair. She was almost never completely at
ease; and only with tremendous exertion could she perform her daily
duties. During the hours of relative freedom from anxiety and of
quasi stability, she was efficient, considerate, seemingly composed,
and quite witty. However, like waters temporarily dammed, tensions
rose again, and she changed into a "witchlike" destructive creature
who, with shrill sibilance, would war against those around her,
especially her mother. Yet she was never assaultive or completely
unable to control her rages. When she sensed the feeling of onrush-
ing disintegration, she craved emotional support which, when available, flowed into her like energy through a lifeline, and kept her
from "falling apart."

In the beginning of her analysis, she improved rapidly, as if she
had borrowed libido and strength from the analyst, which seemed
to counterbalance her destructive urges. Soon, however, her acting
out moved dramatically to the surface, and during a vacation she
could not share with her therapist she eloped, like a character in one
of her favorite movies. With her sudden marriage her affairs went
from bad to worse. But instead of trying to improve her situation,
she wished only to free herself from a marriage in which she felt
driven into dependency, helplessness, and despair.

She could not offer affection which, she stated, was in short
supply. She said she needed "emotional oxygen" for the strength to
counter her destructive tendencies. There was, however, never
enough love, never enough strength, available to her, and this deficit
made her feel like a bottomless, empty pit. Her condition was
aggravated by a narcissistic husband who was neither willing nor
equipped to lend her even the slightest amount of emotional help.
She believed she was rapidly sliding downhill toward her "inescapa-
ble doom." After her marriage, her anxiety, tension, and frustration
grew, and now old obsessions made their reappearance, such as ideas
of self-destruction and suicide. Added to her aggressive thoughts

toward her family, a "fate-driven frenzy" to drag herself down into destruction made her life a constant torture and misery.

A child was born to her; and now at last there was one circumscribed area that remained somewhat undisturbed. She was apparently quite able to care for, guide, and train her first and then her second child.

With her first child particularly she behaved almost normally. She was warm and affectionate with him, and they were harmoniously attuned to each other. The boy appeared to have taken over the task of supplying his mother with the libidinal energy she needed, thus helping her somewhat in her attempts to regain her balance. However, there were times when her anxiety was greater than the strength she was able to borrow from her young son. This was particularly so when unyielding death wishes against herself held her in breathless suspension. She often cried out: "I don't know where I belong or who I am. First I am a devouring monster, then I myself am in danger of being devoured." At such times she was thrown into the depths of misery, and tormenting words plagued her thoughts: "Kill yourself. Kill yourself."

Two diametrically opposed self-images lived side by side; the kindly, charming, good-humored woman, and the tortured, frightened, "witchlike" person obsessed by ideas of suicide. This division she expressed as follows: "I am two. I am twins. I have an awful sister in me. Let's call her Deviline. She refuses to grow up, constantly demanding that I pursue my pleasures, no matter how irrational they may be; and she will not brook delay. If I don't comply immediately, she becomes nasty, and forces me to become obnoxious and destructive." At the height of this split, she felt lost and extremely lonely, forsaken by everybody. During such moments of consuming despair she could visualize only two solutions of her dilemma; either to become the "beastly witch," like Deviline, or to eliminate herself through suicide.

Gradually another solution pressed itself upon her. She intensified her surreptitious drinking and, in frequent alcoholic escapades, she attempted to drown her "twin." However, instead of drowning and poisoning Deviline by the liquor, Deviline rose to real power, and the patient became an unpleasant, cursing, aggressive, destructive person, even against her children, as if she were attempting to tear down whatever she had built up. At the onset of these excesses, she would feel guilty and shout, "I didn't do it. It was not me. It's not my fault." But later she acted as though she were entitled to her misbehavior, and had chosen, instead of a sudden suicide, a slow descent into the gutter, where her "nasty twin" could attain fulfillment.

She tried to explain her all-pervading feelings of loneliness, helplessness, and hopelessness as the result of her fragmented personality, and she deplored the absence of integration in her mind. In order to illustrate her point, she said: "I cannot exist with my self, because I have no self. I am torn apart, or perhaps not put together yet. I need people to complete me, and to fill me in where I am lacking."

She moved in a circle of friends consisting of "impersonal men and women, without identity and with borrowed personalities," who attempted by some peculiar arrangement to schedule the process of "lending strength" by appointing, for a fixed period, a leader whom the rest emulated and considered their ideal of beauty, reality orientation, and direction. The patient depicted this arrangement as follows:

"When I lose my identity and fall apart, which happens every so often, I am nothing, a shadow without shape and character, without strength, color, or content. Then I try to become the mirror image of somebody else, acquiring temporarily her qualities, even those which I detest. I need to feel I am somebody, whoever this somebody might be, because it is better to be anybody than nobody at all. I manage to get along with everybody because, chameleonlike, I can assimilate anyone's personality, anyone's. I have been so many people in my life, it's truly unbelievable. Unbelievably tragic! I am a shifting personality, kept by my destructive twin from being my true self, from becoming a total person. It's intolerable."

The women from whom she had temporarily borrowed her "personalities" were characterized, as she pictured them, by a kind of "unhealthy hostility" which made them fighters for everything unwholesome, evil. They were "destructive Amazons, Mau-Maus, instead of mamas." She soon found it impossible to lean on them "because they change like rainbows. They are not real, but hazy."

However, these shifting and shallow identifications, though they seemed temporarily to strengthen her against the disruptive power of her aggressive drives, ended in a progressive loss of self-esteem, with mounting distress and panic. She felt she had lost more and more ground. Her ego was drowning in the depths of her id.

Although liked by her friends, she felt rejected and slighted. "How can anyone," she asked, "love a person who herself doesn't know love, who wants only to harm herself and destroy her environment. I don't know why I want to kill myself; I want to live so much! I reach out for the good; yet I find my hands filled with dirt and poison." Once, with a feeble smile, she said: "If these opposing forces must fight, why must they choose *me* for their battleground?"

If in her distrustful, doubting, frightened mood anyone reproached her, or doubted the seriousness of her predicament, she felt a heavy black cloud descending on her, hurling her to the ground, evoking sensations of drowning and suffocation. This terrifying state increased her craving for liquor. The bottle, like a comforting mother, would give her peace and relaxation, would liberate her from "this nightmarish cloud" of wretchedness. In these terrifying moments she felt she was standing before a closed door, forbidding and foreboding, from which a black monster, with the shadowy outlines of the terrorizing cloud, would leap at her and bury her beneath its suffocating weight.

Her deep frustrations and fantasies, as she stated, went far back into her childhood. As far as her memories reached, she had never been happy but always sad, despairing, isolated and alone. She felt rejected by her mother and not too eagerly accepted by her father, who had stood in awe of his wife's wrath. Her mother had, at first, not wished to become pregnant. She had tried to free herself from her pregnancy, and finally, "through an accident," had delivered the child prematurely. Nor had the girl's birth been greeted with joy. The patient complained that her buxom mother had refused her breasts to her and that she was handed from nurse to nurse, from maid to maid.

She remembered her father as a temperamental and angry man, who more than once, with terrifying vigor, "beat me to a pulp." One of the reasons for his explosive anger was, supposedly, her sneaking into the parental bedroom where she often surprised her parents in sexual intercourse. In order to discourage her nightly excursions, her parents' bedroom door was locked. But she continued her visits, remaining outside the door, alone and forsaken in the dark corridor. On several occasions, the door was suddenly opened and, pursued by her scolding father, now the black cloudlike monster of her fantasies, she fled to her room, frightened, furious, and fiercely unhappy.

Her longing to be close to her mother and father, to find protection in their warmth, remained unsatisfied. Her wish to be held close to her mother's body, to feel her affection, was unfulfilled. She related how her father granted her greater physical nearness in her later childhood years. She recalled sitting in his lap and rocking playfully to and fro enjoying, as she vaguely remembers, orgastic sensations from these masturbatory movements. This game was often followed by outbursts of anger and abuse by her parents. There was a pattern to these events. Pleasure in secretive play with father was followed by maternal reproach and paternal punishment.

Her report of enforced loneliness was supported by her account of an extremely traumatic experience during the war when she was alone with a maid while their house in London was being bombed.

Her marriage, she thought, would end her isolation. She would gain strength through her husband who would be powerful and overflowing with energy. To enjoy the proof of his power, she wanted to be aggressively taken by him, with violently passionate sexual force; and by their flowing together she would grow into something whole, and thus end her self-fragmentation. Unfortunately, she chose a partner unable to give of himself or to satisfy her wishes. Soon she developed destructive fantasies toward him like those toward her mother. When she was overcome by her destructive urges, crushed by her guilt, and felt thoroughly contemptible, she identified herself entirely with Deviline and at long last seemed to have found, in her alcoholic stupor, a measure of peace.

"When I drink," she said, "I don't suffer from my second half, because like good twin sisters we've become one. We've come to terms on *her* level. I lose my tensions when I drink. In my alcoholic unconsciousness I finally find rest, maybe some sort of harmony with the evil forces battling inside of me."

This patient, her feet fixed on the road to self-destruction, seemed unable to combat her urge to kill herself. Her twin sister, Deviline, was her arrested, immobilized, ungratified, eternally longing and unhappy childhood self, a rebel, not without cause, but without prospect, without hope.

When failure ended her effort to fill her libidinal vacuum with parental closeness, affection, and love, aggression rushed in and drove her to hostile, destructive behavior. The schism, which was never mended for long, was seen and sensed in all areas. Sexual intercourse, for example, brought physical satisfaction, but never relaxed her mind, which violently demanded more and more intense orgastic pleasure; and thus, immediately after coitus, she was driven to prolonged and repeated masturbation. In her dreams, she was swimming in the sea and watching herself from the top of a mountain at the same time; or she was lying in bed and walking through the streets synchronously; or her brain was removed from her skull and placed high in the air, whence her mind observed her body on the ground; or she dreamed that her father fondled the nipples of Deviline while she saw from a distance how he tenderly stimulated her "second half"; or that she was in the analyst's office, a well-behaved child, eager to please and to learn, while her twin sister hid her head under a pillow and screamed, jumping and thrashing about. Her life had never provided her with adequate protection against these frightening denuding emotions that made her a stranger to herself. She said: "Other people are safe. They belong. They don't constantly quarrel with life, as I do. Slowly I am dying, though I've never really lived."

The patient attributed her condition to a serious developmental flaw, "as though sperm and ovum had flowed into each other but had not joined, and were living their separate lives, battling and repulsing each other, instead of engulfing each other and harmoniously working together in the service of my development."

It fits well into this picture that in moments of panic, synthesis and fragmentation "at their worst" made their appearance in her thought processes. This intelligent woman then lost her judgment and was incapable of distinguishing the real from the unreal. A high level of abstraction as well as her capacity for an easy flow of free associations gave way to an apparently absolute block in both areas.

Regression to the level of concreteness and temporary delusion-like accusations and ideas of reference stood out in sharp contrast to her more normal patterns. She had an excellent command of the English language and its niceties; yet she became unable temporarily to distinguish fine shades in synonyms, or to grasp advanced or abstract concepts. She found herself temporarily arrested in a maze of primitive, repetitive, childlike, unrealistic demands. She compared this state of narrow, simple thinking to the desperate racing round and round of a frightened mouse in a cage.

Something prevented her from maturing and developing, something polluted her feelings and forced her into patterns of behavior which she found alien, obnoxious, and despicable. It was a disturbance of neutralization which led to the invasion of the ego by untransformed, untamed drives, particularly the aggressive drive, which disrupted existing functions and structures, and impeded the normal progress of synthesis. If there is a disturbance in the libido Anlage, the process of neutralization is bound to be defective and inefficient; this defect in turn will adversely affect the fusion of the drives.

The lack of fusion may also be due to a disturbed drive constellation, in which the aggressive drive is too strong and stormy, neither balanced nor sufficiently neutralized by libido. The result is a faulty compromise between the two drives, with a disturbed equilibrium that favors aggression.

If the environment is propitious, flaws in the drive endowment and neutralization may be tolerated, and a measure of equilibrium achieved, without paying the price of too deep a regression. Without that compensation, the untransformed, untamed drives may cast their long shadows over the child's whole life.

The preoedipal character disorders with autistic and symbiotic tendencies belong to this picture, in which "the longing for belonging" is an outstanding feature (Silbermann, 1957). It is the need for a continuing supply of libido which persists throughout the life of these patients. Without it they feel starved, and life seems to them an intolerable, forced march on the road to death. These people are wanting in "emotional oxygen," as our patient expressed it. Its absence makes them feel asphyctic, hopelessly empty, slowly strangulating. They correctly feel fragmented, as though they consisted of isolated and contradictory parts barred from useful fusion and cooperation. They may be keen-minded and accumulate much knowledge; but it is unrelated and useless, unsynthesized and unintegrated. They are bewildered people; and they lead a kind of quasi-tangential existence, precariously on the fringe of social contact with people.

The influence of the primary process can be discerned also in the abundance of acting out, in the *pars pro toto* approach, in displacements and condensations, and in the tendency to let quick generalizations replace painstakingly produced principles. This dysfunction of the secondary process is due to the flooding of the ego by unneutralized drives, especially the inadequately neutralized aggressive drive. The transformation and binding of the id drives, and the progress from the primary to the secondary process, release tension and create pleasure. The flooding of the ego with unneutralized drives, on the other hand, causes anxiety, bewilderment, disorientation, and panic.

It seems to be axiomatic that libido will seek out the affirmative, the constructive, the positive pleasure; and that aggression will seek out the destructive, the pleasure of pain. Libido, on the way to gratification, normally moves from forepleasure to satisfaction, which brings about reduction of tension and a state of ease. Aggression runs a different course. It moves through foretorture, torture, to aftertorture.

Patients, like the young woman described here, seem to be on a constant rampage, in search of masochistic torture. They are never able to satisfy their hunger for suffering and self-destruction. They are blessed with no response comparable to that of the orgastic satisfaction of the sexual drive. Theirs is an unyielding demand for more and more torment. There seems to be no orgastic exhaustion of the aggressive drive which apparently derives its energy from some never-ending source.

Pathological fragmentation, which prevents normal synthesis, probably lies at the root of feelings of strangeness, depersonalization, and derealization.

In the patient described above, as in many emotionally disturbed individuals, an interesting phenomenon can be observed. Although their symptoms have recurred again and again, they behave as if each attack of panic differed from those that preceded it, as if they had never before experienced similar symptoms. Each time seems to be the first time. Preparedness or conscious familiarity is absent. There is a lacuna in memory, a break in continuity, an unawareness of causality and sequence. The symptoms are a constant surprise, a foreign body torn out of the Gestalt of their experiences.

It is possible that such disturbances of memory are due to the denial of a narcissistic injury; they may also serve the purpose of masochistic torture. Each assault of panic, endured each time as something new and different, enormously increases the pain and misery. This symptom of surprise, of impaired recall, brings to mind the reaction of children, who, seeing a frequent change of costume, believe they see a different person each time.

This regressive symptom, which in contrast to the *déjà* phenomenon impresses one as a *jamais* phenomenon, can also be observed in many women before the onset of menstruation. They do not recognize the rather typical and recurring premenstrual symptoms. They feel upset and confused each time anew, although those around them show clear diagnostic understanding.

Summary

Once a defective drive endowment and constellation is assumed, imbalance and dysfunction of the drives may also be assumed. If, for instance, the equilibrium is shaken by an overactive aggressive drive, the process of neutralization will not succeed, and consequently too much of the unchanged id aggression will enter the ego and interfere with its manifold functions.

In many cases it appears as though instead of being first externalized and later internalized, the aggressive drive had discovered a short cut: the direct invasion of the ego. So disturbed an ego cannot carry out the tasks demanded of it; moreover, with its imperfect synthesis it cannot integrate the total Gestalt of the self. In that case the superego too, it is clear, will be faulty in its structure. One more agency for controlling the personality's functioning becomes impotent; and instead of a synthesized self we have a fragmented self.

It appears justified to assume that the neutralization of the aggressive drive must be undertaken first, and that its modification must be of greater scope and intensity than that of the sexual drive. This assumption is based on the very nature of the aggressive drive.

The struggle between the two basic drives, aggression and libido, pervades all of life, man's daily activities, his thinking, his sleep, his dreams and fantasies, his strivings for growth, as well as his tendency to regress and his longing for tensionless nonexistence. Pathology in its various forms is the outcome of unsuccessful solutions of that eternal battle in which the balance has shifted in favor of aggression, resulting in disadvantageous and unpragmatic compromise formations. In a system with faulty balance, synthesis and fragmentation will not work "at their best" but will degenerate into pathological functions, causing defective differentiation, with all its unfavorable consequences.

Man's highest aims are his cultural achievements, his struggle for the expansion of his conceptual world, for insight into the eternal laws of nature. This longing is nurtured by libido. Man is permitted to advance to far regions; but he is brought back from them by the regressive drive toward the inanimate world, by aggression, the representative of the death instinct.

Freud's remarks about culture help us to see man as both victor and victim of his drives. He said (1930, p. 103):

[Culture] presents to us the struggle between Eros and Death, between the instincts of life and the instincts of destruction, as it works itself out in the human species. This struggle is what all life essentially consists of and so the evolution of civilization may be simply described as the struggle of the human species for existence.

Culture controls the dangerous drive of aggression, subdues it, and tries to render it harmless. Psychopathology, on the other hand, is movement in the opposite direction, where the drive of aggression, being far from subdued and harmless, has gained preponderance.

BIBLIOGRAPHY

Bak, R. (1939), Regression of Ego-Orientation and Libido in Schizophrenia. *Int. J. Psa.*, XX.
Bleuler, E. (1911), *Dementia Praecox or the Group of Schizophrenias*. New York: International Universities Press, 1950.
—— (1916), *Textbook of Psychiatry*. New York: Macmillan, 1924.
Bohr, N. (1955), Analysis and Synthesis in Science. *Int. Encyclop. Unif. Sciences*. Chicago: University of Chicago Press.

Fenichel, O. (1935), A Critique of the Death Instinct. *The Collected Papers of Otto Fenichel*, I. New York: Norton, 1953.

Flugel, J. C. (1953), The Death Instinct, Homeostasis and Allied Concepts. *Int. J. Psa.*, Supplement.

Freud, S. (1895), Project for a Scientific Psychology. *The Origins of Psychoanalysis.* New York: Basic Books, 1954.

—— (1900), The Interpretation of Dreams. *Standard Edition*, IV & V. London: Hogarth Press, 1956.

—— (1913a), The Claims of Psychoanalysis to Scientific Interest. *Standard Edition*, XIII. London: Hogarth Press, 1955.

—— (1913b), The Predisposition to Obsessional Neurosis. *Collected Papers*, II. London: Hogarth Press, 1948.

—— (1914), Narcissism: An Introduction. *Collected Papers*, IV. London: Hogarth Press, 1948.

—— (1915), Instincts and Their Vicissitudes. *Collected Papers*, IV. London: Hogarth Press, 1948.

—— (1920), Beyond the Pleasure Principle. *Standard Edition*, XVIII. London: Hogarth Press, 1955.

—— (1923), *The Ego and the Id.* London: Hogarth Press, 1949.

—— (1930), *Civilization and Its Discontent.* London: Hogarth Press.

—— (1931), Female Sexuality. *Collected Papers*, V. London: Hogarth Press, 1950.

—— (1937), Analysis Terminable and Interminable. *Int. J. Psa.*, XVIII.

Fruton, J. S. (1955), Proteins. In: *The Physics and Chemistry of Life.* New York: Simon & Schuster.

Hartmann, H. (1939), *Ego Psychology and the Problem of Adaptation.* New York: International Universities Press, 1958.

—— Kris, E., & Loewenstein, R. M. (1946), Comments on the Formation of the Psychic Structure. *This Annual*, II.

—— —— —— (1949), Notes on the Theory of Aggression. *This Annual*, III/IV.

Jackson, H. J. (1861-1909), *Selected Writings of John Hughlings Jackson*, ed. J. Taylor. New York: Basic Books, 1958.

Köhler, W. (1929), *Gestalt Psychology.* New York: Liveright.

Koffka, K. (1935), *Principles of Gestalt Psychology.* New York: Harcourt, Brace.

Kris, E. (1944), Art and Regression. *Trans. N.Y. Acad. Sci.*, VI.

Lichtenstein, H. (1935), Zur Phänomenologie des Wiederholungszwanges und des Todestriebes. *Imago*, XXI.

Menninger, K. A. (1953), Psychological Aspects of the Organism Under Stress. *J. Am. Psa. Assn.*, II.

Mirsky, A. (1955), The Chemistry of Heredity. In: *The Physics and Chemistry of Life.* New York: Simon & Schuster.

Nunberg, H. (1930), The Synthetic Function of the Ego. *Practice and Theory of Psychoanalysis.* New York: International Universities Press, 1961.

—— (1932), *Principles of Psychoanalysis.* New York: International Universities Press, 1955.

Oparin, A. I. (1953), *The Origin of Life.* New York: Dover.

Schilder, P. (1920), On the Development of Thought. In: *Organization and Pathology of Thought*, ed. & tr. D. Rapaport. New York: Columbia University Press, 1951.

—— (1930), Studies Concerning the Psychology and Symptomatology of General Paresis. In: *Organization and Pathology of Thought*, ed. & tr. D. Rapaport. New York: Columbia University Press, 1951.

Schrödinger, E. (1955), *What Is Life?* Cambridge: Cambridge University Press.

Sherrington, C. H. (1907), *The Integrative Action of the Nervous System.* New York: Scribner.

Silbermann, I. (1940), The Psychical Experiences during the Shocks in Shock Therapy. *Int. J. Psa.*, XXI.

—— (1950), A Contribution to the Psychology of Menstruation. *Int. J. Psa.*, XXXI.

—— (1957), Two Types of Pre-oedipal Character Disorders. *Int. J. Psa.*, XXXVIII.

Simmel, E. (1944), Self-Preservation and the Death Instinct. *Psa. Quart.*, XIII.

Slosson, E. (1919), *Creative Chemistry*. Garden City, N.Y.: Doubleday.

Wald, G. (1955), The Origin of Life. In: *The Physics and Chemistry of Life*. New York: Simon & Schuster.

Zeigarnik, B. (1927), Das Behalten erledigter und unerledigter Handlungen. *Psychol. Forsch.*, IX.

ASPECTS OF NORMAL AND PATHOLOGICAL DEVELOPMENT

SOME NOTES ON THE DEVELOPMENT
OF THE BLIND[1]

DOROTHY BURLINGHAM (London)

The aim of this study is to follow the development of the personality of the blind child, to contrast this with the familiar development of the sighted, to show up deviations, and wherever possible to explain them.

The material that we have at our disposal for this purpose is of various types: there are the observations made in our nursery group for the blind concerning children between three to seven years; there is the experience gained from the work with the mothers of these children; further, there is a group of babies now under observation and their mothers who are given help in raising them, and finally, there is the analytic material from five cases, ages between four to eleven years.

The blind are a minority in a world which is focused on the characteristics, needs, accomplishments, and behavior of the seeing. This means that although the blind themselves lack the stimuli provided by the visual sense, all the stimulation which they receive via the object world comes from people who see and bears the imprint of the sighted world. It is therefore hardly possible to study the mental processes of the blind undistorted by the influences which are brought to bear on them from their sighted environment.

EARLY OBJECT RELATIONSHIP

Based on her work with the mothers of blind infants and children, Mrs. E. M. Mason has described repeatedly the difficulties and obstacles which mother and child meet in making their first contact.

[1] The work with blind children and their mothers is part of the Educational Unit of the Hampstead Child-Therapy Course and Clinic and as such maintained by the Grant Foundation, Inc., New York. The analyses of blind children are financed by the Psychoanalytic Research and Development Fund, Inc., New York.

In contrast to the pride and pleasure which a mother feels in her normal baby, Mrs. Mason has shown how the mothers of the blind are affected by the first discovery of the child's visual defect whenever the discovery is made by them and confirmed medically. She has described their feelings of injury, of hurt pride, of guilt, and of the depression which make them withdraw emotionally from the child and sometimes unconsciously or rationally wish for his death. It is only natural that the baby in this most vulnerable period reacts on his side to the mother's withdrawal and in his turn answers with passivity and withdrawal far beyond the degree caused by the visual defect itself. According to our observations, therefore, blind babies who need an excess of stimulation to counteract the lack of visual stimuli receive less than the normal child. This has far-reaching effects on the further development of their emotional life. It also has side effects on the development of all the ego functions of the child, which the present paper is trying to describe.

THE DEVELOPMENT OF MOTILITY

Consequences of Restriction

From our observation of normal mothers of sighted babies we know how much pleasure they gain from each new activity of the child. The first turning toward the mother, the stretching out of the arms to be picked up, the reaching for a toy, the energetic kicking, the crawling, and the first steps all cause the mother great enjoyment. The physical beauty of the baby as he develops his musculature causes the mother to give him unstinted admiration. This in turn stimulates the baby and he answers with a pleasurable forward movement in development. In a recent paper, Joyce Robertson has described this interplay between mother and child as observed in our Well-Baby Clinic.

We know from the observation of children who have had their hands tied in infancy and were kept in cots and prams overlong as toddlers, that there are serious consequences to such motor restrictions. Under such conditions, some develop excessive autoerotic activities, such as head banging, rocking, sucking, or masturbation. Others become passive; others again answer with a retardation of speech or a general delay in development.

According to our observation on blind babies on which Mrs. E. M. Mason has reported recently, retardation and restriction of muscular achievement are the order of the day. We see two reasons for this in babyhood of the blind. Although the muscular impetus is the same, in the absence of vision the blind baby is not stimulated in the same manner to reach out toward people or inanimate objects. Hearing does not seem to give the same impetus to turn toward the source of sound as sight does. Secondly, the baby is not guided by the mother's look or her expression of pleasure in his activity and therefore lacks some of the incentive to repeat achievements. Lack of muscular response on the part of the baby again diminishes the mother's wish to stimulate the child by her own actions, so that a vicious circle is set up. The blind baby although not intentionally restricted yet behaves in many respects like a restricted sighted child.

As Mrs. Mason has reported of her work with mothers, it is essential to encourage them to take the initiative in muscular action with their blind babies. This may include to take the babies' hands or pull their arms before the baby stretches them out in invitation, to put objects into the babies' hands and manipulate their fingers around them. The object of such activity is to prevent the child from remaining in or falling back to a passive attitude which seems as natural to the blind child as it is his greatest danger. Mothers report that their infants do not seem to have spontaneous pleasure in feeling objects with their hands except those that make a sound.

There is another intriguing observation concerning the blind infant's use of arms or legs. Miss Isabel Harris reported on a blind baby boy (from eleven to seventeen and a half months) that he showed a decided retardation in reaching out for objects and feeling them. At the same time he showed decided pleasure in the activity of his feet and legs, stretching them out and kicking. As he reached the toddler stage and could propel himself about, he used his lower extremities in all ways to make noises, banging his feet on the rug, on the floor, against the bars of his cot, experimenting in this manner with movement and sound simultaneously. Another infant under our observation showed the same tendency to find pleasure in his legs rather than his arms, the latter remaining quite inactive.

Similar attitudes can be observed in older children in our nursery group of the blind. The teacher who gives them physical exercises tries to induce the children to be freer in their movements. It is interesting that she remarked that the children tended to express all ideas with their feet; she had great difficulty to get the children to move their arms at all.

On another occasion Mrs. E. M. Mason has reported on observations of the toddler's stage in blind children, how they enjoy their newly acquired skills, how awkward they are, and how they fall about indiscriminately as do the sighted children. Also, just as the sighted child, the blind toddler soon grows confident, becoming indifferent to bumps and injuries. But only in the sighted child does this early confidence lead soon to the next stage of agility, competence, security, rhythm, and grace of movement. With the blind this early confidence is lost gradually. Although at a later stage also the blind child may become more agile and secure again, what counts next is that the difficulties he has to meet in the first instance increase rather than decrease. There is no diminution of the obstacles that the blind child may bump into, nor of the difficult unknown situations which he encounters. Experience makes him more aware of dangers rather than the opposite. Alongside his own fears run the justified worries of his mother and the constant outcry of "be careful" which accompanies all his activities and leads to the future dependence on the mother and other sighted people to be described later.

With sighted children it has been ascertained that emotional disturbances can betray themselves in awkwardness of posture. There is the suspicion that the same is true for the blind over and beyond the awkwardness which is caused by blindness.

Matthew (three years) runs like a scared rabbit, starting in one direction and then turning to another; beyond expressing the understandable difficulties with orientation this is also an expression of his fears.

Judy (four years ten months) walks and runs stiffly, giving the impression of a puppet, this being well in accord with the stiffness and artificiality of her personality.

Gillian (five years three months) is slow and awkward, this being the result of her being handled and treated by her family like a doll with little chance for original expression.

All the children when running have the habit of running in the same spot, i.e., not advancing. This in their case is an understandable reaction, the outcome of a compromise between the desire for motility and a self-imposed restriction on motion in order to avoid unpleasant experiences and shock. But such reactions which start rationally lead easily into fixed mannerisms.

Blindism

All the children under our observation show the so-called blindisms, i.e., rhythmic movements of the body, rubbing the eyes, knocking of the head with the hands, swaying and rocking. There is little or no thumb sucking in our nursery, although the normal amount of masturbation can be seen. It is difficult to say how far these rhythmic activities merely substitute for the more normal muscular activities and discharge of aggression which the children lack, and how far they have the full value of autoerotic manifestations. They certainly share with the autoerotic manifestations a persistence which wins over all the parents' efforts at restraint.

With one child, Helen (seven years three months), it became unmistakably clear in analysis that her swaying movements were substitutions for restricted and repressed aggression.

Orientation

In normal child development, the infant learns without much difficulty to orient himself in increasingly larger space, and except for cases of very serious illness, we will not find often that orientation is disturbed. This is different with the blind. It is only natural that with the absence of vision to guide the child, orientation is slow to come, perhaps much slower than is ordinarily imagined. We find that even with the children in our nursery, in the well-known room, there is often difficulty to find the door, the toy shelves, or the snack table.

Winnie a child of four, who has for months been taken across the street by her therapist and is repeatedly asked to find the door of the Clinic, is, for example, still unable to do so and will also invariably walk into a mail box on her way.

But orientation once learned and mastered is also open to secondary disturbance in every kind of emotional upset. Children who usually find their way in the nursery easily will not do so when there has been trouble in the home or difficulty with the teacher.

They will get "lost" so far as direction is concerned, and getting lost will put them in a panic which resembles the panic of the seeing child who suddenly cannot find the mother. Thus in the young child so far as our own observation goes, the amount of orientation to be expected at a given moment is absolutely unpredictable.

We have so far only made one assumption why this should be the case. When in emotional equilibrium the blind child seems to help his processes of orientation in various subtle ways, such as concentration on listening for some accustomed noise, asking questions to be guided by the answering voice, increased listening, etc. It is possible that these activities which make high demands on the child's concentration and ego functioning in general cannot be kept up when emotions intervene.

It goes without saying that the ease with which orientation is disturbed acts as a retarding factor with regard to all other activities.

DEPENDENCY

There is in every child's life a phase where needs cannot be fulfilled except by the help of another person who on the basis of this function becomes the child's first object, i.e., the anaclitic object. Normally this phase is outgrown with the increasing independence of the child's functions such as purposeful movement, knowledge of the environment, ability to grasp, to fetch, and to make contact with the source of satisfaction. As the child becomes more self-reliant so far as gratification is concerned, the quality of his object relationship changes and the latter is based on other factors besides need satisfaction.

It is this particular earlier stage which we see enlarged and prolonged in the case of blind children. Since vision is one of the important factors contributing to orientation and mastery of the surroundings, the blind child finds himself longer in the state in which need satisfaction is dependent on the objects which substitute in this respect for the function of his eyes.

The mother on her part adds to this dependency. She is realistically aware of the dangers for her child; that without sight he will pull objects onto himself, bump into obstacles, and fall down into spaces he does not see, and she tries to guard him from such accidents. But above all because of her sorrow, and her guilt over her death wishes, she will protect and keep the child near her, thus encouraging dependency.

Wish for Independence

Although dependency can never be given up altogether by the blind child, he has at the same time the normal urge for independence. This shows in our nursery school children; the cry, "I want to do it myself," is the order of the day. They attempt persistently to become independent. The following is an example of a successful achievement.

The teacher starts to open the door for Winnie (four years) who says: "Do it myself." She goes to the door, fumbles with the handle, opens it, shuts it, opens it again, and passes through with a radiant expression.

Attempted Achievement

Matthew (five and a half years) wants to pour the orange juice into his glass. He tips the small pitcher toward the glass, but hardly any juice goes into the glass, the teacher then holds his hand to help him. He does not look very satisfied.

After many such efforts lasting over months, Matthew is able to fill his glass skillfully without help.

Matthew (six years) fills a self-made clay bowl with water. He holds it under the tap and it fills up, but as he holds it tilted, the water keeps running out. The teacher comes and helps him to hold it straight. Matthew says: "I want to do it myself." This is only partly true; although there is the wish to do it himself, his insufficient ability to complete the activity depresses him and he is in reality complaining: "If only I could do it myself."

The wish to complete a task seems to contain the awareness, that if interrupted or helped part of the pleasure is lost.

When the teacher tells Winnie (five years four months) she will show her how to put a screw into her puppet, Winnie asks: "Then will you let go?"

There are many activities which a blind child cannot learn to do even with persistence and skill. It may be too dangerous such as crossing a busy street, or it may be an impossibility such as picking up all the small objects that have fallen and scattered all over the floor.

In all these instances the children realize there are other people, who can be successful where they themselves fail. They find it preferable on these occasions to accept the help of the sighted, i.e., to use the sighted as their eyes. This is another reason for the blind children to forego independence.

Matthew (six years three months) is trying to find the climbing frame; he calls out to Alan, a partially sighted child, "Show me where the climbing frame is."

Using the seeing in this manner became especially noticeable with Matthew (six years) when his younger sister reached the toddler stage and became able to run about on her own. This younger sister, Dorothy, looks up to Matthew in admiration and thinks that he is marvellous in every way. At the same time Matthew can appeal to her for help and use her vision as his own. For example, she fetches whatever Matthew wants, picks up toys that have fallen on the floor and hands him things even before he asks for them.

Reactions to Difficult Tasks

We have often observed how a child drops a toy or a spoon from a table, makes no effort to pick it up, and behaves as if nothing had happened, as the following example shows.

Judy (six years six months) is trying to match buttons; they fall with a clatter on the floor; she sits quite still, her face immovable, her hands motionless on the table. Since no one pays any attention, she moves away soon to another part of the room.

There are several possible reasons for this behavior. She may avoid in this way the difficult task of trying to pick up the scattered buttons. But what is the most likely is that she does not want to call someone to help her. Experience has told her that she will be asked to do it herself, which would take her a long time. Besides, at home, she has experienced the impatience and irritation caused by her slowness and therefore much prefers the task to be accomplished by someone who can see.

The Child's Role in Initiating Dependence

The children do not find their dependence equally restricting if they can initiate it themselves.

Gillian (six years two months) wanted to be as independent as Helen in going to the lavatory, so she asks the teacher to wait in the hall next to her. But at the same time she is very concerned that the teacher should be sure to wait and tells her to "knock on the wall and keep on knocking."

Judy (six years two months) is jumping off a chair and asks the teacher not to hold her. Then successively, as she jumps, she asks the teacher first to stand by the door, next to go as far as the next room, and finally to sit down in the next room. As Judy gains confidence she gradually removes the teacher from her vicinity until she can be certain that no help can be given.

Often children are observed to say, "I want to do it myself," and simultaneously to hold on to the person to whom they have directed this remark. To give expression to the double feeling: "Don't hold me, but let me take hold of you, let me be the active one," seems to be an intermediary step toward independence. In this way the children feel in control and have taken the initiative in spite of the dependence expressed by their behavior.

The stubbornness observed in our blind children is often no more than the expression of the wish to be left alone to try out experiences for themselves.

Winnie (five years two months) is in the far corner of the washroom and refuses to emerge. She asks the teacher to leave her alone so that she can "go by myself."

Fear of Abandonment Leading to Compliance

Blind children are often treated like inanimate objects, picked up and dumped where convenient.

First, when our nursery opened, the children were brought by car service and often by different drivers. The drivers, good-natured men, would pick the children out of the car and deposit them in the hall. You could observe how the child resented being handled in this manner but at the same time would cling to the driver fearing to be abandoned. They know that if deserted, they cannot cope; therefore they prefer to be at the mercy of these strangers.

This remarkable degree of compliance is observed in all our children. They have learned from experience how dependent they have to be on those with sight, into how many dangers they run, and how many of their wishes are unobtainable when on their own. But this manifest compliance is no more than a thin disguise which hides the revolt against dependency. The latter shows in a tense posture, a clenched fist, etc. It shows also when helpful but ununderstanding adults push and lead children about without bothering to explain their actions. This is very different from the occasions mentioned before when a child takes hold of a receptive hand, and demands to be taken where he wants to go, to be shown where a particular object is placed or where a noise invites investigation.

There are also incidences where pride in achievement and fear of independence are blended into a compromise attitude which is meant to please the adult through compliance.

Gillian (five years ten months) puts the plug into the basin herself to wash her hands. She then pulls the plug out, smiles and says: "Gillian cannot do it, you do it for me."

Anger

In the nursery our teachers are familiar with a form of anger characteristic of all children who feel under the impact of continual frustration.

Alan (six years eleven months) tries to snap his belt shut which he has never been able to do alone. While doing this he repeats to himself in a whisper: "Do it myself, do it myself," although he is still unable to do it.

The whispered words seem to express anger over the frustration turned against himself, as well as his anger toward the teacher who finally comes to his help.

Matthew (six years two months) also at times whispers his wish to do something alone, the whisper expressing control of anger and fear of upsetting the teacher.

It is true that some of these examples could be taken as well from seeing children, but they would then occur at an earlier age, between two to three years. The phase of conflict between dependence and independence, which is comparatively short with seeing children, has to be immeasurably longer with the blind. With them it is less a stage of development than a continued testing of their own powers of accomplishment as well as of adult reaction to what they are doing. In reality, compliance with the desires of the sighted adult conflicts with their own desire for achievement. Still, there is no attempt at competition with the seeing, rather a wish to submit to the seeing person's impulsive need to assist the blind. It is only acquaintance with these compliant children which shows up the superficiality of this reaction and the negative attitude hidden behind the positive one. They suffer greatly when they compare themselves with the seeing; they are resentful and angry, and merely control their anger because they realize how much they need the seeing.

AGGRESSION

When comparing our observations of blind children with those of normal children of the same age, we are struck by the comparative scarcity of free aggressive expression, at least so far as our nursery group of the blind are concerned. The reason for this may lie in the two characteristics which have been mentioned before: the greater inhibition of muscular expression and the increased dependence on their objects.

We know from the development of normal children that the child's first aggression is directed toward the first cathected object, i.e., the mother; that it finds violent outlets in the toddler stage where the mother is not only possessed by the child but often maltreated; and that it reaches its height in the death wishes belonging to the oedipus complex. So far as the blind toddler is concerned, he seems to be prevented from treating the mother aggressively by the general curb on his muscular activity; so far as the blind child in the phallic stage is concerned, it seems to us that his death wishes are inhibited by his greater fear of losing the object, i.e., as mentioned before, by his dependency. What we find in our blind children actually is much less aggressive expression and much more fear of aggression.

The Children's Fear of Their Own Aggression

Most of our children, with perhaps one or two exceptions, are excessively sorry for every aggressive act. They show fear when they have hurt or hit another child accidentally. They are unusually concerned when they have dropped almost any utensil and believe it broken. As all young children do, they throw things frequently, but they do so in a curious way; they throw backwards over their shoulders rather than forward. As mentioned before, they do not dare to express open anger with adults when thwarted or interfered with against their wishes. They seldom express anger with their teachers and certainly much less with their mothers.

Although it seems to us that inhibition of muscular action and of death wishes are the major reasons for this behavior of the children, there is no doubt that absence of vision itself as well as the mother's attitude play their part. So far as the first reason is concerned, we can often notice that the children are made uneasy by their inability to check on the consequences of an aggressive action, that imagination at times leads them to believe that what they have done has had catastrophic results, a belief which may be strengthened by either the exclamation or by silence of the attacked child. This fear of aggression is naturally strengthened by their mothers' excessive concern about any damage that they might cause inadvertently. The mothers' protective attitude toward their blind children is matched almost in all instances by an anxiousness to prevent any damage which their child could do to others.

The Children's Fear of Being Attacked

We find that the children are as frightened of being attacked as they are of attacking. While we think that this is due in the main to the fear of their own aggression, it is certainly heightened by their being less equipped for holding their own in any fight with playmates. They are not able to see the angry expression on another child's face or remark a threatening posture; lack of free movement makes it impossible for them to run away or to take evasive action. Also where adults are concerned an angry expression on the mother's or teacher's face does not warn them beforehand of a reprimand. Any such attack whether coming from a child or adult therefore has a surprise quality to which many of our children react with outbursts of despair.

At least in the beginning of our observation, almost all the signs of aggression noticed by the teachers were abortive or merely verbal ones which neither reached nor harmed the object for which they were intended.

Judy (six years eleven months) is having difficulty in hammering one of the pegs through the hammer-peg toy. She changes to another peg and says: "It's hearing a lot of hammering on its head." The teacher asks her if she thinks the peg can feel. Judy says, "No," but rather doubtfully, and appears to give this peg a rest from time to time.

Matthew (four years eleven months) learns that his teacher is not coming that day and he begins to cry and then becomes quite angry, saying to the substitute teacher: "I don't want you. I hate you."

Judy (five years eleven months), while washing up, says for no apparent reason: "I want to splash and splash and splash your eyes right out."

The nearest to an exception to this general picture is Winnie now at the age of five in analysis, who can hit out especially when jealous. But even with her, her violent self-assertive or hostile feelings are expressed more often in profuse swearing than in muscular action. Occasionally Matthew can do both.

Matthew (four years four months) bumps his head on the door, he kicks out at the door and says: "It nearly pushed my blasted eye out."

Verbalization with Blind Children

The role of verbalization in early childhood has been described in an instructive paper by Anny Katan (1961). When describing verbalization as an important ego achievement of the normal child she views it from three important aspects: (1) as verbalization of "perception of the outer world in order to obtain fulfillment of wishes and needs"; (2) as verbalization of feeling which "leads to an increase of the controlling function of the ego over affects and drives"; (3) as verbalization of thought and feeling which "increases for the ego the possibility of distinguishing between wishes and fantasies on the one hand and reality on the other," i.e., of reality testing.

The blind child verbalizes in a manner similar to a sighted one in many ways, but there are differences. In one way lack of sight stimulates verbalization in the blind child, who tries to make up with words for what he does not see. He finds uses for speech that the seeing do not require, that is, for orientation, to collect characteristics for differentiating between persons, to discover some mark by which an object can be recognized. He asks questions, the main object of which is to provide clues.

On the other hand lack of sight makes many words meaningless or gives them a different meaning. Therefore concepts may be completely misunderstood or only partially understood; or words may be used merely to imitate or to parrot the sighted.

With none of the blind children under our observation did we find any attempt to build up a language which is based strictly on their own perceptions and sensations. On the contrary, the use of words and expressions which are different from the sighted cause embarrassment to the children as well as to their mothers. The children evidently fear to display the inadequacy of their functioning of which they are aware dimly and therefore make every effort to conform. The mothers' wishes certainly go in the same direction.

First Words

Naturally this difference does not show in the first stage before verbalization proper, when the production of sounds and syllables is based above all on mouth pleasure and only gradually serves the purpose of communication. In all our blind babies the first babbling seemed to take the course known from normal infants.

Mary, a blind baby (seven months), at the beginning of observation, enjoyed vocalizing and appeared happy playing with the sounds she could produce as she lay in her cot. This went hand in hand with her general pleasure in using her mouth for exploration.

But mouth pleasure in general seems prolonged with blind infants and children. At eating times, even with our children of nursery age, we have observed with surprise certain residues of behavior from the time when they were being fed by their mothers; namely, when eating independently with a spoon, they have a tendency to wipe their mouth with the implement after every mouthful, just as the mothers have done before they fed themselves.[2] Similarly the mouth pleasure derived first from babbling and then from articulation seems to last longer and to play a larger role. More than usual in childhood, besides serving communication, words are also playthings and speaking an activity for its own sake. This play with words is distinctly pleasurable, it serves the child's fantasy activity even more than his contact with the external world and becomes sexualized.

Delay in Speech

When sighted infants start talking the addition of words generally comes rapidly and continuously. With the blind the mothers tell us that just at that time, between sixteen and eighteen months, when other children are daily adding words to their vocabulary, their children rather seem to forget the few words they had learned already or at least do not increase them. There are three reasons for this.

1. So far as the verbalization of perception of the outer world normally serves fulfillment of the infant's needs and wishes, the position of the blind infant differs somewhat from the norm. The very helplessness of the child forces the mother to anticipate his wishes, thereby leaving less scope and necessity for verbal expression.

2. So far as verbalization serves communication with the mother, it is disturbed at this period by the mother's invariable depression and helplessness regarding her child with the almost inevitable withdrawal from him.

3. So far as verbalization is only one among many other ego achievements and dependent on interaction with them, it is influenced by the restriction and inhibition of motor development which has been described earlier.

Progressive Speech Development

On the other hand this delay in speaking is temporary only. When the toddler stage is over, our blind children seem to have picked up speech very quickly and by the time when they have

---

2 We do not forget, of course, that our children cannot watch other people having their meals, and therefore are not stimulated in the same way as the sighted to imitate more adult table manners.

reached nursery school age it is one of their accomplishments that they speak fluently and have large vocabularies, in which they even outdo the seeing.

This is one of the spheres that mothers encourage. Speech provides a longed-for contact that the mothers have missed. They have lacked the response to their glance and to their facial expressions. Speech not only makes up for this but also reassures the mother that her child is not backward as well as blind, a fear shown by all mothers with whom we are in contact.

Parroting

It is only normal for children to imitate their mother's speech. With sighted children this leads to no discrepancy between their concepts and the mother's because the visual impressions which are verbalized are shared by both. We find with our mothers of the blind that it is difficult or even impossible for them to realize the gulf which exists between their own ego apparatus and the child's. When naming an object the mother of a sighted child directs the child's look almost automatically. Her own glance toward something may even be enough to encourage the child's attention even if she does not say expressly "look," which she does almost all the time. It will hardly occur without instruction to the mother of a blind child to be as persistent in her urging to "feel," or "hear," or "smell" the object mentioned, or if she does so, it will not be done as naturally or automatically on her part. "Come to me" is very different for a blind child even if the voice is inviting. The expression on the mother's face, her outstretched arms create a tremendous urge toward her in the sighted child. What I mean is that by this emotional experience words such as "come" will be libidinized, and will be available earlier for independent use in the child's vocabulary.

From the foregoing it seems to us that the blind child's speech is less firmly connected with his sensory experience; also that certain words are less highly cathected than normal. On the other hand the mother's high valuation of the child's ability to speak and the pleasure and praise she shows for this achievement open up the way to the easier path of imitation. The blind child who learns the mother's language takes an easy way out; that is, he appears to acquire understanding while in reality he acquires only words. Since the lack in ego achievement that goes with this is not apparent to the mother, she continues to promote what seems to her a language common to both, but what is in reality her own language and not the child's. It remains to be seen and studied how far this faulty method of verbalization reveals itself later in superego formation and in certain ego characteristics such as superficiality, hypocrisy, overcompliance, which are often considered to be connected with blindness.

Conceptualization

Since in our nursery school work the mother's wish to make the children conform is replaced by the teacher's and observer's desire to see them develop at their own pace and on the basis of their own perceptions, we have the opportunity to watch a gradual growth of their own verbalization and conceptualization. Under such conditions they begin to verbalize their puzzlement about certain concepts instead of merely naming them glibly. It emerges, for example, that they understand a "square" as something which has points, differentiating it in that way from something the contour of which can be followed by their hands without interference. Or, for example,

Gillian (five and a half years) swings around the teacher. The teacher mentions she is going around in a circle, and Gillian asks, "What is a circle?" This is explained as feeling around an object. "But how can I go in a circle?"

It is very difficult for the children to understand the concept "round" unless the object can be contained completely in the hand. A big ball is not always recognized as round.

"In front" and "behind" is also hard to understand. We observed that when asked to grasp something behind the child, the child has to turn around to find the object.

Helen (seven and a half years) asks: "Where do your hands stay?" She does not seem to know where her hands are when not in use, a most surprising statement since we would expect such knowledge to have much less connection with vision than with the body image based on the sensations provided by its different parts.

Peter (four years ten months) feels the leather belt of his teacher and asks: "Have you a collar on?" Here it is easy to find the connection since his own dog has a leather collar. But the association of ideas also reveals that he thinks it quite probable that people wear collars as dogs do.

The following are some of the verbal associations to the sensations they experience.

Winnie (three years one month) plays with sand for the first time and lets it run through her fingers. She says: "Sugar."
Judy (six years five months) drops the little metal Braille letters onto her hand and says: "It feels like rain."

The children often use metaphors in an attempt to describe an object or to explain a sensation or to compare one experience with another one.

Matthew (six years four months) eats potato crisps, one of which is curved. He says: "It is like a mouth."
Alan (six years eight months) shakes a tin box and is for a long time absorbed in the sound he is making. He finally said: "It sounds like people clapping."
Alan (seven years eight months) uses a paper puncher and remarks: "It is as if I am taking a picture."
Winnie (four years eleven months) swears as she often does: "Fucking'ell, fucking'ell" and adds, "It sounds like music to me."

Collecting Information Via Speech

People are far more attractive for blind children than inanimate objects, such as toys, etc. When they meet strangers they immediately ply them with questions: "What is your name?" "Where do you live?" "Have you children?" "Why did you come here?" These questions may seem similar to those put by institutional children, who have no real object tie and who are trying to attach themselves to every casual stranger. But with the blind the purpose of the questions is to collect information and to gain an impression of the person in place of the visual image which they cannot obtain.

The answers to their questions reveal much to them, in the tone of voice used, in the attitude of the person. They do not easily forget details which they have learned in that manner and will have them at their disposal even a year later, when a visitor returns or is discussed.

It is the same with toys or any other inanimate object. To label it by naming it serves recognition, and to recognize it again is more important to the child than the toy or object as such. They are proud of their ability in this respect, they feel they can talk about it or ask for it again as the seeing do. This often obscures the fact that what is cathected here by the blind child is not the person or the thing in itself but the achievement of remembering. Because of this deflection of cathexis in our blind children, memory is well developed.

Orientation by Speech

Questioning has still another use than those already mentioned, that is orientation. The blind children are very clever in trying to find clues for their orientation. They not only ask where they are but put other quite irrelevant questions to whoever is near. The purpose is simply to get a reply and by so doing to locate the person and in that way appreciate their own position. This question takes the place of the glance of the seeing, it serves to give the direction to where they want to go. This device is also used for objects when fallen and lost. "Where is it?"

Gillian (five years ten months) plays with a wooden ball, listens for it, and is quite good at finding it again, but in doing so remains in constant verbal contact with the teacher which helps her to locate her own position in the room.

As I have mentioned before, any emotional disturbance causes a child to lose his orientation; in such an instance a question resulting in an answer is the quickest way of getting reorientated.

On the occasions when the blind children visit the garden of the nursery school for normal children, the teacher of the latter is struck by the difference in the topics talked about. She comments on the constant request for orientation and the lack of the usual subjects discussed by preschool children under similar circumstances.

Drive to Know to Understand

The blind child's normal drive to know and to understand, which seems to lack expression in the earliest years, finds expression following the sudden awareness that the seeing know what is unknown to him. Curiosity with the resulting urge to fathom the puzzling phenomenon of sight sets in. Language is one of the means used for this purpose, and speech centers around the problems of blindness whenever this is not prevented for emotional reasons as it usually is in the child's family.

Judy (six years five months), when told to pull up her sock that has slipped down, asks in a surprised tone: "How can you tell it's down?"

Matthew (five years) asks the teacher whether her daughter has eyes that come out. (Matthew was born without eyes and has artificial eyes.) He is told that she has eyes that stay in. Matthew in a voice full of sympathy: "Yes, I know some people do have that sort of eyes."

Matthew (four years eight months) is in the garden and calls out: "Come, and watch me water the flowers." When the teacher says she will come out, he says: "You don't have to, you can look through the glass door."

The children also want to know how to use the objects the sighted people use and mention.

Judy (six years ten months) asks about pencils and how to write with them.

Matthew (six years eight months), who like all boys wishes to drive cars, asks to be told about steering, gears, and about the switches, this in spite of the fact that at other times he declares that he will never be able to drive a car because he is blind.

The children get the idea that seeing is the prerogative of the adults, i.e., that children are blind but adults see.

Matthew (five years ten months) asks: "Will I see when I am grown up?"

They evidently make an attempt to penetrate the puzzling abilities of the seeing world by imitating it, which leads for instance to the imitation of people's posture. Winnie at times walks like an old woman, an imitation of her grandmother. This might have several reasons but may also be based on a mechanism which Matthew brings to the teacher's attention quite openly in the following manner. He leans down from his chair as if looking for something and says: "I am looking at something."

At another time Matthew (five years eleven months) brings a yoyo to school and wants Judy "to see it, without touching it." The teacher explains that Judy cannot see it with her eyes but could feel it, to which Matthew replied: "She can stand and put her head this way," at the same time pointing with his head in the right direction, showing that he has gathered that people face in the direction in which they look.

The children also become aware of the amount of vision a person has, and differentiate between the degree of sight of two of our partially sighted children.

Judy (six years seven months), who is especially interested in this, asks when Alan, a partially sighted child, drops a lid. "Can he see it?"

Alan (seven years two months) keeps telling Winnie not to look at the sky when told she cannot see it. He says: "Because she is all the way blind. I am a little blind, Judy and Matthew are all the way blind."

It is obvious to us that the children continually test the correctness of what they assume from vague clues.

Talking of Blindness a Relief

Once the children are able to talk about blindness in general and their own in particular it appears to give them great relief.

Judy (six years seven months), when asked to come to "look" at the new cabinet, corrects the teacher: "You should not say 'see' but 'feel.' "

Judy has several times expressed the idea that blind children gain sight when they grow up. Recently she has begun to express the realization that much as she might wish to see, she would not be able to do so. In the following example she is checking up on this fact.

Judy (six years eleven months) when Helen visited the nursery, asks whether Helen is blind and will be able to see when she is a big lady. When asked what she thinks herself she quickly says: "No."

Matthew (six years three months) asked Helen the same question, whether she is blind. When she confirms it and asks about him, he admits that he is blind and changes the subject.

The ability to express their thoughts, fantasies, and disappoint-ments about blindness has a liberating effect on the children so that they are able to verbalize other affect-laden subjects.

Judy (six years five months) has never mentioned her father directly in the three years she has been with us. But when speaking, she uses a deep gruff voice which is thought to be an imitation and impersonation of her father. Now, since Judy is talking of her blind-ness, she is able to mention her father verbally. She asks her teacher whether she can play football. When the teacher suggests that per-haps her father does, Judy says: "No, he never plays games; when I want to play with him, he says, I should not bother him." When it was put to her that he might rather talk: "No, he never talks to me . . . , he never talks to anyone, only growls at my mother." When the teacher thought he might just be shy, Judy said: "He should have got over being shy, since he is grown up now."

It is interesting that this verbalization freed Judy in her move-ments as well. In the music lesson that followed this conversation, she could run fast over a wide area, which she had been unable to do before.

It is noticeable that the acceptance of their blindness increases the children's curiosity about other matters and allows them to use their intelligence to draw conclusions.

Judy (six years four months) in her Braille lesson suddenly appre-ciates the difference between an "a" and a "g" and says: "I am feel-ing them [the dots]. It is going to be all right now, isn't it?" meaning, although blind, she will now be able to learn.

The children are walking along the street and come to a letter box. Matthew remembers the one in Maresfield Gardens and thinks they must be near the nursery. Judy (six years eleven months) cor-rects him and explains: "He thinks it is the same one because it is the same shape."

At another time Matthew (six years) is told they are going to climb a hill and asks: "Is there a hill on the street as well as on the pavement?" Matthew is trying here to understand about inclines.

Winnie (five years five months) takes a head off a doll and tries to put it on again. "Is this how heads fit on a neck?"

While driving for a picnic the teachers explain to the children that they must not talk to the driver as she needs to concentrate on the driving. On arrival at the place for the picnic, they find a tree suitable for the children to climb. Matthew (six years four months) asks to be taken to it and starts to climb. He stops for a moment and says very seriously: "Please don't help me, and don't talk to me, I have to concentrate like you do when you are driving." Matthew then climbs with great agility.

We are inevitably reminded here of the effect sexual enlightenment normally has on children in freeing their curiosity and intelligence from inhibitions. Once they are allowed to talk about their blindness, the way to the exploration of other secrets seems to be opened up for them.

It is not surprising that the subject of blindness and the difficulty of talking about it are so important. It is not only a painful subject for the mothers, but it is also treated by them as a "secret" in the sense that it is not talked about with the children although they hear a great deal about it, as they do as regards sex, birth, death, illness, or other adult matters. What they do overhear can be only confusing and disturbing and in its incompleteness limiting to their intelligence. This latter effect is overcome or avoided whenever they are allowed to share and verbalize their feeling concerning it with the adult world.

As shown before, there are other respects where sight and blindness become symbolic for the sex differences between children and adults, namely, the adults possessing a power and capacity which children lack. But contrary to sex, it is one of the tragic facts, with which the blind child has to come to terms, that the process to see is not acquired gradually through the process of growing up but will be lacking in his life for ever.

BIBLIOGRAPHY

Bergmann, T. (1945), Observations of Children's Reactions to Motor Restraint. *Nerv. Child*, IV.

Blank, R. (1957), Psychoanalysis and Blindness. *Psa. Quart.* XXVI.

—— (1958), Dreams of the Blind. *Psa. Quart.* XXVII.

Braverman, S. & Chevigny, H. (1950). *The Adjustment of the Blind*. New Haven: Yale University Press.

Burlingham, D. (1940), Psychoanalytische Beobachtungen an blinden Kindern. *Int. Z. Psa. & Imago*, XXV.

—— (1941), Psychic Problems of the Blind. *Am. Imago*, II.

—— & Freud, A. (1942), *Young Children in Wartime*. London: Allen & Unwin.

—— —— (1947), *Infants Without Families: The Case For and Against Residential Nurseries*. New York: International Universities Press.

Colborne-Brown, M. (n.d.), The Care, Training and Education of Young Blind Children in the Royal National Institute for the Blinds' Sunshine Home, Residential Nurseries.

Deutsch, F. (1940), The Sense of Reality in Persons Born Blind. *J. Psychol.*, X.

Freud, A. (1949a), Aggression in Relation to Emotional Development. *This Annual*, III/IV.

—— (1949b), Nursery School Education—Its Uses and Dangers. *Child Study.*

Gesell, A. (1940), *The First Five Years of Life*. London: Methuen.

—— (1953), Development of the Infant with Retrolental Fibroplastic Blindness. *Field of Vision*, IX.

—— & Amatruda, G. (1960), *Developmental Diagnosis*. New York: Hoeber.

Gibbs, N. (1949), Some Observations on Blind Children. *Young Children*, II (published by Nursery School Association of Great Britain and Northern Ireland).

—— (n.d.), The Care of Blind Children. National Institute for the Blind, Bulletin No. 18.

Greenacre, P. (1944), Infantile Reactions to Restraint. *Am. J. Orthopsychiat.*, XIV.

—— (1959), On Focal Symbiosis. In: *Dynamic Psychopathology in Childhood*, ed. L. Jessner & E. Pavenstedt. New York: Grune & Stratton.

Hartmann, H. (1951), Technical Implications of Ego Psychology. *Psa. Quart.*, XX.

Johnson, M. (1953), *Our Daughter Is Blind*. New York: American Foundation for the Blind.

Katan, A. (1961), Some Thoughts about the Role of Verbalization in Early Childhood. *This Annual*, XVI.

Keeler, W. (1958), Autistic Patterns of Defective Communication in Blind Children with Retrolental Fibroplasia. In: *Psychopathology of Communication*, ed. P. Hoch & J. Zubin. New York: Grune & Stratton.

Keller, H. (1905), *The Story of My Life*. London: Hodder & Stroughton.

—— (1956), *Teacher*. London: Gollancz.

Kenyon, E. (n.d.), Psychological Problems of Young Blind Children. Boston Nursery School.

Lowenfeld, V. (1952), *The Nature of Creative Activity*. London: Routledge & Kegan Paul.

Mahler, M. S. (1952), On Child Psychosis and Schizophrenia: Autistic and Symbiotic Infantile Psychoses. *This Annual*, VII.

May, C. (1924), *Diseases of the Eye*. New York: Wood.

Mehta, V. (1953), *Face to Face*. London: Collins.

—— (1958), Reading from Records. *Saturday Review* (Sept. 26).

Middlewood, E. (1954), A Child—Though Blind. *New Outlook for the Blind*, March.

Moor, P. (1954), Meeting the Needs of the Pre-School Blind Child and His Parents. *Education*, Febr. (published by the American Foundation for the Blind).

—— (n.d.), A Blind Child, Too, Can Go to Nursery School. American Foundation for the Blind.

—— (n.d.), Toilet Habits. Suggestions for Training a Blind Child. American Foundation for the Blind.

Moss, L. (n.d.), Work with Fathers of Blind Children in Therapy. New York Guild for the Jewish Blind.

New York Association for the Blind. Growing through Experience.

—— The Pre-School Service of the "Lighthouse."

Norris, M. (1956), What Affects Blind Children's Development? *Children*, III.

—— et al. (1957), *Blindness in Children*. Chicago: University of Chicago Press.

—— —— (n.d.), Blindness and Prematurity. University of Chicago Study of Blind Preschool Children.

Pfeiffer, E. (1958), *Study of Joe. A Blind Child in a Sighted Group*. New York: Bank Street College of Education.

Pollock, M. (n.d.), Visual Perception and Attention in Normal and Abnormal Children. New York Guild for the Jewish Blind.

Royal National Institute for the Blind. The Education of the Young Blind Child.

—— Ways of Helping a Young Blind Child to Learn to Feed Himself.

—— Lists of Toys and Equipment.

—— Residential Nursery School for Blind Babies.

—— The Sunshine Home (Prospectus).

Scott, E. (1957), The Blind Child in the Sighted Nursery School. *New Outlook for the Blind*, V.

Spitz, R. (1953), Aggression: Its Role in the Establishment of Object Relations. In: *Drives, Affects, Behavior*, ed. R. M. Loewenstein. New York: International Universities Press.

—— (1955), The Primal Cavity. A Contribution to the Genesis of Perception and Its Role for Psychoanalytic Theory. *This Annual*, X.

von Senden, M. (1960), *Space and Sight*. London: Methuen.

Wells, E. (1955), Twenty-One Years of Guide-Dogging. *New Beacon*, XXXIX.

SOME OBSERVATIONS ON THE DEVELOPMENT AND DISTURBANCES OF INTEGRATION IN CHILDHOOD[1]

LISELOTTE FRANKL, M.B., B.S., PH.D. (London)[2]

Based on Case Material from Patients Treated by

Isabel Harris, Hansi Kennedy, and Veronica Thompson

The need to study the processes of integration and their pathology arose in connection with our work on diagnosis. As diagnosticians we would like to know how successful or unsuccessful the ego has been in achieving integration within the personality.

Every psychological illness can be regarded as a sign that the mediating function of the ego has not succeeded in integrating the child's personality, and the resulting rift manifests itself in symptom formation, character disorder, impulsive behavior, or even childhood psychosis. As Sigmund Freud (1928) said, "For neurosis is after all only a sign that the ego has not succeeded in making a synthesis, that in attempting to do so it has forfeited its unity."

The word "integration" is used frequently among psychoanalysts. Optimal integration is a goal we are trying to achieve as a result of

[1] The content of this paper is based on material collected in the various Departments of the Hampstead Child Therapy Clinic. The Clinic is maintained with the aid of grants by The Field Foundation, Inc., New York; The Ford Foundation, New York; The Foundations' Fund for Research in Psychiatry, New Haven, Connecticut; The Anna Freud Foundation, New York; The Grant Foundation, Inc., New York; The Estate of Flora Haas, New York; The Old Dominion Foundation, U.S.A.; The Psychoanalytic Research and Development Fund, Inc., New York.

Part of an earlier draft of this paper was read at the Department of Psychiatry, University of Colorado, Denver and at the Los Angeles Institute for Psychoanalysis, May 1960.

[2] I am grateful to Anna Freud, Ruth Thomas and members of the Hampstead Child Therapy Course and Clinic for many helpful suggestions.

treatment. When using the word in this way we think we know what kind of personality we are referring to. When it came to defining integration both in terms of the process and its result, we found, in our work at the Hampstead Clinic, that a great deal of careful thought was needed to get a clear picture of what is covered by these terms. We must think of integration in the first place as a tendency inherent in the ego to unify all the elements at its disposal. These elements are derived both from internal and external sources which have to be integrated and assimilated. In this process the ego exercises a function which we refer to as the synthetic function.

Nunberg (1931), in his paper "The Synthetic Function of the Ego," uses the example of the process of identification in the oedipus situation to clarify the concept of the synthetic function of the ego.

> It is in this process of assimilation that we have the first and plainest manifestation of the ego's influence as an intermediary and binding force, that is, of its synthetic function. But the ego's capacity for synthesis manifests itself, during the formation of the superego, not only in its mediation between the inner and the outer world and its assimilation of the two, but also in the manner in which it unites, modifies and fuses the separate psychic elements within itself. The synthetic capacity of the ego manifests itself, then, as follows: it assimilates alien elements (both from within and from without), and it mediates between opposing elements and even reconciles opposites and sets mental productivity in train. [pp. 121-222]. [To this is added the need for causality.]
> [Nunberg expands the] hypothesis that the synthetic capacity of the ego is derived from Eros, whose function is not only to unite and to bind, but also to create from this union a new living being [p. 129].

Nunberg thus centers his attention on the formation of the oedipus situation. The period of development between earliest infancy when Nunberg suggests that "psychic harmony is probably most complete" and the oedipal period is hardly dealt with. Yet, nowadays we would consider that just between these two periods important steps are made in the ego's capacity to assimilate alien elements from within and without, to mediate between opposing elements, and to set mental creativity in train. Further, the hypothesis that the synthetic capacity of the ego is derived from Eros would no longer be universally accepted.

Hartmann (1939), in *Ego Psychology and the Problem of Adaptation*, made further important contributions to the study of the synthetic function of the ego. He raises wider biological issues.

> Biology speaks of an "organization of the organism" by which it means "the lawful correlation of the organism's individual parts" (A. E. Parr, 1926). We are justified in saying that *adaptation* and *fitting together* (in the sense of this correlation) are interdependent; fitting together is usually the prerequisite of an adaptation process and vice versa. This correlation also includes the psychophysical relations, and its psychological expression is the synthetic function . . . , which is thus a special case of the broader biological concept of fitting together [p. 40].

Hartmann, discussing adaptation and ego psychology, suggests that four equilibria have to be considered. An equilibrium between individual and environment, the equilibrium of instinctual drives, the equilibrium of mental institutions (structural equilibrium), and an equilibrium between the synthetic function and the rest of the ego. He refers to the interdependence of the regulators of intrapsychic equilibrium.

Hartmann thus classifies and systematizes the different aspects of Nunberg's concept of the synthetic function further and draws attention to the principles of regulation within the different parts of the ego. He also emphasizes that "the full range of synthetic factors is not yet known: some of them belong to the superego, most of them to the ego, and some of these belong partly to the conflict-free regulative functions of the ego. We understand some of the unconscious synthetic factors; but we know very little of the preconscious and conscious ones" [p. 75].

In his paper "Comments on the Psychoanalytic Theory of the Ego" Hartmann (1950) suggests that a systematic study of ego functions would have to describe them as to their "aims and as to the means they use in pursuing them; energically as to the closeness to or remoteness from the drives of the energies with which they operate; and also as to the degree of structuralization and independence they have achieved." To this we would like to add the genetic approach, the study of the development of a particular ego function, the changes in the course of development in regard to the above-mentioned points.

At the present stage of our knowledge in regard to the synthetic function of the ego and for the purpose of this presentation, a comprehensive systematic study as envisaged above cannot yet be undertaken. We shall have to limit the discussion to certain aspects of the study of the synthetic function only, with the aim of paving the way for the investigation of the development of integration.

We are fully aware of the methodological difficulties in attempting to trace the development of integrative processes in the young child. Direct observation does not give sufficient insight into the inner life of the child. Psychoanalytic treatment which reveals the inner life of children cannot be used in the earliest phases of life because it presupposes that the child has reached a stage of development enabling him to communicate with the analyst in a form that makes the information obtained as a result of this communication valid.

It may be possible to gain insight into some of the primitive integrative processes which normally occur at a time before speech is developed through the study of children who suffer from an imbalance in development. In some of these children the integrative processes may be arrested at an early level, while the function of speech and the development of object relations have sufficiently progressed to enable them to communicate with the analyst. Observations made in these cases can be compared with material gained in the psychoanalytic treatment of neurotic children who suffer from a disturbance characterized by a form of ego regression which allows insight into the early functioning of some of the integrative processes. Finally, material from the psychoanalytic treatment of children, who for pathological reasons predominantly use the defense mechanism of splitting, may further contribute to the study of the integrative capacity of the ego, since the defense mechanism of splitting acts specifically against the continuity and unity of the personality.

The aim of integration can be considered from the aspect of the formation of:

the body ego,
the self,

the mental representation of the most important objects (at first
the mother, later mother-father-child in the triangular oedipus
situation),

the world we live in,[3]

identity.[4]

The sequence of these aims could be regarded as representing
a hierarchy from the developmental point of view. In each case,
slow, gradual development takes place from the first inception of one
aim to a summit in the course of its development which later sub-
merges under stages of development which in the meantime have
become more important. Hoffer (1949) shows that "the inception of
the formation of the body ego begins in the first months of life," yet
the height of this development is reached much later and overlaps
with the prestages of integration leading to the formation of the self,
and the mental representation of objects.

Spitz (1959) has recently drawn attention to the idea that the
prerequisite for the normal development of any one stage is a more
or less undisturbed unfolding of the previous stage. When a major
disturbance occurs in any one of the developmental stages, a deviant
base is laid for the establishment of the next one. He writes:

> When a developmental imbalance is firmly established at one
> level, then it will modify the pattern of the next major organizer,[5]
> in conformity with the law of dependent development. Structures
> which now should emerge may remain absent or emerge in a
> distorted form. . . .
>   But the process does not end there. If each successive organ-
> izer is dependent on the establishment of the structures integrated

---

[3] See Hartmann (1956): "The coherence of this 'world' is dependent, among others,
on the ego's capacities for integration, which in dealing with outer reality at the same
time consider the state of the mental systems. This is a contribution of the synthetic
function to our approach to outer and inner reality." Hartmann characterizes this
"world of immediate experience" as one of two organized systems of orientation. He
speaks of "the transformation, or molding, of data into this more or less coherent
world" (p. 49).

[4] Erikson (1947), studying the integration of the individual into society and the
culture and value of this society, writes: "his individual way of mastering experience
(his ego synthesis) is a successful variant of a group identity and is in accord with its
space-time and life plan."

[5] Spitz's use of the term "organizer of the psyche," coined in analogy to the term
"organizer" used by Spemann in experimental embryology, will be accepted in the context of this paper as a tentative one only. For discussion of this concept, see Glover
(1961).

under normal circumstances through the preceding organizer, then the distortion of the structure pattern of the preceding organizer must lead to a distortion of the subsequent organizing process, whether this distortion be one of delay in time or a compensatory reshuffling of the structures themselves.

In favorable cases these distortions may lead to a relative compensation [in others to regression, disintegration, etc.] [pp. 93-94].

If this is correct, it follows that it is of the greatest importance to diagnose and treat children who suffer from such disturbances promptly, because if treatment is successful, future stages of development may proceed normally, whereas if treatment is not instituted at the right time, the future development of these children might be seriously impaired. The following examples of disturbances of integration also illustrate the complexity of this problem.

CLINICAL REPORTS

Jeffrey

Among the patients at the Hampstead Clinic was Jeffrey, who was referred at the age of nearly three because he could not speak, and he also could not play or occupy himself. The parents reported, for instance, that Jeffrey had never responded to their attempts to show him how to clap his hands, wave good-by, or later build a tower. I do not wish to discuss the psychopathology of this child, nor the question of his progress in treatment. I only want to quote one example from the boy's treatment which showed how he became able to connect, to fit together in quite a primitive way.

For weeks and months Jeffrey had just been moving around the room in his treatment session or would withdraw from contact altogether. At one stage the therapist placed some bricks in a row. Jeffrey became quite angry with her, pushed the bricks away, knocked his head, a sign which was understood by that time as an expression of his anger. Within a few days Jeffrey had given up his resentment in regard to playing with the bricks, but he would not yet do it himself. He took the therapist's hands, moved the hands toward the bricks, and thus gave her to understand that he wanted her to make something with the bricks. The therapist remained somewhat passive, but Jeffrey insisted, moving her hands until she placed the bricks in a row. Only in the course of the next few days did Jeffrey himself begin to place the bricks in a row, and now he did this with great pleasure, whereas before he had completely refused to do anything like this.

Did Jeffrey show in this way a slow motion picture of a process of integration and assimilation which normally proceeds at such a quick rate that we cannot usually see the different stages of this process in normal children at a much earlier age?

Edward

In another child, Edward, who came to the Clinic at the age of nearly six, we could see the process of integration develop one step further. I quote from Nunberg (1955): "The synthetic function of the ego thus manifests itself in the assimilation of internal and external elements, in reconciling conflicting ideas, in uniting contrasts, and in activating mental creativity" (p. 151). Edward, too, was a child whose development had proceeded at a much slower rate than is usual, and who showed an imbalance in his development. In his case it was also not clear how far this was due to external factors, which had delayed his normal development, and how far an inner defect was responsible for his present state.

Edward was able to express himself verbally. At one point in his treatment he showed his upset about his Nanny going on holiday. The therapist, using dolls for the purpose, enacted the scene of the Nanny going away, and the parents and Edward waving good-by to her. The therapist then enacted that the Nanny was coming back from her holiday. Up to this point Edward had been able to play only in imitation of what other people had taught him. Now he became able to integrate what the analyst had conveyed to him in the context of his fantasies and previous experience.[6] Following the therapist's dramatization of the scene of the Nanny's leaving and return, Edward for the first time used the dolls also to express his

6 See Kris (1952, p. 309): "The theoretical, psychoanalytic explanation of the relationship between recognition and recall is that the synthetic function of the ego, establishing a context, is in the case of recognition facilitated by the help of perception (in our example, the analyst's interpretation). Recall then fills a gap, fits into a pattern."

own fantasy in an organized form. He expressed anger against his mother for allowing the Nanny to go away, by letting the mother get run over by a car; then he turned the aggression against himself in fantasy, and played that a boy got killed on the road. From this point onward, Edward became able to use cars and dolls for the dramatization of his fantasies, thus showing that a new area of his mind had become integrated with the rest of his personality and that he had made a step toward sublimation.

Catherine

The ego's capacity for integration in dealing with inner and outer reality was discussed at the Hampstead Clinic in connection with the study of blind children. Catherine, an eight-year-old twin who was blind as a result of retrolental fibroplasia, was retarded in ego and drive development; for weeks on end she spent much time in her sessions putting the tea set into the basin, taking it out, dropping it back into her drawer, shutting drawers, turning on taps, emptying out water. By listening to her instead of watching her, the therapist finally learned to understand that these were the background noises of her life at home, her mother doing the housework, and the impression she got of what went on. The therapist noted in her report: "When I once commented at a much later stage in treatment why all these activities were accompanied by so much clattering and noise; was her mother always angry?" she replied, "That's what it sounds like to me." This may account partly for her idea of a hostile reality. For example, she told the therapist of an accident she had had a few weeks prior, when she fell off the curb into the street. She blamed her sister Mary for this, because Mary had made her run fast to the letter box. Then in describing her pain she said, "I could not bend my foot, it was smacking me." This example shows how the absence of visual external data—in this case, the fact that Catherine could not check what her mother was saying by looking at her mother's face, and seeing that she was not always angry—may have contributed to a later disturbance in the child, namely, to her feeling that the people around her were hostile, confirming the picture of her mother as a hostile figure, resulting from the projection of her own aggressive feelings.

Sandra

In a highly abnormal child it seemed to have been the mother's mode of influencing the child which resulted in what appeared to be an artificial personality with almost complete lack of integration between id, ego, and superego.

In the case of Sandra, there was no doubt that quite apart from the external factors which influenced her integration, there was in addition a basic condition of malfunctioning, a disturbance in the synthetic function of the ego, although it was more difficult to fit her clearly into one of the clinical pictures described by various authors. She was first seen at the age of seven. Sandra behaved more or less like a little robot, obediently doing whatever her mother suggested, repeating whatever her mother said, compulsively tidying and ordering everything in the room. She was exceptionally clean and orderly, and all of her activities were highly repetitive. Over a long period of time and with great effort, her mother had succeeded in training this child so that Sandra was at least to a limited extent socially acceptable; that is, she was toilet trained, she was immaculate, she could speak, and she would obey mother's commands. But it was clear that all this was simply a mechanical adaptation to her mother, a layer of training superimposed on the rest of her personality and in no way integrated.

For example, Sandra's speech was no more than repetition of learned phrases. She could not answer a question, but only repeat it. If she wanted to go home she could not say, "I want to go home," but would instead reproduce the mother's voice, tone, and words, and say, "Would you like to go home?" She did not use first person pronouns. Her reaction to dirt or water was precisely that of her mother —both would leap for a cloth with a cry of distress. Her activities were also a reproduction of the games which her mother had tried to teach her, and she would often interrupt the therapist by shouting in a harsh voice, "Naughty girl—will you stop that noise," or "If you can't keep quiet, you can stand in the corner"—all very familiar expressions of her mother. Altogether, Sandra seemed to be like an exaggerated edition of her mother, and one had constantly to ask: "Where is the child?"

This superstructure of rigid and repetitive behavior was one of the few means by which her extremely primitive ego could defend itself against anxiety, yet it was comparatively easy to peel away. The most extreme of Sandra's compulsions was the ordering of people and things so that everything was sitting on or straddling something else, and all similar objects were in pairs. And this gave a clue as to where this child's real interests and real personality lay. Her ritualistic ordering of all the toys and furniture, so that small dolls and objects were sitting or being carried on larger dolls and objects, was an attempt to reproduce one of the inner images to which she was fixated—namely, being carried on her mother's shoulder.

Gradually, she abandoned her compulsive ordering of things in favor of using the therapist as a means for dramatizing this picture, and it was at this point that she completely dropped her parrot speech. Instead she expressed herself by maneuvering the situation and people, indicating her wishes by actions, and behaving as if she were a nonspeaking child. She demanded that her mother carry her as she had done for many years in the past when Sandra was much smaller, and she screamed whenever she saw a real child being carried by an adult. As a baby, being carried had been the only protection she had had against anxiety. In addition, of course, it was one of her main sources of gratification.

The excessive tidiness and orderliness gave way to the emergence of or regression to what might be called Sandra's anal phase. She demanded a pot, she soiled and wet herself, she insisted on direct anal gratifications from her mother such as being wiped, having ointment applied to her anus, etc. She enjoyed smelling and pouring and smearing, and turned every toy and every game into potting, producing, and playing with feces. She wanted to defecate and urinate in the presence of the therapist, and in every way she behaved like a toddler at the height of the anal phase. Sandra became stubborn and obstinate with her mother, insisting on having her own way and developing all the struggles with her mother which are characteristic of the toddler. It was indeed the outstanding feature of this case that Sandra's mechanical, compulsive, rigid superstructure could, in a period of less than a year, give way to an intense and vivid experiencing of the instinctual impulses and conflicts typical of the anal phase.

The libidinal development brought about decided changes in

her relationships and in her ego development. The speech which had formerly been only repetitive could now be used for the first time to express her own ideas and wishes. It became genuine communication. Instead of pushing and pulling the therapist, she would say, "Go upstairs, go downstairs." When her mother said, "Have some beans," Sandra would not repeat this as in the past, but would say she wanted all the beans, not some of the beans. Instead of saying as she used to, "Would you like to tie the shoe?" she would now say, "Tie my shoes." When she put her foot up to have one shoe tied, she would afterwards put her other foot up and say, "Tie the other shoe."

Changes in Sandra's appearance and motility took place, and she was able to express much more affect and to move with ease and skill. Logical thinking became possible so that she was able to solve problems such as how to get things which were out of her reach by using a chair or a long stick; play became possible as she began slowly to displace her instinctual impulses onto more acceptable materials such as paint and water. Gradually she became clean again, and instead of soiling herself, she allowed her dolls to do so. Sandra was beginning to show signs of being able to incorporate prohibitions. For example, she shouted and grunted when the therapist refused to allow her to enter another therapist's treatment room. On the following day she tried again and grunted when she was again stopped, but after this she could walk past the door to this room, give a little grunt to herself, and control her wish to enter without the therapist's interference, or even in the latter's absence.

Thus, whereas at the onset of treatment, seven-year-old Sandra was at the level of a young toddler, overlaid with the training and restrictions of her mother, she was now back at that level without those restrictions. One could observe more normal ego development belonging to that phase of development in the transition from anal preoccupation to symbolic play, in the internalization of prohibition, and in speech. Previously Sandra had functioned on the basis of strict commands with no attempt at integration of her own wishes with those of the environment. Although the lack of integration in this child's personality could be influenced by treatment, we would envisage the improvement to be limited; owing to the fact that for external reasons Sandra was removed from home after eighteen months of treatment, no conclusions can be drawn as to the possible extent of her improvement in regard to the development of the ego as well as to that of libido and aggression and her object relationships.

In regard to the chances of influencing the integration of the personality, these are no doubt better if the lack of integration is predominantly caused by outside circumstances than in cases where there is an internal defect of the synthetic function of the ego. And it is imperative to spot, as early as possible, those cases of sometimes quite severe lack of integration which are due to external factors, because these children will continue to be held up in their development and some of them may appear clinically like borderline psychotic children.

Sheila

While we do not know whether Sandra would have reached anything like near normality, in the case of Sheila, who also lacked integration of her personality, it was possible to see her attain a stage of development which was within the range of normality as a result of treatment.

Sheila was first seen when she was three years and ten months old. She was acutely anxious and was brought for a sleeping disturbance to a children's hospital. The psychiatrist who saw her at that time had the impression that she was a borderline psychotic child. Her mother reported that at the age of six months, following a short hospitalization for vomiting, she was taken to a hospital for a congenital dislocation of her right hip. She had been laid flat on a frame for four months, and then placed in plaster at the age of ten months in a frog position. She returned home at two and a half years, having been in the hospital for two years. During this period, her mother said, Sheila gave no sign of being disturbed. She became very attached to the ward nurse, who became equally fond of Sheila. She placed the child in a bed which was directly in the line of vision of her office, and they saw each other and talked to each other constantly. She became the favorite patient of the hospital and was always shown off to visitors.

When she returned home, at the age of two and a half years, she became increasingly restless, talked compulsively, was described "as a mass of nerves," behaved spitefully to her brother, and was very destructive.

One of the reasons for thinking that Sheila was borderline psychotic was that although she was clearly of extremely high intelligence, she did not seem to use language to communicate. Her talk consisted of a curious nonstop, anxious mixture of television advertisements, snatches of song and rhyme, sprinklings of adult words and phrases and a bizarreness of thought and ideas, which seemed all the more incongruous for being wedged in between occasional rational remarks. Later this was understood as a fantasy in which she seemed to have twenty-one children. Holding one doll in her arms, she said:

> Now dear, yes dear. I'll get rid of the lot of you.
> Eat castor oil and grow up strong and healthy, it stops dreams it does, castor oil, it stops dreams.
> I have dreams of Jesus, Jesus standing on me, on top of my head, wanting to make me happy. What did He do to me? You know what He did. You were there in the dream.
> Galloways cough syrup, Galloways cough syrup, Galloways cough syrup.
> Jesus was a carpenter, sawing wood on a bench, smooth wood.
> I can't talk in Sunday School, learning lessons.
> God and Jesus make things grow, my plant, God making snow fall, big things like elephants, small things like "mouses." Proud He is, Jesus is proud.
> This baby likes to be cuddled, when he is fed. One is English, one is Indian, one is French. He loves his mother too much to be comfy.
> Bird's custard. I always give everyone Bird's custard. It's not like castor oil, it leaves you as you are. Would you like some?
> I won't go. I'll come with you.
> I'll take you where the lions get you, they'll eat you.

She also broke down into fierce rages whenever frustrated, and attacked the therapist verbally and physically. She would scream, for instance, "You are a misery, an old goat, you old goat, why do you scratch me, I won't go, I'll stay here all day." While this continued she attacked the therapist, scratching her, trying to get a handful of her hair, kicking her shins and screaming. She rushed from one activity to another, and her play was overwhelmed by her profuse fantasy life. She played various roles in her games, but because she switched so rapidly from one role to the next, it was difficult to tell whom at any one moment she was representing.

This was the picture which emerged from the observation sessions. It was not possible to offer her analytic treatment at that time, and she was first seen once weekly. When told that these sessions were "to help her with her worries" there was a dramatic change in the confused and disintegrated picture she had presented earlier. Her fantasies were now brought in the form of more or less organized games; for example, the fantasy of a large family of twenty or more children emerged as a hospital-ward game in which she was a nurse in charge of twenty patients. This introduced material about the whole hospital experience.

Shortly afterwards, when she was taken into analysis, there was a further improvement in her communication. It became very clear that the defense mechanism of splitting was, at this stage, of great importance for her functioning. She split her positive and negative feelings between the mother and the therapist as, we conjectured, she had previously failed to integrate these feelings between Nurse M. and her mother. The disappointing object was "totally bad," the other at the same time being "totally good." With a mother who visited regularly, a nurse to whom she was very attached, and the other nurses who also shared in the physical care of her, she had every opportunity not to integrate her unwanted feelings. It may even be that the sudden change in the direction of greater organization, which occurred even in her weekly treatment, was largely due to the fact that once more she had two objects—the therapist and the mother—between whom she could now split her positive and negative feelings. Thus, while she hated one, she still preserved the other.

The confirmatory material came later in the analysis, when she verbalized the transference feelings which belonged to Nurse M. in the past. She said that it seemed as if she had had two mummies when she was small, and that this had been very confusing. She confirmed the fact that her current splitting of her feelings between the mother and the therapist belonged to the original situation in the past, relating it to her wish to have the therapist as a mother whenever her own mother disappointed her. She added spontaneously that even now when she felt cross with her mummy she still sometimes wished she could go back to Nurse M.

With analysis, therefore, it was possible to integrate Sheila's present with her past, in a way that enabled her to function in most

respects on an age-adequate level. It does seem in this case that we
were not dealing with a primary disturbance of the synthetic function of the ego, but that the external factors in the child's history
were important in producing a picture of severe lack of integration.
Sheila had suffered from two sets of traumata: the separation from
the people who cared for her at the age of six months when she was
removed to the hospital, and at the age of two and a half when she
was again completely separated from those she had learned to love in
hospital. This complete break in the continuity of her life at two
and a half years had the effect that her personality practically fell to
pieces and she appeared like a psychotic child. In Sheila's case we
also must consider how her body image developed, owing to the fact
that she was in a plaster cast, and spent many months in a frog position between the age of ten months and a year and a half. The
summation of traumatic events in her life, the two complete separations from the people she knew and the environment she lived in,
together with the interference of the integration of her body image,
led to the establishment of this pseudo-psychotic picture.

Freud referred to what he later described in his paper "Splitting
of the Ego in the Defensive Process" (1938) already in 1927, in the
paper on "Fetishism." There he refers to two patients who had
refused to acknowledge the death of their fathers. A very important
piece of reality had thus been denied by the ego, in the same way
as the fetishist denies the unwelcome fact of the absence of the penis
in the woman. Freud adds, "I also began to suspect that similar
occurrences in childhood are by no means rare" (p. 156).

Daniel

In splitting of the ego in the defensive process, the defense is
being adopted only by part of the ego, while other parts of the ego
treat the warded-off event or impulse as ego syntonic. This can be
seen, for example, in a boy who on discovery of the apparent castration in a girl on the one hand accepts it as a fact, on the other hand
denies it and builds further development on this denial.

This mechanism could be observed in the course of the analytic
treatment of Daniel. He was brought to treatment at the age of
three because of his compulsion to handle and smell ladies' underwear on or off the body and the urge to feel the panties of his sister

or of any other little girl he met. In his analysis it became clear that this behavior was built on a denial of the difference between the sexes; everyone has panties, signifying that everyone has a penis. His insistence on seeing the panties of little girls was an attempt to reassure himself against his castration anxiety. This anxiety had been exceptionally strong owing to the fact that his mother had been manipulating his foreskin since the age of one. Smelling of underwear was understood also as a denial of knowledge about menstruation, which was equated in his mind with castration. When the denial had been extensively interpreted Daniel brought material confirming that he was fully aware of the "castration" of little girls; for example, he said that a "panty pecker" had pecked a hole in his sister's panties and pecked off her genital.

He thus showed the splitting of the ego as found in adult fetishists where one part of the ego denies the absence of the penis in the female, while another part admits it.

DISCUSSION

In choosing integration as the subject for discussion, we are of course aware that in the course of development each step in the process of integration must be viewed in connection with processes of differentiation. It will be important to study the consecutive levels of integration and differentiation in detail; at present we are by no means yet able to establish a complete and systematic hierarchy. Integration can first be found to take place when, according to Hartmann, gradual differentiation between id and ego begins. Integration of drives and primitive ego functions, integration of different functions within the ego, and structural integration of id, ego, and superego follow.

The clinical examples presented in this paper show how processes of integration can be influenced at certain stages in the development of the child, as a result of internal and external factors. Some of these examples illustrate various forms of arrested development in so far as the development of integration is concerned, i.e., Edward, aged six, showed an arrest of the development of integration just prior to an important stage of activation of mental creativity. How later levels of integration are influenced, owing to disturbances of integration at an earlier level, can be seen in the case of Sheila: the "self," the "mental representation of the most important objects," the "world we live in" were distorted owing to the disturbance of integration at the level of development when these structures were formed, as well as owing to the earlier deviant integration of the "body ego" of this child who spent much time on a frame and in a plaster cast in the frog position. Her "body ego" did not function as a well-integrated basis for the unfolding of the later levels of integration. Relatively normal development in the first place and later unsuccessful employment of defense mechanisms, symptom formation with splitting of the ego, interfering with integration, is shown in the case of Daniel, the young fetishist.

We believe that investigation and clarification of the development and pathology of integration could now go beyond the contributions made by those authors[7] from whom we differ and who speak of "typical defenses of the early ego, such as the mechanisms of splitting the object and the impulses" in explaining happenings in the first few months of life, before integration has taken place to any extent; they also seem to use the identical term with the same meaning when describing defense mechanisms in adult patients who had achieved a high level of integration prior to their illness.

CONCLUSION

In order to predict the response to analytic treatment in a particular child it is important to distinguish clearly between disturbances of integration due to arrested development, imbalance of development, regression from later developmental levels of integration to earlier ones, and disturbances of integration resulting from splitting of the ego in the defensive process.

BIBLIOGRAPHY

Erikson, E. H. (1947), Ego Development and Historical Change. *This Annual*, II.
—— (1950), *Childhood and Society*. New York: Norton.
—— (1953), Growth and Crises of the "Healthy Personality." In: *Identity and the*

[7] See Klein (1946): "Object-relations exist from the beginning of life, the first object being the mother's breast which to the child becomes split into a good (gratifying) and bad (frustrating) breast; this splitting results in a severance of love and hate."

Life Cycle. Selected Papers [*Psychological Issues*, I (1), Mon. No. 1]. New York: International Universities Press, 1959.

French, T. (1941), Goal, Mechanism and Integrative Field. *Psychosom. Med.*, III.

—— (1945), Integration of Social Behavior. *Psa. Quart.*, XIV.

Freud, A. (1936), *The Ego and the Mechanisms of Defence*. New York: International Universities Press, 1946.

Freud, S. (1927), Fetishism. *Standard Edition*, XXI. London: Hogarth Press, 1961.

—— (1928), Dostoevsky and Parricide. *Standard Edition*, XXI. London: Hogarth Press, 1961.

—— (1938), Splitting of the Ego in the Defensive Process. *Collected Papers*, V. London: Hogarth Press, 1950.

Glover, E. (1961), Some Recent Trends in Psychoanalytic Theory. *Psa. Quart.*, XXX.

Greenacre, P. (1953), Certain Relationships between Fetishism and Faulty Development of the Body Image. *This Annual*, VIII.

—— (1960), Considerations Regarding the Parent-Infant Relationship. *Int. J. Psa.*, XLI.

Hartmann, H. (1939), *Ego Psychology and the Problem of Adaptation*. New York: International Universities Press, 1958.

—— (1947), On Rational and Irrational Action. *Psychoanalysis and the Social Sciences*, I. New York: International Universities Press.

—— (1950), Comments on the Psychoanalytic Theory of the Ego. *This Annual*, V.

—— (1956), Notes on the Reality Principle. *This Annual*, XI.

Hoffer, W. (1949), Mouth, Hand and Ego-Integration. *This Annual*, III/IV.

Klein, M. (1946), Notes on Some Schizoid Mechanisms. *Int. J. Psa.*, XXVII.

—— & Heimann, P., Isaacs, S., Riviere, J. (1952), *Developments in Psycho-Analysis*. London: Hogarth Press.

Kris, E. (1951), Opening Remarks on Psychoanalytic Child Psychology. *This Annual*, VI.

—— (1952), *Psychoanalytic Exploration in Art*. New York: International Universities Press.

Nunberg, H. (1931), The Synthetic Function of the Ego. *Practice and Theory of Psychoanalysis*. New York: International Universities Press, 1961.

—— (1955), *Principles of Psychoanalysis*. New York: International Universities Press.

Spemann, H. (1938), *Embryonic Development and Induction*. New Haven: Yale University Press.

Spitz, R. (1959), *A Genetic Field Theory of Ego Formation*. New York: International Universities Press.

Waddington, C. H. (1940), *Organizers and Genes*. Cambridge University Press.

Winnicott, D. W. (1945), Primitive Emotional Development. *Int. J. Psa.*, XXVI.

—— (1954), Mind and Its Relation to the Psyche-Soma. *Brit. J. Med. Psychol.*, XXVII.

—— (1960), The Theory of the Parent-Infant Relationship. *Int. J. Psa.*, XLI.

ADOLESCENT MOODS AND THE REMODELING OF PSYCHIC STRUCTURES IN ADOLESCENCE[1]

EDITH JACOBSON, M.D. (New York)

This lecture will focus on some developmental problems of adolescence, a period which, in the opinion of all analytic experts in this field, has not yet been fully explored.

In her last paper on this subject, Anna Freud (1958) discussed the reasons for our insufficient insight into the confusing emotional manifestations and symptomatology of this interesting phase. In this context, she compared the adolescent's resistances to analytic treatment with the difficulties encountered in patients during periods of mourning or during unhappy love affairs, and she emphasized how much the emotional situation of the adolescent has in common with these two states.

Berta Bornstein and Nathan Root (1957) had already called attention to the significant role of mourning in the struggle of the adolescent, who must disengage himself from his parents and embark on a search for new objects.

But why does the adolescent pass through such violent and peculiar affective crises? Why does he show such a bent for rapid, sudden swings of mood? One week he may be in a state of doleful sadness, of *Weltschmerz* and despair. The next week may be a period of earnest concentration and introspection. Today we may enjoy his sparkling enthusiasm, his burning interest in his studies, or his infectious joyfulness and his high-spirited sociability. But tomorrow

[1] The Abraham A. Brill Lecture, presented to The New York Psychoanalytic Society and Institute, March 7, 1961.

A briefer and somewhat different version of this paper, entitled "The Loss and Finding of the Objects and the Self in Adolescence," was presented at the Tenth Anniversary Symposium, the Child Psychiatry Unit, Massachusetts Mental Health Center, Harvard Medical School. The symposium was devoted to "Psychoanalytic Studies in Object Loss and Depression."

we may be angered by his boisterous activities or his foolhardy reck-
lessness. And this behavior may again be followed by a period of
secret, passionate worship and overwhelming ecstasies.

What are the nature and origin of these moods? And for what
reasons do so many adolescents suffer from recurring painful states
of depression and despair, which may involve not only severe guilt
conflicts, but harassing feelings of shame and self-consciousness to
the point of hypochondriacal body preoccupations or paranoid fears?

Moreover, why do we find embedded in the adolescent's conspicuous and unique emotional manifestations such characteristic,
disturbing fluctuations in his feelings for others and in his self-
feelings, his feelings of identity? Why does he show at one time a
close relatedness to the world, to people, to nature or art or God, in
conjunction with rich experiences of "I am I, I live, and the world
is mine and will be mine," while at other times he has painful doubts
about the meaning of life and of the world, about himself and his
role in the world, or even suffers from desperate feelings of isolation
and lonesomeness and is convinced of the nothingness of his existence, of life, of his own life and future?

Before we embark on a study of the psychic processes causing
these turbulent emotional phenomena, we must visualize the inner
situation of the adolescent, which Anna Freud (1936, 1958) and
Helene Deutsch (1944), among other authors, have so beautifully
described.

In point of fact, adolescence is life between a saddening farewell
to childhood—i.e., to the self and the objects of the past—and a
gradual, anxious-hopeful passing over many barriers to the gates
which permit entrance to the still unknown country of adulthood.
Beginning with his infantile love objects, the adolescent must not
only free himself from persons who were all-important during childhood, but renounce his former pleasures and pursuits more rapidly
than at any former developmental stage. Preparing himself to leave
home sooner or later, he must reach out for adult sex, love, and
responsibility, for personal and social relations of a new and different
type, for new interests and sublimations, and, last but not least, for
new values, standards, and goals which can offer him directions for
his future and aid him in making the most important decisions of
his life: the vocational choice which will determine his work and

his future financial and social situation, and the choice of a love object—ultimately of a marital partner.

This necessitates a complete reorientation, leading to structural and energic transformations, to economic-cathectic redistributions, and to a drastic overhauling of the entire psychic organization.

I do not intend to deal with all the aspects of these processes but shall discuss mainly their influence upon the infantile object relations and identifications, whose vicissitudes find a reflection in the adolescent's states of mood.[2]

We know that all the emotional turmoil and disturbances of this stage are centered around the conflicts caused by the tremendous psychobiological changes in the adolescent. I cannot go into the complexities of the instinctual conflicts aroused by the onset of puberty. Suffice it to point out that the adolescent's instinctual development impressively demonstrates how, in climbing up the tortuous ladder to adulthood, he seems at every new step to experience anxiety, confusion, disorganization, and a return to infantile positions, followed by propulsion and reorganization at more advanced and more adult levels.

Such processes, to be sure, can be observed at any developmental stage. But during the dramatic adolescent period we see what Helene Deutsch (1944) described as a "clash" between progressive and regressive forces. This clash leads to a far-reaching temporary dissolution of old structures and organizations, in conjunction with new structure formation and the establishment of new hierarchic orders, in which earlier psychic formations definitely assume a subordinate role, while new ones acquire and sustain dominance.

The adolescent's propensity to recurring swift temporary regressions in all areas and systems obviously results from the all-too-powerful assault of instinctual forces on his ego. Being engaged, for its part, in continuous growth and change, the ego is certainly bound to reinstate past positions before it can cope with the formidable task of finding new ways of instinctual control and new avenues of discharge, which can help the adolescent not only to relinquish his childhood attachments, but also to gain the optimal and socially

---

[2] Unfortunately, I cannot avoid restating and re-emphasizing in this context many points which have previously been brought to our attention by other authors, especially by Anna Freud and Helene Deutsch.

permissible degree of instinctual and emotional freedom needed for the building of adult sexual and personal relationships.

We know that during this struggle the defenses established during latency become so badly battered that they may partly break down under the onslaught of instinctual impulses. How does the adolescent manage to reconstitute, reorganize, and resolidify his defense system?

At this point, it may be helpful to compare the situation in adolescence with the childhood period of the passing of the oedipus conflicts. The oedipal child had to repress his sexual and hostile impulses in favor of affectionate attachments to his parents. In adolescence, the sexual maturation process leads to a temporary revival of preoedipal and oedipal instinctual strivings, thus reanimating the infantile struggle. But now the incestuous sexual and hostile wishes must be finally relinquished; moreover, the adolescent's affectionate ties to the parents also must be sufficiently loosened to guarantee his future freedom of object choice. This is the cause of his grief reactions, which have no parallel in childhood. What makes this emotional task even harder is the fact that it involves, in addition, a definite and final abandonment of his practical and mental dependency on the parents. This "detachment from parental authority" Freud (1905) regarded as "one of the most significant, but also one of the most painful, psychical achievements."

In fact, the adolescent will soon "come of age" and thereby reach a point of no return, indicating that society regards him as able to be his own master.

Even though his practical dependency may extend to the twenties, or longer, this step signifies that the adolescent's final solution of his oedipal conflicts must also accomplish a liberation from family bonds, which is necessary for the final establishment of the autonomy and independence of his ego and superego. This struggle may be complicated further by irregularities in the concomitant, rapid growth of the ego, which is not always commensurate with the advance of instinctual development.

Superego formation assists the child in the solution of his oedipal conflicts and enables him to achieve a certain independence of external influences even at that early stage. In the adolescent no new psychic system arises from his efforts to break away from his infantile love objects. However, his struggles for maturity and final liberation from his family bonds certainly find support from remarkable modifications and new structure formations developing in his superego and ego.

We know of course that during adolescence the superego becomes readjusted and consolidated, but precisely what does this process of consolidation involve? The necessity for a resetting of the defense system has already been mentioned. However, such reorganization of the defenses certainly presupposes and depends upon a far-reaching remodeling of the superego system. Since the superego is built up by virtue of partial identifications with idealized parental images, with parental standards, demands, and prohibitions, this question leads us directly to the problem of identifications.

We are used to viewing identifications mainly as psychic formations, which, acquiring the function of defense mechanisms, enable the child to tolerate and accept instinctual frustrations, emotional deprivation, or even object loss, and which arise, at least partly, in reaction to these. As we know from grief reactions, identifications may still develop from such sources and serve these purposes in adults. Thus we might easily infer that the adolescent, who now must definitely give up his oedipal love objects, would achieve this mainly by means of even stronger identifications with them in his superego and ego. But what actually happens is not so simple, for good reasons.

From the viewpoint of the ego, we must not forget that identifications originate in the long-lasting psychobiological dependency of the human child and that his infantile ego formation rests upon these identifications. "The weaker the child's ego," says Helene Deutsch (1944), "the more it resorts to identifications with adults in its adjustment to the adult world." But up to his adolescence, even the child with a normal ego strength learns to adapt to society—and to reality in general—less by direct and immediate contact than through the medium of his relations and identifications with his parents and parental figures. To the extent to which his ego has matured and established its secondary autonomy, however, these identifications must lose an essential part of their function. Thus, contradictions must arise between the adolescent's need to cope with the loss of his infantile love objects, by fortifying his identifications with them, and the fact that these very identifications become more and more dispensable.

With regard to the superego we must realize that in comparison with the oedipal stage, its goals and functions must undergo remarkable changes, at least as far as sex is concerned. During the infantile period of superego formation, the child commonly resolves his oedipal conflicts with the aid of defenses which enable him to repress and inhibit his forbidden instinctual impulses to the point of renouncing sexual activities in general. In adolescence the superego once more must enforce the incest taboo, yet at the same time it must open the barriers of repression and lift the burden of countercathexes sufficiently to guide the adolescent on his road to the sexual freedom of the adult and to mature personal and love relationships. These contradictory aims are reflected in the vicissitudes and the reorganization of his identifications, and hence in the changes which superego, ego, and id undergo in the course of adolescence. Before examining these, however, I must first underline certain reservations with regard to my preceding statements.

When we emphasize that the adolescent's identifications with his parents lose some of their significance, or when we speak of his grief over loss of the incestuous love objects, we must immediately add that the final breaking of the oedipal ties, the establishment of new object relations, and the processes of new structure formation and reorganization during adolescence are successful only as long as they do not deplete the libidinous investments or eradicate the identifications of the past. They merely reduce and displace them onto new objects, change their qualities, and subordinate them to new attachments and partly to new identifications (A. Katan, 1951). Putting it from the structural angle: the superego cannot be remodeled, reorganized, and consolidated; new personal and sexual relations, new ego structures and ego functions cannot be built up and integrated unless these new formations are allowed to grow organically from those of the past. As a matter of fact, in adults the survival of unambivalent affectionate relations and of certain fundamental identifications with their parents can almost be used as evidence that in their adolescent past these persons succeeded in renouncing their infantile desires and their dependency on the family.

In the paper I mentioned before, where Anna Freud (1958)

describes the various devices employed by the adolescent in his endeavors to break his ties to the family, she also points to the serious implications of an "inner loss" of his infantile love objects at this stage.

I do not have time to discuss the severe pathology which will develop in case of an enduring cathectic withdrawal from the infantile love objects in adolescence. However, it is significant that even within the margin of normal development adolescents may pass through transient periods of narcissistic retreat to the point of real "inner" object loss. What is decisive is less the brief duration than the reversibility of such states which will normally be followed by a return to the object world and by renewed progression.

Focusing now on the specific vicissitudes of the ego and superego identifications of the adolescent, we realize, first of all, that probably the most incisive and difficult step is the gradual establishment of enduring identifications with his parents as with sexually active persons, who will ultimately grant him, too, the rights of indulgence in sexual and other adult activities.

It is not surprising that these identifications, which were unacceptable in the past, can become fully ego syntonic and attain dominance only to the extent to which superego and ego mature, become reconstructed and consolidated, and reach a new level of strength and autonomy. In fact, these identifications, which open the gates to adult sexual freedom, become only gradually an integral part of the adolescent's ever-widening identifications with the grownups in all areas of the ego which develop under the influence of new or modified superego identifications. This leads us to the changes which the moral codes of the superego must undergo in the course of adolescence.

Simplifying matters considerably, we may briefly define them as follows. Whereas in childhood the superego stated: "If you identify with the parental demands and prohibitions, you will be granted sexual pleasure in the adult future," it must now convey: "You are permitted to enjoy adult sexual and emotional freedom to the extent to which you renounce your infantile instinctual desires, loosen your childhood attachments, and accept adult ethical standards and responsibilities."

This confronts the adolescent with the complex and confusing task of toning down the idealized sexually prohibiting parental images, of reconciling them with realistic concepts of sexually active and increasingly permissive parents, and at the same time of building up new sets of goals and values based on a firm re-establishment of the incest taboo. We realize that this presupposes significant changes in the content and qualities of the ego ideal and in the superego functions—changes which are not merely the result of identification processes but which, as will be shown further on, eventually gain strong reinforcement from new structure formations in the maturing and increasingly autonomous ego. Since these processes involve a reconciliation and integration of the most opposing goals and aims and of very contradictory identifications, they must temporarily weaken both superego and ego. The failure to resolve these contradictions becomes absurdly evident in many of our patients whose concepts of becoming adult may range from the fantasy that growing up means the attainment of complete instinctual freedom to the idea that it means complete instinctual renunciation. Thus it is no wonder that for a briefer or longer period these processes of transformation will cause marked fluctuations in the adolescent's superego functions and in his behavior, and disturb not only his relations to his parents but his object relations in general. Struggling for a partial lifting of his repressions, the adolescent will suffer from severe sexual, narcissistic, and ambivalence conflicts which will become manifest in his attitudes toward persons of the same sex as well as of the opposite sex. During this struggle, his ego will experience increased id and superego pressures and may alternately yield to the latter or rebel actively against it, and in overthrowing it join forces with the id. More or less stormy periods of sexual and aggressive acting out and of narcissistic inflation thus may alternate with periods of repentance, of ascetic ideals, of strictly abstinent, moral behavior, and often of guilt, shame, and inferiority feelings.

From this acting out we indeed gain the impression that the psychophysiological sexual development, the rapid and visible body changes, and the concomitant mental growth of the ego create tremendous amounts of surplus psychic energy, which tend to feed and liberate not only the sexual and hostile impulses, but also the unlimited narcissistic strivings that had once been absorbed by the constitution of superego identifications. In point of fact, to the extent to which he removes himself from his infantile love objects, the adolescent passes through a prolonged stage of overinvolvement with narcissistic aims and preoccupations *at the temporary cost* of truly object-directed goals. Anna Freud (1936) and Helene Deutsch (1944) have both commented on this intensification of narcissism in adolescence. As we shall see, however, this increased narcissism ultimately gains a significant territory for the ego and the object relations.

What lends their special coloring to the adolescent's vacillations and acting out are the regressive features in the defensive operations caused at this stage by the transitory, partial collapse of the superego and by the repressive barriers. Trying to ward off his overpowerful instinctual strivings, the adolescent may again call upon primitive defenses, such as denial, introjection, projection. Or he may use aggression in the attempt to ward off sex, or he may escape from genital to pregenital goals, from heterosexual to narcissistic-homosexual attachments and activities, and back again; from objects of his age to older persons, or even to incestuous objects, and the reverse. This is the reason why the adolescent may develop some forms of behavior which may suggest psychopathy or even psychosis.

In his struggle for a reconciliation between the opposing goals of the superego and the id, the adolescent may find aid from extraneous persons (or also from social, political or religious groups), who at this phase lend themselves better than the parents to repersonifications and reprojections of both superego and id. Pure and saintly or seductive and ruthless men or women may thus alternately become admired and emulated or despised and hated, because they represent his own sexual temptations and ambitions or the virtue, humility, and chastity he seeks. But this is not all. When we observe the types of persons whom adolescents glorify, revere, and emulate, or only imitate for briefer or longer periods, we realize also that the endeavors to remodel ego ideal and superego lead to an intense revival of infantile superego precursors and of values expressive of pregenital and phallic-narcissistic selfish and pleasure aims, rather than moral goals. I have discussed these forestages of superego development in a previous paper (1954). In fact, the adolescent's heroes or heroines may catch his eye because of their physical strength or attractiveness, or because of their sexual successes or their social glamour, their wealth, their ruthless career, and prominence in the fields of sport or art or science, of business or finance or politics, or even of crime. Moreover, his admiration for such persons and groups, or for the values they represent, may find expression in transient but intense homosexual or heterosexual "crushes," which frequently show a rather sadomasochistic coloring.

This betrays that the relationship between superego and ego may become temporarily deneutralized and re-externalized, and that the ego ideal may be partly replaced with pseudo-idealized, glamorous, wishful images of self and objects, which may play a pre-eminent part in the adolescent's daydreams and are representative of his expanding, highly narcissistic, sexual and aggressive strivings. Often the overconcern with such values, interests, and pleasures, which serve narcissistic-instinctual goals rather than truly object-directed ones or aims of the superego, will appear superficial or even dangerous to the eyes of the adult beholder, who is not sufficiently aware of their significance in the adolescent's reconstruction of his superego and ego. Indicative of the advancing instinctual, physical, mental, and intellectual maturation processes, the spreading and temporary boom of such "worldly" ambitions actually has a most stimulating effect on the ego development and normally results in a gradual modification of the superego, with partial delegation of superego functions to the ego. This becomes manifest in the adolescent's struggle with his problems of self-esteem, which his overconcern with the values of these new goals enlarges and extends from the moral sphere to all fields of physical, sexual, intellectual, and social accomplishments, where he may succeed or fail.

To understand these problems, we must, in addition, realize that the adolescent's rapid growth and change necessitate continuous readjustments in his self-representations. This makes the testing of his momentary psychic and bodily reality, and even of his physical and mental potentialities, extremely difficult.

Thus it is not surprising that at this stage intense shame and inferiority conflicts will make their appearance, in conjunction with painful guilt conflicts betraying the sadistic quality which the superego may temporarily acquire. The adolescent's shame and inferiority conflicts reveal that his vacillations of self-esteem originate not only in moral conflicts expressive of tensions between superego and ego, but also in severe tensions within the ego itself: tensions between images of the grown-up, powerful, glamorous, brilliant, or sophisticated person he wants to be, and sometimes believes himself to be, and the undeniable aspect of the physically and mentally immature, half-baked creature between two worlds which he actually is. It is this mixture of moral with such shame and inferiority conflicts that is responsible for the fluctuations in his identity feelings. Since these more primitive narcissistic conflicts cause not only loss of moral self-esteem but a total loss of self-esteem, and may expand his moral and castration fears to regressive-archaic fears of annihilation, they may at times even threaten him with fears of loss of self. Not rarely shame and inferiority conflicts may absorb the guilt conflicts or be used as a disguise for them; but we may also observe the reverse. All these conflicts will subside to the extent to which the adolescent's growing ego becomes strong enough to cope with them.

Characteristically, in late adolescence boys and girls may be simultaneously or alternately preoccupied with highly valued "worldly" aims and pleasures, with questions of manners, form, and appearance, and with very serious ethical and intellectual problems. In all these matters, they may suddenly gain a burning interest and an outspoken position, which may be dropped after some time and replaced with another one. Anna Freud (1936) has described these phenomena very beautifully. The efforts to form and formulate opinions, ideas, and ideals of their own gradually lead to the development of what we call a *Weltanschauung*. It is significant that this term refers merely to the way we "view the world," which is clearly a concern of the ego. In fact, our *Weltanschauung* covers a much broader field than our moral principles. Although it includes and determines our values, ideals, and ethical standards, it extends to our opinions on nature and culture, on sexual, social, racial, national, religious, political, and general intellectual problems.

The beginning development of a *Weltanschauung* in adolescence indicates, indeed, that the ego and the preconscious and conscious thought processes are gaining partial access to both superego and id and can gradually exert a considerable influence on them.

This leads us back once again to the superego identifications. The evolution of a *Weltanschauung* indeed rests on the establishment of identifications with parental figures, who grant—within certain limits—not only instinctual and emotional freedom but also freedom of thought and action. But this very freedom of thought has a curious dual effect on the further remodeling of the psychic systems. On the one hand it supports the ultimate integration and consolidation of those superego and ego identifications which curtail and limit the liberties gained in the course of adolescence. On the other hand it achieves an even further reduction of the role of identifications as such, inasmuch as it favors and reflects the adolescent's final establishment of ego and superego autonomy, which eventually brings about an increasing degree of freedom not only from external (parental and other personal and social) influences, but likewise from outmoded internal (instinctual as well as superego) pressures.

To be sure, for years we will find unmistakable evidence of precisely the reverse, to the effect that id and superego in their turn find open gates to each other and to the ego, and gain a strong foothold in the thought processes. In point of fact, superego and id may infiltrate the ego to such an extent that the *Weltanschauung* may represent no more than a rationalization of either or both. I may here refer again to Anna Freud (1936), and also to Heinz Hartmann's Freud Anniversary Lecture (1960), which is highly relevant to the issues under discussion. Thus, for long periods an adolescent's philosophy of life may vacillate in an almost preposterous way between opposite trends, depending on the predominant influence of either superego or id on his thinking. Today he may surprise his liberal parents and teachers with puritanic, conservative, or reactionary opinions on moral, social, or political matters; and some months later he may suddenly shock them with revolutionary or hedonistic convictions which evidence his need for rationalizations, justifications, and glorifications of his irrepressible instinctual and selfish wishes and behavior.

In discussing the adolescent's asceticism, Anna Freud (1936) pointed out that his estrangement from the family seems to extend to the ego's attitude toward the superego, which is treated as though it were the forbidden incestuous love object. This is certainly correct. But we may go even further in our understanding by considering besides that these defensive attitudes of the ego toward the superego are part of the adolescent's desperate struggle for freedom and for independent individuality, and hence an expression of the ego's rebellious refusal to "submit" or "admit" to any authority or influence, be it from without or from within.

In point of fact, we can observe during periods of asceticism, as much as at stages when the adolescent professes hedonistic philosophies, that he may repersonify and treat any part of the self—that is, not only the superego but likewise the id—as though they were powerful infantile love objects from whose prohibitive or seductive influence the ego must escape, detach, and rid itself. Obviously during such periods the ego calls on archaic defenses, such as isolation, denial, and projection, rather than repression, to ward off overwhelming pressures of the superego and the id (Jacobson, 1957). Thus it may happen that the adolescent's views, whatever they are at the time, may become strangely disconnected from his instinctual and guilt conflicts and from a behavior that may actually show either the irresistible force of his id or the sadistic power of his superego, whose hold on the ego cannot be admitted.

While during this phase of transition the adolescent is naturally apt to employ external representatives whose philosophy he may temporarily accept, borrow, or oppose, he may likewise insist that his opinions are free of such external influences and reflect his own independent thinking. Actually, for a long time he may not be able to achieve more than a pretense of independence, maintained with the aid of such denial mechanisms.

To the adult environment these attitudes become especially exasperating at times when the adolescent's problems tend to become subject to open discussion with his peers and sometimes to violent arguments with parents, teachers, and other persons in authority. It is characteristic that in such arguments he will each time defend his new convictions with the greatest vigor and often with superior, self-righteous, or even arrogant attitudes toward his adult opponents, which reveal his underlying insecurity, suggestibility, and changeability.

It is not surprising that concomitantly with these hectic beginnings of a *Weltanschauung,* we observe in so many adolescents a flourishing of sublimations and of creative urges and activities which may fade out again after maturity has been reached.

Anna Freud (1936) pointed out that instinctual danger stimulates the growth of intelligence in the adolescent as much as in the small child. But it is my impression that during this particular adolescent phase, when ego, superego, and id become accessible to each other, a singular dynamic, economic, and structural situation arises, which is in many ways reminiscent of the conditions we may find in creative individuals.

Of course, during all of adolescence the psychic organization is in a state of fluidity as never before or since. However, at the stage of tremendous instinctual-narcissistic boom, when lasting defenses and countercathexes have not yet been re-established but the ego's heroic efforts at leadership begin to meet with success, a fluid interplay between primary- and secondary-process functioning may develop, which appears to be especially favorable to creative intellectual or artistic activity.

Provoked initially by the instinctual upheaval of this period and by the adolescent's need for orientation and guidance in the threatening world of adults, the development of a consistent and effective *Weltanschauung* is of course a process that continues after adolescence—indeed, through life. I need hardly emphasize to what extent superego and id may still exercise their influence on the philosophy of adults, and even color their scientific convictions.

However, in late adolescence there will be a slow but unmistakable shift of power to the ego, whose gain of strength will manifest itself in its increasing influence on id and superego, causing a partial reversal of the situation. The ego will now play, as it were, the role of an active mediator, who employs the adolescent's worldly strivings as aids for the toning down and readjustment of the superego demands, but then in turn calls on the latter for assistance in restricting the id. The ego's contribution to the restructuring of ego ideal and superego, and to the concomitant curbing of the adolescent's excessive instinctual and narcissistic expectations, will slowly bridge the gaps and contradictions between his moral and his worldly trends. In increasingly close collaboration, superego and ego will thus gradually build up new sets of values which will provide him with more realistic goals and directives—moral and otherwise—for the future.

This advance will find expression in the substance and solidity of the adolescent's judgment, views, and position in various worldly and intellectual matters and in the maturity, stability, and growing effectiveness of his ideals, his moral principles, and ethical convictions.

In view of the ego's role in the development of adult scales of value, we might well question whether it would not be more correct to consider the ego ideal as an ego formation rather than part of the superego system. This was indeed suggested by Bing, McLaughlin, and Marburg (1959). Probably for similar reasons Erikson (1956), too, delimits the superego from the ego ideal, which he regards as a more mature formation, while he does not sufficiently consider the structural and functional alteration and maturation of the superego system as a whole, during adolescence.

From the genetic and functional points of view, the idea of separating the ego ideal from the morally demanding, prohibitive, and critical superego is indeed hardly acceptable, since they undeniably represent a functional unit and arise and mature as such. However, the reasoning of Bing, McLaughlin, and Marburg (1959) is sound. Though originating in the child's identifications with the idealized parental images, the ego ideal can certainly not be disconnected from the more and more individualized conscious value concepts and ideals which are built up during and after adolescence under the growing influence of the ego.

I believe this theoretical dilemma can be resolved when we understand that due to this mutual interaction of superego and ego, which is caused by the receding role of identifications in favor of autonomous thought processes, the ego ideal during this phase gradually bridges the two systems and may ultimately be claimed by both.

In fact, these last stages in the development of the ego ideal demonstrate beautifully the hierarchic reorganization and final integration of different—earlier and later—value concepts arising from both sources into a coherent new structural and functional unit.

But we must realize that this reconstruction of the ego ideal can proceed only in conjunction and close interrelationship with the modification and maturation of the entire superego system and of its functions and with a corresponding growth of the ego's capacity for critical and self-critical moral—and intellectual—judgment.

Evidently, the ultimate evolution of the ego ideal as such a coherent bridge structure connecting and belonging to both systems permits the ego gradually to support, to supplant, and to supplement superego functions and eventually brings about a smooth, intimate collaboration between the demanding, restrictive, and self-critical ego and superego. Subsequently under the influence of its adjunct, the ego, the superego's operational methods become enriched and endued with a variability and flexibility, and with new individual features, which the infantile superego lacks.

Concomitantly with this development, the superego fears and the fears induced by shame and inferiority conflicts will become toned down, less archaic-sadistic in their content and qualities, and—in part, at least—replaced by more realistic anticipations of danger such as Schur (1953, 1958) has described in various papers. This results, in the case of normal development, in a far greater ability of the ego to cope with intersystemic and intrasystemic narcissistic tensions.

Thus we see that these modifications in the superego and ego structures and functions lead ultimately to a remarkable strengthening of both systems. It enables the ego to reset and resolidify its defense organization, despite and precisely because of the fact that they result in the attainment of instinctual freedom, freedom of object choice, freedom of thought, feeling, and action, and greater freedom from external influences and from archaic id and superego pressures. In point of fact, all these liberties can be gained only to the extent to which superego and ego acquire sufficient autonomy and strength to subject them to the necessary limitations and to establish and maintain a stable and durable control system which is in accord with adult reality.

Only at this stage will the fluctuations between periods of narcissistic boom, of sexual and aggressive storms, and opposite phases of instinctual and narcissistic restriction and constriction subside. Subsequently the adolescent will be able to assert himself as an autonomous, grown-up, and sexually mature person, and create and accept a corresponding consistent and durable self-representation. To the extent to which his sexual, his narcissistic and his ambivalence conflicts, and the vacillations of his self-esteem and his feelings of identity pass, will he reach new and more object-directed aims and positions. Especially after he begins to permit himself heterosexual genital activities, he will feel ready to embark on more enduring and profound love relations, and to approach the problem of his future vocation, in a realistic manner. When the adolescent has reached this level, toward the end of adolescence, we may say that he has found himself. Henceforth ego development and identity formation will proceed less and less along the lines of identifications and grant increasing room to critical and self-critical judgment and to the individual, autonomous trends of the ego and its Anlage. I believe this is what Erik H. Erikson (1956) alludes to when he says that "identity formation begins where identification with persons of the past ends." It is certainly significant that at the stage when the adolescent begins to choose the direction in which he wants to move ahead, he may pass through identity experiences which have a significantly new and convincing quality (Eissler, 1956).

We must not, however, underrate the role which identification processes, even normally, continue to play in the further development of personality. The adolescent boy's fundamental and leading identifications with his father as a man extend later on quite naturally to his position as a husband and father, and may determine the young man's vocational choice. In the girl, the identifications with her mother likewise gain considerably in strength after marriage, and especially during motherhood. Here we recall the parents' continually changing identifications with their child and with their own parents, whose significant role Benedek (1959) described so magnificently.

Let me now return to the adolescent emotional and mood phenomena, whose spectral colors reflect the processes here discussed. Evidently the adolescent's erratic emotional vacillations mirror his swings from temporary disorganization, drive deneutralization and regression, causing a partial dissolution of old psychic structures, to dramatic mental progression leading to drive reneutralization and to a restructuring and reorganization of the psychic systems. In the course of his mental trips back and forth, the adolescent will repeatedly be forced to make stops on various and changing infantile levels and to re-establish primitive narcissistic types of object relations and identifications which may bring him to the point of refusions with objects. This was pointed out by Elisabeth R. Geleerd (1961). From the economic point of view, we must visualize that the adolescent is apt to suffer from sporadic aggressive eruptions as much as from libidinous tempests: one day he may feel ready to die of sexual starvation, the next day he may feel consumed by hate and self-hate, and then again he may pour love from every niche of his soul upon others and on himself. At a stage where large amounts of surplus hostility have been mobilized, this hostility may threaten the adolescent with inner object loss and loss of the self, whereas the influence of libidinous storms may expand the cathexis of the self to the whole object world and result in experiences of tremendous richness of his self and of the world.

When we give sufficient consideration to these processes we understand that adolescent states of depression and elation can have multiple meanings and very different causations, and hence involve a great variety of conflicts and mechanisms. An adolescent's unhappiness may express his grief about childhood objects and pursuits that he must relinquish; his sadness may be tinged with painful longings because he can neither go back to them nor yet reach new levels of achievement, of personal investments and pleasures. He may be depressed because he cannot gain the love of a girl he woos, or because he has failed in his work or in other personal conquests and feels physically and personally inadequate, intellectually and mentally inferior. But at other times his depression may be caused by guilt conflicts, either from sexual sources or because of his disproportionate, severe hostility. His depressive moods may once be devoid of regressive features, and then again involve a retreat to homosexual or sadomasochistic positions, or even a hostile and deeply narcissistic withdrawal from the world. Moreover, for the sake of his mental growth, the adolescent needs periods of quiet retreat and introspection, when he feels neither depressed nor lonesome but wants to indulge in being alone and taking account of himself. The same variety of causes can be observed in the adolescent's states of happiness and elation. They may originate merely in loving or enthusiastic approaches to new interests, to the opposite sex, or to other new persons. But they may also be the aftermath of success, of narcissistic-aggressive conquest and victory in the area of work, of love and sex, accomplishments which show him that he has definitely reached a new developmental position. The adolescent may be noisily joyful when he can discharge surplus libido in gay company or in flirtations and sexual play with youngsters. At times these parties may lead to wild activities, such as speeding in cars or boats, which offer an outlet for his excess aggression when he cannot exhaust himself in sports, games, and the like.

Because of this emotional intensity, some teen-agers may be so all-absorbed by a mood that it may set their mind, for weeks or longer, stubbornly and exclusively on one problem or activity or preoccupation.

"Last summer," I was told by the mother of an attractive, lively, intelligent girl of seventeen, "nothing but poetry existed for June. During the winter her only interests were dancing, flirtations and boys. This summer she has spent sitting alone on the rocks, gazing dreamily at the ocean . . . But, after all," the mother added thoughtfully, "what are rocks for?" It is characteristic that this is a girl who graduated from high school at sixteen and is an excellent, serious college student.

During stages when he feels overpowered by libidinal desires, but equally afraid of homosexual and heterosexual attachments, the adolescent may indeed prefer lovingly to embrace mankind and its many causes instead of an individual, to indulge in ecstatic religious experiences of mystical union with God, or to celebrate lonely orgies with nature, poetry, music or art.

Such adolescent states certainly remind one of similar experiences which we can observe in the beginning of schizophrenic processes. In the schizophrenic, as in the adolescent, such ecstatic experiences may be accompanied by rich self-feelings. But commonly the adolescent's ecstatic feelings of self-expansion, though indicative of a narcissistic hypercathexis, include both the self and the world and reflect those floods of libido which have been liberated but cannot yet be attached to new individual objects. Moreover, these states may pass swiftly, to be followed by a sober return to reality and to everyday life activities.

No doubt the long period of narcissistic overexpansion, of concern with ambitious goals and highly narcissistic values, has a dangerous potential and accounts for the adolescent's propensity to such elated and depressive mood conditions. It is the depth of their narcissistic regression which may, even in adolescents who are not grossly disturbed, cause transient depressive states with paranoid and hypochondriacal features, with feelings of utter lonesomeness and isolation, and with identity problems reminiscent of psychotic types of depression.

However, we may observe to our amazement that small events and experiences, which appear irrelevant on the surface, may suddenly and swiftly sweep away not only the depressive mood, but all these alarming symptoms. They may recur again, but ultimately, when the adolescent's search for new love objects and for a new, grown-up self has met with success, they may disappear without leaving any traces.

BIBLIOGRAPHY

Benedek, T. (1959), Parenthood As a Developmental Phase. *J. Am. Psa. Assn.*, VII.
Bing, J. F., McLaughlin, F., & Marburg, R. (1959), The Metapsychology of Narcissism. *This Annual*, XIV.
Bornstein, B. Quoted by Root (1957) as personal communication.
Deutsch, H. (1944), *The Psychology of Women*, Vol. I. New York: Grune & Stratton.
Eissler, K. R. (1956), The Problem of Identity. Read at the American Psychoanalytic Association, Chicago.
—— (1958), Notes on Problems of Technique in the Psychoanalytic Treatment of Adolescents; with Some Remarks on Perversions. *This Annual*, XIII.
Erikson, E. H. (1956), The Problem of Ego Identity. *J. Am. Psa. Assn.*, IV.
Freud, A. (1936), *The Ego and the Mechanisms of Defence*. New York: International Universities Press, 1946.
—— (1958), Adolescence. *This Annual*, XIII.
Freud, S. (1905), Three Essays on Sexuality. *Standard Edition*, VII. London: Hogarth Press, 1953.
Geleerd, E. R. (1961), Some Aspects of Ego Vicissitudes in Adolescence. *J. Am. Psa. Assn.*, IX.
Hartmann, H. (1939), *Ego Psychology and the Problem of Adaptation*. New York: International Universities Press, 1958.
—— (1950), Comments on the Psychoanalytic Theory of the Ego. *This Annual*, V.
—— (1960), *Psychoanalysis and Moral Values*. New York: International Universities Press.
Jacobson, E. (1954), The Self and the Object World: Vicissitudes of Their Infantile Cathexes and Their Influence on Ideational and Affective Development. *This Annual*, IX.
—— (1957), Denial and Repression. *J. Am. Psa. Assn.*, V.
Katan, A. (1951), The Role of Displacement in Agoraphobia. *Int. J. Psa.*, XXXII.
Root, N. (1957), A Neurosis in Adolescence. *This Annual*, XII.
Schur, M. (1953), The Ego in Anxiety. In: *Drives, Affects, Behavior*, ed. R. M. Loewenstein. New York: International Universities Press.
—— (1955), Comments on the Metapsychology of Somatization. *This Annual*, X.
—— (1958), The Ego and the Id in Anxiety. *This Annual*, XII.
Spiegel, L. A. (1958), Comments on the Psychoanalytic Psychology of Adolescence. *This Annual*, XIII.
—— (1959), The Self, the Sense of Self, and Perception. *This Annual*, XIV.

SOME THOUGHTS ABOUT THE ROLE OF
VERBALIZATION IN EARLY CHILDHOOD

ANNY KATAN, M.D. (Cleveland)[1]

Piaget (1923) and Karl Bühler (1934) have explored the development of language, a theme very much neglected by analysts so far; Heinz Hartmann touched upon the subject of verbalization in his article "Technical Implications of Ego Psychology" (1951); and Loewenstein, in his paper "Some Remarks on the Role of Speech in Psycho-analytic Technique" (1956), has explored the importance of verbal communication in the psychoanalytic situation.

These, however, are not the themes of my paper. This paper is limited to the role that verbalization plays in early child development, emphasizing specifically the importance of the verbalization of feelings by the very young child.

It has been my experience with children between three and five years of age that a number of them needed treatment badly but were so lacking in speech, and sometimes in other ways of communication as well, that they could not express themselves in treatment. We decided that these children needed preparation in this area before treatment could be started. Although of course this task could have been accomplished by the therapist, we thought it could also be accomplished by the combined efforts of teachers and parents. Whereas a therapist would have had to spend one hour daily over a long period of time in such preparation, this work could be done just as well or better when it was extended over the whole day and was done by teachers, parents, etc.

Verbalization is considered by us a part of general education, and therefore it need not be confined to the analytic hour. In concentrating on trying to help the child verbalize his feelings and thoughts, I arrived at the following conclusions:

1 Dr. M. Katan has greatly helped me in the verbalization of my thoughts.

184

1. Verbalization of perceptions of the outer world precedes verbalization of feelings.

2. Verbalization leads to an increase of the controlling function of the ego over affects and drives.

3. Verbalization increases for the ego the possibility of distinguishing between wishes and fantasies on the one hand, and reality on the other. In short, verbalization leads to the integrating process, which in turn results in reality testing and thus helps to establish the secondary process.

I

The very young child can perceive the outer world with his perceptive organs—the eyes, the ears, the nose, the skin. The child himself wants to name these outer perceptions early; he needs to verbalize perceptions of the outer world in order to obtain fulfillment of his wishes and needs. In the course of expressing his desires for certain objects in the outer world, he discovers early the advantage of being able to name these objects so that his desires may be understood and fulfilled. This process is helped along considerably by the parents as, with pride, they watch and usually encourage the naming of objects, sounds, smells, etc., by the young child. The parents help to libidinize this process, and their show of visible pleasure encourages the child to become more and more ambitious.[2]

Usually the child is not so quick at learning words to express the inner perceptions of his feelings. The child perceives his feelings, of course, and expresses some of them without words—by crying or laughing, by facial expressions, or body motility. In the very early stages of development, however, these feelings are not usually given names. Often they are not understood by the parents; so the means of communication, like pointing, etc., that exists with regard to wishes directed toward the outer world is nonexistent for the expression of the child's feelings. In this respect, the task of the parents is much more difficult. They have to guess at the child's feelings.

Verbalization of the child's emotions by the parents comes very much later than verbalization of his perceptions of the outer world.

2 I will discuss later the eventual disadvantages of this libidinization (Anna Freud, 1960).

In my experience, feelings of pain or getting hurt are verbalized earlier than are other feelings; then follows the verbalization of feelings of fear, of being scared. Yet such feelings as sadness, excitement, happiness, and anger are often not verbalized for the child until a much later date. In some cases these feelings are not verbalized at all, and the child picks up the words for them as he develops further—is read to, etc.

If the child does not learn to name his feelings, a situation may arise in which there develops a discrepancy between the strength and complexity of his feelings on the one hand, and his modes of expression on the other. If the child could verbalize his feelings, he would learn to delay action, but the delaying function is lacking. Accordingly, the situation may have pathological consequences.

When the child has later acquired the art of verbalizing, he will still cling to the earlier method of acting upon his feelings instead of mastering them through verbalization. This uninhibited discharge may bring him into conflict with his environment, so that he will form either too great fears about the environment or too early feelings of guilt. If this process of acting upon feelings continues for a considerable time, the results will be fully evident. The child's ego will become fixated upon acting upon his feelings rather than attempting an adequate means of mastery. In such children the ego becomes weak, for it is repeatedly overwhelmed by affects.[3]

II

It now becomes clear that verbalization of feelings leads to an increase of mastery by the ego. The young ego shows its strength by not acting upon its feelings immediately, but by delaying such action and expressing its feelings in words instead. To the observers in our nursery school, it was very gratifying to see the changes which certain educational efforts produced in young children who had not yet learned to verbalize their feelings but expressed their feelings through actions. When we succeeded in helping these children to

[3] Children whose acting upon their feelings predominates over verbalizing their feelings can in this way establish a pattern which predisposes them to become "actors out" in later life. I am in full agreement with Phyllis Greenacre's findings on this point as described in her article "General Problems of Acting Out" (1950).

verbalize what they felt instead of acting upon it, we found that they demonstrated a mastery over their feelings and that this mastery led secondarily to a feeling of greater security. It was then striking to observe how they seemed to rise rapidly toward their age level.

We should be very much aware of those situations in which the increase of the child's verbalization does not lead to the ego's ability to express the child's feelings in an advantageous way. I have in mind the type of parents who not only are unable to show their own emotions but also do not permit emotions to show in the child. If such parents speak about their feelings which they are unable to show, or speak about the child's feelings, it is clear that their words are used not to further the expression of emotions but to ward these emotions off. If this is the case, the words are not a bridge, as they ought to be, but are a defense against the emotions. The child may now take over the example set by the parents and also use words defensively.

Anna Freud, in her recent lectures (1960), has made possible the understanding of another disadvantageous type of verbalization. She pointed out that some parents show an inordinate amount of pleasure in certain functions of the child. Accordingly, the child, in order to please the parents, may overcathect these functions. This means that he libidinizes them. They become, so to say, hypertrophic, and this leads to an unwanted distortion of normal development. The energy that should have been invested in other functions is now stored up in these selected functions, with a resulting disharmony of development. It is obvious that this libidinization can also occur in the process of verbalization; the development of other functions may lag behind in favor of verbalization.

In order to prevent confusion, it is necessary to elaborate on the subject of mastery by the ego through verbalization. Verbalization creates, for the child, a means of communicating his wishes and feelings. We have already had an opportunity to speak about the profitable delay of immediate acting upon feelings. This delayed action, as a result of the verbalization, enables the ego to judge the situation. The verbalization as such is a part of the intellectual process, which, according to Freud's formulations (1911), is a trial acting, using small quantities of energy.

Verbalization prevents the fixation of a part of the ego at a certain level and keeps open the transition to further development. Thus, through verbalization, the ego is able to master its affects and does not have to resort to defenses like denial, avoidance, etc., to shut these affects out.

III

Verbalization increases for the ego the possibility of distinguishing between wishes and fantasies on the one hand, and reality on the other. Such children are able at an early age to differentiate between pretend and real. We know that the object relationships of the small child are influenced for a time by the fantasy object relationships. Early reality testing will contradict existing fantasies of grandeur and the child's belief in the power of his magic wishes. More and more he will be able to recognize himself as a child, with the limitations of his age, and accordingly his magical thinking will be prevented from extending over too long a period. It seems to me that such a child will enter the oedipal phase better prepared to weather the storm through his ability to express his feelings verbally, and therefore will feel less overwhelmed and his guilt feelings will not become too strong. The ability to distinguish between a wish and reality will be helpful in the resolution of his oedipal complex. The resolution of the oedipal conflict varies, as we know, according to timing and completeness. The complete resolution is an ideal never achieved. Yet the more complete the resolution is, the better it is of course for the child's continued development—for his early and strong superego formation.

BIBLIOGRAPHY

Bühler, K. (1934), *Sprachtheorie. Die Darstellungsfunktion der Sprache*. Jena: Fischer.
Freud, A. (1960), Four Contributions to the Psychoanalytic Study of the Child. I. The Assessment of Normality. II. The Assessment of Pathology. III. The Therapeutic Possibilities. IV. The Status of Child Analysis. Lectures presented at New York.
Freud, S. (1911), Formulations Regarding the Two Principles in Mental Functioning. *Collected Papers*, IV. London: Hogarth Press, 1925.
Greenacre, P. (1950), General Problems of Acting Out. *Psa. Quart.*, XIX.
Hartmann, H. (1951), Technical Implications of Ego Psychology. *Psa. Quart.*, XX.
Kris, E. (1950), On Preconscious Mental Processes. *Psa. Quart.*, XIX.
Loewenstein, R. M. (1956), Some Remarks on the Role of Speech in Psycho-analytic Technique. *Int. J. Psa.*, XXXVII.
Piaget, J. (1923), *The Language and Thought of the Child*. London: Routledge, 1932.

EFFECTS OF DEPRIVATION ON INSTITUTIONALIZED INFANTS

Disturbances in Development of Relationship to Inanimate Objects

SALLY PROVENCE, M.D. and SAMUEL RITVO, M.D.
(New Haven)[1]

This paper is based on observational data on institutionalized infants who were the subjects of a study carried out by Sally Provence and Rose Coleman Lipton.[2] The infants were deprived of adequate maternal care and this deprivation manifested itself in numerous disturbances in the infants' development. In this paper we will emphasize only two of the general findings:

1. The apparatuses for functioning appeared according to the intrinsic maturational timetable, but they were delayed in being brought under the control of the ego.

2. When the various behavior items should be integrated into more complex action units in the service of developing ego func-

[1] From the Yale University Child Study Center, New Haven, Conn. Dr. Provence is assistant professor of Pediatrics (Child Study Center). Dr. Ritvo is associate clinical professor in the Child Study Center and the Department of Psychiatry.

[2] This study was supported by a grant from the Field Foundation. Since this study, the findings, and the methodology will be reported in full (1962) by Provence and Lipton, we will mention here only a few aspects. In general the findings of the study support the findings of others (Spitz, 1945, 1946; Levy, 1937; Bowlby, 1951; Goldfarb, 1945) who have written about the adverse effects of deprivation of maternal care on infant development.

At regular intervals throughout the first year of life the infants were evaluated by physical and neurological examinations, standardized tests of infant development and a variety of other observations. These observations included such things as feeding behavior, ratings of activity, reactions to illness, and types of responses to the environment and to the routines of care. All available background data on the infants were utilized in assessing their development. The environment in which the babies lived was studied in terms both of the general attitudes and child-care practices of the staff and of the specific environment and experience of the individual infant.

tions, these more complex patterns were delayed, distorted, and lacked richness and subtlety.

The report of Provence and Lipton (1962) will document fully that the deprivation was significant and of many dimensions. Each infant had very little contact from a mothering person. He rarely experienced the sight, sound, touch, or smell of another person who came to do something that made him more comfortable. For example, the feeding experience was markedly barren. While the institution carefully provided a diet that was in every way nutritionally adequate, the methods of feeding were not geared to the infant's emotional needs. Bottles were propped. They were given on an externally determined schedule and not in response to any clues from the baby. When strained foods were added to the diet, they were at first given in the bottle. Later, when the babies were over nine months, solids were mixed together and rapidly spooned into the infant by the attendant. Throughout the first year the interchange with another person around feeding was minimal. This is in sharp contrast to the variety of sensations and wealth of experiences that are a part of the feeding of an infant cared for by the ordinary devoted mother, to borrow Winnicott's term (1945). In addition, the baby in a family has experienced these things at least much of the time in response to his distress signals. With the many repetitions he gradually discriminates what and later who it is that brings him comfort and pleasure. He gradually learns also to make some connections between his expression of discomfort and the response of another person. These experiences are virtually absent from the lives of the institutional babies.

There was a great deficiency not only in being comforted when in distress but also in being stimulated to action or to responding to another person. In the daily life of an infant cared for by his mother there are many situations in which he has some kind of contact with her, and these increase in variety and complexity as the first year proceeds. In these interactions the mother communicates a variety of feelings, positive and negative, which are believed to be important for the development of the infant. In the life of the institutional babies the interest and emotional involvement of the persons who cared for them could only in rare instances approximate a mother's attachment to her own baby. The meagerness of contact, the poverty of experience, and the tenuousness of the emotional tie were striking. Furthermore, the entire emotional atmosphere of the institution was bland, in so far as could be seen by the visiting observers. The place gave an impression of quietude and tranquility. All expressions of feeling of the staff, both positive and negative feeling, were muted and dampened. Thus, briefly, we try to convey that the deprivation was not mild but severe. We believe that the disturbances in development observed in these infants were related both to the degree and to the nature of the deprivation they experienced.

The development of these infants suffered in many ways. Motor development was delayed, although it was less adversely influenced than other areas. Language development was the first area in which retardation was found as measured by infant tests. Language development was retarded as early as the second month and was markedly retarded throughout the first year. Personal relationships were clearly disturbed and became increasingly distorted as the year proceeded. Especially in the second half of the first year, the usual repertoire of affective responses which can be recognized in the average infant was distorted, both in time of appearance and in the manner of expression. The use of toys and play materials was poorly developed. At an age when one expects an infant actively, specifically, and purposively to direct his feelings and interest toward the outside, the institutional baby was inactive and appeared disinterested. Another person, a toy, his own body, all things he could be expected to reach out for, were poorly invested and rarely approached. The infants conveyed an impression of a lack of energy and vigor, although they were physically healthy and well nourished.

As the study proceeded, one general finding became apparent. In several areas of behavior there was a discrepancy between the maturation of the apparatus and its use in the infant's adaptation to his environment.[3] In these areas the investigators found that the apparatus matured according to the biological timetable, but the

[3] We distinguish here between maturation and development. Utilizing the concept and terminology of Hartmann, Kris, and Loewenstein (1946), we use the word *maturation* to refer to growth and differentiation of the infant's inborn equipment relatively independent from environmental influence, and the term *development* to designate those growth processes which are largely determined by the environment. We also distinguish between the ego and the apparatus it uses (Hartmann, 1939).

emerging potentials were not put to use in the normal fashion. Maturation of the apparatus insured that certain capacities for functioning emerged at the time one would expect, but they did not become fully organized in the service of the infant's adaptation to his environment. They did not come under the control of the infant's developing ego as readily as in family-reared infants.

A few examples will illustrate this point. In the area designated as language development on the Gesell scales such signs of maturation as changes in tonal range of the voice and the presence of polysyllabic vowel sounds and consonants occurred on schedule, but the babies were notoriously quiet, vocalized very little, and did not use these sounds in contact with others. In the normally developing infant the *mama, dada, baba* sounds appear at around six to seven months of age and become specific names for the parents during the last three months of the first year. In the institutional infant the *mama, dada* sounds could be elicited, though with much effort, at the expected time, but they did not become the names of people and were not used for communication or social interchange.

A similar observation was made in the evolution of the grasping patterns of the hands. Normally these patterns go through an orderly sequence from ulnar and palmar grasping to radial-digital and pincer grasping (Halverson, 1947). These are elicited in the test situation by observing how an infant grasps the one-inch cubes or the small candy pellet. In the institutional infants the earliest grasping efforts were normal in configuration and time of appearance. Until the age of five to six months these infants approached and grasped the toys, and at such times one could observe that the maturational sequence was undisturbed. But from six months on the grasping behavior deviated from the norm. The infant reached out for the toys less frequently. Hand posturing and finger movements reminiscent of athetoid movements often appeared. The toys were flicked at or picked up briefly and dropped as though they were hot. With these signs one might be concerned about motor-tract damage or defect were it not for the fact that with time and patience one could elicit responses which demonstrated that the maturational sequence had not been disturbed. One could establish that the infants did have the ability to approach, grasp, and manipulate toys, though they put this ability to minimal use and the movements lacked skill and smooth modulation.

A third example is the failure of the infant's development to keep pace with maturation in self-stimulating activities. The hand-to-mouth maneuver appeared at the expected time, but after a few days or a few weeks of some thumb or finger sucking, this behavior disappeared. Similarly the infant's ability to lift his legs high in extension, a prerequisite for the hand-foot and foot-mouth play, appeared on time, but he did not play with or mouth his feet or toes. By the time he had reached the age of six to seven months he had the apparatus available for the many kinds of self-stimulation seen in the normal baby. He should have been able to suck his thumb, play with his feet, tug at his ear, touch his arm or body, poke into his umbilicus, or handle his genital. But these activities, which can be viewed as ways in which a baby voluntarily produces some sensation in himself, were rarely seen. We believe that this observation, together with others in the same area, reflects a disturbance in the development of these infants' body ego, about which we plan to report in more detail at a later time. It is used here to illustrate, in still another area, the discrepancy between maturation of the congenital apparatus and the development of certain aspects of the ego.

We have selected one aspect of the development of the institutional infants, their reaction to the inanimate object, for more detailed description.

Test materials, here designated as toys or inanimate objects, are presented on many items of the infant test. Information can be obtained about some of the baby's adaptation to his environment by observing whether he perceives, manipulates, or exploits the toys or play materials which are a part of that environment. How he makes use of them and manipulates them is also important for assessing his development, that is, whether he mouths, bites, bangs, casts, explores, combines one with another, or uses the toy to initiate a contact with another person. Various aspects of his perception, motor development, and general learning are revealed in these activities. The term investment is used here to convey an impression of the energy directed toward the toy. One can describe the variations in degree of investment in the toy just as one can describe what the baby does with the toy. In the following paragraphs we will trace some of the major trends which can be observed in the average infant and compare these with the institutional babies.

In normal development, responses of increasing differentiation and complexity appear as the first year progresses. In the early weeks the baby responds to the toy as it comes into his line of vision, as it moves or makes a noise, or as he touches it. Some toys are responded to more definitely or more strongly than others because of their size, the type of sound or motion they make, or their nearness to the infant. These responses reflect the state of maturation and integrity of the sensorimotor apparatus. One can observe individual variations in these responses which are probably indicators of inborn characteristics.

The earliest reactions, which are believed to be of reflex origin, gradually give way to more specific and differentiated behavior such as attention to the toy through visual, acoustic, and tactile senses. These are often accompanied by body movements, vocalization, and changes in facial expression. By four to five months one sees the beginning ability to approach and grasp a toy in a voluntary way. The infant reacts to the familiar cradle gym, nursery bird, and other toys commonly suspended over the crib, first by looking at them, later batting and still later grasping them voluntarily. This could also be described as a progression from a passive visualizing to an active focusing, attending, and approaching.

About the time a baby can approach and grasp in a purposeful manner, he can also take a toy to his mouth and can resecure it if it drops from his hand so long as it also remains within his field of vision. By six to seven months he can do these things quite proficiently, and can also bite, transfer, bang, and wave the toy.

The infant's adaptation and learning are indicated in other ways through the use of the toy. From seven to eight months on there are test situations which examine the infant's capacity to combine toys, i.e., to do something with two or more toys simultaneously. These and other situations in which he tries to bring two objects into some specific relationship to each other are assumed to reflect capacities for integration of multiple stimuli.

One type of manipulation of toys seen during the nine-to-twelve-month period has been called exploratory interest. It reflects the infant's increased attentiveness to details and may be seen in the test situation when he investigates the parts of the bell by looking closely at it and poking at its various parts with the index finger or by ringing it purposively and mouthing it, all done with an exploratory and experimental flavor.

In his studies of infants Piaget (1936) has described sequential steps in the development of the child's capacity to have a mental concept of the existence of the inanimate object. In the early months the infant reacts to the toy if it is in sight, and may fuss if it disappears, but there is no indication that he is aware that it still exists when it is out of sight. By the age of nine to ten months, however, he will begin to search for a toy that has been covered or masked, and by the end of the first year he can solve the problem of finding a toy that has been hidden from him by a solid screen. The capacity to solve this problem implies that he can now remember or have a mental concept of an inanimate object which continues to exist and remains the same, although it is out of sight. The infant tests for the first year include several situations which indicate the progress in the infant's development of this mental concept of the inanimate object, and they are of considerable interest because of the contrast between the behavior of family babies and the institutional babies.

In the latter part of the first year a normal baby begins to show a preference for some specific toys over others. There are two types of preferred toys. The infant may develop an attachment to a toy which seems to be a specific substitute for the mother, the transitional object of Winnicott (1953). This may be a stuffed animal, a doll, or a blanket. The sensual quality of the toy is significant here. It obviously reproduces some of the sensations of the contact with the mother. This attachment, which varies from child to child in time of appearance, develops under the aegis of the mother, with the initial attachment to the toy being made possible because of the relationship with her. Later it seems to give some comfort in her absence and at times in her presence. In the first year one sees only the beginnings of this specificity which is more firmly established in the second year.

Another type of preference for one toy over another is seen from nine to ten months on, when the infant gives clear indications of choosing one toy over another, presumably because of some quality of the toy itself such as sound, contour, or mouthing value. At this time, if one tries to remove a toy before the infant is through with it, one often encounters a strong protest which is not alleviated by offering a substitute toy. At an earlier age, he might have shown displeasure at the loss of the toy, but would readily have accepted a substitute.

By the end of the first year, a baby reflects many aspects of his intellectual, physical, and emotional growth in his contact with the toy. With toys, as with people, he expresses feelings of pleasure, displeasure, eagerness, satisfaction, frustration, and anger with increasing clarity as the first year proceeds. He experiments with losing and finding; he shows preferences for some toys over others. He picks up a toy, drops it, creeps across the room for it, fingers, feels, mouths, bangs, or listens to it.

In the institutional infants, the deviant nature and delayed development of the behavior with toys are important aspects of their difficulty. The earliest visual and acoustic responses as well as the early approach and grasping activities are very similar to those of the normal infant. From about four to five months on through the first year there is a decrease of investment and in the approach to and grasping and exploitation of the toys. The looking, banging, biting, feeling, shaking, sucking, fingering, poking, dropping, and picking up again, which in the average baby become more elaborate day after day, are much less prominent in the institutional babies. Even though they appear to get some pleasure from the toys, there is never any evidence of displeasure when the toys are removed. No evidence of preference for one toy over another is seen in the first year, and efforts to recover a lost toy are virtually nonexistent.

The concept of the existence of the inanimate object is also markedly delayed in these institutionalized babies. On the infant tests there are several situations of increasing complexity that are designed to assess this. The first is the infant's capacity to recover a toy that is partially hidden; the next is his ability to recover a toy that is completely hidden. In this latter situation, a toy in which the infant has been interested is placed on the table at which he is sitting and covered with a cloth. To be successful here he must remove the cloth and find the toy. The response of the normal infant who has not yet reached this stage of development is to behave as if the toy no longer exists once it is out of sight. He is likely to get involved with the cloth and may rediscover the toy fortuitously or turn to something else. When he has developed further he can uncover the toy promptly in a clearly purposive way, demonstrating, it is believed, a memory of the toy after he can no longer see it. At the end of the first year he demonstrates a further step along these lines. When a toy with which he has been playing is taken from him and placed upon the tabletop behind an opaque screen, he is able to find it. His first reaction is often a protest at its removal followed by an attempt to pull down the screen. When this is prevented, he must then inhibit his initial motor response and, using a different motor act, make a detour around the screen to find the toy. This appears to require the interpolation of a thought process between the initial situation and the final solution.

In the institutional infants the retardation in development as measured in this series of test items is apparent from the first introduction of the partially hidden toy at the eight-month level. At this level the retardation is mild. However, the ability to recover the toy hidden by a cloth (a nine- to ten-month item) and the screened toy (an eleven- to twelve-month item) are markedly delayed. Observing his reactions to these situations one at first has the impression that the hidden toy either is not remembered or is not important enough to be recovered. By the end of the first year, however, it also appears that the initiative to evaluate the situation, the mental activity necessary to solve the problem of recovering the toy, is blocked; a deficit in thinking seems to be operating.

In general the institutional infants have done best with toys in those activities which they can do by imitation after repeated demonstrations by the adult within the individual testing session. In contrast to this, they give a particularly poor performance on test items which are believed to reflect developing integrative capacities and the ability to handle multiple stimuli upon which some later types of thinking and problem solving seem to depend.

Little spontaneous play with toys is seen in the first year when the infants are in their cribs. The play that occurs most often is a repetitive fingering or banging, with a minimal amount of elaboration, little evidence of enjoyment, and none of the experimental zest of the normal baby. This is not the result of lack of opportunity as some type of toy is suspended or placed in the crib from the earliest months. Although dolls and stuffed animals were available, in no instance did an institutional infant develop an attachment to a specific toy which became a comforter or "friend." There were no transitional objects as described by Winnicott (1953).

The way in which the developing infant reacts to the toy at various ages depends, as do other functions, on the constant interaction of maturational and developmental processes. The importance of maturation of the apparatus in making possible such things as perception, manipulation, and the concept of permanence is self-evident and needs no elaboration here. The importance of the relationship between mother and infant in influencing the reaction to the toy is supported by our material. Katherine M. Wolf emphasized that the infant's reaction to toys and his use of toys depends in very important ways upon the relationship to people. Her hypothesis stated that "the infant's capacity to develop a belief (a mental concept) in the consistency and constancy of the inanimate object, i.e., a world of things, is dependent upon the consistency and constancy of the human object."[4]

Observations on family infants who have a disturbed relationship to the mother suggest still another dimension. In order to use toys with pleasure and interest the infant appears to need both the personal attachment to the mother and some opportunity to play with toys in an atmosphere where he is not asked constantly to interact with another person. The baby also needs some time to himself with his toys, so that he may have an opportunity to exploit and use them in his own way. This is one of the experiences that provide the "detours to mastery and learning through play" which Hartmann (1939) has emphasized as an important part of adaptation. Such opportunities are amply present in the lives of most family babies, but occasionally one encounters parents who, to put it simply, allow the baby no time of his own and consequently he has little interest in and satisfaction with toys.

DISCUSSION

As Rapaport (1960) has recently emphasized in his discussion of psychoanalysis as a developmental psychology, the existence of in-

[4] This hypothesis (presented by Dr. Wolf in a seminar) was first suggested by Heinz Hartmann (personal communication).

trinsic maturational factors in the instinctual drives was one of
Freud's early discoveries. The existence of intrinsic maturational
factors in the ego was assumed when it was realized that the ego did
not derive from the conflict between the instinctual drives and reality
but that both ego and id were formed by differentiation out of an
earlier undifferentiated matrix (Hartmann, Kris, and Loewenstein,
1946; Hartmann, 1950). As numerous authors have pointed out, the
psychoanalytic theory of development unites maturational and experiential factors. It is the constant dynamic interaction of the intrinsic maturational factors of both the instinctual drives and the ego
with the experiential factors which to a large extent determines the
development of the personality.

In this developmental process, object relation plays a central role
as a pre-eminent environmental factor extremely variable in the wide
range of experiences it may bring to the child. The range is great
for different children and may also be great for the same child at
different ages.

The very young infant has two objects for his drives which provide him with a variety of experiences and which play an important
part in the early steps of the process of differentiation of the self
from the outside world. One of the two objects is the infant's own
body as Hoffer (1949, 1950) has described, for instance, for the hand
and mouth; the other object is the mothering person. From the
beginning the mothering person is the agent whose interventions
bring comfort and whose unresponsiveness results in the prolongation of discomfort. At this point a hypothesis proposed by Kris (1956)
is relevant.[5] In its most condensed form it states that in the infant
comfort serves to build object relations, while discomfort stimulates
differentiation and structure formation of the psychic apparatus.
The investment of the maternal object which grows out of the experience of gratification by the mother is essential to the establishment

[5] In a discussion of this paper, Max Schur pointed out that this idea had already
been formulated by Freud. In Chapter VII of the *Interpretation of Dreams*, Freud
speaks of the pleasure-unpleasure principle being operative in the laying down of
memory traces which make the child seek the object which brought gratification by
discharge of tension. Schur also pointed out that this concept became the model for
Freud's distinction between alloplastic action and defense: satisfaction leads to alloplastic action; while discomfort or frustration experiences become the model for
defense.

of a progressively sharper distinction between the self and the outer world. The permanent cathexis of the image or memory trace of the object makes possible the hallucinatory recall of the object from which gratification was derived. Further experiences with the object tend to enrich the memory traces of the object, and the discomfort-comfort sequences associated with the object are progressively more cathected with psychic energy. This development, made possible also by the maturational progress of the child, is manifested in the anticipatory reactions of the infant to the coming feeding situation and in the infant's increasing ability to wait for the gratification. This is one of the many ways in which the cathexis of the object is related to the development and elaboration of the intrinsic or primary autonomous ego factors which eventually have a leading role in controlling and regulating discharge processes.

More than discomfort alone, discomfort-comfort contrast of a certain degree is probably important for facilitating the permanent cathexis of the gratification experience and for stimulating the differentiation and formation of psychic structure. Observations on one of the children in a longitudinal study[6] illustrate the hypothesis that a lack of contrast experiences influences adversely the development of some capacities in the infant in the first year. In this family-reared infant observers had the impression that the discomfort-comfort contrast was so narrow that neither was experienced sharply. This resulted partly from equipment factors in the infant and partly from the mother's lack of responsiveness to the child. The child did not give signs of intense distress in the hunger situation, and the mother was not perceptive to the child's needs and did not easily pick up clues from the little girl's behavior. What discomfort the child experienced was likely to go on for a prolonged time before the mother responded. Moreover, in the feeding situation the mother did not provide the richness of sensory and emotional experience that would have made it more gratifying. Thus the gratification experience was rather meager and was delayed. The child's relatively poor development of discriminatory powers and certain aspects of her learning in

[6] This refers to the Longitudinal Study of Personality Development at Yale Child Study Center, instituted by Milton J. E. Senn and Ernst Kris. This study was supported by a grant from the Commonwealth Fund, New York.

the first year were thought to be related to this particular combination of intrinsic and experiential factors.

In the family infant with the "ordinary devoted mother," the maternal ministration which relieves the discomfort is likely to come more frequently in closer proximity to the peak intensity of the discomfort. Also, because of the qualitative aspects of the care, the family infant may more frequently experience a fuller gratification with a greater degree of comfort than the institutional infant. This results in a greater contrast in the range from discomfort to comfort in the family infant. We assume that this type of experience would in general tend to facilitate and stimulate the permanent cathexis of the memory traces and image of the need-satisfying object (Hartmann, 1952; Anna Freud, 1952) which then can be invoked in a hallucinatory way for the delay and postponement of discharge of instinctual-drive tension.

In contrast to this, the institutional infant's situation is quite different. Less frequently and less regularly will the gratification brought by the attendant be in proximity to the initial peak of the discomfort and drive intensity. Sharp contrasts of discomfort-comfort will not be experienced as regularly and as frequently in association with the mothering person. On the contrary, the institutional infant is more likely to experience prolonged periods of discomfort before the relief comes. Besides, the comfort derived from the propped bottle given by the attendant is not as complete as that experienced by the infant who is held and fed by the mother. Thus the institutional infant has not the same stimulation as the family infant for cathecting the memory trace of the object as it is gradually formed from the feeding and other comforting situations.

Although we may assume that temporary discomfort followed by comfort stimulates differentiation and structure formation, protracted discomfort without relief is likely to have a different effect on the infant. This may be a disorganizing influence which interferes with ego development. Observations on infants suggest that, in general, the infant seems better organized and functions at a higher level when he is in a state between extreme discomfort and complete satiation. In the neonate, focusing and following with the eyes occur most consistently during feeding in the period after the initial intense hunger has been satisfied and before the infant's activity has been obliterated by satiation. With prolonged discomfort and under prolonged stress of instinctual-drive tension, the infant loses signs of the reflex organization which is the basis for this early focusing and following with the eyes. The disorganization of the infant's capacity for functioning when he has experienced prolonged discomfort can be observed regularly. This disruption, or loss, of an already achieved function is an early sign of regression. The same effect can be observed in many everyday situations with older children. Variations can be seen among children in their resistivity to disorganization under such circumstances. There are individual differences in depth and rate of regression which are important to include in the characterization of personality profiles.

One would have to conclude that allowing children to get into prolonged situations of intense distress is so disorganizing as to interfere with optimal development of the ego. These states between peak intensity of discomfort and satiation provide the best conditions for good ego functioning. This leads to the hypothesis that these states between peak discomfort and satiation experienced in connection with the object or part object and with instinctual tension not at peak intensity migh have considerable importance for stimulating the investment with neutralized energy of activities involving progressively more parts of the ego apparatus.

The institutional infants discussed in this paper were certainly deficient in this type of experience. This may account in part for the marked lag in the combination and integration of component units of activity into increasingly complex behavior even though the component units have already appeared through maturation.

In the institutional infant the object does not stimulate instinctual-drive energy to the same degree, and also is not cathected to nearly so high a degree, as in normally raised infants.[7] Consequently the highly cathected object, and eventually its image or memory, is not as available to act as the agent by which the cathexis is displaced from the object to activities and substitute objects such as toys and dolls. Thus one might say that the object is important for stimulating and mobilizing the energy with which the object is then cathected

[7] Dr. Peter Neubauer, in a discussion of this paper, has suggested a hypothesis in respect to the drive energy: Drive energy is not a given which seeks the object alone but depends upon the object for further stimulation.

by the infant, and for facilitating the displacement of this cathexis. As this takes place, the mechanism of displacement itself is structuralized and energized. This follows the suggestion of Rapaport (1960) that primary-process mechanisms may themselves be structuralized and energized by cathexis with neutralized energy. Behaviorial manifestations of these energy transformations can be elicited by the examiner and demonstrated in the institutionalized infants. The infant's interest in the observer can be aroused by persisting in a playful approach to him. If the observer then introduces a toy, the child may shift this interest to the toy and play with the toy for a while. For the institutional infant to carry this out the adult must remain with him, maintain his interest in the infant, and continue to show some pleasure in what the infant is doing. However, he must also withdraw to some extent so as not to compete with the toy, otherwise the infant does not shift his interest from the person to the toy but remains mainly interested, attentive, and responsive to the person. In such an example one can see manifestations of the displacements carried out by the infant and also observe the effects of the human contact first in stimulating the instinctual drives of the infant and then in facilitating the displacement of cathexis.

The institutional infant's inability to reach around the screen for the toy and the deficit in thinking which appears to be present involve the infant's difficulty in cathecting the object and shifting or displacing the cathexis. The inability also illustrates a disturbance in the developmental process by which primary-process mechanisms and primary autonomous ego apparatuses are integrated in secondary-process thinking. Of course, successful solution of the problem of finding the toy behind the screen requires maturation of the perceptual and motor apparatus to a level where the child is capable of registering the movements of the toy and carrying out the movements of retrieving it. In addition, finding the toy behind the screen requires a thought process in which the infant sustains an image of the toy behind the screen. When he is prevented from trying to reach the toy by going through the screen, he must be able to interpose another thought process in which the route around the screen to the toy is imagined and traversed in imagination. For these images to be sufficiently cathected to play a part in initiating the infant's action the toy would itself have to be highly cathected, a process which, as pointed out above, is significantly dependent on the nature of the contact with the mothering person. This cathexis is then available for distribution to the various thought images involving the toy.

Problem solving of this type, which requires linking the past with anticipations of the future and which is typical of secondary-process thinking, thus is seen to be a function which, at least in infants, may be dependent on factors of quality and intensity of cathexis of the human object and on an ability to modulate displacements of cathexis by secondary-process thinking.

SUMMARY

We have presented some of the observational findings from a study of institutionalized infants deprived of adequate human contact. These findings demonstrate that in these infants various parts of the apparatus of the ego mature when they would normally be expected to, but are not integrated or put to use in a normal fashion in the service of the infant's adaptation to his environment. In other words, the maturational sequence and timetable are not disturbed, but development is retarded.

We have described the institutional infant's behavior with toys, his investment in them, and his lack of initiative in approaching and exploiting them. The institutional infant's inability in the second half of the first year to solve the problem of finding the hidden toy is interpreted as indicating a deficit in the type of secondary-process thinking necessary for problem solving.

It is widely known that lack of mothering adversely affects the development of the infant. We have tried to formulate hypotheses about some of the specific mechanisms by which this adverse effect might be brought about:

1. The lack of an appropriate balance between comfort-discomfort experiences impedes the laying down of memory traces of the object and their permanent cathexis.

2. Due to the insufficiently cathected representations of the human object, the displacements to the inanimate objects do not take place in the normal fashion.

3. Therefore, the mechanism of displacement itself does not become adequately structuralized and energized.

These findings and the formulations based on them suggest a way in which the human contact acts as an organizer for the development of the infant.

BIBLIOGRAPHY

Bowlby, J. (1951), *Maternal Care and Mental Health*. Geneva: World Health Organization Mon. No. 2.

Freud, A. (1952), The Mutual Influences in the Development of Ego and Id: Introduction to the Discussion. *This Annual*, VII.

Freud, S. (1900), The Interpretation of Dreams. *Standard Edition*, IV & V. London: Hogarth Press, 1950.

Goldfarb, W. (1945), Effects of Psychological Deprivation in Infancy and Subsequent Stimulation. *Am. J. Psychiat.*, CII.

Halverson, H. (1947), In: *Developmental Diagnosis*, by A. Gesell & C. Armatruda. New York: Hoeber.

Hartmann, H. (1939), *Ego Psychology and the Problem of Adaptation*. New York: International Universities Press, 1958.

—— (1950), Comments on the Psychoanalytic Theory of the Ego. *This Annual*, V.

—— (1952), The Mutual Influences in the Development of Ego and Id. *This Annual*, VII.

—— & Kris, E., Loewenstein, R. M. (1946), Comments on the Formation of Psychic Structure. *This Annual*, II.

Hoffer, W. (1949), Mouth, Hand and Ego-Integration. *This Annual*, III/IV.

—— (1950), Development of the Body Image. *This Annual*, V.

Kris, E. (1956), Decline and Recovery in a Four-Year-Old. Unfinished manuscript.

Levy, D. (1937), Primary Affect Hunger. *Am. J. Psychiat.*, XCIV.

Piaget, J. (1936), *The Origins of Intelligence in Children*. New York: International Universities Press, 1952.

Provence, S. & Lipton, R. C. (1962), *The Development of Institutionalized Infants: A Comparison with Family-Reared Infants*. New York: International Universities Press (in press).

Rapaport, D. (1960), Psychoanalysis As a Developmental Psychology. In: *Perspectives in Psychological Theory*, ed. B. Kaplan & S. Wapner. New York: International Universities Press.

Spitz, R. A. (1945), Hospitalism: An Inquiry into the Genesis of Psychiatric Conditions in Early Childhood. *This Annual*, I.

—— (1946), Hospitalism: A Follow-up Report. *This Annual*, II.

Winnicott, D. W. (1945), Primitive Emotional Development. *Collected Papers*. New York: Basic Books, 1958.

—— (1953), Transitional Objects and Transitional Phenomena. *Int. J. Psa.*, XXXIV.

NOTE ON DR. MAX SCHUR'S COMMENTS ON GRIEF AND MOURNING IN INFANCY AND EARLY CHILDHOOD

JOHN BOWLBY, M.D. (London)

In the last volume of this Annual, following my paper entitled "Grief and Mourning in Infancy and Early Childhood" (1960a), comments on it by Anna Freud, Max Schur, and René A. Spitz appeared. Many of the issues they raise I shall discuss in subsequent papers and in the book I have in preparation. Since, however, Schur has attributed to me a number of views which are other than those I hold, I believe it may avoid misunderstanding if I correct them briefly.

On pages 64 and 65 Schur has attributed to me the following views on instinct theory:

> Bowlby's concept is therefore mainly based on that part of the instinct theory of ethology which assumes the *fully innate, unlearned character of most complex behavior patterns* [Schur's italics]. . . .
> Under the impact of this debate most ethologists, e.g., Thorpe, Tinbergen, and others, have abandoned the rigid insistence on the *entirely innate* origin of instinctive behavior, on the specificity of the drive element and of action-specific energy, and on the "hydrodynamic model"—all of which play such a great role in Bowlby's formulations [Schur's italics].

I am familiar with the work Schur refers to and, I believe, have not advanced the sort of theory he attributes to me; several times, indeed, I have expressed views of an opposite kind. For instance, on pages 364-365 of the paper on "The Nature of the Child's Tie to His Mother" (1958), I have been fairly specific:

> . . . ethology conceives of [the organism] starting with a number of highly structured responses (some of which are active at birth

206

and some of which mature later), which in the course of development become so elaborated, through processes of integration and learning, and in Man by imitation, identification and the use of symbols, that the resulting behaviour is of amazing variety and plasticity.

In an earlier paper (1957) there are a number of passages in which I also make it clear that I regard learning as having a central place in development. For instance, on pages 235-236 I give a series of examples of how, through processes of learning, experiences may lead to the "instinctual" patterns taking unusual forms or even not appearing at all. Near the end (p. 239) I state:

> I hope it is not necessary to repeat that one is not discarding learning theory. On the contrary, for understanding many of the processes of change to which the components of instinctive patterns are subject, it is indispensable and therefore complementary to ethology.

Just how genetic and environmental factors interact in the development of any one behavior pattern is of course a matter for research.

Schur's attribution to me of the "hydrodynamic model" is puzzling since not only is it conspicuously absent from my recent papers but in two separate places I have shown I am critical of it. These are 1957, page 234, "this psychohydraulic model is now discredited," and 1960b, page 313, where I refer to "the abandonment of Lorenz's hydrodynamic theory." It is possible that Schur was misled by my reference to it in a brief paper of 1953, now superseded. Nowhere do I speak of action-specific energy.

Throughout pages 64-69 of his Comment, Schur writes as though both the biopsychologists (Beach, Lehrman, Schneirla) and also the ethologists would disown my formulations. He concludes: "Bowlby's concepts are therefore at variance with the concepts of biopsychologists and of most ethologists." Now, were I to hold the views that Schur attributes to me, I have no doubt he would be right; as it is, however, I think he might have difficulty in finding support for his opinion. Since a main object of my work is to link psychoanalytic theory with modern biological and psychological theory, I have done all I can to ensure that my formulations are in line with the converging concepts of the two disciplines. In attempting this I have been fortunate in having the constant help of, among others, Dr. Robert Hinde, formerly of the Department of Zoology and now of the Sub-Department of Animal Behaviour at Cambridge University. He has read all my recent papers in draft and advised me about many points when further thought was needed. Although he is not to be held responsible for my final formulations, I believe that he has helped me to keep within a framework of theory acceptable to biologists. I am deeply indebted to him.

REFERENCES

Bowlby, J. (1953), Critical Phases in the Development of Social Responses in Man. *New Biology*, XIV. London: Penguin.
—— (1957), An Ethological Approach to Research in Child Development. *Brit. J. Med. Psychol.*, XXXIII.
—— (1958), The Nature of the Child's Tie to His Mother. *Int. J. Psa.*, XXXIX.
—— (1960a), Grief and Mourning in Infancy and Early Childhood. *This Annual*, XV.
—— (1960b), Ethology and the Development of Object Relations (Contribution to Symposium on Ethology and Psycho-Analysis). *Int. J. Psa.*, XLI.
Schur, M. (1960), Discussion of Dr. John Bowlby's Paper. *This Annual*, XV.

CLINICAL CONTRIBUTIONS

A STUDY OF "SCREEN SENSATIONS"[1]

E. JAMES ANTHONY, M.D. (Chicago)[2]

FRAGMENTS FROM THE ANALYSIS OF AN ADOLESCENT GIRL

Lily came into analysis with me a little over two years ago when she was almost eighteen years old. At her first interview, she presented herself as a strikingly beautiful girl with a flat affect and a detached, sleepy, faraway look as if she had only just woken up. As if to substantiate this impression, she told me that her main trouble lay in her feeling of lifelessness and emptiness. Only when she was active or eating or being touched by boys did she lose this deadness, but it soon came back when she was alone by herself. For this reason she could not bear being without company, and yet people meant nothing to her.

It was no new thing. As long as she could remember, she had felt cut off and isolated from others, especially her contemporaries, and this had forced her more and more into the role of spectator, watching but never really participating. She was convinced that she bored everyone and that she had nothing worth while to say to them. When she did find something to say that was not totally banal, she could not express herself. However, she was far from being inarticulate on paper. Since late childhood, she had filled numerous diaries with detailed descriptions of her emotional states and experiences, extracting every iota of feeling out of them. "Everything makes sense inside me, and nothing makes sense outside me," she said but without bitterness. She spoke like someone who had suffered a sensory deprivation from birth.

[1] Read before the Chicago Psychoanalytic Society on January 23, 1961. The discussants included Dr. Joan Fleming, Dr. Paul Kramer, Dr. Gerhart Piers, and Dr. Heinz Kohut.

[2] From the Division of Child Psychiatry, Washington University School of Medicine, St. Louis.

This impression was borne out by her mother. She insisted that Lily had never been any different. Timidity and aloofness had characterized her behavior since infancy, and the slightest unpleasantness in day-to-day living drove her further into herself. She had remained childishly dependent on her mother who regarded and treated her as a child. Lily was aware of this and, at times, resented it. On one occasion, for example, her mother had given her a bottle of perfume which she herself habitually used. Her daughter reacted strongly. "I don't want to smell like you. If I smell like you, I'll be you and I won't be myself. You've never wanted me to be myself. You've kept me sick because you want to look after me and keep me close to you." Her mother was both surprised and hurt, but, as not infrequently, there was a grain of reality in what Lily had said. There was no doubt that the mother had needed her daughter almost as much as the daughter had needed her and had tended to exploit the girl's "constitutional" propensity toward isolation and dependency. As a girl, she too had been shy and seclusive and ill at ease in society.

In Lily's extrafamilial relationships, the sense of unreality and depersonalization predominated unless she managed to establish some form of anaclitic tie on a physical and emotional basis. "I'm like one of those sea creatures," she said of herself. "I get stuck on someone, and then they can't get rid of me. I can't give them anything, and I expect to get everything from them. I just seem to live my life through other people."

Throughout the first interview, I was struck in turn by her immaturity, her detachment, her orality, and her narcissism that added up in my clinical mind to the primitiveness of a schizoid rather than of a frank schizophrenic disorder. I judged her to have enough ego capacity and insight to warrant at least a trial of analytic treatment. I was not too sure about her manifest qualities of naïveté and innocence under cover of which she appeared at times to discharge both sexual and sadistic impulses. The boys who attempted to touch her intimately were made to feel that they had seduced a nun and went off loaded with guilt and embarrassment. Her dreams seemed shorn of all defensive embellishment. "I dreamed last night that my mother was trying to overpower me, and I took an axe and cut her head off."

As might have been expected, within a few weeks she had established a close symbiotic relationship with me. I had given her the option of lying down or sitting up on the couch as she felt the need, and she had treated this concession with great seriousness, using it for purposes that she discussed fully. She sat up, sometimes unexpectedly, when she wondered whether I was dead, asleep, or bored. She lay down when she thought she could trust me completely, and she sat up when she suspected that I was about to attack her. She wanted very much to touch and be touched, not, she insisted, for sexual reasons, but so that virtue might flow out of me and into her and cure her by bringing her completely to life. "I am alive now when I am with you, but I want to be alive away from you," she recently remarked. "I want to do without you just as I'm doing without my mother." She had left home and was working as a lab technician in a biological department, while at the same time taking courses at the university. She was associating with a young man whom her parents wanted her to marry, and she was planning to terminate treatment in the summer and move to another city.

I felt that she had a long way to go yet and took no active part in any of this planning.

The incident that I am about to relate took place at the beginning of her second year of analysis. She had brought me some cookies made from *marron glacé*, and we had become busily engaged examining her motivation. She enjoyed cooking, eating, and serving food to others, but both in real life and in her dreams, she was haunted by the anxiety that what she offered would prove unacceptable. If I ate what she produced, it would be proof that I was accepting her since I would be assimilating her products. Something from her would have gotten right inside me. She imagined the *marron glacé* creeping into my tissues. These and other similar fantasies pointed to animistic "survivals" in her thinking that added strength and concreteness to her already intense oral transference. At the end of each subsequent session, with the question of acceptance still at stake, she would pick up the cookie and depart, only to return with it the next day. As time went on, the need to have her products incorporated by the analyst in this particular concrete way became less and less, until finally one day she was able to throw away the, by now, very undesirable and stale concoction with the remark, "I

don't think I need that stuff to be able to get close to you. I was just
trying to force my way in as if you were trying to keep me out."

For some time during this period, she had experienced hunger
on her way to her analytic session and had called in at a little café
that sold doughnuts of which she had always been inordinately fond.
This insured her not feeling ravenous during the hour, and we
analyzed her anxieties over asking the analyst for nourishment and
being refused. As she put it, "Even if you were a woman and had
breasts, there would be no milk in them. My mother had no milk in
her breasts." The doughnuts were good but not at all as good as she
could remember them from earlier times. She always bought two to
satisfy herself.

One day she was earlier than usual for her session, and, instead
of buying the doughnuts and eating them on the road as had been
her wont, she sat herself down in the shop and ate them there,
treating herself at the same time to a glass of Coca-Cola. What she
actually did was to break off a piece of the doughnut and dip it in
the Coca-Cola before eating it. As soon as she experienced the taste
of the doughnut combined with the liquid in her mouth, she suddenly became extremely nervous and shook all over. A feeling of
wild elation seemed to take possession of her, and she was hardly able
to contain the happiness that surged through her. She felt that she
was on top of the world and that she had everything that she wanted
and that nothing bad could ever happen to her again.

On arrival, she was still extremely excited and kept saying that
it was like something that had happened before, but she did not
know what. She tried hard to associate but could get nowhere with
this, and it left her exhausted and distressed. When I interpreted
along the lines we had been working at, she became irritable and
asked me to stop talking and not interfere with her thoughts. I
pointed out that she was trying to do without me and keep me out
of her thrilling experience. To this she replied, "Just sit there and
say nothing. I just want you to be there, that's all."

That night she had the following dream. She had gone into a
shop to buy doughnuts. There were a pile of these on the counter,
but on close examination she saw that these were stale and of
inferior quality. At the end of the shop, there was a door leading
down to the basement, and she had a feeling that there were better

doughnuts down there. She went down and found some wonderful doughnuts fresh and beautifully made, and she helped herself to several. As she was taking them out, she saw several bottles of Coke, and she took one. The man at the counter looked severely at her and said that the two did not go together and that she should keep them separate.

The patient remarked that in recalling the dream, she also recalled a memory that she had not been able to get at on the previous day. She remembered the exact tasting sensation first and immediately linked it with a childhood experience. She thought she must have been about five years old at the time. For being a good girl, she thought, her mother had taken her to a shop that seemed to her "like heaven." People in pure white coats served delicious hot, sugary doughnuts, oven-fresh. Because she had some difficulty in coping with her big doughnut, her mother had helped by breaking it up into pieces and "dunking" the pieces for her in a glass of Coca-Cola. She remembered the situation as a specially happy one because her brother had been left at home, and she had her mother entirely to herself.

She was also able to recall now that after the doughnut episode of the previous day, the thought had occurred to her, "I have my Coke and doughnut and then I have my session, and this is the very best thing in the world for me, and I wish it were like this always."

The stale doughnuts on the counter in the dream she associated with the poor-quality doughnuts that she had on the way to analysis and also with what she received in analysis. The analyst gave her nothing but words, and words could not fill a stomach. I reminded her that she had tried to fill my stomach and to have an eating session with me and that she probably felt very angry and rejected at my nonacceptance. Her going back to the satisfying eating session with her mother was in part an attempt to highlight the fact that I had failed her. She said that I had a "horrible habit" of separating everything that went together in her mind. I was always talking of "good" and "bad," "male" and "female," "father" and "mother," "thoughts" and "things," and it made her feel that she wanted to squeeze them all together to make one thing. She knew how to deal with one thing. She could eat it up, break it up, mend it, throw it away, keep it; but two things were difficult; she just did not know how to deal with two things. I said that it reminded me very much of the way she kept her father out of her analysis. With her usual air of great innocence, she replied that she never wanted to think of her father ever since she had found him on top of her mother in their bedroom one night. She hated the thought of him being 'in the picture." I said that it seemed to me that in order to achieve "oneness" with her mother, she was getting rid of father. "I don't want him around when my mother's around," she said emphatically. "One of them has to go. The other one makes me feel uncomfortable. I'm more comfortable with my mother." Once again she compared me unfavorably with her mother who had allowed her so generously to mix things. "You want to divide the world into up and down, right and left, and back and front." I told her that I felt that she was talking about the body and not about the world and that she was trying to pretend that all parts of the body were the same. I said that the body was not merely a breast but that she was making it into that. She was complaining because I was not just a breast like her mother. Her answer to this was: "You're more like my mother than my father, but I think of you as half-way between them." She paused for a moment and then added, "That's funny; I usually think of myself as half-way between them. Sometimes I confuse myself with you."

On the following night she had a dream in which she was sitting on two of her father's boots, defecating into one and urinating into the other. It was important to keep them separate, but she was not accomplishing this too successfully so that some mixing was taking place. When she looked into one of the boots, she saw that it contained doughnuts. She immediately wanted to eat one but felt that it would be a very wrong thing to do.

Her immediate association was that I had made her dream her doughnuts into feces by confusing her thoughts about the body. I was also forcing her to become like myself, a separator. She remembered that she used to sit on her father's shoe while he swung her up and down. Occasionally when she saw the analyst's shoe during a session out of the corner of her eye, she had an impulse to sit straddled across it. She had a fear, however, that the tip of the shoe might go into her. That would make her at once want to pass a bowel motion and urinate as if she was having an enema.

She was suddenly distressed as she remembered how severe her mother had been with her younger brother during his toilet train-ing. She was about six at the time. There was a long period of silence, and then she remarked in a low voice that something had come back to her. She had a distinct memory of her mother saying to her, "You must never do big business and small business together. The two are separate, and you must do them separately." This was so irrational that she was sure that she must have imagined it. "I sup-pose that I'm making her into you now and that everything will turn into you in the end." The next morning, on waking, she recalled when she had heard something like this before. She was again about five or six, and she had a vivid picture of herself sitting up in a rather messy bed and of her mother saying to her, "I don't mind you wetting the bed because some girls of your age still do that some times, but I strongly object to you soiling at the same time. That you should have gotten over a long time ago." She had an impression of herself, at first lying pleasantly in a warm gooey mess, and then becoming guiltily aware of her double crime.

Her next dream, two days later, found her sitting in a high chair with two plates in front of her, one full of milk and the other con-taining a meatlike substance which on closer inspection resembled miniature doughnuts. She tried to pour the milk over the doughnuts, but it kept running down the side. She said that she understood the dream from a remark her mother had made the day before. During dinner, Lily had added some butter and milk to her potatoes and made a small mash to eat with her meat. Her mother recalled what a problem she had been as a baby with her food. She wanted to mash everything on her plate with her hands and then stuff her mouth with handfuls in a most greedy way. The mother added that it had taken a good many spankings to cure her of this disgusting habit and to teach her that it was more polite to eat different foods separately.

At this stage, she became quite depressed. "I felt so happy about my mother last week, and now I'm beginning to hate her. I can't imagine how I ever felt differently. She's always been the same. Everything has to be 'just so' and in a definite place. My hair has to be in order and my nails manicured. How could I ever think of her as different." She cried softly to herself. I said that it must be a great sorrow to lose such a lovely feeling, but that giving it up could help her to grow up and enjoy more grown-up feelings. She sat up on the couch and looked at me for a long time, eventually whispering, "I didn't hear what you said but it sounded so very kind. I don't know why I thought of you as a cruel separator. You're the opposite." I told her that she was afraid of being separated from me just as she had been afraid of being separated from her mother; of one person turning into two with the world between them. "You're trying to make it easier for me. You're being very kind." With a deep sigh she lay down on the couch again, and the room became very quiet. I thought at one point that she had fallen asleep, but after ten minutes of silence she inquired in a whisper if I was still there. I did not answer but moved instead in my chair, and she was quiet again for about another ten minutes when she said, "I can hear you breathing. It makes me happy." A little later, she said, "I feel giddy," and curled up on her side. She began to shiver and put her arms round the cushion with her face almost buried in it. She began to mumble not very clearly: "So happy, so very happy . . . so kind . . . everyone kind and happy and good . . . lovely feeling . . . all colors . . . such nice taste . . . good taste . . . I'm flying . . . the blue's coming near . . . it's going away . . . it's gone."

She shook her head and sat up abruptly looking a little dazed. "It was like having a dream when I was awake. I had the same wonderful feeling I had with the doughnut. It didn't come into my dream just now except it could have been the blue blob with the hole in the center. It must have been a very magic doughnut, don't you think?"

I will leave my understanding of this phenomenon and the chain of events that preceded it to a later discussion. At this point, the character of the analysis changed in many respects. It gradually assumed a more classical outline, the patient lying all the time, and obeying to a much larger extent the basic analytic rules. In place of the previous symbiotic relationship, a genuine transference neurosis began to emerge, and rudimentary oedipal elements found their way somewhat surprisingly into the sessions.

Before this, however, she had one final episode outside the analytic hour, about which she wrote to me. I am reproducing it verbatim:

I saw some photographs of war and immediately was transported into another world of stronger emotions. I first felt a little bit asleep. I was walking across the campus and looking at all the people around me. I have the drowsy feeling. I say hullo to acquaintances as if I were on a cloud floating away from them in a wild happy ecstatic state. It's all blue and gold. My eyes have been burning. My feelings are completely immersed in those photographs which seem to be unique. I felt that lack of contact with other people again.

Back in the analytic setting, she brooded irritably for half the session on the war photos, which had simply shown pictures of soldiers and refugees. Quite suddenly, she was "back" in Italy during the early part of the war. She and her brother were standing with their parents outside a house, and her mother was crying loudly, while her father was saying, "Hush!" She took the apple she was eating and gave it to her mother who then stopped crying. (I did a quick calculation at this point and estimated that she could not have been more than six or eight months old at this time.) Lily herself wondered why this horrible memory had given her one of her "glorious feelings." The next day, she came for her session in a very bemused state and quite a bit embarrassed. She had talked to her mother about this memory, and her mother had laughed, reminding her that she was only a baby at the time. Sensing Lily's indignation and distress, she gave the matter more serious and careful consideration and eventually came up with what she believed to be the real fact that Lily had so grotesquely misremembered. In this, she collaborated with her husband who supported her conclusion. The family were trying desperately to get out of Italy and had made numerous applications. On a particular date—Lily was nine months old and still at the breast although they were contemplating weaning her—the family were asked to report to the local police station. With many other people in a similar situation, they sat for nine hours on benches provided outside the building. Both parents described this as one of the most unpleasant days of their lives. Lily was extremely fretful and howled continually, and the mother in desperation would put her constantly to the breast which proved the only effective means of stopping her.

When Lily insisted that she had a distinct picture of giving her crying mother an apple, the latter again laughed and caressed her daughter affectionately. It was true. She remembered something, but it was not in Italy. It was much, much later. They were already in America, and Lily was almost seven years old. Mother was at the end of her pregnancy and had had a few initial pains. They had all gone to the hospital, and while sitting in the clinic waiting for the doctor to appear, mother's pains had worsened and she had started to moan and weep a little. Lily, who had been sitting apprehensively by her side munching an apple, had immediately offered this to her mother. "I was so touched by her thoughtfulness that I forgot all about my pains and started kissing her. We were both very happy for those few moments."

In my own state of "free-floating attention," associations were beginning to well up and ultimately led me to re-examine a famous literary case history in seven volumes which had been out of my mind for many years. It was only during the war years that I had found the leisure time to wade through the whole work.

FRAGMENTS FROM THE SELF-ANALYSIS OF A RECLUSE

Speaking of Marcel Proust, the writer Joseph Conrad wrote: "I don't think that there ever has been in the whole of literature such an example of the power of analysis, and I feel safe in saying that there will never be another."[3]

During the last thirteen years of his life, Proust isolated himself from ordinary life. A victim of chronic illness and afflicted with a morbid fear of dying, he shut himself off in his apartment, swathed himself like an Egyptian mummy, drew the shutters and curtains to exclude the light, and searched feverishly into the past for memories. He could be called a retrospective voyeur since his inner eye was constantly directed toward visions of early life that seemed ineluctable. From childhood, he had regarded himself primarily as a spectator who could only learn about things by watching, and this encouraged him to make watching an end in itself. As a child, he was accustomed to play little mental games in which he would fix

3 Quoted from Introduction to *Past Recaptured.*

his attention on an object and attempt to decipher the reality that lay behind the appearance. He seemed forever intent on peering behind the manifest.

He saw his ill health in terms of secondary gain, since it brought about his divorce from life and allowed him to focus his entire attention and energy on what mattered most—the re-creation of the past as a dynamic, living reality. He recognized as his lifework the recovery of memory impressions "that must be plumbed to their depths, brought into light, and transformed into intellectual equivalents." This was his analytic task. He had already begun making notes for his elaborate work in 1890 when he was nineteen, and the first 700 pages were completed by 1906. (You will remember that *The Interpretation of Dreams* was published in 1899.)

Of special interest to the psychoanalyst was the concern of this highly analytic individual with such problems as psychic determinism, the association of ideas, the dynamic continuity between childhood and adult life, the various psychological selves that punctuate the course of development, and the strange "double orientation" of the human situation that allows a person to look both within himself and outside himself, out into the present and back into the past, geared sometimes to fantasy and sometimes to reality. Like Freud, he had a long and bitter struggle with the idea and significance of death so that his concept of death underwent radical changes during his life.

Like my patient, Lily, he lived a life bathed in sensation, and it was the world of perceptual memories that dominated his attention. Both he and Lily had strong claims to the "unusual hypersensitivities" described by Bergman and Escalona (1949). Scattered through his books are constant references to the scent of chestnut trees, heliotrope, raspberries and sprigs of tarragon, to the appetizing, domestic smells of country life, of warm sweet bread, and of soot in big rooms. Over and over again he returns "with an unconfessed gluttony" to a myriad different perceptions ranging over the five senses but chiefly directed toward the more primitive impacts of taste and smell.

I want to consider briefly his notions regarding memory and its relation to time and sensation. First let us hear him speak of the "infinitely, unrolling past, unconsciously carried" within him, "without break of continuity or cessation of existence." "It still clung to me, and I could recapture it, go back to it, *merely* by descending more deeply within myself." Notice the word "merely." It was certainly not "merely" for him. No one better than Proust appreciated the difficulties of the "descent."

His pursuit of memories is relentless but frustrating. He is in "an abyss of uncertainty," a "dark region," where the "equipment of the mind avails it nothing." In his desperation, he has recourse to three techniques—the association of ideas, a consideration of dreams, and a manipulation of sensations.

The memories recovered by the laborious process of association seem to him lifeless and "artificial." There is no accompanying emotional catharsis, and the feeling is one of disenchantment. There is a cognitive recognition of possession, but the owner of the experience is clearly some former self out of touch to varying degrees with the current self. These actual recollections of the past, says Proust, based as they are on false and limited impressions make it seem tiresome, as tiresome as the present which is always so hopelessly disappointing since it is experienced without any imaginative elaboration.

He next turns to dreams for help in the re-creation of a more vivid past. I will again let him speak for himself.

> The interest I have always taken in dreams was due to the fact that making up in intensity what they lack in duration, they help us to understand better, for example, the subjective elements of love. With what prodigious swiftness do they accomplish what would be vulgarly called "getting a woman inside our skin." . . . Perhaps it is also the preposterous game that they play with time that has fascinated me. Have I not seen in one minute of one night remote periods of my life so far in the past that I could scarcely distinguish any longer the feelings I had at the time. These dreams came rushing upon me full tilt, blinding me with their brightness like giant aeroplanes bringing me all that they had once held for me, the emotion, the shock and the brilliance of their immediate proximity [1928, pp. 1024-1025].

On waking, however, comes the inevitable disappointment as he has to retrace the long distance that the dream has crossed in one bound, and he realizes that dreams were not the means for recaptur-

ing the past although better than the objective exploitation of
memory.

As dreams constituted another of the facts of my life which had
always struck me most forcibly and must have been the strongest
factor in convincing me of the purely mental character of reality,
I was not going to scorn their assistance. . . . I reflected that they
would sometimes bring me nearer to truths and impressions
which would not come through my own unaided effort or even
through natural contingencies. . . . No, I would not scorn this
second muse, this nocturnal muse [1928, p. 1026].

It is, however, to the third muse, the muse devoted to the life of
sensations that he turns with the greatest expectation and the greatest reward. He saw sensations as signs leading back and forward with
more supple facility and dynamism than either memories or dreams.
He refers to this "subjective book of strange signs, which my conscious mind, as it explored my unconscious self, went searching for,
stumbled against and passed round like a diver groping his way."
These "transferred sensations" as Proust calls them bring back as a
living experience the past in all its complex sensory and emotional
complexity, in contrast to the "snapshots [recalled memory] which,"
he says, with the bitterness of frustration, "have never yielded me
anything."

He felt convinced that the "sensations" afforded him a truer picture of the past than anything else, and the accidental quality of their
occurrence supported this. As he puts it,

It is precisely the fortuitous, unavoidable way in which I came
upon the sensations that guaranteed the truth of a past which
that sensation revived and of the mental images released, since
we feel its effort to come up into the light and also the thrill of
recapturing reality. The sensation is the guarantee of the truth
of the entire picture composed of contemporary impressions
which the sensation brings in its train, with that unerring proportion of light and shadow, remembrance and oblivion, which
conscious memory and observation will never know [1928, p.
1001].

This must be seen in relation to Proust's concept of memory.
He compares the process to the belief in Celtic mythology that the

souls of the dead are held captive in some inferior being and lost to
us until a day (which may never come to many) when we pass by
and call the name

> . . . and they start and tremble and the spell is broken. We have
> delivered them. They have overcome death to return and share
> our life. And so it is with our own past. It is a labor in vain to
> attempt to recapture it; all the efforts of our intellect must prove
> futile . . . it is hidden beyond the reach of intellect, and it de-
> pends on chance whether we come upon it or not before we
> ourselves must die [1913, p. 34].

These Proustian ideas are a commentary on the process of self-
analysis, and the technical maneuvers employed by self-analysts to
reach past the defenses into the unconscious without the assistance
of the transference method. The analysis depends heavily on the
accidental factor, and is limited, as someone remarked humorously,
by too much countertransference! It is also a criticism of the way
in which the analysis of sensation has had so little attention paid to
it by psychoanalysts, although seven years ago Felix Deutsch called
attention to what he termed "analytic synesthesiology" as an important technique for increasing our understanding of the analytic situation. According to Deutsch (1954), "the psychological implications
of the psychosomatic process can be fully understood only if the
interaction of the sensory perceptions and their related psychic elements can be traced back to their earliest sources and shown as an
entity." Sensory configurations attach themselves to the libidinized
object, varying from stage to stage of development and from hour to
hour in analysis and indicating the feeling tone toward the cathected
object. Deutsch's procedure is, of course, incorporated within the
transference situation and is more systematically deployed as compared with what Proust attempts to do, but it is correspondingly less
dramatic in its expression. The Proustian sensations lead him to the
very "essence of things." They have the quality of Platonic ideas.
They are eternal.

> When nothing of the past remains [he says], when everything is
> gone and the people are dead and things are broken and scat-
> tered, still, alone, more fragile, but with more vitality, more
> unsubstantial, more persistent, more faithful, the smell and taste

of things remain poised a long time, like souls, ready to remind us, waiting and hoping for their moment to come amid the ruins of all the rest, and bearing unfalteringly, in the tiny and almost impalpable drop of their essence, the vast structure of recollection [1913, p. 36].

With their help, he gets back to the fierce intensity of his early relationship with his mother and re-experiences his feelings, but without any insight. The unconscious is never made conscious, and the seven volumes remain an enchanting exploration of the preconscious but no more. The experiencing of the sensations, however, creates a great hunger for further sensations, but they are few and far between, and only four times do they occur in the gigantic autobiography. So seductive is the moment of sensation, that he feels the present "grappling like a wrestler" with the past, threatening to overwhelm his sense of reality. The former always won, but it was the vanquished that seemed the more beautiful. In his yearning, one is reminded of the well-known lines from Faust:

Then to the passing moment would I cry: linger awhile
Thou art so fair.

If the present scene had not been immediately victorious [Proust (1928) remarks], I believe I should have fainted. During the instant that they last, these resurrections of the past are so complete that they make us oblivious of where we are and compel our entire being to believe itself surrounded by them, or, at least, to vacillate between them and the present scene, bewildered by an uncertainty similar to that which one sometimes experiences at the moment of losing consciousness in sleep [p. 998].

The past memory, like the present moment, has little to offer in itself. The past memory is usually denuded of all its rich concomitant sensations, and the present moment is denuded of all its associations, but it is the coming together of the past and present in the present that proclaims reality.

The five sensations with which he is so concerned are, in sequence:

1. The tinkling of the doorbell.
2. The taste of the madeleine in tea.

3. The experience of uneven flagstones on entering the Guermantes residence.
4. The sound of a spoon against a plate.
5. The wiping of the mouth with a napkin.

It will be at once noted that apart from the first and the third, the sensations are all connected with oral experiences. The first is not a sensation of the kind we have been considering in the preceding discussion. It is a remembered and not an experienced sensation, and my only reason for including it in the sequence is that it opened the door leading to his most important childhood recollection of his mother. Three, four, and five also belong together in a single sequence. The sensations involve sound, touch, and taste.

The "reverberating, ferruginous, interminable, sharp, jangling tinkle" of the little doorbell announced the departure of a guest on a particular night of his childhood and the approach of his mother. Earlier in the evening, he had been permitted to go down to the dining room. Here, once again, I will let him speak for himself, and you will hear for yourself the accent of his ardent young love.

I never took my eyes off my mother. I knew that she would not allow me in public, for fear of annoying my father, give her my usual series of kisses. I therefore promised myself that I would put beforehand into one kiss, which was bound to be brief and stealthy in execution, everything that my own efforts could put into it. I would look out very carefully first the exact spot on her cheek where I would imprint it, and would so prepare my thoughts that I might be able, thanks to these mental preliminaries, to consecrate the whole of the minute that Mama would permit me to the sensation of her cheek against my lips [1913, p. 21].

[Instead of getting his artistically prepared kiss, he is confronted with his father's impatient expostulation: "No, no, leave your mother alone. You've said 'goodnight' quite enough. These exhibitions are absurd. Go on upstairs." Proust, the child, is disconsolate. He climbed the stairs "in opposition to his heart's desire," and instead of going to his room, he lies in wait for his mother in the passageway, his heart pounding violently with terror and joy. Then he hears the bell and her approaching steps, and he throws himself at her. She felt that his father would come and make a scene and whispers to him, "Run away at once. Don't

let your father see you standing there like a crazy jane." He sees
his father's light come creeping up the wall of the staircase, and
he is terrified, but he also uses it to blackmail his mother into
staying with him. Suddenly the father is upon them, and he
involuntarily murmurs, "I'm done for." To his great surprise,
his father's manner is quite mild as he suggests that the mother
should go and sleep with her son. "Go and comfort him," he
orders, "I can look after myself." His mother reads to him, and
gradually his agony is soothed.] I let myself be borne upon the
current of this gentle night on which I had my mother by my
side. I knew that this, the strongest desire I had in the world,
namely to keep my mother with me through the sad hours of
darkness, would never again be repeated, since it ran too much
counter to everything [pp. 27, 28, 33].

This type of memory shows what a strong eidetic tendency
Proust had. His capacity to dissect a scene or situation depended on
this longer and more intense fixation of the image. Lying in the dark
on sleepless nights, he could see his old memories projected in front
of him as a sort of illuminous panel, "sharply defined against a vague
and shadowy background like electric signs on the front of a building." Even this was no comfort during the long dark nights without
his mother.

It was this evening of the bell that he looked upon as the critical
one of his life. "It marked the commencement of the waning of my
will power and my health. Everything was predetermined from that
moment on." The second crisis took place with the death of his
mother, at which point he lost all further interest in current life
and retired completely with his memories into the past. It was after
her death that he rejected any further active participation in society,
but even before this took place, he set out to reconstruct for himself
out of memory and imagination something more satisfactory than
life. The work of remembering, however, went slowly and laboriously and along pedestrian channels until the moment of the
madeleine.

One day in winter when he had come home, his mother, seeing
that he was cold, offered him tea and madeleines. He soaked the
madeleine in a spoonful of tea and tasted it. "No sooner had the
warm liquid with the crumbs in it touched my palate than a shudder
ran through my whole body. An exquisite pleasure invaded my

senses with no suggestion of its origin." All his anxiety evaporated, and he was conscious only of an all-powerful joy. He ceased to feel mediocre, accidental, and mortal, and he lost his morbid fear of death.

Proust became preoccupied with the unremembered state provoked by this first sensation, and he searched for an uncovering technique.

> I retraced my thoughts to the moment of the sensation; I find the same state but no fresh light. I compel my mind to make a further effort to follow and recapture the fleeting sensation, and that nothing may interrupt its course, I shut out every idea and shut my ears to extraneous sound, with no result. Feeling that my mind is growing fatigued, I turn it to distractions which I have just denied it, and allow it to think of other things so that it could rest and refresh itself. And then I make another attempt. I clear an empty space in front of it and put in position before my mind's eye the still recent taste of the first mouthful. I feel something starting inside me, something leaving its resting place and trying to rise like a long-embedded anchor from a great depth. I do not yet know what it is, but I can feel it mounting slowly. I can measure the resistance. I can hear the echo of great spaces traversed. Undoubtedly what is thus palpitating in the depths of my being must be the image, the visual memory, which, being linked to the taste, has tried to follow it into my conscious mind. Will it [he asks himself] ultimately reach the clear surface of my consciousness, this old dead memory which the magnetism of an identical moment has traveled so far to importune, disturb, and raise out of the depths of my being [1913, p. 35].

After many more attempts, and conscious of many resistances, he suddenly locates the taste in time and place. It belongs to a Sunday morning at Combray and it is on a visit to his Aunt Leonie when she offers him some madeleine and lime-flower tea. Immediately a thousand little details ramify through his memory, all of them equally neutral and innocuous, all of them stemming from this bedroom, until the whole of Combray seems to spring into being from his cup of tea, rather like Japanese flowers, which start without shape or character and soon become flowers and houses and people, permanent and recognizable.

Proust was well aware that he had left the essential problem of the madeleine largely unanswered, so when the next series of sensations occurred on his arrival at the court of the Guermantes residence five volumes of autobiography later he was determined to go further than the profusion of "screen memories" that had followed the madeleine. True, they had filled six volumes, but he was now hungering for what lay behind the "screen sensations" at Combray. The three sensations all took place within a short space of time, each one contributing to a deepening of experience.

The first sensation—the stepping back on some unevenly cut flagstones—gave rise to the following complex of sensations, as described by Proust.

The feeling of happiness that came over me was exactly the same as I had experienced while eating the madeleine, but there was a purely material difference in the mental images evoked. A deep azure blue intoxicated my sight, impressions of coolness and dazzling light hovered near me, and, in my eagerness to seize them, not daring to move, I stood there swaying back and forth. . . . The dazzling, elusive vision brushed me with its wings, as if to say: "Seize me and try and solve the riddle of happiness." [The screen sensation led almost immediately to two uneven flagstones in the baptistry of St. Mark's in Venice and associated screen memories. Proust, however, rightly asks himself:] Why did the mental images of Combray and Venice give me such joy, certainty and indifference to death?

[A second signal came to reinforce the first. While in the library, a servant struck a spoon against a plate. Once again there was a burst of happiness, sensations of great heat mingled with the odor of smoke and tempered by the cool fragrance of a forest setting. A butler now brings him a small plate of *petits fours* and a glass of orangeade, and then comes the third and final signal—he wipes his mouth with the napkin that had been given him.] Immediately, like the character in the *Arabian Nights* who rubbed the magic lamp, a fresh vision of azure blue passed before my eyes, but this time it was *pure and saline and rounded upward like bluish breasts*. The impression was so vivid that the moment I was re-living fused with the real present. . . . The napkin spread out in its various folds and creases like a peacock's tail, the plumage of a green and blue ocean. I drew enjoyment, not only from those colours, but from a whole moment of my life which had been brought into being. [The screen memories that now crystalized out of this conjured up his previous stay at Balbec.]

[Proust felt sure that the three sensations and the identical pleasures given by them had awakened in him] something that had no relation to what I used to endeavour to recall to mind about Combray, Balbec or Venice with the aid of a colourless, undistinguishing memory. And I understood how one can come to judge life to be mediocre because this disparaging judgment is based on mental images that have retained no trace of life [1928, pp. 992-994].

Why, he asks himself, is the real impression so much more stimulating than the artificial one, and his answer is that the slightest incident in our lives is surrounded and illuminated by things that have no logical relation to it and which we separate from it by our selective intelligence that has no need for them in its secondary-process functions.

The act or object is wrapped around with irrelevant strains of music, feelings of hunger, yearnings for women and enclosed "in a thousand sealed jars each filled with things of an absolutely different colour, odour and temperature," and when the proper sensory signal comes along, the whole synesthetic potpourri is suddenly released. The individual who is fortunate enough to experience these real sensory impressions does so by "identifying the past with the present, and thus finding himself in the only environment in which he could live and enjoy the essence of things." This environment is outside of time and the privileged individual therefore becomes "a timeless person."

If I was to dare the interpretation of such material outside the analytic situation, I would be tempted to take my bearings from the "timeless person" who to me means the young infant. The sequence of events would then suggest to me the earliest feeding situation in which the baby, held by the two unevenly placed arms of the mother, receives the feeding signal—the tinkle of spoon on plate of a later era—and then reaches up for the "bluish breasts," finally to have his mouth wiped with the napkin. This bold viewpoint receives some confirmation from a further remark of Proust's relating to these sensations.

A single minute released from the chronological order of time recreates in us the human being similarly released in order that he may sense that minute. When the sound or the odour of bygone years is sensed anew, simultaneously in the present and the past, the permanent essence of things is immediately set free and our true self, long seemingly dead but not dead in other ways awakes and takes on fresh life as it receives the *celestial nourishment* [1928, p. 996].

In Proust's case, therefore, the screen memories lead chiefly to what appears to be preconscious oedipal content, whereas the screen sensations, after an intermediary stop at the oedipal fixation points, seem to belong to pregenital oral and anal situations.

In addition to becoming "timeless," the individual undergoing these experiences also loses his fear of death, and in Proust's mind the two conditions are intimately connected. How can you fear death when time has ceased to exist? For much of his life, Proust had lived in a constant, irrational fear of death, as a result of which he developed, not a death instinct, but an obsessional regard. I will let him put it in his own words.

The idea of death took up its permanent abode with me as does love for a woman. Not that I loved death. I detested it; but because I had long pondered over it, it adhered to the deepest stratum of my brain so completely that I could not turn my attention to anything else without first relating it to the idea of death. It was with me as continuously as the idea of myself [1928, pp. 1119-1120].

With the first taste of the madeleine, he loses all fear of death as he returns to the ecstasy of the mother-baby symbiosis and the happiness of the mother-child relationship which he had worked so hard to recapture from the dark past. On reliving these glorious sensations with their "timeless joy," he becomes anxious never to lose them again. He saw his brain as a "rich mineral basin where there was a vast area of extremely varied precious deposits" (among them being his preoedipal and oedipal aspirations). He felt himself "pregnant" carrying around this precious, fragile material. Would he, he asked himself, have time to exploit it? A new "rational" fear of death now developed. He regarded his body as a threat to his mind and its now precious contents. A cerebral hemorrhage or an accident could destroy his body and consequently his mind and its memories. He reverted to his earlier mode of life, isolating himself within his

room and pulling down the shutters on the dangers that threatened
him in the outside world.[4]

THE CHARACTERISTIC OF THE NORMAL AND REGRESSED INFANTILE EGO

For the infant in its first few months of life, the world presents
itself in a most bizarre light judging from the empathic experiences
of adult phenomenological psychologists who have attempted to project themselves into the diaper of a baby. It says a great deal for
the strength of the memory traces left during this early phase that
the many accounts given of "what it feels like to be a baby" show
a fair measure of agreement as to what goes on during "the age of
stupor." The growing consensus holds that more goes on than meets
the behaviorist's eye and that the neonate is more than a "midbrain
specimen" even if his cortex is largely nonfunctioning.

The new infant is regarded as an amorphous being without
boundaries; so he is unaware of where he begins and where he ends.
He is said to be at one with the universe about him, technically
"adualistic." His world is made up of "a mosaic of innumerable
sensations," a "chaos of unrelated sensations and unreflective experiences," in the Jamesian phrase, a "booming, buzzing confusion." It
is thought, therefore, to be largely a world of sensations where
objects are fleeting, insubstantial images in a kaleidoscopic state of
flux, and colors are bright and brilliant. Perceptions are subjective,
syncretic, and synesthetic in this primitive universe, and memories
are tied plastically to immediate sensations.

For the psychopathologist, the world of the young infant is at first
predominantly a breast. It fills the eyes and mouth of the infant, and it
forms the background of his perceptions. In relation to it, he goes
through regular cycles of frustration, crying, feeding, satiation, and
sleep. It moves toward him when it comes to feed him, and it moves
away from him when he has had enough. At the moment of sleep,
it is said to fill his world. His mental life is gradually built up on
the basis of these feeding experiences. It is governed by magical feelings of omnipotence and hallucinatory feelings of fulfillment. Rela-

4 "A recapitulation of the entire work which occurs at the end. It closes the circle
of an endlessly repeating fantasy, with lights shining now here, now there, like the
play of insight which comes and goes" (Miller, 1956).

tions are largely subsidiary to these primary concerns, and have therefore been regarded as narcissistic, autistic, and symbiotic, although Balint (1949) speaks of primary love at this stage, and Klein postulates a complex system of object relationships involving part objects. The Isakower (1938) and Lewin (1946) phenomena belong to this period, and this is also where I have located the sensory impressions from which later screen sensations originate.

This is also the type of world to which there is a reversion in states of diminished consciousness, deep therapeutic and schizophrenic regressions, mystic elations, and toxic conditions. The primitive archaic formations of schizophrenia are not unlike those described in the infant. The deeply regressed ego has the same amorphous quality with loss of ego boundaries and loss of identity, the same oceanic feelings, the same autism and symbiosis, and frequently the same types of perceptual and memory defects.

As the ego advances to the three- and four-year-old level, its basic orientation is still highly subjective, and it places itself securely at the center of the universe. Living is largely a matter of the present, and there is minimal concern with yesterday and tomorrow. For the most part, time concepts are poorly developed, and memory has a short span. Perceptions have been described as syncretic and eidetic, and relationships are directed by the state of resolution of the preoedipal and oedipal conflicts. Certain sensations that resemble the primitive archaic formations of the earlier phase can be understood as masturbatory equivalents. Memory has still to become continuous, and fragmentary screen memories are characteristic of the period. *Déjà vu* phenomena are rooted in deep unconscious fantasies belonging to this phase.

The amnesia that covers these first two stages of development can therefore be pierced by screen sensations, screen memories, dissociated memories (suppression of visual or nonvisual components), and decathected memories. Traumatic experiences may extend and thicken the amnesic curtain and cause screening phenomena to proliferate.

The description of screen sensations, given in this paper, indicates that they are closely related to similar experiences undergone by psychotic and mystical individuals. Five components are generally discernible (Fingarette, 1960):

1. A "letting-go" equated with a cessation of defensive striving.
2. Joy, stemming from the sudden availability of energy previously expended in maintaining repressive processes, and from a diminution of anxiety.
3. Feelings of passivity so that the experience is perceived as something being induced by an outside influence.
4. Insight into the content of the experience which may relate to mystical ideas, psychotic misconceptions, or specific fantasies.
5. A sense of oneness arising from which are "oceanic feelings," "numinous primordial feelings," feelings of mystic union, feelings of magical participation and cosmic identification, "ecstatic self-brooding." According to Freud (1930), it represents a regression to the primal unity with the mother when gratification is direct and complete; and according to Lewin (1946), the whole experience is characterized by a feeling of great certainty. Doubt is banished.

The type of individual prone to such experiences also has certain characteristics which might be summed up in the following profile. He is usually a "borderline," isolated or schizoid individual manifesting what Bleuler (1911) has referred to as a "double orientation" by which he meant someone with one foot in reality and the other in fantasy. This gives him access to two worlds of experience simultaneously and accounts for some of the peculiarities of the phenomenon. These people are also hypersensitive in the Bergman-Escalona (1949) sense and respond intensely to the world of sensations. They often remain eidetic into later life. Their special propensity is toward deep and rapid regressions under the influences of such provocations as sleep, analysis, and drugs. Even with deep regressions, however, they tend to retain their "double orientation" to reality. Considered psychodynamically, as a group, these individuals manifest a high degree of orality with fixation points at an early sucking level. From a psychological point of view, they tend to communicate poorly, although their writings indicate good verbal fluency. They are not particularly good at containing strong emotions, and these are likely to overflow at times into psychomotor activities. Their thinking is often highly emotional and subjective with prelogical and magical components.

Kronfeld (1922) has this to say about the "double orientation":

A relaxation of the psychic apparatus in the highest strata of consciousness takes places. Through the hiatuses are thrust up the representations and projections of archaic formations which are driven upward out of the primitive, instinctual life. These elements set up a magical, mythical, prelogical method of objectification, side by side with or overshadowing the real ego which they tend temporarily to overwhelm.

A Note on Technique

At the level of the deep regressions and primitive phenomena described in this paper, the relationship of the patient to the therapist assumes some unusual characteristics. The boundaries separating the two participants in the therapeutic transaction begin to dissolve gradually and lead to a fusion and confusion of feeling and fantasy that arise from the symbiosis established. The problem of relating the primitive experience to the analytic "here-and-now" is considerable. Searles (1960) considers that only a nonhuman mode of participation can allow the early ego states to be re-expressed. At this level, verbal communication is more of a hindrance than a help, and words conduce to feelings of separation and alienation. If speech is used at all, the voice should be kept especially low and soft, and the ideas expressed in the simplest, most concrete form available. During the brooding period prior to the emergence of sensations, the analyst should be as quiet as possible and interrupt as little as he can. Balint (1949) has suggested that he move his chair occasionally, or breathe audibly simply in order to let the patient know that the therapist is there with him. According to him, this warm, comfortable, and friendly silence allows the analyst to merge himself with the early world of his patient and to assume the qualities of a primary object in complete harmony with him. During this period, it is important for the analyst not to function too much as a separate object, making interpretations, or clarifying the thoughts expressed by the patient.

It might be objected that in the case of Lily her prepsychotic status contraindicated the use of the couch. The process of free association, the therapeutic regressions, and the invisibility of the analyst in the rigorous analytic setting have been regarded as "psychotogenic." I would argue in a contrary direction. In these individuals (and I am excluding psychotics from this category) who are isolates with a "double orientation," the analytic position on the couch certainly favors the development of deep regressions, and deep regressions favor the emergence of screen sensations, and it is the analysis of screen sensations that, in my view, helps to avert psychotic developments and brings about the necessary restructuring of the deeper layers of the personality along healthier lines. As in the case of Lily, the classical technique can be introduced only after the energies bound to early fixation points have been to some extent loosened and released. Free associations and the establishment of transference neuroses are not usually possible initially in these individuals, and the situation is aggravated by the fact that they are inclined to be both uncooperative and uncommunicative. All these factors hinder the development of a true analytic situation so that little progress is made until the sensory life of the patient is brought into full awareness, and the focus placed on it. Thereafter, the recognition, reactivation, and re-experiencing of screen sensations within the analytic setting offers a possible mode of approach to a very difficult and problematical analytic situation.

Kurt Eissler (1953) has spoken of "the formidable problem of technique" in dealing with the emotionality of a schizophrenic patient. He, too, has observed the exaggerated response to interoceptive and exteroceptive sensations and at one point comments on the "blissful feelings" engendered by an effortless bowel movement. He has also raised the two most pertinent questions that arise technically in the therapy of such patients. How can one reach such basic ego disturbances by analysis? And how can one establish a working relationship in analysis? He has tried to furnish several possible answers to these problems, and they merit the careful consideration of every therapist working with such borderline states.

According to him, id analysis must be postponed until the ego of the patient is found capable of forming new structures. Indeed, the patient can only be treated if he has preserved the capacity to form structure. The flow of excitation must be replaced by the formation of mechanisms and functions. Primary processes must be transformed into secondary ones, unbound energies into bound ones, and energy itself must be transformed into structure. Full id analysis is postponed, but it is never completely discarded during therapy although at times it may be reduced to an absolute minimum. An id interpretation is always given when the id demand would become unbearable if not verbalized.

During this first phase, therefore, therapy is conducted in a state of minimal frustration and sufficient wish fulfillment. The therapist must walk the tightrope of "not too much and not too little" since the former state would enhance the patient's feelings of unreality, while the latter would conduce to feelings of total rejection. Eissler does not advocate the use of nonverbal techniques during this initial phase. Instead, he suggests that the analyst and patient interchange on a metapsychological level in which descriptions of psychic processes are brought to the patient's attention, not in technical language but in the patient's own vernacular. Finally, he suggests the use of an additional technique similar to the one that is employed with phobic patients in which the patient, having difficulties with experiencing and expressing his feelings, is deliberately exposed to an affective situation that makes demands on his feelings. It is, in essence, an "active" procedure in contrast to the passive, waiting method described by Balint and myself. Eissler's thesis is that in order to analyze a symptom one must "urge the patient to investigate what his world would look like without the respective symptom. To find this out, he must discard the symptom in crucial situations." Such active directives are not incompatible with the technical suggestions put forward here in this paper. At various times, in dealing with Lily, I have had to balance frustration against gratification in a very concrete way, postpone interpretation until the ego has appeared stronger, talked metapsychology in simple, homely terms, and issued active directives of the kind advocated by Eissler. There are times for all these maneuvers, and the analyst, experienced in the treatment of the borderline case, intuitively makes use of the many different methods at his disposal. There is a time for activity and a time for passivity, and in the situations I have described in Lily's case, the time is ripe for passivity, nonverbal communication, and the creation of a quiet environment that is at once timeless and spaceless.

Summary

In summing up what I consider to be the "conditions" that trigger off these "screen sensations," one would include, first and foremost, the state of regression induced by the analytic process in the analytic situation. The depth to which regression attains has a close bearing on the reappearance of early sensations and is related in part to the quality of the transference development and in part to certain inherent characteristics in the patient.

As already mentioned, the analytic situation and the technique of analysis are designed to facilitate the regressive process. Analytic transactions are carried on with as little verbalism as possible so that the patient's perceptual environment becomes his foremost concern. No contact is made between the analyst and the patient, because this would flood the patient with too much feeling and interfere with the autonomous developments within him. Moreover, contact also creates problems of countertransference which interfere with the analyst's full appreciation of his own role in this delicate world of "suspended transference."

I pass next to the qualities that seem characteristic of these patients and which single them out from among a group of other patients. They have an infantile-primitive aspect that makes them appear "childlike" but not childish. Lily's ego ideal, for instance, took the form of St. Francis of Assisi functioning as a young boy or young girl. She had a special feeling for prepubescent children of both sexes who were "fresh and natural" before the biological occurrences contaminated them. These patients are never psychotic in any clinical sense. Their contact with reality remains persistently adequate, but, at the same time, they live on peculiarly familiar terms with the unreal and irrational features of the primary process. (According to Greenacre [1949], creative people such as artists and writers also have this propensity.) Under certain conditions of provocation and pressure, such as are obtained in the analytic situation, they are capable of sudden, swift, and deep, but transient regressions to very primitive levels of feeling and functioning. In their analytic communications, they frequently express unsatisfied yearnings for incorporation. Speech represents "psychological distance" to them, and they are inclined to feel "dead" unless they can move into very close physical contact, allowing them to "melt" and "mold" themselves to another's body. Through such "contact regressions" or through "sensory regressions" such as I have described in this paper, a feeling of "union" is established in which the various ingredients add up to a quasi-mystical state. Frequently, and especially at moments of loneliness which recur often, an intense orality usually manifests itself in a blatant form. Lily had a long sucking history and would frequently suck at her own tongue during her sessions. She never showed any urge to bite.

The earliest maternal image remains brightest and most alluring for these patients. Each subsequent imago betrays more and more the effects of separation and the replacement of blissful symbiosis with ambivalent dependence. The supreme trauma is the birth of a sibling which brings about the rupture of the symbiosis and an intensification of the basic conflict over separation. Outside the symbiotic cocoon, the world is hard and cold and lonely, and the complexities of social intercourse are difficult to initiate and maintain. What can one do with people who live outside oneself? In the symbiotic union, on the other hand, relations are largely governed by sensations stemming from the mouth, the nose, and the skin. One lives in and through another and not merely by the side of another, and if one is not joined indissolubly to another, one is alone and desolate.

There are, however, contrary and more progressive factors also at work. The desire for symbiosis is matched by a fear of submergence implying loss of individuality and identity. The mother here becomes the great threat to the self. In the analytic situation, the two processes are both allowed full expression so that the basic conflict is clearly exposed. With the move toward submergence, the fear of death disappears, and the individual achieves "timelessness" and "spacelessness." With the move toward separation and individuation, the fear of death reappears. The analyst is able to watch this life and death struggle from the vantage point of the transference. Sometimes he appears to be on the side of separation and emerges into the consciousness of the patient as the great separator, the divider of the umbilical bond, the weaner. At other times, he transforms the analytic situation into a great dark cave into which the patient can retreat. He may see himself with increasing predominance as the separator, but, in true analytic fashion, he accepts and works with the image thrust upon him by the patient at any particular time. With sometimes anxious eyes, he watches the movement of regression into the primordial past, acting as the sheet anchor to reality. The surge backwards is more hazardous in these cases than in the normal therapeutic regressions.

I cannot end without expressing sympathy for my second "patient," Marcel Proust. How often, in his self-analysis, did he bemoan the fact that the great moments of re-experiencing the past were so few and far between and that the coming together of the past and the present in the present had to be left largely to chance. This was indeed true for him, but it soon ceased to be true for others like him. Freud was already making his revolutionary discoveries on the use of transference in treatment, so that the bringing together of the past and the present in the present was soon to become the normal experience of every patient in analysis. Proust knew nothing of this, and this was unfortunate for Proust, the patient, but fortunate for the rest of us. With adequate analysis, he could at last have descended into the unconscious toward which he was striving all his life, but in the process we would have lost seven of the most entrancing, autobiographical statements of our time.

POSTSCRIPT

1. Lily's E.E.G. record and neurological examination were quite normal, no evidence being found of any temporal lobe pathology. Her "sensations" were not considered by the neurologist to be indicative of an uncinate attack.

2. A recent doughnut dream indicates to what extent her conflicts are beginning to shift up the psychosexual scale. A man comes down the street in a van, and the patient goes out to him expecting to buy a cake. He tells her he has no cakes now, only meat (frankfurters). She turns away from him in disappointment, but he comes after her, consolingly, and offers her something wrapped in tinfoil. She cannot at first tell what it is, but she takes it on trust. When she unwraps it, she perceives it to be a doughnut but without a hole (different from her other dream doughnuts), together with a straw, but nothing to drink with it. Once again she is disappointed. She feels sorry for the man as she returns the doughnut and offers to have

a frankfurter. Her associations to this were: "I always expect too much and get disappointed. I used to know what I liked, but now I'm doubtful. No one seems to give me exactly what I want, not even you. I feel I'm disappointing you because you expect too much from me. You want to make me have things I don't want. My father's like that. I'll just eat it to please you, but I know that's not what you want."

3. In a recent letter to me, written over the week end: "Spent the week end with S— [boy friend] who is so spontaneously affectionate. I've not been so free with anyone as far back as I can remember. The evening he left I dreamed that he'd been castrated. I felt angry with him, I believe, and then it seems I may have felt a similar anger toward J— [fiancé], but I'm not sure—I'll be very glad to see you again. I feel more attached to you, more fond of you really than I'd noticed before. I feel fonder of my parents also. Daddy bought me such a beautiful Chinese bowl. Shall leave you now, love, Lily."

Appendix

In addition to her greedy sensuous prehension of the world about her and the acute sensory impressions that impinged on her on the occasions described, Lily shared one other propensity with the celebrated French author with whom I have linked her. She suffered from the same overwhelming autobiographical drive. Whenever she had the opportunity, she would retire with her current diary—there were six volumes in existence by the time I met her in therapy—and set down with minute, analytic precision the events of her day, sometimes with startling objectivity and at others suffused with personal feelings. "I live more in my diary than in real life," she wrote on one occasion, adding, "Writing has always been my greatest comfort—my main comfort and enjoyment." These sometimes achieved a real distinction of style, echoing Proust whom she had not read. The almost infantile quality to her perceptions is strikingly shown in the following passage. She is living in Rome with her grandmother, Nana, and she is waiting to have dinner with her and her cousin, Roberto.

I am waiting impatiently for the moment when the meal is ready. Everything comes up together [note the syncretic nature of her experience]—the sight of the food, the sadness I feel at not seeing on the table what I had thought in delight of eating, the

rising from my chair where I had been reading endlessly, eternally, the change from this into movements and thoughts that are
much more concrete and real, into physical actions which require
no contemplation but which come freely and naturally but which
leave us long moments in between for the torturing thought, the
torturing confusion and the torturing frustration, the joys of
feeling the hot, meat-tasting liquid touch the entirety of my
mouth and soothe my body as it flows down, the pleasure of chewing the tasty meat, the "substancy" meat, tough and thick. But
before this, the waiting, the deadly silence; Nana wishing someone would talk, Nana saying uninteresting things just to make
noise, just so that we have meaning in her life; Roberto contemplating his ever-mysterious life experiences; and I perturbed in
heartful, bursting thought. The air doesn't move. The next plate
to come in brings interest into our blankness. The movements
of Conchita, her blue figure removing the plates from the center
of the table and then each of ours one at a time, placing her arm
carefully in front of us in taking hold of our plate and then from
our opposite side putting in place our new dish. The interest in
the food is all that we share together—the new kind of cheese,
the possibility of cake, the thought of how much of each we can
eat, of how much will fit into our bellies, of how much we would
like. And all the time, Nana wishing to take part in our lives
because she has no life of her own now. She lives only in her
memories and past attachments. Her life is made up of little
details and unimportant actions. She has no part to play as a
necessary person except with her family, no goals to acquire. She
lives only in family preoccupations. She cares for Roberto, and
he accepts her care with a vague indifference. I am very different;
I ask for nothing; I take care of myself; and so she becomes angry
with me that I do not confide in her. I once tried to explain my
feelings, but she, like most other people, felt I was wrong in
being as I am; this, of course, prevents me from continuing these
discussions. Only in the last year have I been able to express a
tiny bit of my feelings, and this is all I can give my friends. If
she is against my feelings, I can do nothing more. She should not
try to be my mother who is a special person with a character
fitting into mine. She cannot take part in our lives—Robert's and
mine; it is impossible to share our thoughts and feelings with a
person so far away from our real lives. We can only eat together.

I could match this passage with many in Proust showing the im-
pressionistic detail, the strong orality, the suspension between the
concrete and the abstract, the hint at powerful feelings seething

beneath the apparent vacuity, and the over-all narcissism which says in effect: if you do not realize what I am experiencing, so much the worse for you. It's your loss, not mine.

June 12. I have the annoying sensation that no one appreciates my qualities and that very, very few like me, especially those who may give me courage or be returning my sentiments by liking me. I don't understand what is wrong with me to make others feel so indifferent or negative toward me. I don't know what to do. I feel completely alone.

May 13. I want to walk in the evening; I want to walk; I want to laugh; I want to feel alive and significant even if only for a moment.

May 6. Just realized myself different from others; feel so different from others, so lacking in contact with them; feel as if I live in my own world, watching everyone else like a Judge. But I take no real part in the outside world. I concentrate on personal problems and am still unable to generalize them; I'm unable to liberate myself from the effects of the tiny experiences in my daily life. The effects prevent me from acting normally and spontaneously. These defects are very great; I still can't understand what use I am to others; what parts of myself I could possibly give to another or even what it means to give of oneself. I have so little faith in myself that I can't conceive of another enjoying my company, of not becoming bored with me, of liking me, of being interested in me. This is so true that it even hurts to say it.

July 31. Mom and Albert [her younger brother] are extremely attached, very affectionate toward each other. When they awake, Albert goes into her bed or she into his. (To explain further hurts; I can't go further.) She helps him in his studies, to write in his diary; she plays games with him, gives him advice, conversation, everything possible. John [her older brother] also got the same help from her. I can't remember ever being treated like this. Now, I am annoyed by any showing of affection toward me, and I am disgusted by it toward anyone else. I am fascinated by couples together and tortured by any warmth they show for each other. Any emotion toward me scares me. I am able to feel close only from a distance.

BIBLIOGRAPHY

Aulagne, L. J. (1949), Essai sur le nocturne Proustien. L'insomnie, le sommeil et les rêves dans *A la Recherche du Temps Perdu* [Essay on the Nocturne of Proust. Insomnia, Sleep and Dreams in *Remembrance of Things Past*]. *Psyche* (Paris), IV.

—— (1952), Les fées d'*A la Recherche du Temps Perdu;* introduction aux mythes Proustiens [The Fairies in *Remembrance of Things Past;* Introduction to the Proustian Myths]. *Psyche* (Paris), VII.

Balint, M. (1949), Early Developmental States of the Ego. Primary Object Love. *Int. J. Psa.,* XXX.

Baranger, W. (1952), Depresion, introyeccion y creacion literaria en Marcel Proust [Depression, Introjection and Literary Creation of Marcel Proust]. *Rev. Psicoanal.,* IX.

Bergman, P. & Escalona, S. K. (1949), Unusual Sensitivities in Very Young Children. *This Annual,* III/IV.

Bleuler, E. (1911), *Dementia Praecox or the Group of Schizophrenias.* New York: International Universities Press, 1950.

Blondel, Ch. (1931), Marcel Proust et l'immensité mentale [Marcel Proust and Mental Immensity]. *Rev. Phil.,* LVI.

Boulanger, J. B. (1951), Un cas d'inversion coupable: Marcel Proust [A Case of Culpable Inversion: Marcel Proust]. *Union Médicale du Canada,* LXXX.

Burchell, S. C. (1928), Marcel Proust, an Interpretation of His Life. *Psa. Rev.,* XV.

Bychowski, G. (1932), Marcel Proust als Dichter der psychologischen Analyse [Marcel Proust as Author Using Psychological Analysis]. *Psa. Bewegung,* IV.

—— (1958), Struggle against the Introjects. *Int. J. Psa.,* XXXIX.

Deutsch, F. (1954), Analytic Synesthesiology. *Int. J. Psa.,* XXXV.

Eissler, K. R. (1953), Notes upon the Emotionality of a Schizophrenic Patient and Its Relation to Problems of Technique. *This Annual,* VIII.

Ellis, H. (1935), *From Rousseau to Proust.* Boston: Houghton, Mifflin.

Fenichel, O. (1927), The Economic Function of Screen Memories. *The Collected Papers of Otto Fenichel,* I. New York: Norton.

—— (1939), The Economics of Pseudologia Phantastica. *The Collected Papers of Otto Fenichel,* II. New York: Norton.

Fingarette, H. (1960), The Ego and Mystic Selflessness. In: *Identity and Anxiety,* ed. M. Stein, Glencoe, Ill.: Free Press.

Freud, S. (1899), Screen Memories. *Collected Papers,* V. London: Hogarth Press, 1950.

—— (1901), The Psychopathology of Everyday Life. *Standard Edition,* VI. London: Hogarth Press, 1960.

—— (1914), Recollection, Repetition and Working Through. *Collected Papers,* II. London: Hogarth Press, 1949.

—— (1917), A Childhood Recollection from *Dichtung und Wahrheit. Collected Papers,* IV. London: Hogarth Press, 1949.

—— (1930), *Civilization and Its Discontents.* London: Hogarth Press, 1955.

Glover, E. (1929), The "Screening" Function of Traumatic Memories. *Int. J. Psa.,* X.

Greenacre, P. (1949), A Contribution to the Study of Screen Memories. *This Annual,* III/IV.

Greenson, R. (1958), Screen Defenses, Screen Hunger, and Screen Identity. *J. Am. Psa. Assn.,* VI.

Heider, F. (1941), The Description of the Psychological Environment in the Work of Marcel Proust. In: *On Perception and Event Structure, and the Psychological Environment [Psychological Issues,* I (3), Mon. No. 3]. New York: International Universities Press, 1959.

Henri, V. & Henri, C. (1897), Inquiry into the First Memories of Childhood. *L'Année Psychol.,* III.

Isakower, O. (1938), A Contribution to the Pathopsychology of Phenomena Associated with Falling Asleep. *Int. J. Psa.,* XIX.

Jaensch, E. (1923), *Eidetic Imagery.* London: Routledge & Kegan Paul, 1930.

Kennedy, H. E. (1950), Cover Memories in Formation. *This Annual,* V.

Koffka, K. (1931), *The Growth of the Mind*. Chapter on The Problem of Memory. London: Kegan Paul.

Kronfeld, A. (1922), Über schizophrene Veränderungen des Bewusstseins der Aktivität. *Z. ges. Neurol. Psychiat.*, LXXIV.

Lewin, B. D. (1946), Sleep, the Mouth, and the Dream Screen. *Psa. Quart.*, XV.

Little, M. (1960), On Basic Unity. *Int. J. Psa.*, XLI.

Miller, M. L. (1956), *Nostalgia: A Psychoanalytic Study of Marcel Proust*. Boston: Houghton, Mifflin.

Pickford, R. W. (1944), *Déjà vu* in Proust and Tolstoy. *Int. J. Psa.*, XXV.

Potwin, L. (1901), Study of Early Memories. *Psychol. Rev.*

Proust, M. (1913), *Remembrance of Things Past. Vol. I. Swann's Way*, tr. C. K. Moncrieff. New York: Modern Library, 1928.

—— (1928), *Remembrance of Things Past. Vol. II. The Past Recaptured*, tr. F. Blossom. New York: Modern Library, 1932.

Rapaport, D. (1942), *Emotions and Memory*. New York: International Universities Press, 1950.

Russell, B. (1921), *The Analysis of Mind*. Chapter on Memory. London: Allen & Unwin.

Saul, L. et al. (1956), On Earliest Memories. *Psa. Quart.*, XXV.

Searles, H. F. (1960), *The Nonhuman Environment*. New York: International Universities Press.

Storch, A. (1924), The Primitive Archaic Forms of Inner Experiences and Thought in Schizophrenia. *Nerv. & Ment. Dis. Monogr.*, XXXVI.

Wijsenbeek-Franken, C. (1941), Marcel Proust. *Am. Imago*, II.

Zilboorg, G. (1939), The Discovery of the Oedipus Complex; Episodes from Marcel Proust. *Psa. Quart.*, VIII.

DISCUSSION OF DR. ANTHONY'S PAPER

PAUL KRAMER, M.D. (Chicago)

Dr. Anthony's absorbing and instructive essay contains much interesting material meriting discussion. Time permits me to select only a few points for comment. Not the least of its virtues is to have demonstrated in a remarkably illuminating, lucidly presented clinical report, the importance of the analyst's concern with the sensations of his patient, his sensory awareness in as wide a context as possible. It is true that the subject has been comparatively neglected by the analytic literature, though perhaps not quite as much by analytic practitioners. I was first introduced to this topic almost thirty years ago by August Aichhorn. When the patient's mind was a blank, Aichhorn sometimes suggested to the analysand that he refrain from searching for free associations but instead observe his own bodily reactions, his sensations, and watch them with free-floating attention, observe their changes in character, location, and intensity, and report on his observation at a time of his own choice. This technical device sometimes had surprising results of circumventing resistances, and leading, through an awareness of bodily attitudes and sensations, to deeply repressed material. Concern with sensory experiences is important and fruitful, not only in work with near-psychotic cases like Dr. Anthony's patient Lily, but in the analyst's everyday work with the average neurotic patient as well. On the whole, the analyst will find himself more familiar with "incomplete" screen sensations in which joy is the least constant component. Instead, it is anxiety rather than joy that our patients perceive when they let go of their defenses, and are about to submerge into the realm of passively experienced sensations. Whether or not screen sensations appear within the analytic situation is in part a function of the analytic atmosphere, of the readiness with which the analyst accepts and encourages their emergence. The analyst's misunderstanding may preclude a helpful approach to the patient's sensory world. For instance, the patient's emphatically expressed need to be touched or to touch may be taken to represent only the sexual demand of an erotized transference and interpreted as nothing but that to the patient. The patient's plea not to be left alone when he is about to be overwhelmed by the world of averbal or preverbal sensory experience then goes unheeded.

I am inclined to believe that in every analysis certain pathogenetic material cannot be reached without recourse to the language of the senses rather than words. Different from screen memories, which are always conscious and available to the ego, screen sensations are not, but tend to emerge suddenly, and take the ego by surprise. The clinician's experience indicates that "oral" sensory impressions (smell, taste) may be the earliest and deepest, as well as the most significant for patients of the type described by Dr. Anthony. In the psychoanalyst's daily work, screen experiences of all sensory modalities prove helpful in lifting the childhood amnesia. In one instance, vestibular phenomena lead to the significant early experiences; in another, muscle sensations are important. I have the impression that screen sensations are more readily observable in adolescence, or in the very young adult than at a later age, probably because of reactivation of early conflicts and transitory erosion of the ego at that age. They appear in older patients only after considerable analytic work.

Dr. Anthony mentions certain characteristics of individuals prone to screen sensations. They are said to be borderline, isolated or schizoid individuals; hypersensitive, responding intensely to the world of sensations; given to deep and rapid regression in sleep, analysis, and under drugs; they communicate poorly; contain strong emotions poorly, and these are likely to overflow at times into psychomotor activities. The analytic reconstruction of the childhood histories of such patients showed that these histories had an interesting feature in common. The children seemed to have been able to, or were prevented from, discharging tension in motor activity, either because of an unknown inherent factor, or because of debilitating illness, or because their mothers were peculiarly intolerant of, and disturbed by, even mild degrees of motor activity. Perhaps sensory impressions in these instances become charged with quantities of energy generally used in and discharged through motor activity. Hence the great intensity of the sensory experience, the helplessness of the young ego which is not yet able to master sensory excitation by gaining distance from it in cognitive self-observation, or through verbalization. The excessive cathexis of sensory impressions is perhaps not unlike overcathexis of thought in compulsive neurosis. I do not know whether anything is known about Proust's treatment as a young child in this regard, but it is of interest that he led an existence of almost total physical immobility for half of his life. We know from Lily's mother that "it has taken many spankings to cure her of the disgusting habit of mashing everything on her plate and stuffing her mouth with handfuls of food."

Lily reproaches her mother with keeping her sick to keep her close to her and in order to look after her. Like my patients, the child may have sacrificed ego functions, such as mobility and capacity for motor discharge, in order to safeguard the all-important relationship with the mother. Very much like Lily, my own patients who had an unusual proneness toward the experiencing of screen sensations were engaged in a profound conflict between two powerful wishes— to reunite with the mother and become one with her; and the opposite wish, to establish and protect an independent identity of their own, separate from and in a sense opposed to that of the mother. Gratification of the former is most tempting, yet it is recognized as a threat to the ego's very existence. Complete gratification of the latter means separation from the mother, without whom the child believes himself unable to survive. There is nothing uncommon about this practically universal conflict, yet it is unusually severe and disabling in these cases. Dr. Anthony quotes Proust as saying that "so seductive is the moment of sensation [the illusionary union with the mother] that it threatens to overwhelm his sense of reality [the ego]. The former always won but it was the vanquished that seemed the more beautiful." There is an everlasting struggle to find a compromise, a solution, never successful, with the result of crippling impairment of all areas and functions of the personality. In exceptional and unique individuals with great endowment, it colors, but does not "explain," their artistic creativity—Proust, Kafka, and others. In a few fortunate instances, the conflict brings the person to the analyst. But in most, less fortunate, persons, it ends at best in a severely limited, distorted existence, at times in psychosis or suicide.

Dr. Anthony's description of Lily's problems clearly indicates this struggle and its many manifestations in the transference. None, to my mind, is more striking than the episode of the "eating session." Lily wanted Dr. Anthony to eat the cookie she had brought as proof that he was accepting her, that something of her—we may add, *in lieu* of herself (her whole self)—would have gotten right into him. This certainly sounds like the ideal oral reunion with the mother, a complete fusion. I wonder, though, whether the act of feeding the analyst is not also an attempt to accomplish the opposite, to assert a degree of independence from him. I should like to remind you of a common observation of an infant between one and two being fed. The average infant will be observed to engage in a characteristic activity in addition to taking his food. To speak with the mother's terms, he makes a mess of his food, and, in addition, he often makes clumsy but determined and persistent attempts to stuff the food in *her* mouth, which endeavor, when successful—perhaps with her aid— elicits an expression of triumphant satisfaction. I do not know whether this behavior has been interpreted by others as I should like to interpret it, as one of the earliest efforts at establishing the child's identity separate from his mother. There is a display of pur- poseful activity where only passivity was present before, a self-asser- tive action which antedates and later overlaps with the "no" stage in the child's development, which was viewed by Anna Freud as an early declaration of independence from the mother. This negativism, she says, is the only way a child of two has at his disposal to express self-assertion. I believe it rather likely that Lily, in the single action of bringing the pastry to feed her analyst, demonstrated to him both the wish to merge with him and the wish to become free and "grow up." The analyst's refusal to accept the offering is at first perceived as a rejection of her desire to come close to him, but a little later she expresses the thought: "I want to do without you as I'm doing with- out my mother." The "no" phase is perhaps reflected in the stage of analysis culminating in her remark, "Just sit there and say nothing," and the uncompromisingly fierce and primitive nature of the conflict between the contradictory wishes is mirrored by the dream: "My mother tries to overpower me, and I took an axe and cut her head off."

It hardly needs to be emphasized that the treatment of patients like Lily makes particular demands on the analyst's technical proficiency. In their treatment, the practice of psychoanalysis is more than ever called upon to become an art in which the analyst has to rely on the sum total of his analytic and his life experience, on his knowledge and his intuition, his mind and his heart. It matters relatively little whether Lily was reclining on the couch or sitting up on it or in a chair, or in what particular way the analyst indicates his presence to the deeply regressed patient. What mattered was Dr. Anthony's understanding of the meaning of her lying still or sitting up, and his capacity to tolerate her needs and anxieties, the "room becoming very quiet," and to respond to them properly.

It was a pleasure to read and to comment on this stimulating and original presentation. In his report on Lily, Dr. Anthony has succeeded in transmitting to us some of the rather special satisfaction of discovery, of observing the appearance of insight and resolution of conflict, that provide the rare rewards of the analyst's work.

SOME ASPECTS OF TRANSFERENCE RESISTANCE IN PREPUBERTY[1]

SYLVIA BRODY, PH.D. (New York)[2]

From a theoretical standpoint, major resistances in analysis should be explainable for the child in the same way that they are for the adult. It is true that those resistances that stem from the analytic position and from the compulsion to repeat are alike for both child and adult; yet to dwell on these major similarities is to blur certain vital distinctions between resistances that are integral to different states of maturity, to childhood and adulthood. For even among those resistances that are alike for both child and adult, there are special qualities in the resistances of children that arise from their very childishness, and which demand special technical measures and theoretical considerations. It is with the latter problems that I shall deal in this paper.

The child consciously assumes a right to withhold information, to deny conflict, and to invite the analyst to act out with him; and it is usual for him to respond to interpretive remarks with deliberate plans to speak, hear, and see nothing in the analytic setting. These childlike and phase-specific resistances present technically difficult but relatively minor problems. The major problems, as is known, come from the child's uneven mastery of instinctual drive derivatives, uneven maturity of ego functions, and not yet moderated superego demands (Bornstein, 1945; A. Freud, 1926). And dominating the child's entire behavior, there is his narcissism: often it appears as if the child perceives a relationship between conflict and character, and feels obliged to defend rather than to permit analysis of his defenses. That is to say, he senses that interpretation will disturb

---

1 Somewhat different versions of this paper were read before the American Psychoanalytic Association in December, 1960, as part of a panel discussion of Resistance in Child Analysis, and before the New York Psychoanalytic Society in June, 1961.
2 Pediatric Psychiatry Service, Lenox Hill Hospital, New York.

his ego-syntonic orientation. To these internal difficulties, which partially appear as well in adults with infantile personalities, there is added the child's closeness to the real persons of the infantile period, toward whom he is liable to turn back for even a questionable safety, or whom he may influence to act out with him, when the insight offered by the analyst is too disagreeable. All of these normal characteristics of the child contribute to his limited capacity to develop a full transference neurosis. Were it not that we ascribe the paucity of transference developments in the child to maturational factors, we should regard it as marking a resistance in itself.

The analysis of the adult becomes a profoundly affecting experience, and usually a therapeutically effective one, because of the transference neurosis, its immediacy and vividness in the living present, its revival of abnormally directed drives, and the palpable resistances against their recognition and dissolution. The child in analysis must undergo a similarly affecting experience. Once he has attained enough psychic development to be capable of being analyzed, and to be neurotic enough to require it, he, like the adult, will have repressed infantile conflicts, and they will have to be revived in the analysis; although, unlike most adults, he can then still direct the drive derivatives back to original objects. The spotty transference phenomena of the child therefore do not simplify, but actually complicate his analysis. They hinder our knowledge about his unconscious life, despite the opportunities for inferences about it which the child's parents may give us when they bring their observations of the child to us.

Just because of the crucial role of transference resistance in classic analysis, it seems useful to consider whether we have not discounted too readily the significance of transference neurosis in children, or relied too little on its appearance. A few authors (Fraiberg, 1951; A. Freud, 1926; Kut, 1953; Waelder-Hall, 1946) have described transference phenomena that mounted to full neurotic proportions for vital periods within a child's analysis, and of course many have reported their transient appearance among children. But impressed as we are with the child's *resistance to transference,* it is possible that in the broader majority of cases we have given too limited attention to the manifestations of transference resistance that do occur in the analyses of children. As childhood is composed of succeeding levels of psychic development, it is at least reasonable to look for changes in the capacity for transference at those different levels, and to try to distinguish any of its phase-specific characteristics.

With these considerations in mind, I shall first comment upon the child's mode of communication in analysis and upon the vicissitudes of this mode in prepuberty. I shall then illustrate and discuss the proposition that a phase-determined resistance of the child who is in or near prepuberty is to be found in the child's struggle to ward off the transference neurosis which threatens to emerge during that period.[3]

In the analysis of a child we do not invoke the analytic rule, knowing that the child cannot allow himself the kind of regression that free association requires (Bornstein, 1951), but we do encourage him to speak as freely as he can, explaining that we will be interested in whatever he can tell us about himself, his ideas, feelings, activities. We make it possible for him to communicate his passing thoughts and feelings with the help of his imagination, and to demonstrate in play[4] that which, if verbalized, might confuse or frighten him. As he plays he displaces his conflict from reality to make-believe; he recreates the conflict at a distance. Then we can talk with him about

[3] Many kinds of transference phenomena are evoked in a child analysis, of course. I deal here with only one aspect of transference, that of resistance during prepuberty. As Dr. Margaret Mahler has properly emphasized (in her discussion of this paper at the meeting of the New York Psychoanalytic Society), in child analysis a greater degree of positive transference must be maintained continuously, without interpretation, than in the case of adult analysis. The positive transference is as useful with the child as with the adult, since it is the medium through which the analyst can most effectively influence the patient, probably through partial identifications (Axelrad and Maury, 1951) or through the revival of earlier libidinal ties, toward that ego strength which is necessary to bear analysis. However, whereas positive transference in the adult must be interpreted if it carries resistance, in child analysis the relatively complete interpretation of positive transference and of the resistance it contains is not nearly so feasible. In the absence of positive transference the child would terminate treatment, physically or psychically. The analyzable adult can keep a positive relationship to the analyst even in the presence of negative transference. Not so the analyzable child. According to my experience, most children are not capable of sustaining motivation for treatment in any prolonged absence of positive transference. It is as if the child's therapeutic alliance depends upon it. The unresolved resistances that it holds for the child may constitute one of the permanent barriers which can work against the completeness of his analysis; and those residual resistances may in part determine the need for further analysis, during adulthood, of persons who have been analyzed as children.

[4] Play is meant here to include dramatizations and structured use of games, toys, or creative media, in which conscious or unconscious fantasy is expressed.

the characters in his play world, involving ourselves in their emotions
and actions, and interpreting them on an imaginary level until the
child becomes aware that those feelings or impulses or the defenses
against them are true even for him. The child's ability to speak to
the accompaniment of or through play is determined by and varies
with his state of maturity, and with the degree and type of his neurosis. But he plays because he must, and not only to avoid thinking
or speaking.[5] Perhaps it is an advantage that he does not understand
the analyst's use of play in analysis. What he cannot know, of course,
is that his play furnishes both the immediacy and the possibility for
objectification that transference factors may serve in the analysis of
the older child or adult.

Freud (1908) remarks that the opposite of play is not what is
serious but what is real, and that although the child invests his play
world with a great deal of emotion he distinguishes it quite well
from reality. In the present context it may be added that often the
prelatency and the latency child make that distinction too readily,
too forcefully. This is one of the reasons why he cannot tolerate our
interpretations of the unconscious fantasies that fashion his imaginative play. He does not care to consider how close the themes of his
play truly are to his own psychological reality, and if we urge him to,
we risk a disturbance in the development of his sublimations (Bornstein, 1945).

There are further differences for the analytic situation between
the activity of the younger child, up to the height of latency, and
that of the older child, nearing or in prepuberty. The older child
may still write poems or stories, although he is now more concerned
with form than he used to be; he may still draw, but whereas formerly he represented whole objects—people, places, animals—and
imbued them with story or fantasy, now to the extent that he draws
those objects he does so with greater concern for realism. More and
more, especially among boys, drawings at this period tend to obscure
emotional content. They rather illustrate mechanical designs, or
schematics for private engineering projects, or complicated maps. As
latency ends, the child frankly sets aside imaginative play in the

---

[5] An eight-year-old, having asked me why I had playthings in the room if I
expected children to talk with me, reflected, and answered himself, "I see! You couldn't
say to a child, 'Don't play.'"

presence of the analyst. An eleven-year-old, referring to his former play, said with chagrin, "I realize now that it must have portrayed my emotions." He felt he had revealed too much. The prepuberty child, having become more dedicated to reality, begins to interest himself in, and many times deliberately tries to follow, the basic rule and to associate freely.

For the prepuberty child, to play freely in the presence of the adult is to run the danger of exposing sexual and emotional excitement, which the child of this age may fear as much as the younger child fears a return to primary-process thinking (Bornstein, 1951). The prepuberty child senses that play can evoke that infantile part of his nature which consciously he wishes to repudiate. The character of the analytic situation, which demands the analyst's continuous observation, and in which the typical prepuberty child can neither play out fantasy nor associate freely, brings him into a direct confrontation with his emotional attachment to the analyst. This he dislikes to acknowledge. In the attempt to avoid strong positive or negative declarations of that attachment, he seeks to do something, to interpose something, between himself and the analyst.

The main way to overcome this avoidance is that of interpretation. Yet however tactfully interpretation is offered, it makes for more difficulties with children of all ages than with adults because, as indicated above, of the essentially narcissistic investment of the child's defenses. The prepuberty child may have developed an adequate degree of that intelligent distance from his own conflicts and from the analytic process itself, to understand interpretation; even his striking advance in vocabulary, and so in abstract thinking, would seem to enhance his capacity to make use of interpretation; but he is, as I have said, more apt than the younger child to curb his emotional response to the analyst, and so to minimize the impact of interpretation.

The child in prepuberty can gradually become free enough to tell about current, and even past affairs, with more or less detail and distortion, and to accept painful and repeated interpretations, as long as he can move about the room at will, giving a part of his energies to some physical activity that serves as an end in itself and is not organized in any conscious activity. It may be assumed that this physical activity contains a discharge equivalent of play. It may be

enough for him to keep himself occupied in small "aimless" actions
while he talks or listens, such as in handling some coins, magnets, or
other gadgets; sometimes he has to keep pounding a pillow or tossing
a ball; and often he has only to keep his body in continuous movement—lying on the floor, under the couch, doing gymnastic tricks,
or following paper airplanes into the farthest boundaries of the room.
The defensive nature of these maneuvers is illustrated by the quickness with which the child turns to physical movement when he is
affected by an interpretive remark, and by the greater degree of such
movement in boys than in girls. These observations are supported
by H. Deutsch's description (1944) of the prepuberty child,[6] where
she stresses the "thrust of activity" occurring in both sexes. It "represents not an increase of aggression . . . but an intensive process of
adaptation to reality and of mastery of the environment made possible by the development of the ego," and it in turn accelerates ego
development. Blos (1958) has also described the increase of diffuse
motility and the resurgence of pregenital aims and activities of the
preadolescent boy; the preadolescent girl he pictures as a young
Diana, "roaming through the wilderness with a pack of hounds,"
aggressively defending herself against the backward pull to the preoedipal mother. Analytic observations coincide with teachers' observations of children of junior high school age, who in good or bad
humor enjoy teasing, challenging, and provoking actions, and who
seem boundlessly noisy and energetic. For children of this age, to
maintain the kind of decorum that adults expect of them is almost
like agreeing to a reduction of their narcissism.

I should like now to make use of material from the case of a girl
who came for analysis shortly before her tenth birthday. I shall then
discuss the following questions: (1) Did a transference neurosis develop in prepuberty to such an extent that its working through was
sufficient for the lifting of repression? (2) Did the patient's attempts
to avoid transference in itself reflect transference resistance? (3) On a
more general level: are there developmental factors in prepuberty
that facilitate transference neurosis and affect the capacity for working through?

    [6] Derived from the analyses of adult women and from interviews with girls of
college age.

CASE PRESENTATION

Sara, the eldest of four sisters born over a period of eight years, came for treatment willingly. She agreed with her parents' description of her as being lazy, dawdling, and irresponsible. They emphasized how she craved continual help and attention from her mother, sulked when these were not forthcoming, and got into such bad moods that the mother, out of her own neurotic needs, felt required to apologize to Sara. Their quarrels then had to be patched up with long, intimate talks, in which the mother urged Sara to tell all her feelings. To these problems Sara added that she had fears at night, of which she had never told her parents, wishing not to upset *them*. But her main complaint was that she felt she was bad. Her symptoms and attitudes suggested the beginnings of depressive states, and a masochistic character formation.

Sara's mother was an impressive figure: tall, beautiful, highly intelligent, slow of movement, and a compulsive talker. In contrast to this majestic appearance, she was severely depressed, quite unable to manage her household and four children, and functioning adequately in only a few areas outside her home. She boasted of her freedom from sexual prudery and of her love of babies. Sara's father was more active and competent but much influenced by his wife's zest for social occupations outside the home.

Sara had been a strikingly beautiful and well-developed infant and young child. Her mother had attended to all of her care with enthusiasm, and Sara had won an uncommon amount of admiration from many adults. Much of this was the result of her very superior language development (her intelligence quotient, measured at age nine, was 170).

The Known Pathogenic Factors in Her History

In her first three years there was probably excessive social stimulation: oral and anal experiences that were made especially exciting in accordance with the mother's delighted preoccupation with all of the infant's body functions; ample exposure to primal scenes; and intense curiosity about childbirth and the male genital, stimulated by the frequent nudity of the mother and grandfather. In Sara's third year, and again in her sixth year, when her first two sisters were born, she was thrust into a too adult position in the family. Up to her seventh year, narcissistic fantasies and activities, augmented by an assumption of the maternal role, were encouraged and rewarded by the mother. At nursery school Sara's social contacts with the children were very poor; she did not play at all, and talked so much and at such an advanced level that no child could relate to her. In her sixth and seventh years, a series of events having to do with death, with the loss of the mother's attendance upon her, and with some sexual arousal and disappointment by the father, precipitated Sara's neurosis. Further precipitating factors were the intrusion of the first sister, Jane, into Sara's relationship with her father; and a year later, the birth of the third sister. Between the ages of six and eight, therefore, confrontation with reality factors forced a reduction of her narcissistic gratifications—mainly related to her conviction that she was already an adult. What was traumatic was the suddenness of the reduction. Her identification with the mother's adoration of babies was retained, but as her oedipal frustrations were attributed by her to the mother's aggressions, Sara's identification with the mother took on an aggressive coloring. The aggression found more than a single outlet: it was turned against her mother, against herself, and against her sister Jane, whom she treated abjectly. The faulty image of her mother was introjected; there was a lowering of self-esteem; and regressive behavior set in, along with unsteady reaction formations. The typical sublimations of the latency period lost their attractiveness. Neurotic and character symptoms appeared: Sara's schoolwork was sloppy and inadequate; she was tense, irritable, sluggish, dispirited, and almost friendless; she felt in danger of impulsive action; and she suffered from nocturnal fears.

I shall present (1) a summary of her actual conduct in her sessions, and (2) a summary of the analytic material relevant to the form of the transference resistance.

Her Conduct in the Analysis

From the beginning Sara was most eager to talk about herself; yet noting that playthings were available, for a time she tried to make use of the simplest games, and then took up a few constructive activities such as would ordinarily be gratifying in themselves—

designing doll clothing, drawing pictures of animals, and amusing herself with the discovery of arithmetic relationships on a remarkably advanced level. Interest in all these productions soon flagged. They all ended up in the wastebasket, and Sara would lay her head down upon the table, to rest. She appeared not to value physical or playful activity as a means of avoiding contact with me—consciously she had no wish to avoid a relationship with me. Rather, she directly sought to have a party with me in each hour, bringing cakes and fruits for us to enjoy together while she chatted all about her family and family friends.

Best of all, she liked to lie prone upon the couch, facing me, and to talk. It was a special problem that by the age of eleven she had read a popular book and some articles about psychoanalysis; one result was that she soon decided to try free association. The trouble was that as soon as she did try to lie supine, or on her side, she felt the need for a blanket so she could curl up and fall asleep. She was also hindered by a great restlessness that made it impossible for her to lie still.[7] She would keep flinging her body about, ostensibly in order to adjust her dress, shoes, socks, belt, her hair, her body positions; or if she again tried to remain prone, she kicked up her legs ceaselessly; but none of these continuously interchanging activities stopped her from keeping an eye on me, bent, as became clear, upon observing my reactions and guessing my thoughts. With these activities she maintained a mild elation. However, when I offered an interpretation that was displeasing, she would hide her face, curl up on the couch, brood on my remarks, and finally plead for sympathy. When she failed to get it she was tormented by feelings of being bad and hopeless.

For almost three years, her physical activity continued to reflect her efforts to ward off general anxiety as well as unconscious fears of masturbatory impulses, in particular. The visual concentration upon me represented, and was acknowledged to be, a conscious wish to divert our attention away from her verbalizations. Finally, after she had gained some understanding of how her fulsome speech brought

[7] Berta Bornstein once reported about a ten-year-old who asked if he might try to lie on the couch and speak his thoughts. She agreed he might try. On the couch, he was surprised to find he had no thoughts—only a certain tune kept going through his head. The tune was, "Don't Fence Me In"; which clearly illustrated the strain that the adult position in analysis would be for a child of this age.

secondary gains, she decided to lie supine and try free association in earnest. Beginning at age thirteen, she voluntarily struggled with the basic rule in an adult manner, although there were of course many times when she sat up and tackled specific issues in the manner of an adolescent.

The Analytic Material

Sara began her analysis with direct reporting about her dislike of any kind of change, her love of nature, her plan to be a veterinarian, and the probability of marriage to a current boy friend. That information out of the way, she embarked upon a process of mourning for the loss of her mother's care. So many things were changing in her life: she had to take care of herself, had to sit before the television set alone, and even had to come to tell me, a stranger, about her feelings. Her clothes, too—just like mother—were now family possessions, hers only until the next sister needed them. Her teacher was negligent also, and let her get by without working—a good teacher would supervise and help her in the same way that mother used to dress, feed, and talk with her; maybe then Sara would learn to be more responsible. Mother was asking too much, too suddenly! Dreamily she would muse about her sweet mommy and their former happy days together. If only she could be a "mommy miser," and be carried in mommy's arms again! At the same time, she yearned to have many babies of her own. She did care for many neighborhood cats, and for all manner of pets in her own home. It is noteworthy that her passionate interest in baby animals and how they are born was matched by a disavowal of interest in sexual activity of any kind.[8] The fact that I could remind her of numerous sexual escapades with men and boys, beginning at age four, did not shake her thoroughgoing denial of sexual curiosity.

As may be expected, outside of analysis Sara's interest lay chiefly in trying to maintain status. At school she was outraged by any sign that a classmate might be favored by the teacher, and she suffered from a lack of popularity, but she warded off her feelings of humiliation by successful manipulations of both teachers and classmates,

---

8 The animals' mating was of no significance to her—just the babies. This became comprehensible years later, when Sara recalled an infantile fantasy that babies came out (are born) whenever the mother wants them to.

and bragged about these to me with a studied carelessness. Outside of school, in safe public places, she initiated conversations with strangers and was flirtatious with men, to whose harmless overtures she would then respond haughtily, like a patrician lady; and then she would recount to me how smartly she had put them in their places. When I summed up her manipulative behavior by calling her a "child manager" she was a little abashed, but mostly proud.

A preliminary interpretation to her of the foregoing material was that she wished to hold me a captive listener, enthralled with the flow of her language and the maturity of her knowledge of adults and their foibles. This interpretation was a serious blow to her narcissism. Greatly vexed, she strove not to get angry with me. She dared not insult me back, for without someone who could share her private excitements and her secrets she would feel lost. My transference interpretation that if I took her mother's place in being impressed by her, she would be saved from becoming aware of her disappointment in and anger toward her mother, gave her pause: for how could she ever be angry with her sweet mommy? *Nobody* in her family *ever* was angry with *anybody!* It was impossible—yet if I said so it must be true. Noting her immediate surrender to me, she added, "I give in so I don't have to be afraid of monsters at night. I'll just give in to dying. I don't want to fight about anything."

This resignation was the end product of infantile conflicts which were partly reconstructed from a group of fantasies that had appeared consecutively between the ages of three and seven. There were four main fantasies, and each lasted for a period of months:

1. At age three, Sara would stand at the window and have conversations with an imaginary neighbor who was always announcing the birth of yet another baby, for which Sara repeatedly congratulated her. The neighbor's name contained Sara's initials.

2. At age five, when her mother was twenty-nine years old and had two children, and her father was a sergeant in the United States Army, Sara pretended that she was a woman of thirty-nine, had three children, and was married to a four-star general of the British Army, with an aristocratic name.

3. At age six, Sara played out a phallic fantasy employing her sister Jane, in which Jane was a horse named Janie and Sara was

the gallant masculine rider. Dramatic rescues of young women by strong men on horseback provided the repetitive theme.

4. At age seven, elaborating upon an earlier Cinderella fantasy, Sara made believe she lived in Gold City (*gold* was part of the name of a much-admired grandmother). The houses there were made of gold plus some copper, gold being so expensive. Only ladies lived there, and as they were all friendly they gave their extra clothing away to a central collection from which any one of them was at all times free to choose whatever she liked. Houses were also interchangeable, via specific arrangements, not in the casual manner of the community garbage collection, or grab bag. In Gold City there was no such thing as rent or eviction, and all the ladies had gold cars. Other gold was hidden in the garbage.[9]

No men were there, although a man might sometimes be adopted in marriage by a woman who had resided in Gold City for ten years. There was, however, a Society for the Prevention of Cruelty to Men on the outskirts of town, and it provided five men, to collect garbage, or just to have nearby in case of need. Once there was an invasion of men into Gold City, so the women gave them something to satisfy them and sent them off. The women, having no army or navy to fight with, held a discussion as to whether women should be armed, and decided no, better play dumb and pretend that the houses are worth nothing. Or, if the men insisted on invading and robbing, the women would just show the men the incinerator and then push them in, as Gretel did the witch. Or they could figure out which men were coming to invade, and attack them where they were weak. The men who came to Gold City, Sara explained later on, were something like aphids, which have to be plucked off flowers and destroyed.[10]

These fantasies tell of Sara's competitive identification with her mother, the subsequent turn to her father, the oedipal disappointment, and finally a compromise sought in a vengeful turning from the father along with a regressive return to the mother, with renewed emphasis on anal and phallic restitutions from the mother. The

9 Sara lived in a kibbutz for about two years in early latency. Many aspects of Gold City could be traced to her experiences there.

10 Such clear, rich, and consecutive fantasies are not usually reported in a child analysis.

regression, and the conflict attendant upon it, were demonstrated in the positive transference resistance that became subject for interpretation. The interpretation led to a few dynamic shifts: Sara recognized her identifications with both the hypomanic and the depressive sides of her mother's personality, and her own wish that analysis should make her a good and compliant girl again. Impelled by the anxiety these insights aroused, she vowed to improve her behavior at home and at school, and to some extent she actually did so. At the same time, her preoccupations with baby animals and with the management of adults lost some of their intensity, and she slowly relinquished her fantasy that life would be perfect if she could run away to the country, have summer always and enjoy nature freely. Sara accepted my interpretation in such a way that she still remained safely within a state of passive compliance, which unconsciously she wished to prolong. She of course knew nothing yet of her oedipal demands and of the penis envy that were hidden by the regressive compromise.

The content of the analysis soon revolved about three themes related to her mother, her father, and herself. The first centered about a fantasy in which her mother was beaten up by intruders and left helpless until Sara and her father drove home to the rescue (cf. the rescue fantasy at age six). This fantasy swept Sara into a struggle against becoming aware of her dismay and her resentment regarding her mother's neglect of home and children. She tried desperately to rekindle her old love for her mother with memories of being cuddled, and of telling secrets and anticipating her mother's reciprocal confidences about sexual activities with her father. She recalled how she had helped her mother take care of Jane; how she had wished that mommy would get into the carriage and let Sara be the mother, proudly wheeling the carriage along. But then she also had to recall the days, in early latency, when she had felt bewildered and pained upon being faced with the fact that she, Sara, was her mother's *child*, and that mother was the real manager of her children—then Sara had felt obliged to treat Jane roughly. Nothing in her whole analysis up to this time gave Sara so much distress as my reminder that she and Jane belonged to the same generation. This was an insult she could not forgive; it was true, but something I should not have uttered.

Before Sara had reached her twelfth birthday she felt quietly convinced that her mother did not love her any more. Her rage about this was still displaced, mainly to teachers and to her sister, Jane. Sara could not recognize the isolation behind this, but she was impressed by repeatedly experiencing the fantasy that her mother was beaten up. (The belief that her mother no longer loved her was not a projection. The mother, partly in envy of Sara's attachment to me, had quite lost interest in reporting to me about Sara; and Sara's father had been informing me that his wife was greatly threatened by Sara's growing independence, had turned sharply away from her, and was devoting herself almost exclusively to the younger children.)

The second theme appeared in several dreams which revealed the fantasy that the father's value as a love object had increased, but that he was regarded as an awesome substitute for a prior love object whose permission had to be granted before Sara could aspire to gaining his favor. Much later I saw that Sara had unconsciously perceived aright: her mother really did speak of husbands as convenient sources of pleasure, and did often boast to Sara of her enormous sexual enjoyment, not too subtly encouraging her to follow suit. As this material developed, Sara began to appreciate her father not only as a jolly comrade but as a masterful person who would not yield easily to her blandishments.

The third theme was Sara's rising discontent with her slow breast development, and her fear that Jane would begin to menstruate before she did.

Throughout these unhappy days of disappointment with and grudge against her mother, longing for her father, and anxiety about her own sexual maturation, the transference resistance was developing. Having observed that I did not overlook her parents' grave lack of attention to even the physical needs of the children, Sara worked diligently to show me, by regular reports of their latest faults, how much they were to be condemned. She wished, of course, to repeat with me the bygone talks with her mother, the mother herself now being the main subject of her gossip. The mother was, in fact, referred to like a naughty child whose behavior had to be reviewed, judged, and reprehended. As a result of these reports, Sara became less unhappy and less anxious. She talked much and rapidly about daily events, about her astute treatment of boys, and her own sexual sophistication. She condescended to stop for comments or questions from me, and then apologized excessively for not really having listened, for having actually only waited for me to finish so she could resume her monologue. Often she tried to anticipate an interpretation that she thought was in the offing—she understood so well how an analyst has to listen to and observe a patient! She tendered her approval of my techniques as if I were, truly, in the baby carriage that she was wheeling along, and I had to listen passively and in bewilderment to the flurry of her chatter with all the people whom she met along the way and who did not even notice my existence. Certainly she was not in the carriage—in using the couch she merely took advantage of my equipment to run the analysis.

Much of this material, delivered in a joyful mood, was based upon a positive transference. Yet it was not purely positive: her condescension shone through, and it was the negative feeling behind that condescension that was interpreted: she was expressing toward me the scorn and the arrogance that she had felt toward her mother, in defense against the pain of her position as a little girl who could not change places with her mother. This interpretation bore fruit: it aggravated her patronizing attitudes toward me and increased her boasts of the character assassinations she perpetrated at school. She saw to it that certain boys got punished for her misdeeds, and by the man teacher, so making a fool of him as well. She told the mother of the smartest boy untrue stories of his bad conduct. These aggressions hid an entirely unvoiced current rage against her mother, for the boys whom Sara attacked had all been accepted at special high schools, while she, having been persuaded by her mother that study for entrance examinations was unnecessary, had been rejected. Insight into the displacement of her anger yielded further complaints about her femininity, complaints very hard for her to recognize, as she had always felt a profound preference for the female of all animals, birds, and even fish.

The onset of menses, when Sara was thirteen and a half, increased her defensive elatedness. She stopped worrying about her small breasts and about the sexual maturity of classmates more advanced than she. Menstruation was a nuisance, it was true, but typically Sara rather dwelt on the imminent dangers of pregnancy she now naturally faced. The following weeks were devoted entirely to the elaboration of most intense resistances. Sara would bounce into the room with a marvelously carefree manner, and would rattle on in language restricted to jargon and cliché, seldom addressing me directly. She was the worldly woman, reeling off clever opinions about teen-agers to someone whose reactions were of no consequence, anyway.[11]

The interpretation of this transference resistance, in which Sara tried to re-experience with me the oedipal strivings of her past, had to be reiterated on many levels for many months. In the process of working it through, Sara was confronted by her instinctual conflicts, and her analysis moved into its next phase, beyond prepuberty.

DISCUSSION

I shall now return to the questions raised above, regarding the extent to which the transference neurosis developed, the presence of transference resistance, and the more general question of developmental factors in prepuberty that may promote transference neurosis.

The Transference Neurosis, the Working Through,
and the Lifting of Repression

In the beginning Sara had tried to build up an intimacy with me, repeating attenuated wishes that formerly had been directed primarily to the mother. Here was a transference phenomenon such as is usually observable in younger children as well, in that it only brought current history into the analytic hour, and represented the employment of positive transference resistance. Its interpretation led to some symptomatic changes: a reduced demand upon the mother and mother substitutes, and more inner disturbance about her own passivity. As her positive attachment still grew, Sara became light-hearted during her hours; her bad moods lifted as she interested herself in my techniques and in psychoanalysis. She applied herself to schoolwork with explicit intentions of gaining my approval. She also praised my possessions, my brilliance, and my husband, whom—in line with her childhood fantasy—she believed to be British. She was avidly curious about and flirtatious toward

[11] The fact that she did not menstruate a second time until six months after menarche contributed significantly to her defensive high spirits.

any workman she saw in my apartment or in my building, and made sure to let me know how cleverly she had handled them. She wished thus to identify with the overestimated preoedipal mother, and to compete with the oedipal mother, and she anticipated gratification on both levels. Her narcissism was such that she responded to painful interpretations of her positive transference as resistance by falling into a mood of hopelessness and self-accusation, just as she had done with her mother before analysis began. If I understood something ahead of her or was not impressed with her recitals or questioned any piece of her behavior outside the hour, she felt reminded of being an awkward child, excluded from the world of adults. As a little child she had felt herself to be a participant observer of that world. The narcissistic injury at being cast out from her mother's domain was worked through to a considerable extent during the period of positive transference, which corresponded to the years of intimacy with her mother.

When her status as a child and as a girl became harder to deny, Sara reacted with hypomanic defenses. The role of "child manager" was effectively related in analysis to the humiliation she had felt in her exclusion from parental sexual activity, beginning in her third year. As this humiliation was re-experienced, more symptomatic improvements occurred: her nocturnal fears and her sibling rivalry decreased markedly, and social and academic progress was conspicuously increased. And during these changes Sara's competitive, boastful relationship to me flourished and so led us to the interpretation of a severe transference resistance. The interpretation forced Sara to recognize certain determinants of her anger against her mother, and the fact that the anger stemmed from her frustrated wish to keep sole possession of her mother. That wish, which was rooted in both the preoedipal and the negative oedipal positions, appeared in the transference earlier than material related to the positive oedipal position. (This may be attributable to the sex of the analyst.) Her insight into the demand for an exclusive hold of her mother's love was followed by convincing memories of old, ardent hopes that she would one day share her mother's eminence in the family, probably through some special qualification that made her adult while still a child; memories of attempts to enjoy infantile oral pleasures well into latency, of resentment against each of the sisters as they appeared, and of her own anxieties about growing up and having children.[12] Her phallic ambition to outdo her mother emerged later, as shown in her intense curiosity about me and my work, and in her exhibitionistic and managerial attitudes toward me. In the days when she was working through the resistances underlying these attitudes, two childhood events that had been forgotten came to light: they clarified two disturbing incidents that had occurred during latency.

The first incident occurred when Sara was seven. Walking in the street on a Sunday afternoon, with many people about, Sara had set off a fire alarm. During analysis she suddenly recalled an event that had impressed her vividly at age five and a half, not long after her second sister was born. Sara had taken a walk in the country alone; by chance she had come upon a crowd watching a dramatic attempt to rescue a little boy who had fallen into a water hole and been drowned. Remembering her own watching of the rescue equipment (fire equipment), and of the sobbing mother, Sara had another memory: shortly after that exciting scene, Sara's mother had carelessly given away Sara's favorite doll, to Sara's immense grief. When about a year and a half later, soon after the birth of her third sister, Sara had rung the fire alarm and brought out the rescue trucks, she apparently had expressed her identification with the lost boy and the lost doll. The incident occurred in just that period when her neurotic behavior—the bad moods and the demands upon her mother—first became evident to her parents.

The second disturbing incident took place when she was eight. Sara was in a playground with her mother, and climbed to the top of a jungle gym. She refused to come down when called, and finally she shouted down to the children below, "Watch out!" pulled down her pants, and urinated from on high. In the analysis a screen memory was recalled: at age four Sara had attended a wedding, and as flower girl she had been strictly enjoined by her parents that no matter how long the ceremony lasted she must stand absolutely still.

---

[12] Through a dream shortly after menarche, in which an S.O.S. signal was visually prominent, we learned that the lady in her early fantasy (age three), the one whom she had so often congratulated for having so many babies, had always made her think of the color *red;* she had given that lady the name of *Mrs. Sos;* now Mrs. Sos was linked up with the warning, *S.O.S.,* and so Sara recognized that blood and babies did arouse her anxiety.

Sara remembered standing with her back to the bride and groom, they being on a higher platform; she faced the congregation, which sat on a still lower level, and which was separated from her by a brass rail. As she stood motionless, she became tormented by "an ordinary normal itch" in a place that she dared not touch, and she felt on the verge of bringing upon herself an extraordinary humiliation. In the later public incident, her urination from the elevated position behind the bar of the jungle gym expressed the sexual excitement she had felt at the wedding, the derision of the children and of her mother (below), the envy of her little sisters' freedom to wet their diapers, and a proud imitation of boys and men whose urination she had observed. The screen memory of the wedding emerged in the period when I was interpreting that behind her denial of masturbatory excitement there was a continuing wish to persuade me that she was not a foolish child but a dignified adult in full command of her impulses. Sara made the spontaneous connection between the memory and the later defiant act on the jungle gym.

The recognition that her anger was truly aimed against her mother, rather than against teachers, classmates, or Jane, led Sara to develop a loving alliance with her sister Jane, and freed her for greater libidinal investment of her father, so that she could proceed with the analysis of her oedipal wishes. The full measure of her rage against her mother did not become conscious to her until later in analysis.

The Attempts to Ward Off the Transference

It would at first appear that Sara moved into a transference relationship smoothly. Consciously she craved emotional contact with me. She had tried to verbalize all her thoughts as if to gain insight thereby, but for a long time her pressure to keep talking and moving about interfered with her endopsychic perception, and kept her in a state of retreat from contact with me. The pleasure she derived from her stream of words was prominent. Cathexis of content would shift rapidly to pride in her narrations, and she seemed scarcely to notice my presence. She had always felt that she had a child's body but an adult mind, so it seemed to her natural that she should be concerned with my methods and understand the ways of analysis. Her manner

of interrupting herself to adjust clothes, to shift positions, to look
out of the window; her ways of dropping hints about matters she
did not pursue; her occasional chuckling at her private thoughts—
all these were meant to excite my curiosity about what was going on
in her, and to keep me in suspense. Speech and motility thus absorbed
a major part of her energy, allowed for little introspection, and
fulfilled the purpose of those excessive repetitive activities previously
described as reflecting attempts to ward off the transference in
prepuberty.

An aspect of her positive attitude toward analysis that contained
special resistance lay in the quickness with which she took over my
interpretive remarks and made them hers, commented admiringly
upon my insight, and tried to make me join her in discussion of
how that insight might apply to others. Partly she would thus
attempt to work through an interpretation by taking the position of
a colleague or an assistant, and partly she would thus avoid being
affected by an interpretation. For example, she was so ready to agree
with all of her mother's criticisms about her that what seemed to
become paramount was a mature understanding of her mother's
troubles, even an altruistic desire to help her mother. On an occasion when her notable tolerance of her mother's complaints was
remarked upon, Sara responded with the same ready submission to
me, as if now she was obliged to *me* to *not* agree with her mother and
to launch, instead, into complaints about the mother.

So, through her overt obliging manner, her conscious determina-
tion to change her behavior by intellectual mastery of it, and to
associate freely, she had seemed to express an acceptance of analysis.
Actually she had worked to avoid a surrender to the oedipal mother.
That is to say, her neurosis had compelled her to play the confident
adult, free to display her impulses without compunction, and artfully
to attack those whose status she deplored. Analysis of these conflicts
had been warded off by resistance contained in the positive transference, in which she expressed longing for the lost love of her mother
and envy of her mother; and in the gradually rising negative transference, in which she treated me with the overweening aggressive
rivalry that she felt toward her mother. Quite late in her analysis
she gave me to understand that her short-lived use of playthings, in

the first months of treatment, had been a childish waste of time; she had merely indulged me by trying them.

The Relation Between Developmental Factors in Prepuberty and the Capacity for a Transference Neurosis

I return now to my earlier remarks about the need for physical action in prepuberty. Physical activity facilitates verbal and affective responsiveness in the child of this age, because through them he keeps a measure of autonomy, enough to save himself from what he would feel to be an emotional surrender to the analyst (A. Freud, 1952), revived from his own past. But the same physical activity often becomes an excellent vehicle of resistance, most readily observable in the way the child then balances what he *does* as against what he *says*. As action drains off affect, words or their meanings may be so little cathected that a certain sterility is cast over the verbal communications. If then the child's tensions mount in response to interpretation, and action or speech no longer suffice to contain his instinctual arousal, he may complain of restlessness and boredom, and call to mind all the disadvantages of being in treatment.

From a number of cases, of which Sara is but one example, it has appeared to me that where there is a balance between a freedom for activity in the analytic hour, plus a strong enough wish to get rid of symptoms to be influenced toward introspection, we have optimal conditions for analysis at this age. This balance will appear in an alternation, within the hour or from hour to hour, between states of physical activity (which reflect a rise of resistance), rest, and introspection. Since the form and degree of the child's activity—or nonactivity—are likely to reflect his ways of dealing with his affects and his impulses, much care must be taken to nourish the transference resistance it may contain; and as much delicacy is needed for the interpretation of that content as is necessary with respect to interpretation of the young child's dramatic play.

Greater difficulties occur with the child who is too regularly either extremely active or extremely inactive physically, during the hour. The very active children are often those with severe impulse disorders, and their treatment may approximate that of the delinquent. The very inactive ones, who are too inhibited or too restricted to engage in tangential activities, often tend to be silent as well; they are unable to make use of what I think of as a normal safeguarding physical activity fitting to prepuberty, and they are apt—as Sara sometimes was—to attempt a pseudo engagement with the analyst, keeping a fixed attention upon him. Such attention is essentially defiant and withholding, and constitutes a provocative demand that the analyst commit *himself* in speech and action, while the patient thereby receives cues and aids toward further repression.

In either case, of exceeding or sparse activity, the overt behavior often covers intense passive aims toward the analyst, and swells resistance against the experiencing of affect in his presence. This situation, in which a prepuberty child cannot expend a moderate part of his energies in playful or physical activity, is liable to provide him with a means of avoidance of a relationship in depth, in the way that a desire for a face-to-face arrangement may be expected to do so for the adult patient. The fact that the need of the prepuberty child for motor discharge is biologically determined does not mean that it has to be spared from interpretation, for when the need is libidinized and serves resistance it requires analysis. The essential point is that as speech is the primary phase-specific mode of expressive discharge for the adult, and play is such a primary mode for the child approximately up to the height of latency (A. Freud, 1945), so physical activity is such a primary mode for the prepuberty child. As a modicum of freedom for speech in the adult, and for play in the child, makes analytic communication possible, so a modicum of freedom for physical activity in the prepuberty child may be regarded as necessary for effective analysis at that period of development. In each phase of maturity, command of the phase-specific mode of expression would signify ego strength sufficient to convey unconscious material to the analyst, and to absorb interpretation.

The development of a transference neurosis at any age begins to become possible at the point where the patient identifies with the analyst and his purposes. After that, it depends not only on maturational factors but on the patient's readiness to seek gratification from objects other than the original infantile ones, and on the degree of abstinence that the analyst can maintain and still keep the patient in at least a minimally positive analytic relationship.

In the period between latency and puberty, several requirements for transference neurosis are normally approached.[13] These are: (1) The child has acquired independence from his parents in many matters of everyday life, with the result that we need to rely much less upon the parents, and the child can have a more exclusive relationship with the analyst. (2) The child regards his parents more objectively than before, and he values more distant objects as heroes or villains. (3) He has largely dismissed the more childlike forms of play and has a higher degree of intellectual activity; these permit him more abstract forms of communication and less direct gratification than formerly. (4) Object choice, however narcissistic, takes on greater value than identification, and opens the way for the focusing of the symptoms on the person of the analyst.

A basic problem in the analysis of the young child comes from his energetic push to act out and to repeat rather than to remember his unsatisfied emotional strivings. As his capacity for delay, for suspended judgment, and for abstract thinking are limited, he is likely to develop transference reactions quite soon in his analysis, but the capacity to bear a neutral analyst and to understand interpretation of the transference may be beyond him. It may well be that the analysis of defense is relatively successful during the latency period because then resistances from the ego are prominent, and the interpretation of defense measures, if they are not too libidinized, often attract the child's intellectual curiosity, whereas interpretations related to the forces of the superego or the id are more threatening.

The problem for the prepuberty child is this: he has a maturer intellectual understanding of the value of free association and of interpretation, but this very understanding may drive him into efforts, sometimes almost deliberate, to avoid the transference developments that do indeed transpire. That is to say, the nature of the analytic experience and of neurosis impel him to displace his impulses and their derivatives. Yet he parries, temporizes, holds back,

[13] This is not meant to imply that a full transference neurosis may regularly be expected to develop in prepuberty; nor that, if it does develop, it can be sustained steadily through puberty, or adolescence. In addition, it is not a condition of transference neurosis that all neurotic behavior outside the analytic hours is arrested, but rather that the neurotic conflicts are represented in the hours and endure there long enough to permit perception, interpretation, and working through. In every analysis there are peaks of transference development, and so peaks of resistance; even the adult in a properly moving analysis does not experience the same degree of transference neurosis throughout.

battles with himself as to whether or not to speak his thoughts. He tries to discharge tension in the repetitive, idling activities which, as I have described, may accompany his verbalizations and demonstrate his moods, and without which he would feel too vulnerable to his own instinctual strivings, displaced upon the person of the analyst. Only the force of the repetition compulsion brings him unconsciously to reveal his anxiety in the transference. Then, seeking relief from that anxiety, he can tolerate interpretation.

BIBLIOGRAPHY

Axelrad, S. & Maury, L. (1951), Identification as a Mechanism of Adaptation. In: *Psychoanalysis and Culture*, ed. G. B. Wilbur & W. Muensterberger. New York: International Universities Press.
Blos, P. (1958), Preadolescent Drive Organization. *J. Am. Psa. Assn.*, VI.
Bornstein, B. (1945), Clinical Notes on Child Analysis. *This Annual*, I.
—— (1951), On Latency. *This Annual*, VI.
Deutsch, H. (1944), *The Psychology of Women*, I. New York: Grune & Stratton.
Fraiberg, S. (1951), Clinical Notes on the Nature of Child Analysis. *This Annual*, VI.
Freud, A. (1926), *The Psychoanalytical Treatment of Children*. New York: International Universities Press, 1951.
—— (1945), Indications for Child Analysis. *This Annual*, I.
—— (1952), A Connection Between the States of Negativism and of Emotional Surrender (author's abstract). *Int. J. Psa.*, XXXIII.
Freud, S. (1908), Creative Writers and Day-Dreaming. *Standard Edition*, IX. London: Hogarth Press, 1959.
—— (1912), The Dynamics of Transference. *Standard Edition*, XII. London: Hogarth Press, 1958.
Kut, S. (1953), The Changing Pattern of Transference in the Analysis of an Eleven-Year-Old Girl. *This Annual*, VIII.
Waelder-Hall, J. (1946), The Analysis of a Case of Night Terror. *This Annual*, II.

THE SIMULTANEOUS ANALYSIS OF A PAIR OF IDENTICAL TWINS AND THE TWINNING REACTION[1]

EDWARD D. JOSEPH, M.D. and JACK H. TABOR, M.D.

(New York)

In view of the widespread interest aroused when the subject of identical twins is raised, the literature is surprisingly scant. Almost everyone can recount a personal experience with identical twins, and in all cultures, from antiquity onward, identical twins have had special significance. It may not be a coincidence that the founders of both the Jewish group (Jacob and Esau) and Rome (Romulus and Remus) were identical twins (Niederland, 1961). Apollo and Artemis, Castor and Pollux, Heracles and Iphicles were all twins of Greek mythology (Larousse, 1959). A present-day Nigerian tribe has customs in which twins—identical or fraternal—are honored and glorified (Report of the Delacorte Gallery, 1960).

Scientific interest in identical twins dates from the work of Galton about one hundred years ago. More recent investigators, such as Kallman (1948), Newman et al. (1937), and Slater (1953), have tended to use identical twin pairs as experiments in nature useful to determine the relative roles of heredity and environment. Fraternal or binovular twins have been ignored in such studies because they are regarded as distinct individuals whose development would not throw light on the relative role of heredity and environment in psychologic development. As Arlow (1960) points out, these are not studies of twins but studies on twins. Psychiatric studies along these lines have been appearing with increasing frequency (Jacobs and Mesnikoff, 1960; Lowinger, 1960).

[1] Presented at the panel on the Psychology of Twins, Annual Meeting of the American Psychoanalytic Association, Atlantic City, May 7, 1960; the Canadian Psychoanalytic Association, Montreal, Quebec, February 16, 1961; and the New York Psychoanalytic Society, January 31, 1961.

The psychoanalytic literature dealing with twins is not large, but shows a surprising uniformity of conclusions. In 1933 both Cronin and Hartmann, publishing separately, reported the first psychoanalytic studies on twins. Hartmann continued his reports in 1935, and Orr (1941) described the analysis of a fraternal twin in which the factor of twinship led to a rivalrous situation and a mutual problem of establishing a self-identity. It is noteworthy that in his review, Orr cited the work of Grotjahn, Knight, Menninger, and Steinfeld, all of which were personal communications not otherwise reported in the literature.[2] In the past fifteen years there have been sporadic publications by Peto (1946),[3] Abraham (1953), Arlow (1960), Joseph (1959), and Leonard (1953, 1959). Of these last studies, all but that of Hilde Abraham have been of identical twins, in contrast to the earlier analytic studies which were on fraternal twins. The most extensive work in this field has been done by Burlingham, whose earlier reports (1945, 1946, 1949) of her observations of twin pairs (three identical and one fraternal) were summarized in her book *Twins* (1952).

Without summarizing the detailed findings of each contributor, it can be stated that each found that being a member of a twin pair (either fraternal or identical) had profound effects on the personality development. By and large there is a mutual interdependency and failure completely to differentiate one's self from the twin, so that a complete self-representation is not found. Study of the protocols of the various case reports shows that this state of affairs exists to varying degrees in all of these patients. While mindful of Hartmann's admonition (1933) that not everything that is found in the personality of a twin should be ascribed to the twinship itself, where such a finding is so universally reported in all studies, it seems significant.

CASE PRESENTATION

Over the past years we have had a pair of identical twins in analysis. They were studied separately, with each of the analysts

[2] This situation still holds, as was shown at the recent panel on Twin Psychology at the May, 1960 Meeting of the American Psychoanalytic Association. Many discussants had analytic experience with twins which has not been reported in the literature.

[3] Peto's report is the only case in which both members of a pair of identical twins were treated by the same analyst: he analyzed one twin for three years and then had the other twin in treatment for only three months.

reporting to a third analyst for two years. We did not discuss the material with each other until the preparation of this paper. We intend to present a clinical report of the analysis of each of these patients as it unfolded on the couch of each of the co-authors. Later we will attempt to correlate the findings and draw certain conclusions which seem to be indicated by the clinical observations. It should be pointed out that these patients are still in analysis. There are gaps in our knowledge of them and hence gaps in our theoretical considerations.

We shall focus on a phenomenon which this pair of twins presented in an extreme form but which is not uncommonly encountered in other patients who are not identical twins, not even fraternal twins, not even necessarily siblings. This is what we call a "twinning reaction" and consists of (1) mutual interidentification, and (2) part fusion of the self-representation and the object representation of the other member of the pair. This leads to a diffuseness of ego boundaries between the two people. This reaction may occur in siblings who are relatively close together in age, or it may be encountered, for example, between a husband and wife who have been married for a period of time. It should be understood that we do not feel that this reaction accounts for all the clinical phenomena. There is much more to the development of these individuals than the "twinning reaction."

Histories

B came to one of us for help in a state of acute anxiety, essentially a homosexual panic. Demonstrating the twinning reaction, A soon contacted the referring analyst, stating, "If my twin needs analysis, then I must need it too." There was not the acute anxiety that had motivated B, but there were indications for analysis which was started some five months after B. The analyst who was first consulted had little doubt in his mind that these were identical twins. The factor of genetic identity has not been established by means of detailed physiologic studies.

Twin A

The family history is that of a middle-class Jewish family consisting of father, mother, brother, three and a half years older, and the twins of whom A is the older by three and a half minutes. The birth of twins was unexpected; mother wanted a girl to the extent that she had not even considered choosing a boy's name in anticipation of the birth, although a girl's name was prepared. The father, who was omitted for a long time in the analysis, was considered to be a meek, passive man of no consequence in the household. He struggled to eke out a meager existence and succeeded in this only with the aid of the mother. Mother, on the other hand, was considered a brilliant, dominant woman with many virtues, who was hard-working and upon whom fell the burden of running the family. The older brother was a much more prominent figure than the father since he was mother's favorite as well as an individual in his own right. The patient considered the family to be divided into mother and older brother on the one side, with father and the twins on the other as the more inconsequential members of the family unit. Of note, also, was the fact that mother and older brother were regarded as members of mother's family, the prominence of which was much emphasized throughout the years. This contrasted with father's family and the father unit, where the members of the family were quite unimportant. In this early family grouping there was also father's mother, who lived with the family until she developed a senile psychosis and was hospitalized, dying in a state hospital. One of the patient's early memories was of seeing his grandmother standing at the foot of the stairs, helpless and indecisive. He has often linked himself with this grandmother in her senile psychotic state.

Among childhood events the patient emphasized his falling out of a second-story window when he was four, but not being hurt, and outbursts of temper. About the age of seven or eight he and the twin brother required herniorrhaphies, twin A having a two-stage bilateral procedure done, while B had only a unilateral operation. Early in the analysis he also recalled that around eight he became angry with B and stabbed him in the buttocks with a pair of scissors, causing a deep gash. The twins were constant companions throughout school and in their school activities. B was the leader of their activities and the one who would protect the two of them in fights. A regarded himself as the weaker and less masculine so that he was very surprised when he outwrestled the twin brother, and in one instance defeated the older brother in a fight. He felt that his twin brother was his superior in all aspects: appearance, strength, intelligence, ability, etc., contrasting with his own unintelligent, unattractive, unaggressive self. This belief was strengthened by his recollection that in grade 1A he was left back while B was promoted. However, B, in order not to be separated from him, refused promotion, insisting on their remaining together.

Many evidences of the favoritism shown to the older brother were described. These consisted of his getting larger portions of food, being served first, being consulted by mother with regard to family affairs, etc. Of importance in A's development was his sitting next to father at the dinner table and receiving blows on the head from father's newspaper, which was father's method of emphasizing various points about the news. He also felt that his twin brother was preferred by the parents, citing as proof the fact that the twin brother was more gracious and was more of a dandy, being called "silk-hat Harry."

The family name was changed when the patient was about fourteen or fifteen in order that the older brother might be more successful in getting into a college and graduate school. The desires of the twins were not considered. When the time came for them to go to college, they went to separate colleges. This was their first separation. During the winter months they were both extremely unhappy, so that at the end of the first year A was joined at his college by B. They attended the same college for one term, after which, because of his failing in his work, A entered the army. B also left college at this point, to join the army with him. During their entire three and a half years in service they managed to remain together, resisting all attempts at separation. Upon discharge they re-entered college, again separating, with A going to the college that B had attended, while B went to the one at which A had started. After graduation they joined each other at the same graduate school, obtaining marks within one tenth of 1 per cent of each other, with A having the slight edge. While at graduate school they roomed together and later took an apartment together. In this apartment, A looked after the cleaning, laundry, food purchases, and the cooking, while B supplied some money. This was the situation which existed at the time the analysis started.

A started his analysis with a characteristic act, to be repeated in many forms thereafter. Upon indicating that he was ready to lie on the couch, he took off his jacket, rolled up his sleeves, saying "Let's get to work." This characteristic act indicated his use of his body to illustrate thoughts. It soon became apparent that whenever he spoke he did not refer to himself as "I" but as "we." This led to his awareness that he thought of himself as part of a pair. Following this there emerged his intense fears of being separated or of being different from his twin brother. At first this was associated with his great love for his twin brother, a love of which he could readily speak. Within the first six months or so of the analysis he was able to describe overt homosexual behavior between the two of them, starting from the age of seven or eight when they first learned to masturbate and continuing on into their college days. Essentially this consisted of mutual masturbation, the "doggie" game, which involved getting down on all fours, biting and snarling at each other, and attempting to mount and perform anal intercourse. This was successful on several occasions. The final form of their mutual sexuality occurred around age eighteen or nineteen when he performed fellatio upon B. He vigorously denied, however, that this mutual acting out was occurring at the present time. Toward the end of the first year of analysis though, he was aware of fantasies and desires to resume the "doggie" game with his twin brother. To defend against this, he impulsively left his brother, setting up and furnishing his own apartment. He felt completely lost, stating that B was his "cock and balls." He developed a series of fantasies of incorporating the twin brother which served a dual purpose. He was not alone, but was always with his incorporated brother, and it also preserved B from being destroyed by A's hostile, orally destructive fantasies. At the same time he had other fantasies—looking in the mirror while lying on his bed and feeling sure that the image he saw looking back at him was that of the twin brother. Until this time they had managed to obtain about the same salary at different jobs, but after the separation B apparently went ahead to obtain a much better situation.

From the start of the analysis A had been involved with a woman, non-Jewish, with whom he often considered the possibility of marriage, ultimately reaching the point that marriage was undertaken. He recognized readily his need to be joined with someone else and that this girl represented a twin to him. He was quite dismayed following his marriage to find out that she was not the same as he, nor the same as his twin. She was much more of an individual, with her own thoughts, desires, and anatomy. Later she also came to represent mother to him, and he often spoke of himself as a child, a *single* child, living with mother. The arrival of children aroused intense sibling rivalry. At the same time he would identify with her pregnancy, having birth fantasies that were lived out via body sensations.

A feature of this patient's analysis has been the oft-repeated incidence of rapid identification with objects, even those with whom he has a very transitory relationship. Soon after the birth of his first child he spent an hour lying on the couch, eyes fixed on the ceiling, unable to speak, his arms moving at random. When his hands suddenly went across his eyes he was able to say, "I have a hand." With his eyes he then followed the hand down the arm and saw that it was connected to his own body. This identification with his infant daughter was facilitated by a reactivation of his desires to be nursed and suckled by the feeding mother-wife.[4]

It became possible for him to recall various aspects of his earlier development and relationships. For example, before the age of four or five he was given to frequent outbursts of temper, on one occasion smashing his hand through a window, breaking the glass and cutting his hand. About the age of four or five, while at the dining room table, he made the conscious resolve to be like mother. His personality changed and he became a "good boy" who helped mother around the house, setting the table, cleaning, etc. At the same time, he would secretly take the food she gave him and throw it behind the radiator. He was well aware, at this age, of being one of a twin pair, and was treated as such by the family. An early picture of the two of them, dressed alike, with long hair, looking like girls, was remembered. The family always regarded them as the twins, never as A and/or B. At about the age of four and a half, while sleeping alone because of an illness, he enjoyed having a bed completely to himself and was reluctant to return to sharing a bed with his brother. There was a

[4] On other occasions he would have to feel parts of his body or raise his head from the couch to locate the rest of him. This dissociation of his body image points to a very early disturbance of ego formation which was complicated by the sight of his "other self" in the person of his identical twin.

resolve that henceforth he would be a single individual. On the other hand, another fantasy of this period was that all people were twins; mother and father were a twin pair, and the older brother was a twin who had incorporated his twin. This, he felt, accounted for the brother being larger than either he or his twin. One consequence of fantasies of this type was additional confusion about the nature of the people around him. He did not know whether mother was female or male, and what father was.[5] At times he felt that they were identical, both possessing a male genital. Mixed in with this were primal-scene fantasies and observations, as well as observations of mother's undressing. The latter became connected with his masturbation, in which he used mother's stockings or panties. The twins shared in these observations, attempting to act out intercourse on each other. At about seven he had nightmares, all ending with the sensation of being bitten by crabs. He would rush in to lie next to mother for protection. These memories came out in the context of his great hostility to mother associated with oral biting fantasies which were acted out on the couch by marked clamping of his jaws and grinding of his teeth. Much later these same memories were associated with positive oedipal feelings toward mother.

During the many years at home practically no experiences were shared with the older brother who, seemingly, pursued an independent course, with his own friends and activities. In marked contrast to this, the twins shared everything, whether some form of mischief or pleasurable activity. The family attitude encouraged this unity. Within this unity he was aware of intense rage toward B. He denied this by word and action for several reasons: there was genuine love for B; he felt guilty about his murderous impulses; and finally he needed B as a source of narcissistic supply. It was possible to see that he used his twin brother as a substitute, replacing first mother, who disappointed him, and later father. At times he felt B to be the older of the pair.

Currently he maintains contact with his twin brother, feels competitive with him and defeated by his business successes which

5 This confusion extended to his own self-representation. Once while waiting for a bus he saw his reflection in a window. He did not know whether it was he or his twin brother looking out at him (see Elkisch, 1957). The image then changed to a beautiful woman with long hair and a voluptuous figure. He then identified it as himself.

contrast with his own relative lack of success. At the beginning of his marriage he regarded his wife as his twin. He has developed many tender feelings for her which alternate with periods of fighting. He has become fond of his children and is now able to treat them not as rivals for his wife's (mother's) affection but as children whom he can protect and look after.

There are several personality traits of great interest, namely, his punctuality for sessions and promptness in paying his fee. In his work he is punctual, keeps his records up to date, and takes care of the necessary manifold details. He is also intensely desirous of managing everything for himself which conflicts with a deeper desire to have everything done for him.

From the beginning of the analysis it was very clear that this patient used extensively the mechanisms of denial, isolation, and projection as his chief defensive maneuvers. This was coupled with an extensive use of intellectualization and rumination. It was possible on many occasions to work out with him the fact that his obsessive ruminations served to deny something ranging from a desire to cheat his company to such infantile thoughts as the nature of the female genital. At other times this same defensive maneuver was used to protect himself from the orally destructive desires directed toward his boss (a father figure), the analyst, his wife, etc. He often attributed all his problems to the twinship which, he felt, complicated everything that happened to him.

A striking feature of his personality is his passive compliance which results in seeming acceptance of interpretations which are then warded off through a form of isolation or projection. Often they were accepted only if he repeated them to himself with the fantasy that hearing them in his own voice meant they came from the twin brother who knew what he was thinking. As the transference developed this was no longer as important because the analyst became his twin; consequently he felt it unnecessary to state many things because the "twin-analyst" knew them already. Coupled with his passive compliance has been a marked feminine attitude, at times with the conviction that he is a woman who wants to be attacked by the male analyst. This feminine identification which shows up in many situations is facilitated by the ease of identification described before. When he stayed home with his wife for any period of time he felt he was becoming like a woman. Therefore, returning to a male environment became a necessary procedure. At the same time, in his relationships with his business contacts, he was the seductive young male homosexual, able, thereby, to obtain more business for his firm. This provided him with a great deal of narcissistic gratification, compensating for a lack of financial recognition.

This account has not described the flavor of many of his sessions in which he will run the gamut of feelings and emotions quite openly. He will at times become very excited, yell, and pound the couch. On other occasions he will illustrate feminine fantasies by cupping his hands on his chest as though he had breasts, then putting his hand down to fondle his genital. Often these activities in the session became the clue to early memories or to the reconstruction of early experiences. For example, toward the end of a session centering around his need to see the analyst or some other person in his environment, he fell silent. Suddenly he began to shake his legs and arms. Inquiry led to the recall of his lying still on a bed and looking over at his twin at about the age of one and a half years. Both children were still; he then moved his legs and arms, noting that the twin did not move his limbs. In this way he could distinguish himself from the other person in his visual environment.[6]

He is extremely scrupulous in keeping his appointments and paying his bills, but has no compunctions about padding his expense account. He will, however, ruminate for days as to whether to put down one sum or another for an expense-account item, overlooking completely that the item is fictitious and that he is not justified in putting down either amount. His superego formation was much affected by using the twin state as differentiating him from others, so that he is "an exception."

Twin B

The patient is now a thirty-seven-year-old, white, Jewish male, who was initially referred to the author in a state of acute anxiety,

---

[6] Dorothy Burlingham (1952) states that the intertwin identification develops about two years, or more, after the period of individuation has passed. In this example the confusion as to where he was—here or over there—was resolved, not visually, but by means of a differentiating movement of his limbs. Since the other self did not move, he could then differentiate himself from the other self existing outside. This suggests that both individuation and interidentification are processes that go on simultaneously rather than in separate phases.

mixed with depression. In the initial interview the patient announced that he was one of a pair of identical twins. The next sentence was that they were so identical that in a two-year course at graduate school, although they had not attended the same classes, they had achieved an average which was identical to the second decimal point. The expression with which he made this statement was mixed with pride and wonder.

The following data were obtained to some degree in the initial interviews and during the patient's analysis. Information essentially the same as for A is omitted for brevity.

The birth seems to have been uneventful except for the condition of multiple birth, with B being born three and a half minutes later than his twin. The mother was surprised by the birth of twins, having expected and wanted a girl. The mother had been a schoolteacher and did some teaching after the birth of the twins. The patient many times described the solicitous attitude that the father had toward the mother, treating her as though she were a precious, fragile thing, to be adored. One persistent recollection has been that of an enormous oil painting of the mother in her wedding dress. In every home they had, the patient felt this painting dominated the household. The mother was a fairly severe disciplinarian, demanding cleanliness, punctuality, and driving them, a little later in their lives, to being academic successes. The only consistently nice thing that the patient recalled his mother saying about the father was that the father had a deep-seated love of knowledge. The mother would make envious and disparaging remarks about the large, well-kept estates in the vicinity of their home. She compared them with the affluence of her side of the family, and at the same time implied that no one could make that much money honestly. The patient recounts and remembers this with a great deal of bitterness because he felt that it meant that he and his brother were inferiors and not as desirable.

B made a very clear-cut division in the family constellation. He divided his mother, older brother (the nontwin), and father in one grouping, and his twin and himself in the other. The patient felt that the mother was extremely partial to the older brother, and at one time he reported with a good deal of satisfaction that she had even made a slip of the tongue, referring to him not as her son but as her husband.

Father was a hard-working man who even through the depths of the depression managed to make a living. He was relatively small in stature and unathletic. This was at variance with the patient's wish for a so-called typical American father who would be a pal and go fishing with the boys. For the most part father was quiet, came home tired from work, and was attentive to his wife. The patient had the feeling that his father considered himself fortunate to have such a wonderful wife. Occasionally the father would have explosive outbursts of temper. Once the father, while holding a bag of eggs, flew into a furious rage, dropped the bag of eggs and kicked them violently with his foot, splattering them over the living room. The patient was frightened, but had a secret feeling of glee that some of the egg had splattered father's precious books. One type of experience was to provoke his father into chasing him around the house. The father would chase the boy who would run in a circle until the father would give up. He described his feeling of excitement in this kind of activity.

The older brother always seemed exceedingly distant and vastly superior to the patient. He was looked upon as the family genius. He was very able in school, which brought the mother pleasure and she bestowed a great deal of praise on him.

Parenthetically, when the twins began school they were very poor students and had a reading block. They had to remain in the first grade and repeat the first half—much to their intense humiliation. The patient felt that the brother's position, in the good graces of the mother, was absolutely unassailable.

He and his twin brother were practically inseparable. He recalled a picture of himself and his twin in white dresses with long ringlets. One of his earliest memories was that of sitting in a high chair and pulling the bib up over his face, calling out expectantly, "Why doesn't somebody laugh?" Nobody laughed. He put the bib down and to his amazement and chagrin, the bowl of food had been taken away. Another childhood memory of importance was his falling headlong down a flight of stairs into the basement of the house, promptly leaping to his feet and calling up to his mother, "I'm not hurt." (Denial.) His general affective memory of his childhood was one of continuous tension. He felt he was a second-class citizen in the family, he and his twin being a pair of wormy runts, troublesome, and badgered by the mother with regard to cleanliness and school. He has not recalled any specific early masturbatory experiences or memories or fantasies about sexual activities in the household.

During latency things seemed to be looking up, with one recollection of a negative character: it was discovered that both twins had hernias, possibly congenital, and both underwent herniorraphies. B only had one. His twin brother had a bilateral herniorraphy. When B first reported this he was not sure which of the two had had the bilateral procedure. Similarly, when he spoke about an experience of having been stabbed by his twin brother with a pair of scissors, he was not sure whether he had stabbed his twin, or the twin had stabbed him. In both cases, the next day he reported that by inspection of the scars he was the one who had one hernia, and also had been the victim of the stabbing. The patient's schoolwork improved, and he was near the top of his class. At this time too the twins engaged in what they called "dog play." They would get down on all fours and snarl and bite at each other, nip and smell each other's genitals and anal regions. This was a very exciting form of play. The patient and his twin brother had practically no real friends in the community, being self-sufficient together.

The patient continued to do fairly well in school, but he felt lost in the large high school. He was always uneasy because of the presence of people whom he had not known previously. He began to masturbate with fantasies of attacking young girls and engaged in mutual masturbation with his twin brother, fellatio, and perhaps attempts at anal penetration. B is extremely loathe, to this day, to really describe just what did take place, sexually, with his brother. The twin brothers began to go out with a pair of twin girls. B always felt that the other twin was making out better, was better liked, was handsomer, while he was just barely tolerated. He tried to compensate for these feelings by a great deal of bravado, boasting, doing acts of derring-do. This latter earned him the family title of "the professor." His relationship with the twin girl with whom he was going broke up sooner than his twin brother's relationship with his girl.

B had several other desultory relationships with girls, but of no depth or seriousness. He recalled his father's repeated admonition not to waste his time on girls, but to be a good student. B always tried to keep A in the background. For example, when there was the possibility of a fight with another boy he promptly pushed A behind him, leaping forward to do battle. His motive was that A should always look up to him as the better fighter and never find out how well he could really fight.

The boys had a fair academic standing. The parents felt that it might be better if the boys were separated, so each went to a different college. B took his mother to the admission interview, feeling that she would impress the registrar. His acceptance, he felt, was due to his mother's presence. This is a pattern that he reverts to, calling it "hiding behind somebody's skirts." He was lonely at college, sloppy, and neglectful of his work. At the last moment he would cram and work frantically getting passing grades. He felt isolated and attributed this to his religion despite his awareness that other Jewish men on campus were not as isolated as he. He worshiped from afar the captains of the football and ski teams. He relied on his eccentricities to get some measure of attention, if not acceptance, being known as the "mad genius." After the first year of college he applied for admission to his brother's college. Before graduation, however, they enlisted in the ski troops of the army—this was his fantasy of being a Nordic hero. On assignment to the initial training camp, somewhere in the South, B was seized with panic when one of the men in the barracks grabbed a bayonet, jabbed it into one of the wooden supporting pillars, saying, "That's what I'm going to do to the Heinies." He was overcome with anxiety and called his parents. They were able to have the twins transferred to another unit.

Their army experiences are literally unbelievable. They were never so undisciplind as to evoke direct action, but they were transferred from one outfit to another and not infrequently transferred themselves by falsifying papers. Overseas they followed the same process. Once they tormented their sergeant by bouncing pebbles off his helmet. When he challenged them to a fight, they stood together threatening to beat him up. After honorable discharge from the army they returned to school and were graduated.

B obtained a job with a small firm. His work pattern was erratic, but he was able to be so productive that he rose in company ranks. He worked practically every night until 10 or 11 o'clock in the company of his secretary. She took A's place. She awakened him every morning by phone, reminding him of things he had forgotten, giving him information about the boss, doing his typing, and staying at the office with him until late at night. He spent at least one evening a week at her home where she prepared dinner for him. Except for one experience, he did not have sexual relations with her. He has used her as his guide into the world of people. He felt defective when it came to judging the people about him. She was able to do this for him. He alternated in feelings of wanting to marry her, and of never marrying her. When he went out with other girls he felt enormous guilt toward her. His sexual life consisted largely of masturbation with violent fantasies of attacking and crushing women, and his emergence as their adored hero. He overwhelms them, which is his fantasy of a salesman who has to ram the product down the customer's throat. When away from home on business trips he occasionally had fellatio experience with a prostitute. On some occasions he suffered from premature ejaculation. On the whole, he led an impoverished life, had few relationships with others, and spent almost all of his waking hours in business. He quarreled frequently with his boss, competing with him and never listening to suggestions. Despite his real value to the company, he suffered from a fear of displacement. He rarely went to a movie, theater, concert, or read a book, although he professed a very great interest in all of these activities.

When the twin brother left the apartment the patient was distressed and depressed, but he thought the twin would come back. When A married, B was bitterly opposed, having nothing pleasant to say about the girl. He felt that his brother had been hooked and snared, and was now being deprived of all the appurtenances of manhood. He tried to seduce his brother by inviting him to play tennis or go skiing and told his brother with great relish of the wonderful times he had. It was a severe jealousy reaction. Later, however, he began to wonder whether his twin brother did not have something more of a life with companionship and a relationship, despite the ups and downs of his marriage. As for B himself, his sources of gratification were skiing in the winter and tennis in the summer, when he fancied himself as a Nordic hero who vanquished all. He had several accidents while skiing.

During the first year of the patient's analysis, the material produced had a vague, shimmering quality. This applied both to recent and past information. There were so many "ifs," "maybes," "perhaps," "about," "it might have been," "it could be," that it was difficult to obtain a clear picture of the actuality of a given occurrence. For instance, an incident involving the police was so disturbing, he repressed the memory of the whole event and did not know what had happened, or even whether the event itself had occurred. This also occurred in regard to any material relating to sexual play with his twin brother, or his sexual experiences with women. So great was his castration anxiety and separation anxiety that this mechanism was imperative: at all costs he had to avoid being held to account. This became known in the analysis as his "crystal-gazing" attitude. Another motivation for this defensive attitude was to be chased by the analyst, as by father. There is also a denial of self in this as well as an inability to take individual responsibility.

The patient had great difficulty following the basic rule and preferred to narrate the details of his external life. He wanted to enlist the advice and services of the analyst for the purpose of guidance and counseling. When this was denied him, he turned more and more to his girl friend, D. On occasion, when he did gain a bit of insight into his defenses and motivations, he would say, "I'll probably forget it by tomorrow anyhow," which in the majority of instances was true. When reminded of the previous day's insights or material, he reacted as though it had never happened. Each session was an entity unto itself. Interpretations were received, and disappeared as though into thin air, only to come up again weeks later either as an original thought or as the remark someone else had made. This has abated and at present he listens to an interpretation, interrupting when he gets the drift to "carry the ball" himself, and outdo the analyst. The entire analytic process consists of slowly working out small pieces of information about defense and drives which he discerns individually but keeps fragmented and separated. His conflicts over his self-image are unresolved. He sees himself as half a female, which frightens him because either he must fuse with someone else to be complete or he must take flight. He alternatively uses both methods. A brief summary of his progress to date is contained in the following statement that he recently made: "I know I'm not *him* now, but who am *I?*" He has felt that the pair is like a tripod; without one leg they would both collapse. A most salient feature has been B's denial of his deep need for his twin. Incidentally, in contrast to A, B has not made much in the analysis of the age difference, nor of the role of the twinship as causing problems for him.

DISCUSSION

Comparing our material, the most noteworthy feature is the striking characterologic difference between this pair of identical twins.

A tends to be more passive, compliant, and feminine; while B is more overtly active, masculine, and hostile. Upon closer examination it appears that this difference between them lies in a different attitude toward their feminine identifications: A has accepted the feminine role, while B is constantly denying it. A could describe the homosexual relationship that existed between them, while B can either hint at its existence or express it openly only if coupled with a denying statement.

Another striking difference is seen in the degree of narcissism manifested by each of them. While somewhat narcissistic, A has been able to establish a relationship with his wife and children for whom he has developed tender feelings, and he is capable of expressing openly his loving tender feelings for his brother. B, on the contrary, consistently denies any such feelings, even toward A, and has been able to establish a relationship with a woman based either on a mother-child or on a twin-twin relationship.

Both twins failed to establish a complete self-representation, but A seems to have a greater sense of identity, while B feels himself not as an "I" nor any longer as part of a "we."

Another striking contrast is the presence of greater reaction formations in the character of A. The punctuality, the concern about money, the cleanliness, the tendency to deep guilt feelings of A are in marked contrast to the direct acting out of the flowing away of money of B, delayed payments, sloppiness, consistent lateness, and lack of overt guilt.

On the other hand, there are many similarities in the material of these patients. There are many commonly shared experiences which are described as though they had happened to both, regardless of who was involved in the experience. At times though, certain experiences of A are described as though they were completely his own, to the exclusion of B, with the reverse occurring in B. There have been many fantasies in common. Both show a relative lack of reality testing, manifested, for example, by a failure to know to whom individual experiences had happened. Each has an image of the other as the better, stronger, healthier, more intelligent, more attractive individual than himself. At the same time there is a depreciation of the other, so that this also becomes a shared type of fantasy regarding each other.

Both depend on each other, love each other, and have envy and hostility for each other. A admits this more readily; B denies it. There is a commonly felt guilt toward each, which B again attempts to deny, while A lives it out. Each twin has many grounds upon which to base his feelings of guilt. B realizes that he has attempted to "con" twin A into believing himself inferior and feels that he has gotten away with this deception. A, on the other hand, feels guilty toward B on the basis of having beaten him out by being born first, and also because of fantasies about B disappearing so that he, A, can have mother and all the good things of mother completely to himself. Such fantasies also exist in B and form a similar basis for the feelings of guilt that exist but are denied. There is similarity, also, in the use that each twin makes of the other as a source of narcissistic supply, when this is needed, and as an object upon whom certain fantasies derived from the oedipal period, for instance, have been acted out.

Part of A's overvaluation of his twin brother was based on an image of him as a father figure. In this regard he felt he could never equal B's achievements in, for example, the business world. When they lived together A was the "mother" of the household, while B was the father. Only in their sexual relations did A reverse the role by being the aggressor based on an identification with the father and the phallic mother. B, on the other hand, saw himself in the paternal role and consistently hid his feminine identifications.

To sum up, and put it briefly: The essential differences between these two lie in the fact that A has developed greater reaction formations and a "stronger" superego which enable him more correctly to judge situations and to respond with feelings of guilt. B, on the other hand, does not seem to have as strong a sense of reality and as strong a superego, with the result that he uses such primitive defense mechanisms as denial, isolation, and projection more extensively. It should be emphasized that A uses the same defenses, but not to the same degree, so that he is able in the therapeutic process to regress more readily "in the service of the ego," while B must guard himself and battle with the analyst. To regard it another way, A can more readily accept a passive role in his relationships and more readily accepts his feminine identifications than B.

The question arises as to how to account for this difference between the members of this pair of identical twins. A has often described his feeling of being a middle child, squeezed between a favored older brother and a favored younger brother. Evidence for this favoritism exists with regard to the older brother, and in the fact that the family store of memories are of cute things concerning B. Thus, the bib story, related by both, is part of the family folklore, as are such expressions as "silk-hat Harry," etc. B, on the other hand, knew that he was the youngest and the one whose existence created a twin pair. Thus, his fantasies that where two identical things exist, one is dispensable certainly played a role in his development. In terms of their interrelationships, the fact of one being older and the other younger, even though by a very brief period, was also of seeming importance. A had fantasies of intrauterine play between the two of them in which he beat out his brother and was born first. This, he felt, gave him an advantage which he had to attempt to deny. Part of his denial was his acceptance of the reversal of roles in terms of older and younger.

Such other external events as the nature of the surgical procedures seemed to have played but a minor role in their development as far as is currently known, but an event of major importance was the exposure of A to father's "beatings" on the head during dinners which accentuated a tendency toward masochism already present. There is no comparable material from B. However, these factors do not seem to account fully for the differences.

Both twins developed an identification with the mother and a passive, masochistic attitude toward father and older brother. A was better able to accept this situation, becoming clean, neat, etc., like mother; while B attempted to deny this by a pseudo-aggressive masculinity. A's identification with the phallic mother went to the

extent of carrying out fantasies of a vagina dentata, for when performing fellatio on B, he had fantasies of biting off B's phallus.
B's fantasy of a vagina dentata is more covert and acted out in B's
avoidance of heterosexual contacts and symbolic displacements. Both
twins in effect thus identified with mother and gave her what she
wanted, i.e., girls. But they did it as a form of diverging from each
other in an effort to develop an individual ego which could win
mother's favor. This drive for individuation ran into more than usual
difficulties.

It is in this regard that we see the twinship playing a large part
in their development. From the clinical evidence it is clear that these
individuals have not differentiated themselves from each other, and
yet they have to some extent. Aside from the close physical proximity
imposed upon them by their environment, aside from the drive
toward unity expressed by the family, aside from their need for each
other as a source of the narcissistic gratification so often denied by
the need-satisfying objects, aside from the use of each other to live
out instinctual conflicts, and aside from the need to deny guilt at
hostile feelings toward each other by remaining a unity—they still
are different individuals. This seems to have come about in two
interrelated ways: (1) through an identification with different aspects
of mother's personality: A with the more feminine, and B with the
aggressive and domineering; and (2) through a desire to separate
from each other and obtain the benefits of being a single individual.

To consider the last one first, each was aware from very early in
life of the advantages of being single, i.e., brother and father—in
relation to what could be obtained from mother. Each felt therefore
that he could court mother best if the other did not exist, and could
please mother by imitating her. Their choice of method seems to
have been partially determined by a desire to differentiate from
each other, for what we see clinically is: if A, then not B, and vice
versa in many situations. We know that A was aware of the delights
of being alone, and he was also aware of mother's approval of B
because of his wearing glasses and his cute sayings. This also shows
that in B a process of differentiation had already begun, encouraged
by the mother and by the fact that B needed glasses and A did not.
For A, competition with B reached its peak at the oedipal period,
when he could not compete with both father and B. He adopted a

more passive and masochistic solution. He turned to father and was the seductive young lover toward him. At the same time he included father in his family group of three, so that he, twin brother and father could continually live out his oedipal fantasy of being father, mother, and only child. In this way he could gratify many fantasies including those of castration, femininity, masculinity, twinship, and aloneness. In his present-day relationships and in the analytic transference he attempts alternately to live out all aspects of this solution of his phallic and oedipal conflicts. To some extent he established B as an ego ideal and part superego; B did the same with A, but then denied the superego aspects of his relationships with A because of its more feminine nature.

The desire to differentiate manifested itself early in their lives, aided no doubt by such chance occurrences as having to wait for feedings, for diaper changes, and mother's preferences. Later situations—different colleges, jobs, etc.—further this process. But it is also clear that the desire to differentiate and separate ran into powerful internal obstacles which were based on the need for each other and the initial hostility and guilt. Other fears also opposed this, such as B's fear that as an individual he would be "swallowed up or dissolved." A expressed the same concept and warded it off by fleeting contacts with outside objects. Being swallowed up or dissolved in the twin was not dangerous because it represented a fusion of object and self-representations which already were so alike as to be poorly separated.

The essence, then, of the "twinning reaction" is represented by a fusion of object and self-representations in which the two merge, leading to a loss of ego boundary between the two individuals and a loss of identity. In the transference A could allow this, which led to certain technical difficulties; B fought it off, for part of his identity is based on being rebellious, while A's identity is based on complying.

It is important to realize that the "twinning reaction" is not peculiar to these neurotic identical twins; it may also occur between different-sexed fraternal twins (Orr, 1941), between siblings close in age, between nontwin individuals (Deutsch, 1938), and even between a husband and wife who are married to each other for a period of time. The factors present in the twins reported here may also be operative in these other situations just mentioned.

To consider the situation of the identical twins first:

1. Contemporaneity and simultaneity. The occurrence of relatively simultaneous passage through the progressive phases of maturation and development facilitates interidentification. The daily bolstering of similar impulses versus the shaping and critical influence of the parents—especially the mother (Demarest and Winestine, 1955; Gardner and Rexford, 1952; Leonard, 1959; Plank, 1958)—threw them almost literally into each other's arms. This is similar to adolescents who make common cause against the adult world through mannerisms of speech, dress, and actions. In these twins the antagonists were primarily the mother and older brother and secondarily the father.

2. Physical similarity. The physical similarity of identical twin pairs eases the path of mutual interidentification (Gardner and Rexford, 1952). This factor exerts an early influence at a time when the separation of self and nonself occurs; this separation in identical twins is more difficult because of the existence of a physically similar individual coexisting simultaneously.

3. Mutual object of libidinal and narcissistic gratification. Being disappointed in the need-gratifying objects of their environment increased the importance for each as a source of gratification for the other. Each statement to the other of "that's great" for the smallest achievement had in it the desire for a return of the compliment. Additionally it served as a defense against envy for the other and amounted to an altruistic surrender in favor of the other.[7]

4. Defense against hostile impulses. Based partly on a need for each other and partly as a defense against hostile, murderous impulses toward each other which arose in their struggle for sole possession of the mother, mutual interidentification served a defensive role in permitting a state of coexistence in which neither gained an advantage over the other, and the libidinal ties between them were strengthened.

5. Influence of the environment toward nondifferentiation. Because of the actual difficulty of telling them apart and because of the parents' unconscious attitudes toward them (Gardner and Rex-

[7] Freud, in a footnote to his paper on "A Case of Homosexuality in a Woman" (1920, p. 159), describes this mechanism as operative in a pair of twin brothers, one of whom was homosexual.

ford, 1952; Plank, 1958), the tendency was to regard them as "the twins" not as "A" and "B." (This applies to married couples, for example, who are often referred to as the "Joneses" and not by their given names.)

Many of the factors enumerated are operative to a lesser degree in the situations in which a "twinning reaction" exists in nontwin individuals. What may also be observed in these twin and nontwin relationships is that each sets up the other person as part of his ego ideal. This occurred in these identical twins.

Lest it seem that the relationship and psychologic development of identical twins such as these appears too simple, this drive toward the "twinning reaction" is opposed in the course of maturational growth by a drive toward separation and individuation. It is the interplay between the "twinning reaction" and the striving for individuation that forms the matrix for the behavior of twins and for understanding the nature of the twinship.

CONCLUSION

Fragments from the analysis of a pair of identical twins have been presented. Some aspects of their development, such as body image, self-representations, object representations, superego formation, could have been discussed in much greater detail. We have, however, attempted to focus upon some of the factors relating to the psychology of being a twin that have gone into their ego development to account for the differences in personality as seen in the individual analyses of these patients. The transference reactions of each of these individuals have been strikingly different. We have considered the possible role of difference in the personalities of the analysts as playing a part in the different transference reactions, but it is evident from the material that these reactions seen in the transference are repetitions of attitudes that were present in all of their relationships outside the analysis. Therefore, it has been felt that the personalities of the analysts have not materially influenced the nature of the particular reactions, so that these are in reality valid findings of the analytic situation. Even aspects of the early mother-child relationships have not been discussed in any detail in order to focus on the twinship itself.

What we have attempted to describe is the nature of the "twin-ning reaction" each of these patients has shown, and account for the difference on the basis of a slightly different environment for each and a desire to differentiate from each other that encountered difficulties from both within the self and from outside. We have not attempted an exhaustive dynamic formulation of all aspects of the development of this twin pair, but only mention one consequence of the constant presence of a contemporary going through the same developmental phases simultaneously.

BIBLIOGRAPHY

Abraham, H. (1953), Twin Relationship and Womb Phantasies in a Case of Anxiety Hysteria. *Int. J. Psa.*, XXXIV.

Arlow, J. (1960), Fantasy Systems in Twins. *Psa. Quart.*, XXIX.

Burlingham, D. T. (1945), The Fantasy of Having a Twin. *This Annual*, I.

—— (1946), Twins. *This Annual*, II.

—— (1949), The Relationship of Twins to Each Other. *This Annual*, III/IV.

—— (1952), Twins: *A Study of Three Pairs of Identical Twins*. New York: International Universities Press.

Cronin, H. J. (1933), An Analysis of the Neurosis of Identical Twins. *Psa. Rev.*, XX.

Demarest, E. W. & Winestine, M. C. (1955), The Initial Phase of Concomitant Treatment of Twins. *This Annual*, X.

Deutsch, H. (1938), *Folie à deux. Psa. Quart.*, VII.

Elkisch, P. (1957), The Psychological Significance of the Mirror. *J. Am. Psa. Assn.*, V.

Freud, S. (1920), The Psychogenesis of a Case of Homosexuality in a Woman. *Standard Edition*, XVIII. London: Hogarth Press, 1955.

Gardner, G. E. & Rexford, E. N. (1952), Retardation of Ego Development in a Pair of Identical Twins. *Quart. J. Child Behav.*, IV.

Grotjahn, M. Cited by Orr (1941).

Hartmann, H. (1933), Psychiatrische Zwillingsstudien. *Jb. Psychiat. Neurol.*, L.

—— (1935), Zur Charakterologie erbgleicher Zwillinge. *Jb. Psychiat. Neurol.*, LII.

Jacobs, E. C. & Mesnikoff, A. M. (1960), Alternating Psychosis in Twins. Presented at the American Psychiatric Association.

Joseph, E. D. (1959), An Unusual Fantasy in a Twin. With an Inquiry into the Nature of Fantasy. *Psa. Quart.*, XXVIII.

Kallman, F. J. (1948), Heredity and Constitution in Relation to the Treatment of Mental Disorders. In: *Failure of Psychiatric Treatment*, ed. P. Hoch. New York: Grune & Stratton.

Knight, R. P. Unpublished material cited by Orr (1941).

LaCombe, P. (1959), The Problem of the Identical Twin As Reflected in a Masochistic Compulsion to Cheat. *Int. J. Psa.*, XL.

Larousse (1959), *Encyclopedia of Mythology*. New York: Promotheus Press.

Leonard, M. (1953), Twins, Myth and Reality. *Child Study*, XXX.

—— (1959), Problems of Identification and Ego Development in Twins. *Bull. Phila. Assn. Psa.*, IX.

Lowinger, M. (1960), Problems of Development of Identical Twins. Presented at the American Psychiatric Association.

Menninger, W. C. Personal communication cited by Orr (1941).

Newman, H. H., Freeman, F. N., & Holzinger, K. J. (1937), *Twins: A Study in Heredity and Environment*. Chicago: University of Chicago Press.

Niederland, W. (1961). In: Panel on The Psychology of Twins, reported by E. D. Joseph. *J. Am. Psa. Assn.*, IX.

Orr, D. W. (1941), A Psychoanalytic Study of a Fraternal Twin. *Psa. Quart.*, X.

Peto, E. (1946), Analysis of Identical Twins. *Int. J. Psa.*, XXVII.

Plank, E. N. (1958), Reaction of Mothers of Twins in a Child Study Group. *Am. J. Orthopsychiat.*, XXVIII.

Report of the Delacorte Gallery, New York (1960), *Twin Rites Among the Yoruba Tribe*.

Slater, E. (1953), *Psychotic and Neurotic Illness in Twins* [Medical Research Council, Special Report No. 278]. London: Her Majesty's Stationary Office.

Steinfeld, J. Cited by Orr (1941).

PROBLEMS IN IDENTIFICATION AND EGO DEVELOPMENT IN TWINS[1]

MARJORIE R. LEONARD (Stamford, Connecticut)

Psychoanalytic theory of the development of personality generally assumes that we are talking about the development of an individual resulting from a single birth. To date no attempt has been made to explore what modifications, if any, might be necessary to describe the personality of twins. We find, however, that twins relate to each other in a manner differing in certain respects from other inter-personal relationships. It is the nature and origin of this intertwin relationship and its effect on the personality development of twins as individuals with which this paper is concerned.

An understanding of the nature of the intertwin relationship may help us to further our comprehension of other close bonds. Twinlike relationships exist more frequently than is usually realized, often as a result of the mutual support such a relationship offers. The bond between married couples, for instance, often takes on many of the characteristics ascribed to twins. One of the most striking examples of supportive relationship gained through artificial twinning is described in the Anna Freud-Dann (1951) account of the group of six children brought up without parents until three years of age in a German concentration camp. The authors describe the relationship between these children as similar to twins in whom an identification "prospered on the basis of common needs, common anxieties, common wishes, in short, on the similar reaction of two beings of the same age living in close proximity under the same external conditions." Brewster's case (1957) of two unrelated polio

[1] Read to the staff of the Child Study Center, Mount Sinai Hospital, Los Angeles, California, October, 1958; the Los Angeles Psychoanalytic Society, March, 1959; the Los Angeles Society for Child Psychiatry, April, 1959; and the Annual Meeting of the American Psychoanalytic Association, Philadelphia, April, 1959.

patients who found mutual benefit from a twinlike relationship probably has many parallels which have escaped our attention.

Artificially created twinships are not always supportive, however. Some parents, in an effort to treat siblings who are close in age as equably and fairly as possible, stress the similarities between them, rearing them almost as though they were twins. Other environmental situations in which it is advantageous to minimize individuality as much as possible create "twinning *en masse*," as for example the parochial schools, the armed services, and prisons. The reasons why this type of twinning may have a deleterious effect on the personality of the individual will, it is hoped, be understandable as the relationship between real twins is clarified.

In the case of every twin whose analysis has been reported, the twin relationship was considered the prime reason for that individual's emotional disturbance. Hartmann (1933) pointed out the striking similarities in the mental illness of twin pairs, not infrequently resulting in *folie à deux*, which he laid to identification between the twins. Orr (1941), Beckwitt (1954), and Abraham (1953) also stress identification, in these instances between fraternal twins, each pointing out the pathogenic influence of the identification.

My personal observations of twins as well as intensive study of the observations made by others have led to the conviction that the intertwin relationship differs from most other interpersonal relationships because of certain characteristics peculiar to the intertwin identification. The purpose of this paper is, therefore, to explore the nature of the intertwin identification and the reason for its possible pathogenic influence on the development of personality. Before a discussion of intrapsychic mechanisms can be undertaken, certain factors specific for twins and influential to their development must be made clear. These factors are: (1) the cultural attitude toward twins; (2) the parental attitude; (3) the physical similarity of the twins; (4) the socioeconomic situation.

The Cultural Attitude Toward Twins

By "cultural attitude" I am referring to the mythlike beliefs, the clichés which, by their very existence, serve as barometers of the social climate in which the twins are being raised. "Twins look alike, think alike. They never fight. They have a closer relationship than any other known to mankind." These are some of the frequently expressed ideas about twins, regardless of whether the twins in question are identical or not.

Corollaries to these notions are ideas which have to do with the upbringing of twins. "Twins are something special. Parents who have twins are 'doubly blessed' and as a matter of course do everything to emphasize and maintain the twin relationship. Therefore, twins should be given twin names, should be dressed alike, and treated just as much alike as possible." Anyone who treats twins in any other way is considered to be depriving them of their special heritage.

Generally speaking, the cultural attitude emphasizes the positive aspects about having twins, and about the twin relationship. It is strikingly unrealistic, it omits completely the frequent problems in pregnancy and delivery, the problems of handling two small infants simultaneously, the intensified sibling rivalry, and others which will be discussed later. This attitude is in the nature of a mass repression. It probably occurs as a result of the wish to be a twin (Burlingham, 1952) or its substitute, which seems to be nearly as prevalent, the wish to be a parent of twins (Leonard, 1953).

There is evidence that the cultural attitude varies in different countries as well as in a given country, according to the particular socioeconomic status. As far as this study is concerned, the attitudes described are those commonly found in urban communities in the United States. These attitudes exert a constant influence, not only on the parents' handling of the twins, but on the educational environment, on the attitude of relatives and friends: they create the climate in which the intertwin relationship develops.

The Parental Attitude

As has already been mentioned, the cultural attitude toward twins influences the conscious attitude of the mother toward them. She is aware that only one mother in a hundred[2] is so blessed, so that she feels both privileged and proud of her achievement. Thoughts of "double trouble" or of deeper emotional dissatisfactions are quickly put out of mind. Only within the framework of a group of mothers of twins were some mothers able to speak freely of their

[2] Twins occur in one out of ninety-seven births (Guttmacher, 1953).

frustration, a sense of being cheated of those expected quiet moments with the baby. "There was always the other one who needed attention." Of those whose twins were their first-born, several mothers indicated that one reason they wished for a third child was in order to have one baby toward whom they felt they could justifiably devote their whole attention. The frustration of the need to identify with the child is probably felt more keenly when mothers have not had this experience before giving birth to twins.[3]

In recent years Mothers of Twins Clubs have sprung up all over the country. Just being together with other mothers of twins serves as a narcissistic gain, reinforcing their pride in their unique social status, enabling them, as Emma Plank (1958) has described it, to identify "in a group of peers which simulates a sibship or even a twinship . . . almost a fulfillment of the old fantasy of having a twin who shares everything of importance." This identification probably also substitutes for an identification with the child, difficult if not impossible to achieve with two-at-a-time.

Whether fathers of twins also experience a narcissistic gain, or whether theirs is mostly reflected glory, has not been investigated. They are expected to share many of the drudgeries as well as "bring home the bacon" for that extra mouth to feed. Time for compensating fun with the children is rarely found. It is little wonder that most men, when they hear of the birth of twins, laugh uproariously. They feel it to be a good joke on the other fellow.

Negative feelings concerning twins are rarely expressed consciously by the parents. The positive attitude is more easily maintained because it gains support and emphasis from the accepted attitudes in our society. Despite this cultural sugar-coating, the

[3] The psychological reactions of the mother on giving birth to twins needs further investigation. If we accept Bibring's thesis (1961) that pregnancy and motherhood represent a maturational crisis, we can speculate that the mother who finds simultaneous identification with two infants impossible does not go through the same maturation process as does a mother of singly born infants. One solution of the problem seen all too frequently is the identification with one of the twins, rejection of the other (Demarest and Winestine, 1955).

Unconscious avoidance of such a psychologically harmful solution may explain the former custom among Apache Indians of killing one twin. The Indians "considered the birth of twins a hardship visited upon the mother by witchcraft, due to someone's hostility to her, and the second twin might carry the onus of witchcraft and eventually kill the mother" (Boyer, 1961). This belief can be understood as a projection of the mother's unconscious hostility directed toward one of the twins.

reality problems of handling two-at-a-time exist and must be met. From the moment the twin infant is born, his environment must necessarily differ from that of a singleton. Mothers will welcome, even seek, a helping hand whenever possible, with the result that the infants may become confused by the many changes of routine, by the many adult faces and voices which approach them. It is of utmost importance in understanding later development to realize that the one human being who is most constant within the twin infant's range of perception is not his mother but his twin.

In recent studies of normal maturation there has been an increasing awareness of the significance of the infant-mother relationship. We have come to realize the importance of the interplay between the infant's expression of need and helplessness through his crying and the mother's readiness to respond. It is generally assumed that a healthy, unneurotic mother responds intuitively to the cries of the infant, and since such crying is the infant's only way of indicating his needs, quick response to them is important.

It can readily be seen that the mother of twins finds herself in a quandary. It is a rare set of twins who conveniently fit their demands into a schedule which would permit the mother to feed one while the other sleeps. The quiet, peaceful period of breast feeding which gives the mother a sense of being "in tune with her child" is rare in the case of twins. A striking exception is one case (Trainham et al., 1945) in which twins were not only nursed, but were kept on a self-demand schedule. This mother even went to the extreme of occasionally nursing the babies simultaneously, one at each breast. However, this was admittedly "not satisfying for the babies, and too fatiguing for the mother to be practiced often." All too frequently and frustratingly, the feeding of one is accompanied by the screaming protest of the other infant.

From approximately the fifth or six month on, the twins are sufficiently aware of each other so that being together seems to have a quieting effect. Too often parents, preoccupied with the mechanics of caring for the family, rely on this fact, leaving the children to themselves as long as they seem to be reasonably contented. In just the same way that the mere presence of the mother in the room will quiet an infant's crying, even though she makes no move to pick him up, in those early months the little sounds and movements that each baby makes seem to be sufficient to give them a sense of not being alone. From this early awareness a relationship between the twins gradually becomes noticeable. Whereas in the earliest months the crying of one infant does not disturb the other, unless he happens to be awakened by the noise, in the later months of the first year there often seems to be a sympathetic crying response. There is an increasing influence of the mood of one upon the other, and as lallation commences one has the impression of the beginning of communication.

If we now link these two sets of circumstances, that of the children being left in each other's company a large part of the time and that of the relatively little opportunity to relate to an adult, one factor important in the personality development of twins becomes clear: namely, the scene is set for the twins to identify with each other rather than with an adult object.

Physical Similarity

The intensity with which twins appear to be drawn to each other and therefore to identify with each other seems to be strongly affected by the degree to which they resemble each other. Contrary to what one might expect, the degree of similarity is not necessarily correlated with the type of twins in question. Some identical twins differ more in their weight at birth and therefore in appearance than do some nonidentical twins. On the other hand, just as singly born siblings often tend to look very much alike, fraternal like-sexed twins may be difficult to distinguish.

For our present consideration the important point is whether, fraternal or identical, they resemble each other closely. Understandably, when pronounced physical differences exist at birth, each child will receive different care. It can even happen that the relationship of the mother to each infant is quite different (Demarest and Winestine, 1955). Because the smaller child must remain in the hospital, she may not be permitted contact with it for several weeks. In the meanwhile she has had opportunity to feed and fondle the larger twin. She may reject the smaller twin with a feeling that it is imperfect. To another mother, the smallness and weakness may cause the baby to have a special appeal once she is able to assume its care. In instances of different-sexed twins, even the most unneurotic mother will have differing "normal" feelings toward a boy and a girl. The variations in her reactions toward fraternal, like-sexed twins will be subtle, and their explanation would no doubt involve understanding her unconscious reactions.

One point is clear, however: it is much easier for the mother to relate to twins as individuals when distinct differences exist than to those who are very much alike. Burlingham (1952) emphasizes the importance of being "able to identify with each of them in order to love them. If the twins are alike she finds this impossible and as a result her emotions cannot have free play." A one-to-one relationship seems to be dependent on distinct delineation of one twin from the other and the possibility of being alone with each one, at least for brief periods of time. The more alike identical twins are, the stronger the tendency on the part of the environment to treat them as a unit rather than as individuals. Such treatment will, of course, emphasize their identification with each other and will tend to make them feel as though they belonged together, rather than that each has a right to an individuality of his own.

The Socioeconomic Factor

Parents under economic stress will be particularly hard put to find time and energy to give the twins individual attention. They may frequently be left to "entertain each other" or in the company of older siblings. Parents lacking in higher education may be more influenced by the accepted cultural attitude toward twins and therefore further emphasize the twin relationship.

IDENTIFICATION AND EGO DEVELOPMENT

The four factors just described provide a combination of circumstances, all of which may serve to emphasize intertwin identification. However, in addition to these factors which are peculiar to twins, the identification between them has certain specific characteristics. In the first place, identification between twins is usually mutual, i.e., reciprocal and of equal intensity. It is identification with an individual on the same level of development, instead of with an adult or older sibling. This libidinal tie to the other twin conflicts with and has to adapt itself to the parent relationship. In the second place, the intertwin identification appears to have commenced so early that its origin is difficult to determine.

We can assume that as individuals each twin goes through the same developmental process as singly born infants, i.e., through an undifferentiated phase in which id and ego are one (Hartmann, Kris, Loewenstein, 1946), and no boundaries exist between the self and the outside world, to the time when his ability to perceive develops and he becomes aware that the mother is not an extension of himself. With the beginning awareness of separation comes the first stage in the process of identification, a striving to maintain the unity with the pleasure-giving object through incorporating it into the ego. Primary identification with the mother is the result of this early incorporation.

In the case of twins, each infant not only must go through this same process of becoming aware of himself as separate from his mother, and the ensuing primary identification with her, but he has an additional task, that of separating himself from his twin. If the intertwin identification is assumed to originate in a similar manner, we would have to show that one twin has the ability to satisfy some need or drive in the other. However, the twin infant does not need his twin in the sense that he needs his mother, so that it is unlikely that the intertwin identification takes place through oral incorporation. To the infant, everything outside of himself is an extension of himself, until through frustration he perceives the separation. Therefore, to the extent to which one twin is aware of the existence of the other in the first weeks of infancy, there must be a sense of oneness, or rather a lack of perception of separateness. As a result of this lack of differentiation, a state of psychological syncytium[4] exists, a condition preceding an awareness of body boundaries.

Maturation of sensory perception is necessary before one twin infant can begin to perceive himself as separate from the other. A few examples will, I hope, make this clear.

1. Twins, approximately three months of age, were lying side by side in a twin-sized baby carriage. Both infants were sleeping peacefully on their backs, the thumb of one twin in the mouth of the other.

[4] Term suggested by Boyer (1959). Introduced in his papers (1956, 1960).

2. At a later stage of development, approximately in the seventh month, these same twins were seated on the bed opposite each other and were playing with each other in the manner that a single child might play with a mirror held up to him, namely, reaching out and touching. However, this particular situation had other elements in it; each baby seemed to be exploring the body of the other in a way that, if left to himself, one baby explores his own body. Fingers were poked into the navel of the other, toward the eyes and into the mouth.

Certainly there was a partial awareness of separateness as evidenced by the laughter (Jacobson, 1946) which accompanied these pokings. The play was abruptly interrupted, however, by a shrill cry. A finger poked into the mouth of the mirror image was bitten!

To the observer, there seemed to be considerable surprise mingled with the expression of pain. It must be experiences such as this last-described one which eventually enable the twin baby to perceive that his twin is really another individual, not an extension of himself or his mirror image. Parallelism in behavior which exists in any two infants of the same stage of physical development must contribute many similar instances in which one twin perceives the other as though observing himself in a mirror. Conversely, he is likely to think his own mirror image is his twin. Burlingham (1952) tells of one twin whose name was Bill, who at two years five months called his brother, "other one Bill," and seeing his own reflection in the lavatory mirror when urinating, said, "other one Bill do wee-wee."

In these early years there appears to be a continuum, never a sharp delineation between a sense of oneness with the twin and the realization of separation. Incomplete differentiation is characteristic of the intertwin relationship at this period. Continued visual confrontation with the mirror image leads to identification through visual incorporation and the gradual transition from the phase of psychological syncytium to that of primary identification.

This primary intertwin identification resembles the primary identification with the mother in many respects. Concerning primary identification, Edith Jacobson (1954) states that it "plays a predominant role in the mental life—throughout the preoedipal and early oedipal phase and to some extent even later. In fact, it will find its place within the mature psychic organization. . . . Even when the baby has progressed to a full awareness of himself and of his love objects as individual entities, his dependency on the mother in regard to most of his instinctual needs and ego functions is still bound to prevent the complete separation of maternal and self-images."

The influence of the primary intertwin identification is similarly evident in later stages of development, in some instances throughout the life of the twins. This identification with the twin often retards the maturation of both individuals, causing language difficulties and interfering with the formation of other object relationships. Just as the dependency on the mother prevents complete separation of the maternal and self-images in the single child, the dependency of one twin on the other often causes their self-images to remain blurred.[5] Many examples can be cited to illustrate this continued blurring of images or confusion of identity; one of the most convincing is the result of a study by Irène Lézine. In a test at twenty-four months in which the child was supposed to say his own name, only 40 per cent of twins passed, as compared with 60 per cent of nontwins. At the same age level, the children were supposed to be able to point to parts of their own body and to identify them on a picture. Here again 42 per cent of the twins passed, as compared to 60 per cent of the nontwin control group. A confusion of identity was observed in other situations as well; a child would come when his twin was called, or he would point to parts of the body on the body of his twin instead of on himself (Lézine, 1951).

This confusion of identity is one of the results of the primary intertwin identification. It has a serious effect on the further development of the personality, since it must necessarily cause a retardation in the development of the ego. As Fenichel (1945) states it, ". . . in the development of reality, the conception of one's own body plays a very special role. One's own body becomes something apart from the rest of the world and thus the discerning of self from nonself is made possible. . . . the so-called body image constitutes the idea of

5 Dr. Edward D. Joseph, who discussed this paper at the 1959 meeting of the American Psychoanalytic Association, reports an excellent example of the persistence of this relationship into adulthood: ". . . watching his reflection in a store window, he became uncertain whether he was seeing himself or his brother. Suddenly the image that he saw was perceived as that of a beautiful woman with a glamorous figure. He then knew that the reflection was himself. This hallucinatory experience showed not only that his self-representation was incomplete, but also that it was distorted. It was not clearly defined, but rather one that fused the brother and a female figure."

I and is of basic importance for the further formation of the ego."
The Lézine tests clearly show the difficulty twins have in separating
self from nonself.[6]

The continued inability of the twins to see themselves as
separate identities can be illustrated with several observations.
Dorothy Burlingham, for instance, points out that some twins seem
to represent two sides of the same personality, as though, added
together, they would make a well-balanced whole. On the other hand,
there are instances in which twins appear to switch attitudes almost
as easily as they might exchange a set of clothes. One set of twins
observed used to take turns crying whenever the mother left home.
Finally one day the mother asked the twin who was being "good"
and not making a fuss, how it happened that she was not crying too.
"Sister's crying," she was told, "I don't need to."

As evidence that this type of interchangeability does not end at
the toddler stage is the scene between twin girls, age five, in the
process of trying on new dresses. Lacking a mirror, one of them said
to the other, "Stand over there so I can see how I look."

Although these examples illustrate the continuation of the
primary intertwin identification and the resulting lack of individuation, they are not in themselves any indication of a serious disturbance in personality development. If, however, added to the existing
primary intertwin identification we find one or more of the four
factors (the cultural and the parental attitudes, the physical similarity, and the socioeconomic situation) exerting a strong influence,
the effect may be pathogenic. These factors cause an intensification
of the primary intertwin identification with serious ego retardation

---

[6] A similarity in the relationship of one twin to the other and that of a single child
to a transitional object as described by Winnicott (1953) has been mentioned by several
discussants of this paper. Robert M. Dorn, discussant at the Los Angeles Psychoanalytic
Society stated: "The twin relationship sets up a perpetual twenty-four-hour opportunity for an animated transitional object—one that sometimes 'intrudes' whether he is
wanted or not." This comparison is only valid to the extent that the intertwin relationship is concomitant with the object relationship to the mother. However, undue
persistence of transitional objects is the *result* of the slow development in object
relationship to the mother; whereas persistence of the intertwin relationship *interferes*
with the development of object relationship to the mother. Moreover, the twin fails
to serve the purpose of a transitional object in Winnicott's sense because the actions
of one twin cannot be controlled by the other, and because the twin cannot be the
passive receptor of feelings of hate and aggression. Many of the twins whom I have
observed not only make use of the transitional objects as Winnicott describes, but
also show all the evidence of a strong bond to each other.

as a result. Here again we see a striking similarity between primary intertwin identification and primary mother-child identification. The one serves to preserve the unit, twin-twin; the other, the unit, mother-child. When the singly born child does not progress from the stage of primary identification to object-libidinal cathexis of the mother, we speak of a fixation at the early mother-infant symbiotic phase. The mother remains fused with, not separated from, the image of the self. According to Mahler (1952), such fixation is at the root of symbiotic psychoses.

Intensification of the primary intertwin identification causes comparable disturbances to personality development. Such an intensification may occur as the result of lack of opportunity of the individual twin infant for adequate contact with the mother. "Bodily contact with the mother, that is, fondling and cuddling, is an integral prerequisite for the demarcation of the body ego from the nonself within the stage of somatopsychic symbiosis of the mother-infant dual unity" (Mahler, 1952). With possibly only half the opportunity afforded a singleton for contact with the mother, the twin infant would normally be delayed in developing an awareness of self as well as in relating to the mother as a love object. In other words, the primary intertwin identification persists because no other relationship interferes with it, and as a result, the twins fall back on each other in the way a singleton remains autistic when there is a lack of opportunity for adequate object relationship.

Normally the child progresses from the early primary identification with the mother to a more active type of primitive identification through imitation of the love object. As Edith Jacobson (1954) puts it, "These early infantile affectomotor identifications seem to precede and usher in imitations of the parents' functional activities. . . . The child's own expanding motor activities, his learning to walk and talk and to behave like the parents, his cleanliness training which is expressive of a beginning instinctual control . . . all these accomplishments . . . mark the onset of ego formation."

Spitz (1957) calls our attention to the mutuality in imitation, stressing the role of the parent's imitation and identification with the infant, without which "the development of the child into a human being would be impeded . . . the mutual imitation of gesture and word have a powerful effect on the progressive unfolding of the child's personality." The mother's difficulty in being able to identify with two infants at a time has already been emphasized. The transition from primary intertwin identification to object relationship with the mother is hampered from two directions: insufficient response from the mother to each individual child, and the constant presence of the twin as object for imitation and identification.

The effect of the intertwin imitation is dramatically described by Burlingham. Bill and Bert, confusingly identical twins, were in the Hampstead Nursery from the time they were about four months old to the age of three years. At about thirteen months of age a game of imitation developed:

> One would start to shout and kick and the other would watch him and laugh; then the other would take his turn to shout and kick and the first one would watch and laugh. . . . Both twins tried to find new ways of entertaining the other . . . grimacing, making sudden jerky clownish movements, . . . [They would become] more and more excited until the game was like an orgy. . . . Wild movements about the room, aggressive actions against adults, children and each other were generally the result of these games. . . . In the last months at the Nursery it was felt best to separate them [Burlingham, 1952].

Another set of identical twins, Johnny and Jimmy, were brought to my attention at about four and a half years of age because their speech was almost unintelligible to anyone but themselves. With these youngsters, as with the Burlingham twins, separation brought about a solution, each child being sent to a different school. It was interesting, however, that during the summer vacation following the first semester of separation, when the children were once again constantly in each other's company, what had been a marked speech improvement was completely lost. Several years in separate schools were necessary to effect a permanent improvement.

Johnny and Jimmy were also strikingly similar twins. They were true mirror-image twins, one left-handed, the other right-handed, one with the heart on the right side of the body. In contrast to Bill and Bert, they were brought up at home and there being no other children, they should have had ample opportunity to relate to their parents. However, the family finances were limited, and the mother did all her own work. As a result, the twins were left to "amuse themselves" as much as possible, while the mother looked after the housework. Thus we see that the economic factor as well as the physical similarity played an important part in the background of these twins. Evidence of the influence of the cultural attitude is seen in the manner in which the twins were named, and in the fact that they had usually been dressed alike.

In both sets of twins a multiple number of factors were present, all of which worked in the direction of intensifying the primary intertwin identification. In both, the physical similarity was especially marked and was probably the most important single element of influence. Both suffered inadequate opportunity for object relationship.

The retardation in the ability to speak intelligibly for the one set of twins had the same effect as the imitation game for the other: both fostered and strengthened the intertwin tie, at the same time putting an obstacle in the way of relationship to others. In both instances we can speak of a continuance and intensification of the primary intertwin identification as the dominant characteristic of their relationship. One other aspect of this becomes clear: there is a tendency for the primary intertwin identification to be self-perpetuating. Once it has become intensified, it inhibits progress toward communication with individuals other than the twin and thus hinders the development of object relationship.[7]

Disturbance and retardation in twins of the important ego function, the use of language, has received considerable attention and study on the part of educators and psychologists although little has been offered in the way of explanation of its occurrence. The well-known studies of Davis (1937) and Day (1932) in which they compared only children, singletons with siblings, unlike-sexed twins, and like-sexed, clearly established a continuum in the direction of retardation. Like-sexed twins were apt to be the most retarded, while only children who have had no constant companions other than adults averaged superior in speech development. Davis found that children of parents in the upper occupational groups, i.e., higher

7 We do not yet have sufficient observations on twins to determine whether or not marked autoerotic symptoms always accompany retardation in ego development in twins. However, it is interesting that in both these sets of twins bed rocking was noted: with Johnny and Jimmy from three to seven months of age, with Billy and Bert, up to three years. For the latter, head banging and masturbation were also reported. Since such symptoms regularly occur in singly born children with disturbances in object relationship, it should not surprise us to find the same to be true for twins.

socioeconomic level, have practically overcome their language handicap by nine and a half years, while those from the lower occupational groups have made relatively little progress.

In my experience, preverbal communication is normal and usual between twins, commencing at the phase of lallation when the infant begins to play with sounds. An instance at a somewhat later period was observed in twin boys about one year of age, who did not yet speak any words. One had been removed from the bedroom to be dressed, while the other was just beginning to wake from his nap. Suddenly the one who was being dressed noticed the absence of his twin. He sat bolt upright and let out a shrill "Ay-y!" An answering "Ay-y!" was heard from his brother across the hall. "Ay-y's" flew back and forth for several minutes. This, obviously, was communication. Echolalia between the twins is the probable reason for the frequent appearance of nonsense words or syllables in their "vocabulary" which is unintelligible to anyone but the twins themselves, and often reported by parents as a "language of their own."

Piaget (1923) has said: "In talking to himself, the individual experiences sufficient pleasure and excitement to divert him from the desire to communicate his thoughts to other people." The twin, a second self, must make this "self-communication" even more enjoyable and exciting. Nevertheless, not all twins are slow in learning language. There seems, however, to be a correlation between retardation of this ego function and the intensity and persistence of the intertwin identification. It is possible that further study of the conditions under which such language retardation occurs will give us a clearer understanding of the conditions under which the intertwin identification may have a pathogenic effect on ego development as a whole.

Turning to nonidentical twins, we find that generally speaking dissimilarity serves to lessen the intensity of the primary intertwin identification to such an extent that the relationship of the twins to each other differs little from that which we would find between any two siblings. The parents are able to distinguish between them from birth and to relate to them as individuals. However, some parents have their own unconscious need to see a continuation of the intertwin relationship. Douglass W. Orr (1941) describes the analysis of one member of a set of nonidentical male twins whose problems he traced to an attempt on the part of the environment to suppress the differences between them.

The differences between twins, while helping each achieve an identity of his own, often intensify sibling rivalry. From the point of view of the parents, the insistent clamoring for attention on the part of each twin can be unbearably harrowing. Not realizing how important it is that twins fight it out and learn to accept each other as different individuals, parents frequently do everything in their power to try to make the twins conform to the culturally accepted picture of what the twin relationship should be like. Apparently the parents of Orr's patient were of this type. This man was unable to develop a sense of his own identity, feeling guilty when aware of the differences between himself and his brother.

Nonidentical twin girls, Linda and Susan, who had been dressed alike and in other ways treated like identical twins, developed complementary personalities, one predominantly compulsive, the other phobic. Both girls showed evidence of fixation at the anal-aggressive level, and at age sixteen their immaturity in ego development was marked by their interdependence and inability to assume age-appropriate responsibilities in daily life. Susan was brought for treatment because of multiple phobias, of which her fear of rain and thunder was most prominent. In the course of treatment, as she became aware of the underlying fear of boys and men, in particular of her father, the phobic symptoms gave way to exhibitionistic acting out, aggressively castrative behavior toward boys, and defiance toward parental authority. Despite her emancipation from her dependent attitude toward her parents, she continued to cling to her twin, needing her twin's approval concerning her behavior, manner of dress, and choice of friends. Linda was the only person who could impose a restraining influence on Susan's new-found impulsivity. On the other hand, Linda, who had not had treatment, continued to be the obedient daughter, the good student. Having difficulty with social relationships, she relied on Susan to "break the ice" for her. The sadomasochistic relationship resulting from these sharply contrasting attitudes caused endless conflict between them. At this point believing that sisters and especially twins should not fight and being totally unable to cope with the rivalry they had previously been able to hold within bounds, the beleaguered parents interrupted Susan's treatment.

Beckwitt (1954) and Abraham (1953) both describe analyses of the female half of different-sexed twins. Both emphasize the importance of the identification with the male twin in the etiology of the neurosis and the tenacity with which the patient clung to the fantasy of possessing a penis. Obviously, for a girl to have a male twin adds continued insult to supposed injury. To maintain equality with the male twin, the primary intertwin identification must be preserved; therefore, the illusory penis persists in order to continue the denial of femininity.

In some instances, differences in maturation rate even between identical twins serve to diminish the effect of the primary intertwin identification. This was the case when one member of eleven-year-old identical girl twins began to menstruate before the other. Her emotional maturity kept pace with her physical development and she felt ready to break away from the closeness of their intertwin tie, while the other still seemed quite dependent on it. The more mature twin became angry and disturbed. She complained: "Judy follows me around all the time. I can't do a thing without her tagging along. She's such a baby, I'm ashamed of the way she acts." For her, the intertwin identification was no longer a source of support; rather, it represented a narcissistic injury to conceive of herself in terms of what she felt her sister to be. Her mirror image now appeared to be all that she was trying to discard and posed a threat to the identity she was trying to establish for herself.

To date there have been few opportunities to follow twins observed in infancy to the point of maturity. When I learned that James Shields had used Bill and Bert in his study, "The Social Development of Twins" (1954c), I asked him for a report. They had had so much difficulty in forming object relationships, it was not surprising to learn that at twelve and a half years they were still too unmanageable and aggressive toward one another to live with the rest of the family. They were in a hostel for maladjusted children, had not made close friends with other boys, and had remained extremely lively, excitable, and undisciplined. These same twins are referred to by Anna Freud in her paper on Adolescence (1958). Diagnosed as psychopathic personalities,[8] they had undergone treatment.

8 Personal communication.

In their treatments it transpired that the "adolescent revolt" against the love objects of infancy demands the breaking of the tie to the twin in no lesser degree than the breaking of the tie to the mother. Since this libidinal (narcissistic as well as object-directed) cathexis of the twin is rooted in the same deep layer of personality as the early attachment to the mother, its withdrawal is accompanied by an equal amount of structural upheaval, emotional upset, and resulting symptom formation. Where, on the other hand, the twin relationship survives the adolescent phase, we may expect to see a delay in the onset of maturity or a restrictive hardening of the character of the latency period . . . [p. 266].

For the majority of twins, although observable remnants of the primary intertwin identification remain, the effect does not seem to be nearly as pathogenic as one might expect. In the Slater and Shields study of psychotic and neurotic illnesses in twins (1953), it was shown that the percentage of twins in mental hospitals was no greater than the percentage of twins in the population as a whole.

One reason for this may be that the social adjustment of the pair as a pair is sufficiently normal so that they do not as a rule come to the attention of a psychiatrist. Such an instance was described by Shields in a personal communication (1954b) concerning adult twins, Barbara and Carol. When Shields made their acquaintance, he was struck by Barbara's dominance over Carol. Later Carol described several disconcerting and embarrassing situations resulting from the fact that her twin viewed Carol's possessions and experiences as her own. However, Carol tolerated her sister's psychotic behavior, leading us to the supposition of a complementary disturbance in her own personality. An interdependence such as this masks the need for psychiatric intervention.

It is interesting that Carol and Barbara had undergone several periods of separation. The first occurred at two weeks of age, when Barbara was taken to the home of her paternal grandmother. Until age five, they met only on rare occasions. Then they lived together until they went to different universities at seventeen. It is to be hoped that at some future date, there will be opportunity to analyze twins who, as in this instance, have developed an intense intertwin identification despite having gone through separation. An understanding of the dynamics of such a dependent relationship could perhaps help explain twinning relationships in nontwins. It is possible that the loss of individual identity may in large measure be compensated for by the supportive aspect of such a bond. The reassurance and security gained appears to counteract whatever weakening may have been suffered by the individual ego. The identity *à deux* substitutes for an identity as an individual.

When such an identity *à deux* developes, or when the primary intertwin identification persists beyond adolescence, we can conjecture that a psychosis might occur in one or both of the individuals at a time when life brings about a separation. This is an area not yet investigated.[9]

In order to understand the nature of the intertwin relationship, certain psychological processes have been postulated. These processes, peculiar to twins (and possibly to other children of multiple births), are concurrent and frequently conflict with the usual developmental processes. Commencing with a state of psychological syncytium, a gradual transition takes place as the infants begin to distinguish between self and nonself: primary intertwin identification occurs as a result of visual incorporation. Constant confrontation with a mirror image retards differentiation of self and twin, and inhibits clear delineation of body boundaries. The continuing primary intertwin identification resembles in effect the continuation of primary identification with the mother in so far as it prolongs the mutual interdependence, brings about retardation of ego identity, and interferes with object relations to others.

Ordinarily these difficulties appear to be overcome in the course of development. However, in some instances when the primary intertwin identification is emphasized by one or more of the four factors —the cultural attitude, the parental attitude, the degree of similarity, and economic pressures—the effect may be pathogenic. Implicit to this conclusion is the assumption that prevention of pathogenic development must occur through measures taken to counteract the influence of those four factors.

[9] In discussing this paper when read to the staff at Mount Sinai Hospital in Los Angeles, Dr. Sheldon Selesnick reported having seen several such cases in twins who had been separated during military service.

BIBLIOGRAPHY

Abraham, H. C. (1953), Twin Relationship and Womb Phantasy in a Case of Anxiety Hysteria. *Int. J. Psa.*, XXXIV.

Beckwitt, M. C. (1954), Some Observations on Penis Envy in a Girl Twin. Read at the Los Angeles Society for Psychoanalysis.

Bibring, G. L. (1961), A Study of the Psychological Processes in Pregnancy and of the Earliest Mother-Child Relationship. I: Some Propositions and Comments. *This Annual*, XVI.

Boyer, L. B. (1956), Maternal Overstimulation and Ego Defects. *This Annual*, XI.

—— (1959), Personal communication.

—— (1960), A Hypothesis Regarding the Time of Appearance of the Dream Screen. *Int. J. Psa.*, XLI.

—— (1961), Personal communication.

Brewster, H. H. (1957), Identical Pair of Poliomyelitis Patients: A Study in Twinning. Read at the Western Divisional Meeting of the American Psychiatric Association.

Burlingham, D. (1952), *Twins. A Study of Three Pairs of Identical Twins.* New York: International Universities Press.

Davis, E. A. (1937), *Development of Linguistic Skill in Twins, Singletons with Siblings, and Only Children from Age 5-10 Years.* University of Minnesota Press.

Day, E. J. (1932), The Development of Language. *Child Development*, III.

Demarest, E. W. & Winestine, M. C. (1955), The Initial Phase of Concomitant Treatment of Twins. *This Annual*, X.

Fenichel, O. (1945), *The Psychoanalytic Theory of Neurosis.* New York: Norton.

Freud, A. (1958), Adolescence. *This Annual*, XIII.

—— & Dann, S. (1951), An Experiment in Group Upbringing. *This Annual*, VI.

Greenacre, P. (1952), *Trauma, Growth and Personality.* New York: Norton.

Guttmacher, A. F. (1953), The Incident of Multiple Births in Man and Some Other Unipara. *Obst. & Gynec.*, II.

Hartmann, H. (1933), Psychiatrische Zwillingsstudien. *Jb. Psychiat. & Neurol.*, L.

—— & Kris, E., Loewenstein, R. M. (1946), Comments on the Formation of Psychic Structure. *This Annual*, II.

Jacobson, E. (1946), The Child's Laughter. *This Annual*, II.

—— (1954), The Self and the Object World. *This Annual*, IX.

Joseph, E. D. (1959), An Unusual Fantasy in a Twin. With an Inquiry into the Nature of Fantasy. *Psa. Quart.*, XXVIII.

Leonard, M. (1953), Twins; the Myth and Reality. *Child Study*, XXX.

Lézine, I. (1951), Les étapes de la prise de conscience de soi chez les jeunes jumeaux. *Enfance*, III.

—— & Brunet, O. (1951), *Le développement psychologique de la première enfance.* Paris: Presses Universitaires de France.

Mahler, M. S. (1952), On Child Psychosis and Schizophrenia. *This Annual*, VII.

Orr, D. W. (1941), A Psychoanalytic Study of a Fraternal Twin. *Psa. Quart.*, X.

Piaget, J. (1923), *The Language and Thought of the Child.* New York: Humanities Press, 1951.

Plank, E. N. (1958), Reactions of Mothers of Twins in a Child Study Group. *Am. J. Orthopsychiat.*, XXVIII.

Shields, J. (1954a), Personality Differences and Neurotic Traits in Normal Twin School Children. A Study in Psychiatric Genetics. *Eugenics Rev.*, XLV.

—— (1954b), Personal communication.

—— (1954c), The Social Development of Twins. *Case Conference*, I.

—— (1958), Twins Brought up Apart. *Eugenics Rev.*, L.

Slater, E. & Shields, J. (1953), *Psychotic and Neurotic Illnesses in Twins* [Medical Research Council, Special Report Series No. 278]. London: Her Majesty's Stationery Office.

Spitz, R. A. (1957), *No and Yes. On the Genesis of Human Communication.* New York: International Universities Press.

Trainham, G., Piliafian, G. & Kraft, R. M. (1945), A Case History of Twins Breast-fed on a Self-demand Regime. *J. Pediat.,* XXVII.

Winnicott, D. W. (1953), Transitional Object and Transitional Phenomena. *Int. J. Psa.,* XXXIV.

REFLECTIONS ON DEPRESSION[1]

BERTRAM D. LEWIN, M.D. (New York)

In previous centuries, psychiatry did not use freely the term *depression*, as it does now, to indicate a pathological complex of symptoms. The old literature was apt to speak of *melancholia* instead, and the history of the melancholia concept from Hippocrates to Kraepelin constitutes a large part of the history of psychiatry. That the word *depression* has replaced it so extensively may be due to the authority of Kraepelin and his use of its cognate adjective in the diagnostic label, *manic-depressive*. In one application, *involution melancholia*, the older word survives, and it was current at the time of Freud's early writings. We find Freud and Abraham writing of *melancholische Depression*, implying thereby that they meant one form of depression—a structured complex of symptoms.

Present-day psychiatry has not completely rejected the concepts which Kraepelin used in regard to manic-depressive psychoses, but it has let them lie fallow. Not much, for example, is done operationally with Kraepelin's organic assumptions, and indeed the idea of symptom, in its nineteenth-century meaning of sign of a disease process, has fallen into desuetude. The word symptom remains, but it has a new meaning. In manic-depressive psychoses, in other psychoses and in the neuroses, symptom has come to mean a psychological structure, as Freud defines it in *The Problem of Anxiety* (1926). Psychiatrists are gradually getting away from the word's original denotative implication.

Certainly, in psychoanalytically pervaded thinking, there has been an inevitable, insidious change of meaning not only in the concept of symptom, but also in the concept of depression. Although depression

[1] This paper was presented at the Tenth Anniversary Symposium, the Child Psychiatry Unit, Massachusetts Mental Health Center, Harvard Medical School. The symposium was devoted to "Psychoanalytic Studies in Object Loss and Depression."

is still the diagnostic label of a psychosis, it is predominantly the label of a definite set of mechanisms. These mechanisms, which include as elements aggression turned inwards, identification, tension between ego and superego, narcissistic and oral regression, are familiar to us all. In our thinking, depression has come to mean this complex of mechanisms rather than a disease process; the metapsychological concept has largely replaced the psychiatric-diagnostic one. A third meaning of the word depression creeps into our writing and thinking, and in a way too this is due to our background of Kraepelin's psychological assumptions. I refer to the everyday idea of depression as an elementary feeling. As the song puts it, "The blues ain't nothing but a good man feeling bad." Beneath all the Kraepelinian nosological system lies a faculty psychology which assumes that an affect is something elemental and unstructured, pure and pristine. If this has come to seem a matter of common sense and something obvious, we must remind ourselves again of the philosopher's remark that what we regard as common sense is apt to be the residue of habit and that today's common sense was yesterday's bias.

Let us therefore look more closely at the idea of depression as a sad feeling. Psychoanalysts have many opportunities for observation and assessment of this feeling. Gerö[2] has remarked that it appears, along with anxiety, in any analysis, even in the analysis of persons called normal, that is, those who have no specific neurotic and psychotic symptoms—students in analytic training, for example. The emergence of feelings of anxiety and depression during an analysis is indeed a corollary of what we believe to be a feature of the analytic process, namely, the uncovering of conflict. During analysis, conflicts previously latent become manifest. Those between ego and id are attended by the evolution of anxiety, those between ego and superego by depression. We think of these technically as feelings indicative of the conflicts, and we are attentive to their presence as signs and signals. Such transient anxieties and depressions, we also believe, are not unlike those which could appear in anybody, and they are of an intensity usually which one would say was within the range of the normal. Particularly is this true if the person who experiences the feeling is able to account for it rationally or through rationalization.

[2] Personal communication.

Also, offhand, we are apt to think of the feeling as a pure and elementary process in the sense of faculty psychology, as an elementary affect. We conceptualize signal anxiety especially and do not usually attend to cognitive elements nor to questions of special genesis and structure.

Yet the simplicity we predicate, on second thought, is purely conceptual. On the couch, we see that the anxiety is a sign of id-ego tension, but we also observe that it occurs in various forms and in different settings. The same anxiety that shows us the presence of open conflict tends to have more or less of a structure. We even approximate a sort of classification, for we note that sometimes the anxiety makes its appearance in the form of a mild phobia, that is, it includes or is linked with displacement. Or in other instances, where there is projection, we may speak of a paranoid anxiety. When we think in this way, we already imply that there is a possible diagnostic and metapsychological aspect even in the case of signal anxiety. Genetically too, since the publication of *The Problem of Anxiety*, we know that we may be dealing repetitively in the analytic situation with anxieties that are formed at various stages of development, and we speak accordingly of separation anxiety, castration anxiety, social anxiety, and the rest. Though we know that anxiety on the couch has its genetic history and structure, conceptually and in the context of analytic technique we neglect this in favor of its major meaning of a signal or sign of conflict.

On the couch, the more or less passing depressive affects, which could be characterized as blue feelings, unhappiness, etc., can be subjected to the same considerations that were introduced concerning anxiety. Depression, like anxiety, is a sign of conflict within the personality; and the forms we meet on the couch range from what may present themselves as nearly pure affect, in the old-fashioned sense, through the various forms known to us from psychiatry. Thus we speak of anxious depression and paranoid depression, and we have even designated one familiar form by a label originating in psychoanalytic technique. I refer to the negative therapeutic reaction. Gerö (1936) has stated that this is a common occurrence in the analysis of cases diagnosed as depressions. The negative therapeutic reaction may not show itself starkly as a depression. But when it does, it is possible to recognize in it various structures.

I do not wish to suggest an exhaustive classification of the forms of negative therapeutic reaction, and I particularly wish to leave any list of depressive forms entirely open-end, but it might be useful to mention examples. One example would be a young woman whose every analytic step that gave promise of possible instinct satisfaction was regularly followed by a guilty depression. The superego here was a lineal descendant of a really very jealous mother and older sister, and her guilt had originally been displayed in real appeasing gestures, designed to curry their benevolence and ward off their jealousy. Internalized, this became visible during the analysis in fantasy. We speak in such a case of moral masochism and a fear of object loss. But it is noteworthy that so far as the patient's introspections were concerned, all of this was for a long time unknown, and even the precipitating actual event for the reaction was not connected in her mind with the ensuing depression. If she had been examined for diagnosis during one of the episodes, she might have been called a case of anxious depression, though the diagnosis would have been qualified by some such term as "subliminal" or "mild."

I have not carefully distinguished in my language between guilt and depression, leaving it to my audience to understand the level of exposition. Theoretically, of course, I follow our usual terminology in this respect. The main point here is that when we find a transient depressed mood appear during the analytic hour—even if it is "reasonable" or rationalized—we can usually find in it one or more of the familiar features of the depressive mechanism, such as turning of aggression against the self, reaction to an object loss, etc. Under the microscopic scrutiny of analytic procedure, we do not find examples of simple affective elements.

I should like to pursue this somewhat further. The studied cases of momentary sadness show a mechanism and are not pure affects in the old faculty-psychology sense. Let us therefore make a radical assumption, somewhat as follows: that in the depressed moods and momentary sadnesses of everyday life, in adults at least, such a pure affect never occurs and that sadnesses, blues, and the like all are complicated reactions involving instinct and ego psychology. To make this idea more concrete through a hypothetical example: I hear of a friend's illness and I become sad. Faculty psychology would predicate two elements—a stimulus (the bad news) and the response (sadness). Such two-term stimulus and response would be considered the elemental model for the origin and appearance of an affect. According to the idea presented above, which is suggested by experience with transient moods in the analytic hour and their analysis, the model would be as follows. Bad news such as the friend's illness is a stimulus, but it is what psychiatry calls a *precipitating* event. The reaction is not a pure simple feeling, harmonious and appropriate (as common sense would say) to a bad situation. The bad news has the form of a threatened object loss, hence in psychological reality *is as if* an object loss and the response is a form of grief, which under scrutiny could be empirically analyzed into aggression turned inward, identification, and more or fewer of the classical elements of the depressive symptom complex. I realize that this hypothesis implies a kind of psychiatrization of psychology and would surely meet with many academic objections. What we have been naïvely calling a normal emotion turns out to be a minor neurosis. Yet I should like to point out that psychology has benefited many times from the introduction of this point of view. My model is Freud's attack on the genesis of anxiety. In considering the hysteric attack, he said that this might be considered an artificial emotion, and turning the matter around, that the original modeling of anxiety on the trauma of birth would mean that the emotion repeated an original "attack."

I shall not speculate further about the genesis of emotions in general, but instead call attention to a clinical difficulty encountered in the study of elation. For many years, elation of low intensity passed relatively unobserved in clinical psychoanalysis. The subject was joyful, one supposed, because things were coming his way. Only when elation did not fit our common-sense preconceptions of when it was to be expected did we give it more intensive study and develop psychological models and explanations. Yet the mild elations encountered during an analysis proved a fruitful field of study. They revealed mechanisms, now well recognized. They could be understood in terms of denial, of coalescence of ego and superego, of identification, and the rest. It is possibly the case that everyday joys too are structured. They are probably not simple responses to simple stimuli, like a reflex, but can be shown to have a structure as complicated as a pathological elation. The organic analogy would not be a reflex, but the firing of some of the complex structures called to our attention by modern neurophysiology.

In the light of our assumption of the individual specificity of affective responses, we may attempt a kind of shorthand metapsychological restatement of some of the above. As an example, we may take the transient depression of individuals in whom, as we say, there is a paranoid coloring. We would assume here the bad news of a friend's illness leads not only to a sad response but to a suspicion that this illness was caused by mistreatment this friend may have been subjected to by his wife or employers or physicians. Such transient suspicions would perhaps disappear with the friend's recovery but might be revived under later stresses. Plainly, we should have a bringing into play of ego defenses other than those classically present in the Freud-Abraham model for depression, notably projection designed to shift an unconscious sense of guilt. Or the sadness could take on a secondary exhibitionistic quality, seeking an outlet for unconscious aggression—if the occasion was used to nag the environment, the friend's family, for example. Such forms would, I think, still come under the head of intelligible reaction and on the whole not be thought particularly pathological.

I have no wish to get involved in an attempt to define normality as opposed to pathology. My standpoint here would be approximately that expressed by Freud (1937) in the following quotation in regard to the ego in analysis:

> If we want to make a compact with the patient's ego, that ego must be normal. But such a normal ego, like normality in general, is an ideal fiction. The abnormal ego which is of no use for our purpose is unfortunately no fiction. Now every normal person is only approximately normal, his ego resembles that of a psychotic in one point or another, in a greater or lesser degree.

This is a profound statement, and I should like to use a partial paraphrase for the sake of exposition to comment on the emotions. The normal emotion is an ideal fiction; emotions we encounter are no fiction. Every one of them is only approximately normal in the sense of faculty psychology. They resemble a psychosis in one point or another, in a greater or lesser degree.

Such a point of view, which admits more factors than are accounted for by faculty psychology and its corollary, Kraepelinian nosology, appears more adaptable to that state of affairs which led Kraepelin to formulate mixed manic-depressive states and the other dubious syndromes in his classifications. It would also, I believe, shed some light on the matter called "the prognosis of the attack." The guiding principle in psychiatry has been roughly that the more pronounced the affect in a psychotic attack the better the prognosis. More accurately one would wish to have stated not whether an attack is temporary but which elements in the attack will probably persist into the so-called period of recovery, and which will not be present. Notably there are variations here, and we still need a study of what particular mechanisms tend to be tied together in different individuals.

As examples of the approach for which I have outlined a sketchy methodology might be mentioned studies by Fenichel (1934) on boredom and by Greenson (1949) on apathy, which are contributions from pathology to the psychology of affective states.

Up to this point in our exposition, the main effort has been to see what Freud's idea as to the genesis of an affect, as elaborated in *The Problem of Anxiety*, might contribute to our conception of the affect, depression. Now, using the same text, we may apply other ideas of Freud to the concept of depression as a combination of neurotic mechanisms. In the main and in principle this has already been done, so what appears here are truly reflections. During years of teaching, I have noted that when the matter of symptom formation is under discussion, we all make many references to Little Hans and the Wolf Man. The references, however, are not often to the original case histories but are more apt to be to the formulations given by Freud in *The Problem of Anxiety*, where the infantile phobias of these two patients are used to illustrate Freud's concept of phobia formation and the role of anxiety and the ego in this process. Indeed, in this context, Little Hans and the Wolf Man come to stand for simple phobia formation. This has become evident from the follow-up work done on the Wolf Man, first by Ruth Mack Brunswick (1928), now by Muriel Gardiner (1953, 1958), and other material gathered for the Freud Archives. This new material has had to do somewhat with the Wolf Man's famous dream and with his phobia, but it has illuminated other parts of his personality and other features. The more we consider Freud's statements in *The Problem of Anxiety*, the more we realize that so far as Little Hans and the Wolf Man are concerned, he has given us there not a bit of case history but an abstract model for the formation of a simple phobia. The model gains in sharpness by the abstraction, that is, by Freud's cutting to the psychological core of the matter. We can say that in general conflict of id and ego are shown by signal anxiety; and that in the simple phobia repression and displacement appear in response to the anxiety.

But even in these simple phobias, the anxiety (except for conceptualizing) is not a simple one-element process. In the case of the Wolf Man, after attributing the anxiety in the main to a fear of castration, Freud adds that it also contains an oral component which arises from a previous period of development and contributes to the manifest fear of being eaten. In Little Hans the fear of being bitten implies a similar oral component. However, we are left with the idea that this is an adventitious rather than a constant matter. The phobia, we are to understand, is a genital neurosis, and the anxiety is typically castration anxiety, while the oral coloration is an individual peculiarity of the two little patients. Some years ago (1952), I gathered material which showed that the façade of other, especially adult phobias (claustrophobia and agoraphobia) also showed traces of oral components, and I thought I could demonstrate in them elements that sprang from the nursing situation. My method in that study was based on Freud's comparison of the façade of a phobia with the manifest content of a dream.

I should like here to take some of the thoughts presented above and transpose them to a similar frame of reference, to speak now of the façade of a depression, and to invoke for the depression a state of affairs such as we find in phobias. The variety in the manifest picture of the phobia led to the invention of a variety of neologistic combinations with the Greek root *phobia:* claustrophobia, agoraphobia, aleurophobia, gephyrophobia, and the rest. That the façade of a depression may show variety was, I believe, adumbrated by the psychiatrists before Kraepelin; for example, when Kahlbaum invented the name *cyclothymia*. But on the whole, these psychiatrists were concerned not with the façade nor the manifest content. They emphasized the course and the form, as the name just mentioned illustrates. The namers of phobias impressed us with their manifest variety, contrariwise Kraepelin and his predecessors and successors ignored variety. In the depressions and elations, they stressed a presumptive unity and sameness. Traditional psychiatry has alerted us to variety in the phobias and to uniformity in the depressions. There is no general terminological agreement concerning the variety of depressions. In the different official classifications, the subheadings designed to indicate varieties of depression differ widely.

Here, I think, the psychoanalysts are beginning to make their contribution. However, they are not following the tradition of the phobia-namers, nor yet that of the descriptive psychiatrists who spoke of *folie circulaire*, simple depression, simple mania, etc. Analysts have instead seen variety in the psychological sense; for example, in the types of identification that can be demonstrated in different patients (Reich, 1954), and in other specific features of the ego (Jacobson, 1954). This type of clinical approach is very different from the one of naming and descriptive classification, and we hope will ultimately replace it. Ultimately, too, such replacement may go far to extend the psychoanalyzation of psychiatry and to substitute for an outworn psychology, based on faculty psychology, a true dynamic model.

I have elsewhere (1954) stated my conviction that all psychoanalytic statements concerning the neuroses must be tested by sleep and dream psychology. This conviction is based on Freud's crucial finding of the sameness in essence of the dream and neurosis psychology, and by the empirically successful application of this idea. I should therefore like to repeat here briefly a comparison I once drew between the depression and a certain type of dream, in which I continue an idea Freud introduced by comparing the phobic façade and manifest dream content. As a frequent manifest façade of the depression, I select the standardized picture used by Freud and Abraham.

Our first approach to treating the melancholia picture as if it were a manifest dream façade assumes that *narcissistic* has the same meaning when it is used in connection with the regression in melancholia and with the regression during sleep, where it implies a dreamless state. Hence, what appears in the manifest picture of melancholia is an analogue of the manifest dream picture, the result of intruding impulses from id and superego which are the analogues of stimuli that threaten to waken the sleeper. In other words, the manifestations of the classical picture of melancholia are the façade ultimately derived from the distorted expression of such impulses.

In this respect we may say further, the depression is an unpleasant dream manifestly, in which the latent narcissistic wish for sleep at the breast is disturbed in its fulfillment by an opposite intruding tendency, that is, by weaners and wakeners. Like the narcissism of sleep, the narcissism of the depressive regression is subject to disturbance by impulses and memories, and these get analogous representation. As in the well-known dream of the burning child in Chapter VII of the *Interpretation of Dreams*, they are represented in a way which is influenced by the need to preserve the narcissistic regression. In the example mentioned, you will recall, a father dreams that his dead child, whose body is laid out in a nearby room, comes to him, shakes him by the arm and whispers, "Father, don't you see I am burning?" The father wakens and finds that one of the candles has started a real fire. Freud uses this dream to show the operation of the wish to sleep, for the dreaming provides the father with a moment more of sleep (Freud, 1900, pp. 533-534).

The well-known superego commands, if they are considered as wakers and weaners, are demands that the depressed patient give up the breast, hence are analogues of the real fire which disturbed the father's sleep. The handling of these by the depressed patient is analogous to the dream distortion and serves the same purpose, namely, to preserve the narcissistic regression. In the dream example, the real arouser, the fire, becomes a dream sentence. In the depression, the superego injunctions are distorted expressions of commands to waken. Their form tends to guard the analogous narcissistic regression of the depressions. The narcissistic sleep analogue of the depressed person is constantly being intruded upon and told, "Get away from your mother's breast! Wake up!" But the demand is not obeyed. The persistence with which this command is repeated over and over shows that it is heard but not heeded. As long as the depressed patient is thus admonished, he is evidently secretly or unconsciously still maintaining his regressive place at the breast. The admonition is treated in the way a dreamer treats a stimulus from within or without—it is given attention and registered but the narcissistic regression is preserved.

I have chosen a very simple type of dream, that of the burning child, as the analogue of a frequent simple form of depression, in which prominent symptoms are due to guilt and oral regression. Freud commented on the contrast between the conscious sense of unworthiness and the unconscious narcissistic grandiosity in such cases. There is a similar paradox in the conscious pain of this disagreeable melancholic picture and the unconscious pleasurable wish fulfillment of sleep at the breast.

To return now to the point made above in regard to the forms and classification of the depressions, we could take the variety of the means used to preserve the narcissistic regression and the different defense mechanisms of the ego that are invoked to preserve it as the source of the individual coloring and varying mechanisms found in different depressions. We have type dreams which, like that of the burning child, are relatively simple and can be used to demonstrate a basic mechanism. In fact, Freud used the dream of the burning child in this very way, as a type to indicate a feature of all dreaming. So, in the analogies drawn above, we have been dealing with a type, and as in the case of the dream, with something which in one way or another may enter all depressions, while the façade presents an analogous variety.

BIBLIOGRAPHY

Brunswick, R. M. (1928), A Supplement to Freud's "History of an Infantile Neurosis." *Int. J. Psa.*, IX.
Fenichel, O. (1934), On the Psychology of Boredom. In: *Collected Papers of Otto Fenichel*, I. New York: Norton, 1953.
Freud, S. (1900), The Interpretation of Dreams. *Standard Edition*, IV & V. London: Hogarth Press, 1953.
——— (1926), *The Problem of Anxiety*. New York: Norton, 1936.
——— (1937), Analysis Terminable and Interminable. *Int. J. Psa.*, XVIII.
Gardiner, M. M. (1953), Meetings with the Wolf Man. *Bull. Menninger Clin.*, XVII.
——— (1958), How I Came Into Analysis with Freud, by the Wolf Man. *J. Am. Psa. Assn.*, VI.
Gerö, G. (1936), The Construction of Depression. *Int. J. Psa.*, XVII.
Greenson, R. R. (1949), The Psychology of Apathy. *Psa. Quart.*, XVIII.
Jacobson, E. (1954), Contributions to the Metapsychology of Psychotic Identification. *J. Am. Psa. Assn.*, II.
Lewin, B. D. (1952), Phobic Symptoms and Dream Interpretation. *Psa. Quart.*, XXI.
——— (1954), Sleep, Narcissistic Neurosis and the Analytic Situation. *Psa. Quart.*, XXIII.
Reich, A. (1954), Early Identifications as Archaic Elements in the Superego. *J. Am. Psa. Assn.*, II.

ON SADNESS AND GRIEF IN INFANCY AND CHILDHOOD

Loss and Restoration of the Symbiotic Love Object[1]

MARGARET SCHOENBERGER MAHLER, M.D. (New York)

There is a conspicuous gap in our understanding of the connecting links between those conditions which Spitz (1946) has described as "anaclitic depression" and other psychotic pictures in early infancy. While anaclitic depressions occur in the second half of the first year of life, the other psychotic conditions may, or may not, have their prestages in the first year of life; however, they definitely develop during the separation-individuation phase of normal development, that is, from twelve to thirty-six months of age.

According to Spitz, anaclitic depression is the equivalent of "primal parathymia," which was described by Abraham (1924) as the infantile prototype of a later depressive psychosis. Spitz considers the syndrome of anaclitic depression a psychosis, although, due to the immaturity of the psychic apparatus, the signs and symptoms differ from those manifested in the psychoses of later life. He feels that by the second half of the first year of life, the ego is sufficiently well organized to control motility and express negative and positive affects. An extreme disturbance in these ego functions could therefore be considered to be psychotic. The chief signs of anaclitic depression in the infants Spitz observed were a dejected expression and posture, and a distaste for motility.

We are all agreed that the cardinal etiological agent in this syndrome, as in other forms of infantile psychosis, is the object loss

[1] This paper was presented at the Tenth Anniversary Symposium, the Child Psychiatry Unit, Massachusetts Mental Health Center, Harvard Medical School. The symposium was devoted to "Psychoanalytic Studies in Object Loss and Depression."

This paper is based mainly upon research supported by the National Institutes of Mental Health, United States Public Health Service, Grant M–3353.

suffered by these infants. In this connection, Spitz explains that after six months of age, an infant can seek out an adult—that infants who have suffered object loss will attempt to regain the lost object world, as do adults. In infancy, this involves finding a substitute object. The infants in the particular institution Spitz studied had little opportunity to find a substitute object because few could in reality be found.

There is another important etiological factor involved here, and one which we cannot afford to minimize: these anaclitically depressed infants were deprived of maternal care during the second half of the first year of life. *I conceive of this as the symbiotic phase of development, and consider a need-satisfying mother-infant relationship during this period a prerequisite for normal growth.* In previous publications (1952, 1955, 1958, 1960) I delineated my concepts of developmental phases—those of normal autism and normal symbiosis, and of separation-individuation—which form the core of my formulation of infantile psychosis.

In that twilight stage of early life which Freud designated as primary narcissism, the infant shows few signs of being able to perceive anything beyond his own body. He seems to live in a world of inner stimuli. The first weeks of extrauterine life are characterized by what Ferenczi (1913) called the stage of hallucinatory wish fulfillment. Whereas the enteroceptive system functions from birth, the perceptual conscious system, the sensorium, is not yet cathected. This lack of peripheral sensory cathexis only gradually gives way to perception, particularly to distance perception of the outside world. This earliest extrauterine phase, which may be considered a normal autistic phase of the mother-infant unity, gives way to the symbiotic phase proper (from the age of three months on). During his wakeful, hungry periods, the three- to four-month-old baby seems to perceive, temporarily at least, the Gestalt of that small part of external reality which is represented by the mother's breast, face, and hands—that is, what is perceived as her ministrations.

I wish to emphasize the fact that normal symbiosis implies a complex interaction between the baby and the mother. The Gestalt of the mother's ministrations is a component of the Gestalt of the symbiotic partner, with its highly libidinized affective quality. This stage of development is characterized by the specific smiling response which the symbiotic object elicits, and the discriminatory anxiety and fear of strangers which the infant exhibits at or around eight months of age (Spitz, 1950). The importance of these responses cannot be overestimated. I would also point out that whereas the development from normal autism to normal symbiosis occurs within the matrix of the oral gratification-frustration sequences of the normal nursing situation, it is dependent upon, and synonymous with, need satisfaction only in a very broad sense. This development involves much more than the satisfaction of oral and other vegetative needs. The primitive ego seems to possess an amazing ability to absorb and synthesize complex object images without adverse effect, and on occasion even with benefit. Thus, the Gestalt of the nurse, who may be relegated to the function of providing immediate need satisfaction, is synthesized with the Gestalt of the mother, who may be available only as an additional or transient external ego. However, it is truly impressive that although the mother may be less involved in the actual care of the infant, her image seems to attract so much cathexis that it often, though not always, becomes the cardinal object representation. This crucial phenomenon is rarely mentioned in the literature, and to my knowledge has never been investigated in a systematic study. Freud's paper on Leonardo (1910) and Helene Deutsch's "A Two-Year-Old's First Love Comes to Grief" (1919) are thought-provoking classics in this direction.

Although the representations of the symbiotic object are extremely complex during this crucial phase of development, and although the Gestalt of the need-satisfying object and her ministrations are highly specific, there seems to be dim awareness only of the boundaries of the self, as distinct from the boundaries of the "symbiotic object." During the symbiotic phase the infant behaves and functions as though he and his mother were an omnipotent system (a dual unity) within one common boundary (a symbiotic membrane, as it were).

Toward the latter part of the symbiotic stage, we generally assume, primary narcissism declines and gradually gives way to secondary narcissism. The infant takes his own body, as well as the mother, as the object of his secondary narcissism. The concept of narcissism, however, remains rather obscure in both psychoanalytic theory and usage unless we place sufficient emphasis on the vicissitudes of the aggressive drive.

During the course of normal development, protective systems safeguard the infant's body from the oral-sadistic pressures which begin to constitute a potential threat to his body integrity from the fourth month on (Hoffer, 1950a). The pain barrier is one such device. In addition, Hoffer (1950b) particularly emphasized that adequate libidinization of the body, within the mother-infant relationship, is important for the development of the body image.

Only when the body becomes the object of the infant's secondary narcissism, via the mother's loving care, does the external object become eligible for identification. To quote Hoffer (1950a), from the age of three or four months on, "primary narcissism has already been modified, but the world of objects has not necessarily yet taken on definite shape." Identification enables the infant to separate from the mother gradually, and to leave her outside the hitherto "omnipotent common orbit," by cathecting the "self-boundaries" (p. 159).

Normal symbiosis paves the way for the separation-individuation phase, which overlaps with and replaces the symbiotic phase (from the age of twelve to eighteen months on). As a result of the maturational spurt during the second year of life, the normal toddler achieves relatively advanced physical autonomy. At this time, the autonomous ego function of locomotion may become the most conspicuous paradigm of discrepancy between the rate of maturation and the rate of personality development.[2] Locomotion enables the child to separate physically—to move away—from the mother, although he may be emotionally quite unprepared to do so. The two-year-old becomes aware of his separateness in many other ways as well. He enjoys his independence, and perseveres with great tenacity in his attempts at mastery. In this way, large quantities of libido and aggression are utilized by the ego. On the other hand, some children react to this newly acquired autonomy adversely and with increased clinging to the mother. The realization that they function separately may elicit intense anxiety in vulnerable toddlers, who then try desperately to deny their separateness and to struggle against re-engulfment by increased opposition to the adults in their environment. At the Masters Children's Center we are currently investigating the

---

[2] Hartmann, Kris, and Loewenstein (1946) have introduced the helpful distinction between the concepts of development and maturation.

various reactions of separation-individuation.[3] This research project involves the intensive study of the interaction between the infants from twelve to thirty-six months of age and their mothers. It is being conducted in a natural and informal indoor-playground setting. We are gathering participant and nonparticipant observational material of normal development, with particular emphasis on the specific steps in the various processes of disengagement from the symbiotic object, which we know so little about. In a second research project, we are investigating symbiotic psychotic toddlers. This study is being conducted within the framework of a therapeutic setting, in which the children and their mothers are simultaneously present (Mahler and Furer, 1960).[4]

The toddler is able to experiment with, practice, and enjoy the autonomous functions of his ego only if personality development and maturation proceed at a comparable rate. Mastery of these functions gives the child secondary narcissistic pleasure, as Hendrick (1942) has pointed out. Moreover, such experiences eventually help the child to acquire a sense of individual identity.

It must be quite obvious at this point, theoretically at least, that the toddler is not able to cope with the demands of the separation-individuation phase of development unless the preceding symbiotic phase has been satisfactory.

The most severe traumatization during the symbiotic phase is that suffered by anaclitically depressed infants who had actually been separated from the central love object during this phase. They had suffered object loss in reality—and substitute mothers had not been available. Yet, when the mother was restored to the baby, and when this occurred within a reasonable period of time, before his ego had suffered irreversible damage, the infant recovered. It is interesting to speculate which mechanisms account for this striking recovery potential in these anaclitically depressed infants.

We are similarly puzzled, though for quite different reasons, by another fact: the anamneses of children with autistic and symbiotic psychosis do not indicate, or only very rarely, that separation, of any

[3] This research project had been sponsored by the Field Foundation and is currently supported by the Psychoanalytic Research and Development Fund, Inc., and by the Taconic Foundation.
[4] It is sponsored by a grant from the National Institutes of Mental Health of the United States Public Health Service.

significant duration, from the mother actually occurred. In the majority of these cases, there was no real loss of the symbiotic object, beyond those brief separations which most normal infants experience in the course of the first two or three years of life. I refer to such ubiquitous traumata as transient separation from the mother due to the birth of a sibling, or due to hospitalization of either mother or child. When such events occur at the end of the first year of life, or during the crucial separation-individuation phase, there is no doubt that the toddler suffers considerably. However, most toddlers and most babies are able to accept substitute love objects if these are at all available during the mother's absence. They seem to be able to develop and sustain the mental image of the original symbiotic object. This enables them to enjoy need satisfaction from a substitute temporarily and then to restore the original image after reunion.

Two groups of babies come to mind which bring this seeming contradiction in our prognostic formulations into even sharper focus. The infants I am thinking of were subjected to unusually frequent substitution of need-satisfying (symbiotic) objects. Concurrently, they had to cope with the permanent loss of the original love object—the mother. I refer to the infants described by Anna Freud and Sophie Dann (1951) and the group studied by William Goldfarb (1945). The children described by Anna Freud and Sophie Dann had been in concentration camps. Their mothers had been brutally taken from them. Nor were they able to establish a stable symbiotic relationship with the succession of substitute mothers who were abruptly taken from them also. The babies in William Goldfarb's studies, referred to by Bowlby (1951), had been placed in foster homes, and moved from one home to another with great frequency. Yet, amidst the most trying circumstances, these infants were able to extract, as it were, substitutions for the actual loss of mothering. Although they may have paid the price for this object loss with neurotic disorders, character distortions, or psychopathic difficulties later in life, they *never* severed their ties with reality. We must assume that their rudimentary egos were able to sustain some kind of memory trace of earlier need satisfaction from an external human source, that some vestige of confident expectation remained operative, that they could integrate whatever meager substitute maternal care was available, and that they were able to utilize to the utmost the autoerotic resources of their own bodies and probably also of transitional objects (Winnicott, 1953). In other words, they were able to create a nondehumanized narcissistic orbit for themselves.

Edith Jacobson's work (1954) regarding the ego's capacity to create mental representations of the self and the object world, which complements the concepts of Anna Freud (1952) and Heinz Hartmann (1952) of ego development as dependent on the libidinal object, is particularly pertinent here.

In what follows I shall attempt to apply Jacobson's concept of mental representation to those cases of so-called atypical development where the psychosis was not due to *actual* separation from the symbiotic object. The pivotal disturbance in early infantile autism— or *primary autism*, as I would prefer to call it (Mahler et al., 1959)— lies in the child's inability to perceive the Gestalt of the mother, and concomitantly the Gestalt of her vital functioning on his behalf. There seems to be no perceptual differentiation between an inside world as opposed to an outside world; the child seems to have no awareness of his self, as distinct from the inanimate environment.

The symbiotic psychotic syndrome (Mahler, 1952) represents fixation at, or regression to, the *second undifferentiated stage* of the mother-child unity, which is characterized by delusional, omnipotent symbiotic fusion with the need-satisfying object.

In the cases described in the psychoanalytic literature as atypical, psychotic, primarily depressed, schizophrenic, etc., authors have duly and emphatically explored the minute details of the traumata inflicted by fate, or by the nature of the mother's personality, upon the mother-infant dual unity in the early life of those infants.

1. In one group of such cases there were repeated separations from the mother. It was either immediately evident, or was reconstructed by the parents in retrospect, that these infants would not accept substitutes for the original maternal care, although such substitutes were available.

2. In a second group there was overwhelming proprioceptive stimulation and painful illness, coupled with a hampering of affectomotor tension release. The disturbance in these cases did not come to the fore before the peak of the separation-individuation phase.

When it did become manifest, the environment was confronted with the fact that the infant had suffered a severe break with reality.

3. There is a third group of children whose anamneses contained both factual and exaggerated retrospective accounts, provided by parents who were motivated by a deep sense of guilt and a desire for atonement, of multiple traumatizations, which were inflicted on the primitive ego by a cruel disregard of the child's needs and signals.

4. In another group of cases there was an abnormal bodily closeness between mother and child, a primitive, exclusive appersonation, inflicted on the child during the first eighteen months of life by the mother, which then might have been abruptly ended by some fateful event. Concomitantly with this exclusive, mutually parasitic symbiosis, there was an utter disregard of the infant's need for individuation—indeed, any differentiated needs other than purely vegetative ones were disregarded. The sequelae of these conditions included a blurring or extinguishing of the perceptual awareness of the gratification-frustration sequences. As might be expected, the symbiotic relationship in such cases was stifling, the emotional relationship empty and joyless, providing little opportunity for promoting mutuality and object constancy.

5. The most conspicuous factor in the fifth and final category of these atypical cases is the grossly unpredictable quality of maternal attitudes. There is evidence of crude overstimulation and all kinds of seductions of the baby, alternating with abrupt withdrawal and abandonment, leaving the infant to his own devices.[5]

In reviewing the cases in the literature, and those histories with which I am personally familiar, I found many examples in which the mother's relationship with the child was undoubtedly gravely deficient. I would emphasize, however, that I also found many which indicated that there was a reasonable emotional response on the part of the mother, and where, furthermore, the infant seemed to have shown signs of pleasurable anticipation of need satisfaction by the living object, at least during the first twelve to eighteen months of his life. I am thinking of that group of cases of early infantile psychosis in which, temporarily at least, marked symbiotic interaction between baby and mother did obtain. We are further puzzled by the

[5] In my clinical work as well as in our research project, we have seen an increasing number of cases which would fall into the last two categories.

fact that although in the majority of cases we find abundant traumatization of the mother-child unity, there are many cases in which
neither the timing, nor the severity, nor the multiplicity of these
insults would account for the severe fragmentation and regression of
the ego of these infants.

The foregoing description of the various categories of anamneses
does of course permit us to draw certain conclusions about the
personality of the mothers of these children. Undoubtedly, there is
a large percentage of infantile personalities among them; there is a
sprinkling of detached schizoid personalities; there are many who
have acted out symbiotic-parasitic claims upon the infant, overstimu-
lating and then abruptly abandoning him. Many of the mothers
had suffered from a measure of postpartum depression. But on the
whole, we are impressed with the number of mothers who would
have been accepted for membership in Winnicott's large group of
ordinary devoted mothers. Many experienced workers in the field—
e.g., Bender, Despert, Anna Maenchen, and Annemarie Weil—have
reached the same conclusion regarding these so-called "schizophreno-
genic" mothers.

We thus become increasingly aware of the enigma which confronts us. On the one hand, in the face of serious insults to the
mother-infant symbiotic relationship, most infants progress without
severing their ties with reality. On the other hand, these atypical
children, whose traumatization was no more severe, either in quality
or quantity, have broken with reality, regressed, and fallen back to
their own devices—that is to say, regressed to the autistic state.

Obviously, some unknown factor, or combination of factors, is
at work. I believe that the cardinal precipitating event in these
cases of infantile psychosis is the breakdown of that highly subtle
"circular process" to which Emmy Sylvester (1947, 1953) has called
attention: the mutually reciprocal relationship which enables mother
and infant to send out, and receive, each other's signals, a compatible
predictable interreaction, as it were.

If the infant's signals do not reach the mother because he is unable
to send them, or if the infant's signals are not heeded because the
mother does not have the capacity to react to them, the mother-infant
circular interreaction pattern takes on a dangerously discordant
rhythm. Gratification-frustration sequences are unpredictable, and

utter disorientation as to inner tension versus gratification from an outside source obtains. Under such circumstances, the infant cannot develop a capacity for confident expectation (Benedek, 1938), for basic trust (Erikson, 1950), which would enable him, from the third or fourth month on, to keep disruptive impulses toward immediate tension discharge in abeyance—a first prerequisite for the formation of ego structure.

Another vicissitude of the earliest mother-infant dual unity stage (which represents the normal autistic stage in the infant's development) may derive from the fact that the infant is handled as a purely vegetative being and consequently is unable to develop signals to indicate his needs. His hunger is saturated and stifled before he can become aware of tension from within. Furthermore, the gratification of oral and other purely physiological needs is dissociated from the more subtle and complex satisfaction of those human needs which David M. Levy (1937) has called affect hunger. I mean by this that there is no integration of the memory traces of oral and other purely physiological gratifications with their affective concomitants, that is, the complex Gestalt of human maternal ministrations. In short, there is no incentive for the infant to anticipate tension release from an outside need-satisfying agent, and no realiable beacon to orient him toward such a pattern.

Whereas the primarily autistic child has never been able to develop the complex mental image of the symbiotic maternal partner, there are other infants, particularly those with an inherently great sensitivity (Bergman and Escalona, 1949) and very low tolerance for frustration, who seem to develop the complex representation of the symbiotic object and seem to proceed to the symbiotic phase. However, they seem to be able to achieve homeostasis only by permanently drawing the need-satisfying object into the inner milieu in Hoffer's sense. Hence, there is fixation to the omnipotent symbiotic dual unity without the quality of fluidity which pertains to its normal form and which should pave the way to separation-individuation. In such cases, the mental representation of the symbiotic object is quite rigidly and permanently fixated to the primitive representation of the self. When in the course of maturational growth the ego is confronted with the incontrovertible *fact of separateness*, the fused symbiotic representations of self and object do not allow for progress toward individuation. We then see the catastrophic rage-panic reactions, which I have described as typical of the symbiotic psychotic syndrome. However, no organism can tolerate chronic panic. Hence, there occurs regression to secondary autism and other primary symbiotic and secondary autistic mechanisms in various combinations. The sequelae of object loss were described by many authors, among them by Rochlin (1953a, 1959), Mahler and Elkisch (1953), Elkisch and Mahler (1959), and Mahler (1960).

In a rather advanced conceptualization, Spitz equated, or at least compared, anaclitic depression in infancy with melancholia in adulthood. Spitz suggests that whereas in melancholia the aggression of the superego is turned against the ego, in anaclitic depression the superego is still the external love object, whose sadism is turned against the infant.

We know that systematized affective disorders are unknown in childhood. It has been conclusively established that the immature personality structure of the infant or older child is not capable of producing a state of depression such as that seen in the adult (Zetzel, 1953, 1960). *But grief as a basic ego reaction does prevail.* This implies that as soon as the ego emerges from the undifferentiated phase, the mimetic, gestural, and physiological signs of grief do appear, albeit in rudimentary form. The child's grief is remarkably short-lived because his ego cannot sustain itself without taking prompt defensive actions against object loss. It cannot survive in an objectless state for any length of time (Mahler, 1960). Mechanisms other than bereavement, such as substitution, denial, and repression, soon take over in various combinations. Children recover from transient reactions of mourning, accordingly, with lesser or greater scar formation.

Edward Bibring (1953) pointed out that both anxiety and depression are basic ego reactions. Bibring's definition of depression as the emotional expression of a state of helplessness is generally applicable, I believe, and contributes to our understanding of the ego's fluidity and vulnerability during the phase when the dim self-image and symbiotic object representation are differentiated. Bibring emphasized that frequent frustrations of the child's needs may at first mobilize anxiety and anger. However, if frustration continues, despite the "signals" produced by the infant, his initial anger will be replaced by feelings of exhaustion, helplessness, and depression. The emphasis in this hypothesis is not on oral frustration and subsequent oral fixation but on the infant's or young child's shocklike experience of, and fixation to, feelings of helplessness. Freud (1926) made the following statement concerning grief:

[The infant] is not yet able to distinguish temporary absence from permanent loss; when he fails to see his mother . . . , he behaves as though he would never see her again, and it requires repeated consoling experiences before he learns that such disappearance on his mother's part is usually followed by her reappearance. The mother promotes this knowledge . . . by playing with him the familiar game of covering her face and then to his joy revealing it again. Thus he is enabled, as it were, to experience longing without despair. . . . Subsequent thereto, repeated situations in which gratification was experienced have created out of the mother the object who is the recipient, when a need arises, of an intense cathexis, a cathexis which we may call "longingful" [pp. 118-119].

We may define grief as the reaction specific to object loss, and anxiety as the reaction specific to the danger which this loss entails. This connection, this kinship, between the affective state of longing and the modulated, ego-filtered emotions of grief and depression was emphasized by David Rapaport (1959) in his paper given in memory of Edward Bibring. This subjective affective reaction, reminiscent of depression, seems in children to consist of a vague realization of helplessness, of the ego's apprehension lest the libidinal object fail to come to its rescue in the face of mounting inner tension. But I would emphasize that the ego must be structured enough to permit enough respite to mobilize sufficient vestiges of confident expectation and hence must allow for the secondary process to delay discharge. Only if these conditions obtain is it possible to experience the subjective affect of longing, which, to my mind, is a precursor of the ego-filtered affect of sadness and grief.

I shall illustrate the dynamics of this process by briefly citing some of the findings we have so far amassed in our therapeutic action research with symbiotic psychotic toddlers. This therapeutic research aims at facilitating the child's capacity to restore the need-satisfying symbiotic object, to create a representation of the good object, as it were. We have been particularly interested in observing the general feeling tone of the child's affective manifestations and moods during this process. It is a well-known fact that the affective responses of the psychotic child who has regressed to a comfortably restricted autistic world of his own will be minimal unless this autistic, omnipotent, dedifferentiated world is upset. Thus, when both therapy and the unfamiliar, inanimate environment of the Center impinge upon his autistic withdrawal, his affective reactions may range widely from wandering off and searching,[6] to incessant, hyperactive, irritable restlessness and fretting, to abysmal panic reactions, fits of rage, temper tantrums, head banging, self-biting, and other grossly autoaggressive acts, until he reaches a state of exhaustion or extreme apathy. Then, as the child begins to retrieve the symbiotic object and to cathect its representation with libido, we observe more ego-filtered moods and emotions. These manifestations mark the first stage of giving up and replacing autistic defenses; they also mark the ego's emergence as a functional structure of the personality.

These processes could be observed in several children. Amy, at the age of three and a half, was aimlessly preoccupied with such stereotyped activities as pouring water or sand all over. She was unable to focus and instead seemed to look through people. She urinated and defecated whenever she was so prompted by an urge for bodily discharge; and darted about, snatching at objects. The slightest change in the environment evoked loud shrieks or prolonged whining. Amy reacted to frustrations, however minor, with desperate temper tantrums and excessive hyperactivity.

In the course of our therapeutic action research, Amy became noticeably attached to her therapist using the latter in a most primitive way as an extension to her ego, as a need-satisfying tool. Concomitant with this development, Amy retained her stools and held other tensions in abeyance as well. At this point the child who previously had alternated between reckless hyperactivity and exhausted lethargy occasionally began to display by her mien and gestures sadness and even grief.

By restoring the human object, therapy had helped Amy to form some representations of a symbiotic object. Yet, precisely in this phase of therapy Amy cried inconsolably at the sound of such trigger

[6] Compare Imre Hermann's work (1936).

words as crib, blanket, lying down, going to sleep. Though her sleep itself was not disturbed, it seemed to us that Amy at this point showed a mechanism resembling those which transiently occur in the normal sleep disturbances of two-year-old normal toddlers.

In a panel on Sleep Disturbances in Children (see Friend, 1956), Anna Maenchen considered "the *unspecified maturational reluctance* to retreat from all the activity and autonomy of waking life" in early childhood. Marianne Kris mentioned Dr. Frankl's experience as a newspaper consultant in London. Dr. Frankl had "most requests for help with sleep disturbances in a two-year-old group." The intimate connection between the loss of object relationship and considerations of regression is important in these transient sleep disturbances. It is interesting that we, as well as other investigators of psychoses in children, have had the experience that predominantly autistic children did not suffer from sleep disturbances, while those who were predominantly symbiotic sooner or later did develop sleep impairments. Maenchen feels that the child "once withdrawn into its autistic shell is no longer afraid until he comes out of the withdrawal." Conversely, the appearance of sleep disturbances, according to her, could be an indication that progress in ego development is being resumed. In Amy's case, I think her anxiety reaction and fretting when words reminding her of the state of ego regression in sleep were mentioned indicated a growing awareness of human object relationship. When Amy began to evolve the image or concept of a symbiotic object, she became aware of the danger which losing the symbiosis with this object in sleep entailed.

When Michael, another three-and-a-half-year-old psychotic child, came to our attention, he had achieved a much higher level of integration than Amy. When he arrived with his "ordinary, devoted mother" at the Center he wore at times the frozen expression which is so characteristic of primarily or secondarily autistic children. He responded to his mother and usually was in contact with her—albeit in a rather primary-process fashion. He later established a similarly patterned relationship with his therapist, provided his demands were correctly guessed and promptly fulfilled. His little face lit up immediately, however, when someone suggested the game of telephoning his daddy. He assumed a longing, wistful expression while on the toy telephone he carried on his imaginary conversation with his father. Michael also engaged in a passionate contact with a male doctor in our research group, snuggled up to him, and looked crest-fallen and sad whenever the doctor left the room. Michael's peculiar symbiotic relationship with his father gave way only very gradually —via a re-experiencing of the symbiotic relationship with the thera-pist, and subsequently with his mother, by externalizing split-up representations of self and object, and by concentrating libido on the representation of the good mother and projecting his aggression onto the image of the bad mother. Only after the delusional, patho-logical symbiotic tie with his father was loosened could Michael experience, for the first time, the communion he had missed in his relationship with his mother. During this phase, which began after Michael allowed himself to spit at people, his therapeutic sessions involved endless babbling, cooing, and gurgling with his mother. Incidentally, his mother said to us: "Michael seems to be having the same experiences with me now that his two older brothers had with me when they were babes in arms."

Within the framework of our research, the emotional manifesta-tions of psychotic children have been observed to range widely, from unmitigated, extreme affective and affectomotor phenomena, which are characterized by the predominance of unneutralized aggression and tension-discharge processes, to the more ego-filtered, amalga-mated emotional accompaniments of the secondary process which Edith Jacobson (1957) has described as moods.

In therapy, we have also observed that restoration of the libidinal object renders these toddlers susceptible to sadness and grief. In fact, once their autistic armor has been pierced, they become particularly vulnerable to emotional frustration, helplessness, and despair.

David Rapaport (1959) has pointed out, as Bibring (1953) im-plied, that grief is a genetically late, "tamed" reactivation of feelings of helplessness. In our present frame of reference this concept must be amplified by additional genetic considerations. Grief is dependent upon that measure of human object cathexis which prevails from the second half of the first year on; it is dependent upon the cathexis of the living Gestalt of the need-satisfying mother.

In the conventional therapeutic setting, the goal has been to permit the child to relive in a corrective way the missed and distorted developmental stages. However, all too frequently, this goal is under-mined by the fact that it requires superhuman effort and endurance on the part of the mother.

As early as 1952, I realized the inadequacy of treating the psychotic child who had regressed and organized his defenses for adaptation and survival within his secondarily created autistic shell, without
full participation of the original symbiotic object, the mother. At that
time I wrote:

> . . . If the [primarily or secondarily] autistic [child] is forced too
> rapidly into social contact, . . . he is often thrown into a catatonic
> state and then [into a] . . . fulminant psychotic process. . . . if
> such catastrophic reactions cannot be avoided, it seems that such
> autistic infants are better off if allowed to remain in their autistic
> shell, even though in "a daze of restricted orientation" they may
> drift into a very limited degree of reality adjustment only. Diag-
> nosis of their "original condition," of course, then usually escapes
> recognition; they are thrown into the category of the feeble-
> minded [p. 303].

A most dramatic episode occurred in little Lotta's life, who was
brought for treatment at the age of three years four months as a mute
autistic child. At four and a half years of age, after she had established a symbiotic relationship with me in the second year of analytic
treatment, the family moved to a distant suburb. As a result, her
treatment was interrupted and her inanimate environment was radi-
cally changed. I subsequently received a call from her desperate
mother, and visited them. Lotta epitomized the most heart-rending
and tragic picture of utter bereavement. She was unable to focus on
me; instead she behaved as if she wished to ward off the very perception of my presence by agitated creeping and sliding on her buttocks
on the garden grounds, by rocking and throwing garden earth onto
her disheveled little head with both hands; by whining pitifully, but
without tears and without any sign of appeal to the humans around
her. All the signals which she had learned in therapy, and which
had enabled me to fulfill Lotta's needs, were lost. This signal language, syncretic in nature, but well libidinized, had involved confidence and pleasurable anticipation. Now Lotta warded off any
approach from either her mother or me. Needless to say, it was most
difficult and needed great effort to re-establish contact with Lotta
when she was brought back for treatment.

Lotta's ego suffered a similar, but much more permanent, and,
in fact, irreversible psychic damage when, at the age of about six,
she was placed in an institution which housed autistic and organically brain-damaged children. Ironically, she was placed there after
she had made a spurt of development in therapy and attained an
extensive, though automatonlike vocabulary. This vocabulary had

been taught to her by her mother, who had also been able to teach her to perform automatized mental operations which were quite remarkable in their complexity, including the ability to read. Unfortunately, Lotta reached a plateau in this automatic learning, and her mother, preoccupied with a new pregnancy, was unable to meet Lotta's needs which were manifested in the form of a very distorted and very delicate reaching out. Both parents decided it was just "no use."

Lotta's mother wrote to me about her visit to the institution. The description of Lotta in that letter sounded like the description of an adult in a state of acute melancholia. Lotta did not speak, merely pleaded desperately with her eyes. Her movements were slow and listless; she walked with a shuffling gait. The mother also reported that she refused to eat. Lotta was subsequently taken home, and nursed back to life, so to speak—an utterly automatized and delibidinized life. Her mother was able to train her successfully enough so that Lotta was accepted and enrolled in the public school of the community.

Lotta was brought to my office to visit when she was nine. Her responses were automatic; there was no recognition of me as a person. She remembered syncretically the most minute details of the playroom, and enumerated, in primary-process fashion, all the objects around her. There was an amazing execution of commands which her mother had obviously given her beforehand. For example, whenever I tried to say something personal to her, she would ward off an aggressive impulse from within by loudly reciting, in the voice of a town crier: "Always be polite"; "You should love all the children"; "Go to the blackboard"; "I can do long divisions, I can spell"; "The elevator will take you down"; "You will go home"; "You will sleep home." She used these internalized but unintegrated commands to tame her anxiety and basic mistrust.

Precisely such experiences as those with Lotta and similar ones prompted Dr. Furer and myself to design a therapeutic approach in which the mother can be fully engaged in the treatment process and thus helped to lend herself to her child for re-experiencing the missed and distorted developmental phases. Within this newly developed tripartite therapeutic design, the therapist serves as the catalyst, the transfer agent, and the buffer between the child and mother. Such an approach should forestall the irreversible and catastrophic reaction to the disintegration of a recently established therapeutically imposed symbiosis as we witnessed in Lotta's case.

In a recent paper, David Beres (1960) stated succinctly: "only with the development of the capacity to create mental representations of the absent object, does the child progress from the syncretic, sensory-motor, affective, immediate response to the delayed, abstract, conceptualized response that is characteristically human." This intrapsychic image, this mental representation of the temporarily absent symbiotic object, seems to serve as an indispensable catalyst in that it enables all the potentially autonomous capacities of the primitive ego to become functional. I consider it the spark which ignites the ego's capacity for human affect, for human social and emotional development.

In psychotic children, the breakdown of the ego's basic functions —of all or many of them—can be attributed to either one of the following conditions: (1) the ego's inability to create the relatively complex intrapsychic image of the human symbiotic object; or (2) the loss of a precarious mental representation of the symbiotic object which, because it is excessively linked to need satisfaction on a symbiotic-parasitic level, cannot grow toward object constancy, and which therefore cannot cope with the demands of the separation-individuation phase. We are all familiar with the chronic sequelae of these psychic events. *What we seldom see, and what is rarely described in the literature, is the period of grief and mourning which I believe inevitably precedes and ushers in the complete psychotic break with reality, that is to say, the secondary autistic withdrawal.* In this paper, I have also tried to show that sadness and grief are the first signs of progressive development and seem to be obligatory accompaniments of the child's emergence from the de-animated autistic world through restoration of the libidinal object.

BIBLIOGRAPHY

Abraham, K. (1924), A Short Study of the Development of the Libido, Viewed in the Light of Mental Disorders. *Selected Papers on Psycho-Analysis*. London: Hogarth Press, 1927, p. 469.

Benedek, T. (1938), Adaptation to Reality in Early Infancy, *Psa. Quart.*, VII.

Beres, D. (1960), Perception, Imagination and Reality. Paper read at the New York Psychoanalytic Society, May 31.

Bergman, P. & Escalona, S. (1949), Unusual Sensitivities in Very Young Infants. *This Annual*, III/IV.

Bibring, E. (1953), The Mechanism of Depression. In: *Affective Disorders*, ed. P. Greenacre. New York: International Universities Press, 1954.

Bowlby, J. (1951), *Maternal Care and Mental Health*. Geneva: World Health Organization Mon. No. 2.

Deutsch, H. (1919), A Two-Year-Old's First Love Comes to Grief. In: *Dynamic Psychopathology of Childhood*, ed. L. Jessner & E. Pavenstedt. New York: Grune & Stratton, 1959.

Elkisch, P. & Mahler, M. S. (1959), On Infantile Precursors of the "Influencing Machine" (Tausk). *This Annual*, XIV.

Erikson, E. (1950), *Childhood and Society*. New York: Norton.

Ferenczi, S. (1913), Stages in the Development of the Sense of Reality. *Contributions to Psychoanalysis*. Boston: Richard C. Badger, 1916.

Freud, A. (1952), The Mutual Influences in the Development of Ego and Id. *This Annual*, VII.

—— (1954), Psychoanalysis and Education. *This Annual*, IX.

—— & Dann, S. (1951), An Experiment in Group Upbringing. *This Annual*, VI.

Freud, S. (1910), *Leonardo da Vinci: A Psycho-Sexual Study of an Infantile Reminiscence*. New York: Moffat, 1916.

—— (1917), Mourning and Melancholia. *Collected Papers*, IV. London: Hogarth Press.

—— (1926), *The Problem of Anxiety*. New York: Norton, 1936.

Friend, M. R. (1956), Report on Panel on Sleep Disturbances in Childhood. *J. Am. Psa. Assn.*, IV.

Goldfarb, W. (1945), Psychological Privation in Infancy and Subsequent Adjustment. *Am. J. Orthopsychiat.*, XV.

Hartmann, H. (1952), The Mutual Influences in the Development of Ego and Id. *This Annual*, VII.

—— & Kris, E., Loewenstein, R. M. (1946), Comments on the Formation of Psychic Structure. *This Annual*, II.

Hendrick, I. (1942), Instincts and the Ego During Infancy. *Psa. Quart.*, XI.

Hermann, I. (1936), Sich anklammern—auf Suche gehen. *Int. Z. Psa.*, XX.

Hoffer, W. (1950a), Oral Aggressiveness and Ego Development. *Int. J. Psa.*, XXXI.

—— (1950b), Development of the Body Ego. *This Annual*, V.

Jacobson, E. (1953), Contribution to the Metapsychology of Cyclothymic Depression. In: *Affective Disorders*, ed. P. Greenacre. New York: International Universities Press.

—— (1954), The Self and the Object World. *This Annual*, IX.

—— (1957), On Normal and Pathological Moods. *This Annual*, XII.

Levy, D. M. (1937), Primary Affect Hunger. *Am. J. Psychiat.*, XCIV.

Mahler, M. S. (1952), On Child Psychosis and Schizophrenia: Autistic and Symbiotic Infantile Psychosis. *This Annual*, VII.

—— (1958), Autism and Symbiosis: Two Extreme Disturbances of Identity. *Int. J. Psa.*, XXXIX.

—— (1960), Perceptual De-differentiation and Psychotic "Object Relationship." *Int. J. Psa.*, XLI.

—— & Elkisch, P. (1953), Some Observations on Disturbances of the Ego in a Case of Infantile Psychosis. *This Annual*, VIII.

—— & Gosliner, B. (1955), On Symbiotic Child Psychosis. *This Annual*, X.

—— & Furer, M. (1960), Observations on Research Regarding the "Symbiotic Syndrome" of Infantile Psychosis. *Psa. Quart.*, XXIX.

—— —— & Settlage, C. (1959), Severe Emotional Disturbances in Childhood: Psychoses. In: *American Handbook of Psychiatry*, I, ed. S. Arieti. New York: Basic Books.

Rapaport, D. (1959), Edward Bibring's Theory of Depression. Abstract in *Bull. Phila. Assn. Psa.*, IX.

Rochlin, G. (1953a), Loss and Restitution. *This Annual*, VIII.

—— (1953b), The Disorders of Depression and Elation. *J. Am. Psa. Assn.*, I.

—— (1959), The Loss Complex. *J. Am. Psa. Assn.*, VII.

Spitz, R. (1946), Anaclitic Depression. *This Annual*, II.
—— (1950), Anxiety in Infancy. *Int. J. Psa.*, XXXI.
Sylvester, E. (1947), Pathogenic Influences of Maternal Attitudes in the Neonatal Period. In: *Problems of Infancy and Early Childhood*, ed. M. J. E. Senn. New York: Josiah Macy, Jr. Foundation.
—— (1953), Developmental Truisms and Their Fate in Childrearing: Clinical Observations. In: *Problems of Infancy and Early Childhood*, ed. M. J. E. Senn. New York: Josiah Macy, Jr. Foundation.
Winnicott, D. W. (1953), Transitional Objects and Transitional Phenomena. *Int. J. Psa.*, XXXIV.
Zetzel, E. R. (1953), The Depressive Position. In: *Affective Disorders*, ed. P. Greenacre. New York: International Universities Press.
—— (1960), Symposium on "Depressive Illness." *Int. J. Psa.*, XLI.

"IT ISN'T FAIR"[1]

The Treatment of a Blind Child

EVELINE B. OMWAKE, M.A. and ALBERT J. SOLNIT, M.D.
(New Haven)[2]

The treatment of Ann, a congenitally blind child, presented opportunities to study the impact of blindness on the establishment of object relations, secondary-process functioning, and body-image formation in a young girl. Ann's therapy became an avenue for the child to leave her shut-in infantile world in order to unfold her very considerable capacities that had been hidden under a covering of autistic retardation. In subsequent papers more attention will be devoted to specific aspects of ego psychology that Ann's treatment illuminated. In this presentation the narrative of the treatment and her recovery are offered as a survey of insights and questions raised by the "rebirth" of this child.

> Why can't I write with my eyes? Why did I always want to touch my mother? Where does the loving go when the scolding comes in the voice? Can you see the echo come back? What color is it when it is blue?

Through these and many similarly profound, sensitive, and confusing questions the child revealed a few of the problems she faced as she discovered what it means to be blind when the other people in her life can see and constantly speak to her from the experience of vision. The nature and phrasing of the questions suggest how pervasively the defect of blindness affected the intellectual functions

[1] Supported by the Children's Bureau, U.S. Department of Health, Education, and Welfare; the Connecticut Department of Health; and the Grant Foundation.

[2] From the Child Study Center, Yale University.

We wish to acknowledge with warm appreciation the helpful suggestions and criticisms of Laura V. Coddling, Ruth S. Eissler, Marianne Kris, and Elizabeth Marvell.

of her language, thought, comprehension, and conceptualization. Our title statement, "It Isn't Fair," represents this child's judgment of her plight and was made when she was six and a half years old as she played out a scene in her family life. Its manifest reference was to the fact that she was a twin and had to share her mother with her sister, but it also referred to a dawning awareness of the difference between herself and her sister. The depressed mother, overwhelmed by the premature birth of unexpected twins, one of whom had retrolental fibroplasia, had to leave a good share of the care of the blind child to an infant nurse. Thus as an infant, Ann's gradual awareness of a specific object was of one that is shared by somebody else and referred to both her mother and nurse. The implications of her blindness and her experiences with her objects in the first eight years of Ann's development will be the focus of this presentation.

CASE PRESENTATION

Early Development[3]

Ann was the second-born and smaller of identical twins, a footling presentation, and weighed 3 lbs. 12 oz. The twins were seven to eight weeks premature according to the estimated delivery date. During the first four to five weeks, because of respiratory distress compatible with a diagnosis of hyaline membrane disease, Ann was in an incubator with oxygen concentrations of 40 to 50 per cent. At the time of Ann's birth the role of oxygen in the production of retrolental fibroplasia had not been discovered. Her care was in accordance with the best pediatric knowledge available at that time. There were no detected pathological changes in her eyes during the period of hospitalization, and she went home at the age of five to six weeks in good condition. Her twin sister had arrived home about two weeks earlier. The retrolental fibroplasia developed in the weeks following discharge from the hospital. At the time of her first developmental examination at nine and a half months, her nurse, Leta, reported that Ann seemed to perceive strong light but apparently had no useful vision. Her twin did not develop the disease.

Ann was seen for developmental examination on four occasions by the same examiner prior to the beginning of her treatment: at nine and a half months, seventeen and a half months, twenty-three

[3] This section was prepared by Sally Provence, M.D., Chief of Developmental Evaluation Unit of Child Study Center, Yale University.

months, and thirty-nine months. At the first examination—as on later occasions—the question was raised how much her development was impeded by the sensory defect, how much by possible brain damage linked to prematurity and respiratory distress, and how much was due to environmental influences. The examination indicated that Ann was doing as well as a premature, blind infant could be expected to do. She had no signs of mental deficiency nor of brain damage, and prognosis for future development was considered to be favorable within the limits of disability imposed by the blindness.

At that time (nine and a half months) she was described by her nurse as a predominantly happy infant who smiled, laughed aloud, and vocalized responsively. Her most mature behavior was in the language and social areas which were adequate for her age when one corrected for prematurity. She was imitating syllables and had begun to vocalize nonspecific mama and dada sounds. She showed a definite discriminatory reaction of discomfort in strange places and was reported to be most comfortable in her own crib or on the bed of her nurse where she was often placed for dressing or play. She had found her thumb and sucked usually the right one with some signs of comfort and pleasure. Her nurse felt that when Ann was upset she was most easily comforted by being placed in her own crib rather than being held or cuddled. This appears to be one of the early indicators of the lack of cuddling and holding which were later understood to have contributed in important ways to her sensory and emotional deprivation.

Her motor development revealed a wide scatter. Finger skills were only slightly below her age and were adequate for the manipulation of toys. However, such gross motor skills as sitting, standing, and creeping were severely retarded. There were no localizing neurological signs in respect to the motor system, and the motor delay was considered to be the result of the combined influences of the prematurity, blindness, and some degree of understimulation.

Her lack of vision interfered with the measurement of some of the adaptive functions, but when she was oriented to the test materials by having them touched to her hand she could grasp them. She also banged or rattled the toys in apparent enjoyment of the sound and activity and did a good bit of exploratory mouthing. Moreover, she had enough interest to try to find a toy she had dropped or to locate by sound such a toy as the bell. Her interest, persistence, and drive toward the materials was considered a good sign. On the whole the examiner was optimistic about the prognosis.

The importance of providing a variety of stimuli and experiences with people in order to promote her general development was stressed in discussions with the mother and nurse. However, the extent of the mother's depression as an influence in her care and the tendency of the nurse to treat her as a very young infant were not fully appreciated at the time of the first contact.

Ann's development never again was as appropriate to her age until she was six and three quarter years old in the third year of her treatment. At the subsequent early examinations one was impressed with her retarded development. At seventeen months she could control her trunk muscles well, but characteristically sat in a slumped position with head set forward and face usually averted. Though she had the physical strength and motor skills required for creeping, she rarely moved about, and while she could support her weight on her feet, she often refused and had resisted efforts to get her to walk. Her interest in toys had declined in the eight months since her first examination. She smiled fairly frequently, but more often in response to music than to people. Her passivity in respect to motor development, relationships to people, and capacity for play gave cause for concern. She was making less effort to communicate verbally or in any other way, and her language development had progressed very little.

When she was twenty-three months of age, though she had made some progress, her development was proportionately more retarded in comparison to her age. She was not walking, though it was clear that she had the strength and the motor patterns to do so. She was withdrawn, but could be stimulated to respond, and had a few words. However, she did not call to mother or nurse when she wanted or needed something and would fret, cry, and beat her head with her hands at such times. She reacted with signs of intense displeasure to the feel of sand, grass, and furry toys, and avoided touching them. She accepted hard metal toys, but had little interest in them. She continued to have a poor tolerance for what would be considered minor degrees of discomfort in a normal child. The examiner felt that there was much preoccupation with bodily sensations and inner stimuli.

The development of a touching inhibition and her extreme passivity imposed particular problems in the approach to helping her and added to the disability imposed by the blindness. On the other hand, throughout the early years, there were some signs of maturation, evidences of discrimination in respect to people, and certain glimmers of interest in her environment—factors which warranted intensive therapeutic efforts. It should be said, however, that without the encouraging finding of the first examination, one would have been much less optimistic. It would have been difficult, or perhaps impossible, to exclude some basic mental defect or brain damage if one had seen Ann for the first time at the seventeen-and-a-half, twenty-three- or thirty-nine-month examination.

It was the test at thirty-nine months that led to the referral that resulted in therapy. When she was age six years, ten months, in the fourth year of her treatment, Ann could again be satisfactorily tested with a standardized intelligence test. This test confirmed the impression of her basically normal intellectual capacity; it reflected the dramatic progress she had made in her treatment; and it demonstrated some of the remnants of her difficulty which are the subject of this presentation.

Plan for Treatment and Early Therapeutic Contacts

The first contact with Ann began when she was three and a half. At that time she was tyrannizing her family with a demand for the constant physical contact and undivided attention of her mother. She refused to talk, walk, or move about, to handle toys, or to become involved in any kind of play either of a manipulative, dramatic, or social nature. When the mother moved out of reach of Ann's hand or hearing, the child screamed, flung her body about, and bumped her forehead on the floor. She ate poorly, did nothing for herself, and no one had been able to attempt toilet training. The few experiences in her life which regularly brought pleasure included the sound of rain, one or two phonograph records, her bath, and being in her crib. Ann ignored the sporadic efforts of her eight-year-old brother, six-year-old sister, her twin, her father, aunts, uncles, and grandmothers to elicit a social response or offer a toy. At their approaches, she dug her fists in her eyes and screamed angrily, turning her body away. Her world included only herself and her depressed, harassed, discouraged mother. An old, lumbering, almost blind shaggy poodle beloved by the rest of the family did not at that time appear to exist for Ann, though later it became clear that she had been fully aware of his presence.

The state supervisor for blind children, Miss M., who had been visiting Ann regularly since she was two and a half, had been impressed by the lack of stimulation and support available to Ann at home. People seemed to try to involve her from time to time but gave up in discouragement. Miss M. observed that Ann's mother was accustomed to tiptoeing stealthily from the room in the hope that Ann would not notice her departure. Miss M. reported some progress in her own efforts to bring Ann out of her withdrawn state, as evidenced by an occasional fleeting smile from Ann and by the fact that Ann would allow her to approach. No actual play or conversation had developed between them, but Ann would allow her mother or nurse to leave the room when Miss M. was there. This was the state of affairs when Ann was between two and three years of age.

At this time both her parents and the pediatrician hoped that Ann could attend the nursery school in the Child Study Center on a limited time plan. They felt that by extending her horizons through the introduction of new people and experiences in the educational environment of a nursery school Ann might be helped to overcome some of her negativism and be more yielding to their simple appropriate expectations for independence.

The nursery school director was skeptical of the value of the normal nursery school experience for so withdrawn, infantile, and angry a child. She thought that the noises, suddenness of movements, and vitality of a well-ordered group would serve to increase the fright that must exist behind the anger and resistance of this child. When Ann was first seen she was a pale, thin, waifish, dejected-looking scrap of a child, slumped on her mother's lap with hands fisted in eyes. It seemed as if Ann and the nursery school children could only overwhelm each other. It was clear that it would be necessary to do some preliminary work with her individually before she could adapt to a group of sighted children. However, it was agreed that a modified form of nursery school experience was most likely at that point to help Ann and her mother in a relationship that seemed deadlocked.

Therefore, on the basis that it was important to help Ann separate from her mother and find some pleasure in play, the nursery school director became Ann's therapist, and also maintained regular contact with Ann's mother for guidance as well as to obtain information about the child's home life. The therapist had not only had special experience in teaching blind children but had also been for many years closely associated with a developmental research project involving the psychoanalytic therapy of young children.

In the beginning the therapist's role had been seen by all concerned as primarily that of a teacher. As Ann's psychological problems came to light and life so dramatically during the second year of the contact, a consultation was planned around referral to a psychiatrist. In the pedagogical approach one maintains a certain distance from the conflict, and now that Ann's need for help with her conflicts was apparent, it seemed appropriate to focus the treatment there and to continue her education on the outside. After consideration of (1) the difficulties in communicating with Ann, (2) the need for a therapist with knowledge of blind children, and (3) Ann's well-established trust in the nursery school director, it was agreed that the program most useful to her would be a continuation of the existing relationship now directed toward verbalizing, clarifying, and interpreting the child's conflicts. This required regular supervision by a child analyst. Implicit in such a plan was the need to focus the play sessions on the revelation and working through of her problems through verbalizing her feelings, thoughts, and fantasies, and to interpret her defenses and wishes—to make verbal and conscious what was unconscious. This was the beginning of therapy, conducted along psychoanalytic lines, regularly supervised by a child analyst. Practical considerations limited the interviews to three times a week. The indoor area of one of the nursery school classes was utilized as a versatile playroom for the treatment.

At the same time Miss M., state supervisor, became Ann's regular teacher, and this provided an educational program that was rich and meaningful in terms of exposing her to more experiences outside her own home, such as walks, rides, visits to stores, etc. Since that time, in the treatment, many opportunities have arisen for giving Ann useful information, clarifying her confusions, helping her with techniques of solving educational problems, and inspiring her with a desire to learn more about the world outside herself. However, the therapist has avoided offering unsolicited information, correcting her errors, or directly testing her skills or knowledge.

Ann and her parents were informed of this plan, and the aims and method of the treatment as compared to the educational approach were translated and explained to Ann when she could understand. She continued to refer to the therapist as her "special teacher." Miss M. was referred to as her "other teacher." Later she elected to refer to the therapist by her first name, as though further to distinguish the treatment from the educational work.

TREATMENT

First Year (Age Three and a Half)

When I met Ann in our waiting room she looked like a sad and malnourished child slumped on the lap of an unhappy, unmoving mother. The drooping head and fists in eyes immediately suggested blindness, but the sadness was more pervasive than blindness itself could explain. The child gave no sign of awareness of change when her mother carried her into the nearby playroom where she continued to hold Ann on her lap as I tried to make my presence felt by talking softly about the room itself and the things in it. For two months her mother continued to hold Ann either in a chair facing me or beside me at the piano. I offered toys and talked to Ann, hoping in this way to elicit her interest. Occasionally she muttered "S'at?" ["What's that"] at a noise, but the tone suggested apprehension rather than curiosity.

Gradually she came to tolerate my advances, but she refused to touch the toys that were offered. She permitted me to shake rattles or bells, sing, to tell her about the playthings in the room and what children enjoyed doing with them. I introduced a doll but Ann gave no indication of interest. I held the doll in my hand and talked as follows, "Here's one of the dolls the children like to play with. They pretend it's a child. I'm dressing it now. This is a girl doll and I'm putting on panties, a dress, and socks and shoes like you have. I can make the dolly sit down. Now I will play she is going to bed. . . ." Our session proceeded in this way as she remained sitting limply, fists in eyes, refusing to touch the doll or the clothes. Eventually she let me hold her hands to clap them and to touch her hair, hands, eyes, shoes, etc., but she reached for nothing and made no verbal requests.

She was inclined to brighten up slightly when we moved to the piano where I would play "Doggy in the Window," a song her mother reported that she enjoyed hearing at home. She thus revealed her responsiveness to an acoustic "touch"—one could make a contact that had intensity and satisfaction through what was offered to her hearing senses.

When this interest could be counted on, it was planned for the mother to leave briefly. In the eleventh session I told Ann that two sessions hence her mother was going to sit in the waiting room while she stayed with me. I expected that she might well refuse to leave home at all. However, her mother described the usual brightening-up behavior on being told that it was a "school day" even though she was also reminded of the planned separation. On the third day she had ten minutes on her mother's lap and then I gently lifted her off as her mother said good-by, but was unprepared for the fighting tantrum which ensued and had to put Ann on the floor to avoid dropping her. She thrashed about, screamed, and knocked her fore-head so violently that I could scarcely pick her up again to hold her writing body. Her mother returned within a few minutes, and Ann's tantrum subsided as completely and quickly as it had begun. For the remainder of the session she showed more responsiveness and interest than she had at any previous time. This pattern of tantrum followed by relief of tension and release of fresh energy continued for another month, after which she offered no physical resistance when her mother said good-by before leaving the room for the full session.

The temper tantrum served to establish and consolidate the personal contact with the therapist. It became an avenue for relating by libidinized aggression to a specific, gratifying human object. This is often seen in autistic psychotic children as the first evidence of their intense relationship to the love object. Aggression, libidinized or not, is often the first permissible or useful instinctual tie to the human object outside of themselves.

The only change reported at home during this period was that on "school days" she seemed brighter, and the routines involved in the preparation for coming proceeded more smoothly than usual.

During this time the hours settled into a routine. After her mother's leave taking and the ensuing tantrum, I would walk Ann to the piano. Her gait was stiff-legged; it was necessary to hold both her hands and lift her to the piano bench where she would remain, listening to piano playing and singing. The songs were usually about Ann and what she could do, but I also tried a few traditional melodies that she might hear on records or from her siblings. The keyboard was the first thing she voluntarily touched, and she often would put her hands tentatively on the keys but would refuse to push them down. Her unexpected and excited pleasure at certain loud rhythmic numbers was manifested by stiffening, flushing, and jerky arm and leg movements.

It was apparent that Ann masturbated fairly constantly although her hands were never seen to be involved. She rubbed her thighs together and often looked as if she was deliberately rubbing the genital area against her mother's knee when she stood near her. Her legs were quite often moving when the upper part of her body and arms were rigidly still.

The masturbation suggested that the relationship to the mother had developed irregularly beyond the anaclitic stage. Since this is a continuing treatment, the full significance of autoerotic genital activity in this congenitally blind child cannot yet be fully evaluated.

After the piano play I would lead her to the sink where she would stay for twenty minutes or so bobbing floating toys in a basin with the flat of her hand or unskillfully filling and emptying small receptacles. She could not yet push or pull the faucet in order to turn it on or off, but she could pull up the edges of an enamel basin to dump it full-force down the drain. The filling and emptying of the basin went on endlessly. Sometimes I would carry her outdoors for a short while, but at that time she did not enjoy it. Two years later she recalled from that period walking on pebbles, listening to birds, and four years later being carried up some stairs. She often brought her brother's baseball mitt and kept track of it throughout the session, asking from time to time if it was still there and whimpering, "Git it" if it dropped to the floor. The mitt was used much as a transitional object (Winnicott, 1953).

Ann's language was meager and she used "her" or "you" interchangeably for "I" and "me." She regularly said "Eee" meaning no or yes, which was interpreted from the inflection. Later she used "no-ee" for negation and retained "eee" for affirmation. She had a way of attaching "erm" to words or sentences as if to indicate that she had more thoughts than she had words to express them. A typical quotation from her fifth year was, "Show me how to do it a little half-erm," a sentence which communicated to me that she wanted to learn to cut—to half—with the scissors, but did not want me to expect too much of her. This sentence is one of many which suggested that she had to enact physically an experience before she could deal with it verbally. After this first trial with a scissors she could say, "I want to cut it." The complexity of language and concept formation in Ann will require separate attention in a subsequent report.

When the contact was interrupted in June because of the vacation period, there was some increase in liveliness and interest but play was meager indeed. The clearest clues to her fantasy were: (1) a moderately pleased response to two pieces of music; (2) an attachment to her brother's baseball mitt; and (3) heightened excitement expressed in flushing and other signs of vasomotor reaction when I played a piano piece suggesting a clock ticking. Despite the clinical impression from the developmental evaluation in infancy that the prognosis for good intelligence had been favorable and a hunch that the intensity of the protest at her mother's departure was an indication of strength, her shell still appeared to me to be impenetrable.

During the summer a college girl was employed to live with the family to assist in the care of Ann. As it turned out, Ann rejected her so the student took over the other children, and the mother devoted herself to Ann. In retrospect, it was not until this time that Ann and her mother began actively to explore each other's personalities. As Ann was able to improve, the mother could respond more positively to the child.

Second Year (Age Four)

In September the contact became organized as a treatment. Ann was moving around the room more freely but still refused to try walking without holding someone's hand. She continued to spend the greater amount of time at the piano or the sink, but around these two major activities she would sit briefly at the table and idly finger cups, plates, etc., as they were handed to her; listen to one or two records; or even walk around the playroom with me. The telephone interested her for a moment or two, as did a color tower and pegboard, but she was not inclined to explore their properties or to improve her manipulative skill. When she brought a doll, Floyd, along and demanded endless repetitions of a song, "Floyd Is a Boy Doll," I could not interest her in dressing it even though the clothes were easily slipped on and off. Ann refused the suggestion to wash the doll or the clothes at the sink and to use a doll carriage. Even though she would occasionally accept a suggestion to try something new, her response was meager and her feeble efforts dwindled. Around this time it became apparent that she gave up any task that she could not perform successfully on the first try. She found no pleasure in the process of play or in the mastery or problem solving, both of which help to keep the healthy child involved in play.

At the piano, however, she showed marked eagerness to begin and reluctance to stop the play. The only substitute she willingly accepted was the play at the sink. Both activities evoked excitement manifested by jittery movements, a shrill voice, and high-pitched laughter. But this was in response to my activity rather than her own, although gradually her hands moved along with mine as she played the piano or manipulated the sink toys. Her inhibition about touching was compounded by the actual fact that her fingers were weak and inept. However, both her willingness to touch and her physical strength improved to the extent that by Christmas of the second year she responded to encouragement to press hard enough to sound a note on the piano and kept time with a one-finger accompaniment to whatever I was playing. Ann could anticipate and hold the rhythm and also select notes which were in harmony with the songs I played.

At home during this period some gains in self-help had been achieved, although her mother reported low interest and minimum success. However, Ann did "get the idea" of the toilet, according to her mother. Once she proved she understood what was wanted, the mother's demand for cooperation met with strong resistance in the form of withholding stools. Toilet training remained a battleground between Ann and her mother until the summer when Ann was five. Then, under vacation living conditions, Ann gave up the fight in a twenty-four-hour period. Toward the end of the year Ann helped to pull off her clothing, to bathe herself, and to hold her own spoon and scrape her dish at mealtime. She would occupy herself at least for a few minutes with her doll or in listening to records, and she could be left for brief periods in the family playroom without a stormy protest. Also, she talked more and was overt in listening to the conversation around her. Up to this time her family had con-

sidered her to be too withdrawn to be aware of their actions, interests, or conversations. Her faint efforts to make contact with her
siblings were pronounced "silly" by them. For example, she was
calling her twin "piano" and when the other children laughed, she
would repeat it until they grew bored and ignored her again.

Although the improved home behavior and responsiveness to
the piano play were encouraging signs that it was possible to engage
her interest, there was still little evidence to support the assumption
based on her infant test that she was capable of average or better
than average intelligence. However, after several months of sessions
spent at the piano, Ann suddenly offered an idea of her own. This
episode was momentous in that it was the first time she said anything
that had not first been said to her, except "no" or "git it," and
her expressed idea was highly dramatic for the unusual burst of
energy that accompanied it. I had begun the "clock song" when she
suddenly interrupted shouting, "Leta spank you," and pounded the
keyboard with her hands. The name of Leta, her infant nurse, had
recently been mentioned in the household in connection with a
Christmas visit, at which time Ann had not responded to friendly
advances of the latter. For the first time she had initiated a play
theme. Whatever produced it, the event marked a critical point in
the treatment because from that time on she began to introduce her
personal thoughts and feelings even though I had to supply the
voices and action.

For two more months Ann used the play at the piano to reveal
the vague ideas and feelings which confused and often frightened
her. With her voice and posture, and with a display of energy she
attacked the piano, and in this way communicated her feelings of
helplessness, anger, excitement, and dependency which she had been
unable to express in a way that they could be dealt with. Through
such piano play, strange as it was, she found her first medium for
communication associated with pleasure, mastery, and excitement.
Around the four-handed spanking concerto during which she would
frequently take her hands from the keys and "spank" Floyd who
was face down on her lap, she would listen to my speculations about
spankings, but she herself would not elaborate the initial "Leta
spank you" phrase. The crescendo of laughter and hitting of the
keys was interpreted as enjoyment of the excitement of spankings.

As confirmation of the interpretation, her laughter which had been strident and harsh took on more normal modulations, and sometimes I detected the reassuring gleeful chuckle of a normally excited child engaged in mischief.

After a period of dealing intensively with the spanking of Floyd, Ann produced his feminine counterpart whom she called Rena. Floyd appeared to be the doll that was first invested in a preferred manner. As differentiation of the self proceeded, Rena became more important. The basis on which the Floyd doll was first preferred is not clear, although it is likely that this preference represented a forerunner to later sexual differentiation. Whereas Floyd was spanked excitedly because he was a "bad boy" the girl doll was continually being scolded harshly for specific offenses such as refusal to eat, soiling, and incessant crying. My first clear picture from Ann of trouble at home came from hearing her say to Rena, "You feed yourself. If you don't, I won't feed you. O.K., you are a good girl, I will feed you." Her worst epithet was: "You *child!*"

She now was using personal pronouns correctly and therefore must be advancing toward a clearer concept of herself as a person. Feeding equipment was kept within reach, but when there was an attempt to introduce these for a more realistic form of dramatization than the piano playing she angrily insisted, "Play it," referring to the piano. Gradually, as I continued to speak gently about using the toys, she permitted me to perform the motions of feeding and within a month Ann herself took over the task of pretending to spoon food into the doll.

As the feeding and scolding play increased, Rena moved upstage in the drama, but Floyd remained on the scene. Eventually he was relegated to a favored place by her bed at home, while Rena regularly accompanied Ann to her sessions until she was six, and thereafter turned up periodically in times of special stress. Many times when exposed to unexpected events such as a fall on the stairs or a missed session, Ann's immediate plaintive request was "Tell Rena" or "Comfort Rena." In piecing together the meaning of these two important characters to Ann at that particular time, it appeared that Floyd, the doll, had taken the place of her brother's baseball mitt— it was used as a transitional object. If she made any sexual differentiation at all, she seemed to express a closer affinity to or interest in inanimate objects representing masculine rather than feminine associations. In this connection it should be noted that Ann was strikingly lacking in tactile experience with people. Her father, a gentle, quiet person, had taken over her care briefly from time to time in order to relieve the nurse and mother. Of the siblings, her brother was reported to speak to her occasionally and made considerable noise around the house, but by and large she was physically isolated and ignored.

Gradually through making Rena behave in sessions as she herself was doing at home, Ann revealed her yearning to be understood and accepted as she was. She did this through dramatizing provocative and resistant behavior in her treatment. Thereafter for many months she continued in an infinite variety of teasing ways at home to test the strength of her mother's love and anger.

During the latter course of treatment Ann often would say that she *was* Floyd or Rena when her own behavior would lead to the comment that she reminded me of the dolls.

In the last month of this treatment year Ann introduced the topic of dogs which three years later was to become a major subject of conversation as well as play. This came about through her reacting to the barking of some dogs during the sessions by first observing sadly that they wanted their mother and second by ordering me to play "Billy squeaks" on the piano. I was able to deduce from her vague references that she wanted me to improvise around the sounds made by the family dog as he was coaxed upstairs at night to his basket in the hallway near Ann's room. Billy had died at the veterinarian's the year before where he had been sent after developing arthritis and cataracts. Only much later when her language became more adequate was Ann able to communicate to her family and to me how much she had absorbed of the household difficulties around the ailing pet.

Her final sessions for the year were devoted entirely to the care and feeding of Rena and the struggle to clear up confusion around the nature of dogs. I felt that she now had some understanding of a baby's needs and feelings and a concept of herself as someone who could engage in play around such a theme. Her concept of dogs was considerably less clearly established because she was not yet able to make a distinct differentiation between animals and humans.

The summer was spent at a beach resort. The major events reported were the accomplishment of toilet training referred to earlier, her willingness to visit in an aunt's house nearby, and enjoyment of splashing in the ocean. While she continued to plead, "Don't go" to the mother when the latter left the house, she was entirely cooperative and pleasant with the father or aunt who cared for her in the mother's absence. The twins' birthday was duly celebrated with a family party, cake with candles, singing, and presents. On earlier birthdays it had been assumed that Ann would not participate, but on this, her fifth, the family plans included her. Ann sat crouched and quiet with hands in the eyes refusing the party food— an attitude which was later understood as indicating rapt attention to the situation rather than withdrawal from it. One of her many gifts was a set of twin dolls. One of the dolls, Baby Ann, named by Ann herself, became her constant companion.

Third Year (Age Five)

When treatment was resumed Ann picked up where she had left off—at the piano. Rena was sung about, fed, scolded, and tenderly comforted during the mother's absence. However, while such play set the tone for each session, Ann introduced a "rain" theme which she worked on intensively in the piano play. Together we composed rain, thunder, lightning, and the lull-after-the-storm music. She substituted the phrase "It's raining" for "Sing about Rena or Floyd" in her greeting to me. Her many ways of inflecting her voice, hammering or lightly striking the keys suggested masturbatory fantasies. It also was clear that there was a connection between the rain fantasies and her recently achieved control of urination. The rain play replaced the spanking concerto. Throughout the year while playing with dolls, Ann would murmur or shout, "Is it raining?" This led to interpretations of excitement, its manifestations, and its control. Two years later she occasionally referred back to toilet training by asking, "Why did I used to say 'Is it raining?' " Often Ann used a question with a question mark to advance an idea of her own for the therapist's approval.

After two months of concentration on rain and Rena themes, Ann brought her birthday doll, Baby Ann, which was used to dramatize the child as an infant.

In play with both dolls, Rena and Baby Ann, Ann devised a system of simultaneously playing out two important problems: first, the normal dilemma implicit in separating and gaining independence; and second, the confusing concepts of blindness and being a twin. Many times it was very clear that she saw herself as a baby compared to her twin sister.

During the year of play "Baby Ann" was represented as a *baby* wanting her mother's constant attendance—"She wants to *touch* her mother"—with no resources except to cry. Rena was represented as a provocative, hitting *child* who was actively fighting the mother in feeding, dressing, and sharing attention. Much later phases of the treatment revealed that touching referred not only to the need for constant contact with the mother, but also to her curiosity about the mother's body. She substituted touching for seeing to some extent.

In the "Baby Ann" period Ann often became a tender, loving, reliable mother. By this time she had picked up some knowledge of neighbor babies and her teacher had capitalized on this interest by providing her with Brailled words and stories having to do with babies. She also took Ann to visit an infant. Ann spent weeks discussing how and when babies gurgle, cry, and want to be held and fed. "Is this the way the mother comforts the baby?" she would ask as she laid her doll on top of her shoulder, or "How do you make a gurgling noise?" as she wanted help with perfecting her own excellent reproduction of the sound. But despite her preoccupation with the subject she would "freeze" when outsiders tried to engage her interest in this seemingly safe subject. In Ann's play, as in the reality, "mother" frequently tried to read, "work with her bills," write letters, or commit the unpardonable offense of listening to the radio while the "baby" cried. The baby stopped crying only when the mother interrupted her tasks to hold her. The nurse (therapist) was always present, and the mother instructed her to "comfort Ann," but this was to no avail. The baby cried in the nurse's arms until the mother picked her up.

The Baby-Ann theme was still in full swing when Ann left for summer vacation, during which she had her sixth birthday. Her family found her amazingly free and happy on the beach and in the water, and she was more comfortable with various relatives in the same situation than she had been before. However, she insisted that her mother be near her when she was at home and would eat with no other person. When the mother was away at mealtimes Ann pleasantly accepted whoever was assigned to her supervision.

Fourth Year (Age Six)

When Ann returned to treatment in the fall she introduced many new variations in the family play. Her stage became populated with the whole family. Relatives came to visit, their dogs and cats bit and scratched, got lost, were sent away for fighting or were loved, fed, and rewarded for learning tricks. The father went to work after letting the dog out and making coffee; the parents went out to dinner in the evening, and the children teased the baby sitter. For the first time it was possible to form a more complete, though still distorted, picture of Ann's family life. According to her mother, Ann chose to stay in her room at home except when the children were in school. Then she would stay downstairs with her mother imitating the latter's kitchen and housekeeping activities and protesting strongly if the latter wrote, read, or appeared to be ignoring Ann. The radio had been a source of trouble between them for a long time. As this difficulty came up in the treatment, it appeared that, for Ann, the mother's listening to the radio was like talking to someone else, thus excluding Ann. Also, distracting noises regularly bothered Ann, who liked to listen to the radio and records but not as a background sound when something else was going on.

In the family group play all members of her family were represented. I was the maid who fed, bathed, and put the "baby" to bed. Ann's way of directing the play suggested her conception of her own role in the family as an onlooker. According to her mother, this was self-imposed since strong efforts were made to get her to eat with the family, enjoy the predinner hour in the living room, and go to bed when the twin did instead of two hours earlier. Ann herself insisted on the early supper with her mother and then bed as if she found it less painful to listen from upstairs—off stage—than to be a part of a group with whom she could neither communicate nor compete successfully.

In her therapy hours Ann continued to play the character role of "the baby," while she directed the scenes. She used me as her eyes and to fill in the details of the world as well as to put the characters through their paces. The following illustrates the course of a typical session of that period in the treatment. Ann: "Now let's play baby. What could be the mother? No, not that one, that's Leta." A cursory fingering of the doll I offered showed her that it was indeed the same one we had used earlier for that character. "O.K., but she has to wear shoes. Get them! Let's see. O.K., now she's going to feed the baby. How can we make the baby sit on her lap?" "Now the baby must have her bath."

The scene changed as Ann in her role of baby walked from the kitchen to the section of the room temporarily designated as the bedroom. The bath over, the baby was tucked into bed where she lay in the prone position with fists in eyes and legs either frogged out, in the sleeping position of a diapered baby, or held tightly together as she masturbated by rhythmic sliding up and down. While the baby lay in bed listening, Ann excitedly called, "Now the children must be in the TV room. Did you get the TV? Let me see. Make the mother and father go out to dinner. Did you get the father? Make him drive the car. No! The same place!" The parent dolls had to be seated in a car which she and I in an earlier session had created out of a bench and steering wheel attachment. Her directions were timed to my audible movements, and she allowed time for the character to complete one act before beginning another.

From then on a typical family evening was played out as the children complained about the food but ate it; the maid did the dishes and then urged bed. The children protested bed but finally gave in after the big brother had carefully shut the dog in his own room so that he could not get to the "baby" and the cat was put in the basement for the same reason. The sitter read the paper as she listened to the radio until the parents returned. They checked the baby, retired, and "talked" together.

The vicarious excitement enjoyed by the family member who retired early but remained awake until the rest of the family were all asleep was only too obvious through the loud laughter and chuckles of Ann who shouted "make the sister to do and so," to me until each member had been put through his paces.

In such family play never once did Ann refer to herself as "I" or "me." She did not use the names of the other children, although she accepted my doing so. She referred to them as "the big brother," "the big sister" and "the twin sister." She seemed to know that she was twin to the latter and could by virtue of age share the privileges of the "children," but this was a painful secret, not to be discussed. During this period, Ann arranged to have vicarious membership in the family at night by insisting on an early supper and bedtime despite her mother's urging that she remain up to eat with the family.

Sound effects were important. The dog's collar must click on the stairs; the door must shut as the cat was put out; and the father must go up and downstairs in his slippers, not shoes. If she included giving the dog fresh water, she insisted on my running the faucet so she could hear it. The playroom took the form of her house as she knew it and areas were assigned as certain rooms. When these changed as her play developed, she would say, "The top of the stairs could now be the hospital."

She craved to organize her sensory and perceptual expressive experiences, and through the technique of authoring, casting, directing, and acting in her own plays, she could at once be the active participant and passive observer. In this way she was able to dramatize and verbalize the organization of her world so it made sense— was logical, thematic, and sequential rather than chaotic, whimsical, capricious, and engulfing as she invested her feelings in this outer world.

As the months went on, dolls were found either from the nursery school collection or from her own assortment at home to represent everyone with whom Ann was involved—near and distant relatives as well as the immediate family, the housekeeper, a neighbor, the owner of the kennel from whom the family purchased a puppy, and a variety of neighborhood dogs and cats. Her world became more extensive and specific. Ann's mother was surprised to learn that Ann recognized the existence of any of these because she so rarely spoke to or of other people at home.

So far as the dolls themselves were concerned they were very specific personalities in our play. Ann's quick fingering was as effective as the sighted person's glance in checking to make certain that the doll assigned to a particular role was the one being used. At one point she was using the six members of her own family, an aunt, the latter's maid, a neighborhood baby who cried a lot and its mother, a veterinarian, three different dogs, and two cats. Dolls for eleven people and five animals had to be accounted for in each session. Some of the doll representatives came from home and had to travel back and forth with Ann. This caused considerable difficulty for whoever brought Ann, because she herself needed much physical help in getting in and out of the car and entering the building.

Ann's knowledge of the whereabouts of the doll figures was infallible, and no one challenged her authority when it came to locating a lost object. Her kinesthetic and auditory impression of her immediate surroundings was so precise that she rarely made a false move in reaching for something she herself had put down. This ability to keep her physical environment in mind plus the ease with which she could marshall her doll family through their day's activities suggested a high degree of organization in thinking and a good use of nonvisual memory. However, only in fantasy play in the therapy sessions could her cognitive capacities be recognized and followed. For this reason her parents were unable to feel optimistic about her social and intellectual future. Behavior at home was quite different. She screamed angrily when the other children were talking, feeling ignored and frustrated. The mother's response was to take Ann to her room where she always quieted down and engaged in solitary fantasy play with dolls and animals. Thus, her feeling lonely and ignored was confirmed and fantasy play became a substitute for social experience at home.

The therapist had become a trusted vehicle for the expansion of Ann's experiences in the external world.

Early in this treatment year Ann made her first direct approach to the concept of her blindness. Her parents had decided to buy a dog for the brother though Ann had plaintively insisted, "Don't get a dog." Despite some frightening situations Ann had seemed to have a genuine fondness for some of the relatives' pets.

When Ann was six years seven months old she told me of a dog named Bonnie. In setting the stage for play she said: "The children were in the garden with a picnic" and referred to aunt, uncle, cousins, their collie pup, and her own siblings. The relatives had "stopped off." In dramatizing this scene in the first session in which it was introduced, she asked me to "put the baby [herself] in bed," and then ordered me to scold and hit the dog for jumping up. In subsequent sessions she played the same scene, but the dog was chastised *before* the baby went to bed. Eventually it was clear that the dog had knocked a child down, but my picture of the scene was that one of the other children had been the subject of the attack and not Ann herself. Later I learned from the mother that Ann had been around two years four months of age when the relatives had "stopped off." She had been in the garden for a very brief time when the dog bumped into her, and her total collapse could be handled only by taking her to bed. Her mother had not remembered the episode until asked if Ann had ever had an unpleasant experience with a dog. At first she reported that there had been none, but in a later reference to Ann's knowledge of her visiting cousins the mother was suddenly reminded of the garden scene which involved the attack of the dog.

From the time the decision to get a new dog was made Ann opened each play session with "Why are they going to get a dog when I don't want them to." But she would then quite happily play out a trip in which the other children went with the father to the kennels to choose the puppy. During the period of preparation for the dog all the playroom rubber and stuffed dogs became the dogs she had known. For weeks she vividly recalled Billy, the blind, incontinent, enormous poodle who had died shortly before she was four years old and who had first come up in the treatment a year later. Billy, in his cumbersome way, had interfered with her early physical independence by always being in the way. He had been taken to the veterinarian who said he was too old and too sick to cure and was "put to sleep." In the play another dog was sent away because he could not be house trained. It became clear that the two dogs who were sent away had Ann's own problems—blindness and toilet training.

She enjoyed the play involving the dogs and laughed delightedly at the dilemma they created. At the same time she became increasingly angry and anxious as her family proceeded in the plans to get another dog. She also tried to enlist my aid in opposing the acquisition of a dog. I pointed out ways in which she could participate in the care of the dog and encouraged her family to fence off areas so Ann could always know where he was. On the day that the new dog, Monty, entered the household Ann arrived for her session saying confidingly, "Monty's shaking" as she indicated his trembling by making her hand to do likewise. Her empathy for the dog away from his mother in new surroundings was immediately apparent. Despite continued avowal that she did not like him and would never forgive her family for not respecting her wishes, she obviously began to love the dog who in turn loved her as well as her brother.

Ann suffered another insult when the older sister acquired a cat. Ann was also empathic with this pet as she insisted that his cries be responded to with food, fondling, or being let outdoors. A year later a second dog in the family was eagerly welcomed by Ann as well as the other children.

The dog incident provided the background for the discussion of her blindness. All the dog toys in the playroom had been rejected by her for the Monty role because they had already had other names and personalities. She turned down a teddy bear offered as a substitute but allowed a collection of zoo animals to be put in her lap. When she selected a rubber lion and asked, "Could we use this?" I agreed without identifying it as a lion. She immediately named it "Pronty" and spent an intense session introducing the dog to the family group, comforting him, feeding him, and generally relieving his feelings of homesickness. She then asked to take him home without further clarification that it was a lion being used as a dog. I readily agreed but immediately hesitated as it became clear that the children at home would see that Pronty was a lion. Ann, picking up the note of hesitation, then inquired, "Is Pronty a dog?" For two months thereafter she attacked me at the beginning of each session with "Is Pronty a dog or a lion?" as she carried her animal back and forth from home to the treatment sessions. I repeatedly explained that in play he had served as a dog but that the features were those of a lion. She learned much about lions. I then interpreted that she was wondering how other children knew it was a lion when she did not, and was in this way asking about blindness. Her response was: "Tell me all about blindness."

For sessions thereafter Pronty served as the cue to blindness talk. "Tell Rena" was the way of indicating the painful nature of the subject. Her practiced interest in babies permitted her to become fascinated by the setting of the infant nursery with attentive nurses caring for twin girls, one of whom needed to be watched especially closely. Ann played the baby in an incubator and in this scene for the first time insisted that her twin be nearby and cared for in the same way at the same time. For the first time it was apparent that the twin was uniquely and closely important to Ann.

This was followed by a week of concentrated play and discussion of the care of the tiny twins, including the incubator treatment. The twin was taken home from the hospital two weeks before Ann who remained for continued careful attention by the hospital nurses. The blindness was discovered when she was about four months old. In the play, the care for two hungry babies and the introduction of a nurse to help so that they would not have to wait was the scene that evoked Ann's statement, "It isn't fair."

After that she dropped back to the dog play in which Pronty was discussed, described, and played with as a strange dog in a new household who "was shaking" and needed frequent reassurance as well as training. Ann would accept no references to the real dog, Monty, and steadfastly maintained at home that she did not like him and never intended to. Her regular greeting in therapy, "Why did you call the dog a lion?" changed to "Why did you call the lion a dog?" as she struggled with her confusion and feelings of disillusionment. Her first spontaneous comment to people outside the family was, "Is Pronty a dog or a lion?" as she tested them on their ability to identify the animal. I firmly interpreted Ann's dismay and resentment that she was blind and her fear that I had tried to "fool" her with the animal substitute. Eventually an earlier interpretation was repeated, "You are wondering about what it means to be blind." Again she faced the trouble directly asking: "Are you blind? Will I always be blind? Will I be blind when I am a grown lady?" This was a very moving moment because she had been standing when the conversation opened and dropped into a chair with a sudden and overwhelming loss of physical strength. That evening her mother called to inquire about the session because Ann had seemed "different"—more relaxed and affectionate. At bedtime she had asked for the first time if she was blind, and then if her mother was blind also.

In the ensuing sessions she repeated an earlier play sequence of beach play in the vacation setting. In the game she was a little girl learning to swim and running on the beach with her favorite aunt, with the important theme of dogs having to be tied or trained not to jump up on helpless children.

She then demanded new toy dogs from her family and from me. It was agreed that a new character was needed to represent Monty the real dog, since she had to learn to live with him and wanted to dramatize her difficulties in the treatment. The new "Pronty" was carefully specified by her as a "blind dog." To indicate this she used the expression, "Make him to be blind." All new dogs were named "-onty" and she groped carefully through the alphabet for unused initial consonants to make unique names for the new pets.

During this period Ann began to work more productively with her teacher who had introduced a Braille typewriter. She was interested in experimenting with the keys and in dictating stories. However, it was becoming increasingly clear that the tutoring sessions should be moved outside of the home, and a satisfactory place for school was found in the fall. Ann adamantly refused any such move. One aspect of this was that Ann never mentioned her real teacher in the therapy and resented my references to Miss M. She felt that her relationship to me was threatened if she made any advances in learning. In the play interviews there were discussions of the different roles of the adults in her life, and she was reassured about the continuity of the treatment.

At that time the plan for a psychological test was introduced. Despite careful preparation, she regularly declared, "But I don't want a test." It was clear that she had made a commitment when, offered a choice of playroom or office for the examination, she readily announced that it was to be in the playroom. It appeared that she recognized her own development when she said that if Dr. Provence tested babies she should not be testing six-year-old children.

The test went unexpectedly well. She was interested, cooperative, and worked hard. Surprisingly, she performed up to age level in various items, over age level in some, and under only in those tests involving use of numbers. Her anxiety was revealed at the beginning when she announced to Dr. Provence, "Pronty just threw up." When the test was over and it was clear that she felt relieved and successful, she staunchly defended her stand, "But I won't go to that school." The event of the test did much for Ann. Her relatives were impressed and surprised as much by the fact of her cooperation as by the results, since she was still generally remote and unresponsive at home. She gained considerable status with her siblings who were also relieved to have this strange sister experience anything so normal as a "test." Her brother's delighted announcement that Ann had "passed the test" indicated the importance of this success for the family.

After the test episode a month still remained before summer vacation and Ann's seventh birthday. Ann, relieved of her test, having dealt with the blindness to some extent, and looking forward delightedly to the summer at the seashore, presented a new development in play style. She adapted for her use a popular recording of a current musical dealing with the life and works of a teacher. Ann was fascinated. She learned the songs; she put me in the role of the lead character and asked many questions suggested by the new words she was hearing, e.g., "What is a stage, a theater," etc. This was a fortuitous subject because through discussing the "teacher" in *The Sound of Music* she revealed her interest in hearing about the many things to be learned, why the children in the story loved and needed the teacher, and how teachers in general can help children. We agreed that I helped her to understand many things about herself, but that Miss M. would enable her to learn reading and writing, and all the tools she would want for the understanding of the world around her. She then revealed her fear that if she successfully adapted to school and formal education, she would be in danger of losing me.

In her treatment Ann relentlessly held her ground when she had once taken a stand. This often continued with her mother. For example, her mother would periodically renew her effort to withstand Ann's insistence that certain records not be played in her presence. Inevitably the mother would either give in, become very angry, which in turn provoked a tantrum in Ann, or take her to her room.

After her blindness and the psychological test had been discussed she brought up her fear of sirens. In the presence of sirens she panicked. Tensing her entire body, she would inquire, "Why do my shoulders go like this?" as she hunched them and held her breath until the siren sound faded in the distance. Around this she produced a fantasy of "I am afraid the siren will blow away my furry animal." In reality there had been an episode of riding in the car with her mother and having to draw to the curb while a fleet of fire engines rushed by with blaring sirens. She had let go of the furry cat she had been clutching and could not find it immediately. A dream she referred to revealed considerable preoccupation with the fear of losing the furry cat at night.

The anxiety about sirens led to the castration fear, and to an unusual double displacement—the blindness was displaced downward and the castration threat was also displaced onto the loss of the cat. One likely supposition was that the sirens produced a loss of auditory orientation by the overwhelming volume and rapid approach of the shattering sound—this was a reminder of the helplessness, the castrated feeling, produced when visual and auditory organizers were ineffectual.

When the vacation began Ann was apprehensive and asked plaintively, "Who will teach me?" At the same time she happily anticipated a summer at the beach. She was anxious about the loose dogs but accepted reassurance that the family knew how she felt and would help keep them under reasonable control. A college girl spent the summer with the family, and she and Ann got along well. Ann enjoyed the water and was unexpectedly daring in the waves.

The twins' birthday celebration was enjoyed by Ann in a way earlier ones had not been. She participated in the family party and eagerly opened her gifts. For her birthday I gave her a furry lion. Her parents reported that she had fingered it thoroughly and announced "It's a lion," adding, "But why didn't she send it in a cage? Lions live in cages."

Fifth Year (Age Seven)

Ann returned in September noticeably taller and more robust looking. For the first time she appeared as a healthy seven-year-old of slight build and delicate features except for the sightless eyes and guarded gait. After greeting me with "You have never seen this new dog," she entered the playroom inquiring, "What smells?" in recognition of the fact that the chairs had been painted a month before. Ann regularly tested the smell as well as the sound of new and old places and objects either to establish or to re-establish her concept of them.

Once launched in the session she spent the hour reviewing each old subject briefly as she worked her way back into the familiar world, checking my memory for mutual associations. She managed to cover them all and leave five minutes at the end of the session to protest entering school.

The fifth year of treatment was important in a variety of ways: Ann was definitely better although there was still much evidence of her psychological vulnerability and learning problem. Within a week she showed her mother and her teacher, although not me, that she loved going to school for two hours a day. Despite her efforts to deal with her anxiety at school by controlling the teacher, by late winter she was learning to read, and by spring was occasionally joining her age group of normal children for certain parts of the second-grade program. In treatment she became more flexible, more physically active, very noisy, and increasingly spontaneous in expressing her feelings. In her sessions her repertoire of spontaneously expressed feelings now ranged from strong feelings of excitement, pleasure, anger and love to laughter, screaming, shouting, and tantrums. She pleaded to see me more often and know more about me personally.

Around her memory for early events Ann's way of asking questions about the past indicated that she was now seeking information about herself rather than introducing a familiar topic for discussion. An incident that occurred when she was seven and a half illustrates one of these memory traces. I had used the expression "toward you" in directing Ann to turn a handle. The thoughtful way in which Ann repeated the words led me to inquire whether she was remembering something about them. Although she denied having anything particular in mind, the child's hesitancy suggested that the phrase was familiar although she could not place the time and setting. I described how when she was learning how to regulate the faucets in her sink play at age three and a half the expression "toward you" had been said many, many times to teach her the "on" position. Ann commented: "But I don't remember things like that."

Her language development was excellent so far as vocabulary and phraseology were concerned, although her need to concretize prevented her from clearly or concisely expressing her thoughts; e.g., she had great difficulty in telling how she gave herself "tests" at her new desk at home. She could impressively communicate her understanding of feelings through inflection and choice of words. For example, once she chided me with, "Put the lovingness back in your voice" when she detected a slight remoteness in the midst of a conversation. Although she herself would repeat the same question and play out the same drama relentlessly, she commented when I repeated a statement: "That's repetitious." Her language imagery for describing bodily sensations and experiences was remarkable: e.g., when a heavy door slammed shut she observed, "It throws air at your face." Stamping her feet she described as "kicking up and down to the floor." When handling a new, large teddy bear she observed, "I'm feeling it from place to place." To describe the texture of a furry animal she referred to its "sweatery back" as she reached behind her to stroke the cashmere of her own cardigan. She used the expression, "My blood goes like *this*" to refer to whatever physical concomitant of emotion she was experiencing when hearing a cement mixer grinding outside. Later this expression changed to "My stomach goes like this." When asked what "this" felt like, Ann said, "It curls." "Lying down is a little bit like standing up," she observed as she was lowering herself into a sleeping position in baby play.

Her words and expressions indicated developing feelings of identity with her generation. She would say, "That's real cool," "That's keen," or "Let's trade." She experimented hesitatingly by addressing me as "Stupid," "Dope," or "Liar," and liked to discuss why she used those names and why it was permitted. Her mother reported that Ann was never heard to talk in these terms at home, adding that Ann's language was the best in the family. When her brother's swearing provoked comment from the parents, Ann asked, "Have I ever sweared?" and forthwith began to do so in her sessions coining a few new words such as "God pest!" "Pest" became her favorite epithet for me when she was aggravated. During the interviews she referred to me as "Dear" and by my first name at home. When she used the term "dear" it was clear from her intonations that she was assigning different roles to me. These included the roles of playmate, compatriot, teacher, mother, sibling, etc.

As in other years the gains could be observed in play with dolls and animals. However, this year's dramatic productions benefited from her closer contact with reality, broader experience, and the improved inner organization which permitted greater flexibility and motility. Also, she was able for the first time to count sequentially and demonstrated some understanding of number concepts.

The underlying themes of blindness, twinship, body image, and object choice continued but were worked on at a level more appropriate to her age. Household play developed from washing dishes to serving meals and cleaning the house. Both at home and in therapy she wanted to clean up real dust and dirt and have her efforts taken more seriously. She pretended to serve meals, re-enacting family scenes in which there was conflict about cleaning the plates and who was to be served first. She mixed cocktails or tea to set the stage for "entre-nous" conversation. At such times she discarded the doll or animal characters.

Several weeks were then spent on her curiosity and fearful reaction to a vomiting episode of the twin. Ann herself had not vomited since infancy. The sound and olfactory sensations had been frightening, and exciting.

In the family play, the brother, older sister, and father were often absent, while the twin sister, the maid, and Ann were the main characters. Although the maid played the adult's role in disciplinary situations, Ann quite regularly announced that the mother had gone away and would not be back.

By December, animals had been replaced by "purses" as something she brought from home. These were jammed with pieces of paper representing bills, mail, money, a wallet, change purse, and the usual items in a lady's handbag. She was very curious about my purses. Her own were described and identified by shape and degree of shininess of the leather or plastic finish.

As she was dealing with purses, house cleaning, and playing out the sister's vomiting episode in the treatment, an illness of mine necessitated a two-month interruption. During this period Ann continued to work well with her tutor. Her home behavior changed little except that she began to pretend that she was a Siamese cat and would communicate all her needs with inflected "miaows." The family members were openly annoyed, but she persisted in her cat language at home until two weeks after treatment resumed. There had been an earlier reference to Siamese twins.

On the day she returned to treatment Ann brought Rena whom I had not seen for almost a year. Her opening greeting was a whispered, "Comfort Rena." She followed with, "Tell her about your operation." However, before I could say anything, she shouted that I should talk like the maid with whom she had spent much time. It became clear that her insistence that I not use my natural voice was based on her attempts to ward off reactions to the thoughts that I had been sick and absent. This insistence was sustained until she was able to question the nature of the illness about twenty sessions later. Her first genuine angry outburst since the original tantrums was precipitated when I refused to mimic the maid's flat, dull tones for more than a brief play episode. I told Ann that I did not think it would help her to have me assume that role for a full session. In her outburst she screamed, stamped her foot, and flung everything her hands could find. When I did not try to stop her, the intensity subsided as she asked in a pleading, frightened voice, "Where were you?" Apparently relieved that I had not left her alone when she expressed her anger, she then "staged" daily tantrums for my benefit, laughing delightedly when they were over, asking "Was I too, too mad?" Our sessions focused on the voice controversy to the exclusion of other play themes for some two weeks and her behavior at home was reported as "impossible." She relentlessly questioned her mother about things to which the answer had in the first instance been made clear and definite. She switched the tantrum display in her sessions to a whining "When will you? When? When? When?" on the matter of the voice. The interpretation that freed her from this repetitive behavior referred to her attempts to use this aggressive questioning to indicate her distrust of me for becoming ill and leaving her. Most specifically this referred to the cancellation of her session on the first day of the illness. Discussion of this event served to relieve the mounting irritability which was her way of expressing anger and anxiety about the stability of our relationship.

After this Ann introduced the most elaborate of all her family life fantasies in play. The focus was the content of the musical recording of *The King and I,* which Ann's mother had bought for the family to enjoy during a four-day absence of the parents that had occurred during my illness. In *The King and I,* as in *The Sound of Music,* there is a teacher who becomes involved with the father of a group of children whom she is employed to teach. The drama Ann produced in response to "Anna" and the "King" relates artistically her view of her life's situation. It is presented in the natural scenario form that Ann created. The dialogue is condensed in the interest of economy of space.

Act I   Scene 1

A trip to the music store to purchase the record. I in the role of the maid take the twins with me on the bus. During the ride the two little girls tease the maid by hitting and "swearing" which brings the threat of "no more bus rides." From Ann's direction of this scene, and from her style of acting her own role, it was clear that she wished to share pleasure, excitement, and punishment with the twin. In real life she did not take part in such play with the twin but did with the older sister.

Scene 2

The walk from bus stop to home with the other children in the family eagerly awaiting the twins' arrival with a surprise. Ann patiently unwraps the package while the "other children" shout impatiently to her to hurry. The maid cautions, "It's for the *whole* family." Ann shouts gleefully, "It's the *King and I!*" and she pulls the record folder from the wrapping. Other children plead to be allowed to hear it played.

Act II   Scene 1

In the living room with a pretend record on a pretend record player. The family is settled for listening, while the maid "works with her bills." Ann suddenly screams because she does not like four songs on the record and is sent to her room for "spoiling it for the *whole* family." Children clamor, "Oh, stop that noise!" Maid chides, "It isn't nice to scream. Wouldn't you like to go to your room?"

Scene 2

Ann substitutes a doll, Ann, for herself in the lead role. She puts on the doll's slippers and places her in bed in her room, a block arrangement Ann and I had made. Her hands are in her eyes and she is "thinking." For the first time in her treatment Ann was quite direct about her own feelings via the doll. The "doll Ann" no longer preferred isolation from the others—"She doesn't want to leave the other children"—but she can't help "spoiling" the music because the lyrics of certain songs evoked more feeling than she could safely contain. These lyrics deal with anger, disappointment, fear, Siamese (twin) children, and teasing. In one song, Anna is "too, too angry . . . like the mother" when she shouts to the King in an imaginary conversation, "You're spoiled!"

Scene 3

The painful songs are over and Ann is returned to the living room to listen to the safer songs about romantic love. As she lies on the floor with her hands in her eyes she is told to remove them and sit up straight.

Act III   Scene 1

The record is still playing for the "whole family." The doll Ann remains listening, while Ann introduces a play within a play by having us go to the kitchen adjoining the playroom for "bakery goodies." She and I sit at the table. While she eats candy we discuss how angry Anna gets at the King, and she requests two dolls for acting out the scene. Ann then says, "Tell the twin sister about how I used to touch my mother," followed by, "Tell her how I got blindness," and then "Tell her why I come here." The device of having me speak to the third person instead of to her directly is a familiar one for softening the effects of painful topics. When the subject became too uncomfortable Ann said, "The needle is stuck. The doll Ann wants it fixed."

Scene 2

We return to the original play and remove the record. The play is ended and the session time over.

This play enjoyed a four weeks' run. Then Ann shifted the focus of our session back to simple role playing which dealt directly with the problem of blindness. The following episodes illustrate the manner in which Ann introduced the subject of her blindness:

Ann (age seven and three quarters): "Let's pretend you are Ann, and the record player is on and you are in the living room by the table with the plant on it. Make pretend your knees are on your chair and this part of your body [patting her abdomen] is touching the table and your hands are in your eyes. Pretend a grownup comes in and says, 'Ann, take your hands out of your eyes' and then make your blood go like this."

This was the first time that she had experimented with having me play her role as the blind child. The reference to "blood goes . . ." was Ann's way of expressing indirectly her affective response when her parents told her to remove her hands from her eyes.

A week later she again brought me into her own world when I tripped over a chair leg and she, knowing exactly what had happened, responded with delight and understanding in her voice, "Did you bump into a chair?"

A month later Ann said: "Get me a newspaper so I can be the maid reading the paper. Is this right." I showed her how to hold it in front of her. She chuckled as she found she could effect the familiar sounds of the newspaper being opened by a reader. "Now! Am I reading it?" Such scenes were the springboard for plunging into conversation about reading print and Braille and the puzzling subject of sightedness for the blind and vice versa.

She always wanted it made clear that both the seeing and the blind have trouble understanding how the other person perceives his world. Another version of "reading" play from the same period illustrates Ann's method of dealing with the more practical aspects of the subject of Braille versus print. At Ann's request I had provided a copy of the *Reader's Digest*.

Ann: "Now you be Ann and ask to see the *Reader's Digest*—not the Braille one; the print one."

Therapist: "And who will you be?"

Ann: "I'm Maud [an occasional maid]. I'm reading the *Reader's Digest* and you ask for it."

Therapist: "Please give me the *Reader's Digest* now?"

Ann: "You can't have it because you are blind."

Therapist: "I know that, but I want you to give me the *Reader's Digest*."

Ann: "But you're blind."

Therapist: "But I want to do what you are doing."

Ann: "But you can't see print. It's because you are blind."

Therapist (guided by the observation of Ann's way of fingering over and turning the pages of magazines during which process she picks up all finger smudges, torn pages, insertion of pictures with glossy finish, etc. Actually she can identify many print books by their "feel." Ann often makes up some news or a story as if she is reading it): "I told you I know I'm blind but you don't seem to understand that I want the *Reader's Digest* anyway. I keep trying to feel that print you talk about all the time."

Ann (impatiently): "But you can't have it because you are blind and can't see with your eyes."

Therapist: "But I would like to have it anyway. I sometimes like to pretend that I am not blind and can read print. When I have a magazine I find all the shiny pages and the torn edges and when I am pretending to read I make up a story in my mind."

Ann (even more impatiently): "But you can't have it, Ann, because
    you are blind."
Therapist: "But when I got the Braille *Reader's Digest* everybody
    wanted it. People are always asking to look at my Braille books."
Ann (back in her own voice): "Why do they?"

Back in my own voice I commented about the difficulties on both
sides and Ann's struggle to be understood, referring to how other
children must find Braille very interesting and also want to hold
the book in their hands and study it with their fingers in order to
learn about it. They wonder how Ann can read those dots on the
paper when they cannot, adding that Ann has a similar interest in
print. Further comment about how Ann and other children are alike
in this respect brought no response from Ann, although she did not
interrupt or shout "Pest" as she ordinarily did when she preferred
that I drop a subject.

For several weeks Ann introduced such scenes in the early part
of each session and then before leaving requested that we "talk about
Monty." This led to the recapitulation of the lion-dog confusion of
the preceding year.

Ann could then deal extensively with the story of her own birth
and infancy. She asked questions about childbirth, how the doctor
could tell the babies were girls, etc. This made it possible to clarify
some of her confusion about sexual differences and procreation.
Then, her castration fears became much more accessible to treatment.

When I commented that it was indeed difficult for people who
are blind and those who are not to understand each other, Ann said
in tones which indicated a capacity for self-observation, "Poor Ann.
Poor Ann's eyes."

It was clear that she was developing a sense of the extent of her
defect—its impact on others as well as herself. Earlier she had tended
to wish that others were blind like she was, but this was changing.
Now she experimented with the magic of denial and would say
teasingly and sometimes defiantly, "I can see," or tentatively, "You
are a liar." When she was four she had used the expression, "The
eyes are for tears" during the time that she was building an image
of her body through discussing the functions of various organs and
body parts. Then she had said the words with no particular affect.
Now four years later, after insisting that I say that Ann could not see

with her eyes, she said, "The eyes are for tears" with her affect clearly stating, "And I can now cry."

DISCUSSION

In the study and treatment of Ann, a child who from earliest infancy suffered from blindness, we have been concerned with the effect of blindness on the libidinal and ego development, on the establishment of object relationships, and on the role of the other perceptual modalities in the child's development. It is essential to keep in mind that Ann's mother was overwhelmed by the unexpected birth of the twins, one of whom became blind soon after birth. The mother's reaction to this trauma contributed to the fact that Ann not only was understimulated but also received less guidance than she optimally required for overcoming her handicap.

We are selecting for special emphasis in this discussion the consideration of four of Ann's difficulties and their implications for her development as they appeared in her treatment: (1) an arrest of libidinal and ego development; (2) the development of an inhibition of touching, a function ordinarily hypercathected in blind children; (3) the disorganizing effect of the eruption of memories of painful experiences from the first three years of life; and (4) Ann's slowly emerging sense of a defect and eventually of the specificity of her blindness. We shall also attempt to relate the unbalanced perceptual development to a defect in the ego's capacity to repress, and to demonstrate the repair of this rent in the ego's structure. There are many other aspects of Ann's treatment and development that will be considered in future reports.

It is extraordinarily complicated for the child who becomes blind soon after birth to comprehend the absence of visual capacity that the sighted world takes for granted. In order to gain an impression of himself, his love objects, and the world in which he lives, a blind child depends more than the sighted child on all of his other senses and the protection, guidance, and interpretation of reality by his parents. The mutual adaptation of mother and child has an additional hurdle when the child is blind from birth. The mother as an auxiliary ego attempts to provide substitutes and compensations for the absence of the visual experiences which are so important for the mastery of the developmental tasks of early childhood. These tasks were recently summarized by Greenacre (1960):

> During the first two years after birth, one of the main tasks of the infant undoubtedly has to do with making a sound separation from the mother and the commencement of an individual existence, with the later establishment of the sense of reality, of early object relationship, the beginning of secondary process thinking, and the first stages of the sense of identity, in conjunction with, interdependent with and under the mediation of the young ego [p. 579].
>
> [In the same article Greenacre states:] . . . vision is not only an adjunct but an indispensable one in establishing the confluence of the body surface and promoting awareness of delimitation of the self from the non-self. 'Touching' and taking in of the various body parts with the eyes (vision) helps in drawing the body together, into a central image beyond the level of more immediate sensory awareness. Further the very functioning of visual perception in a focussed way . . . , as different from the reciprocal contacts between body parts by cutaneous touch, may offer a kind of nuclear beginning to an ego development at a mental level. It is a self-observing function which gains significance as it combines with and oversees the self-perception of touch to form some kind of image of much of the body self, and to separate it from the other objects, both animate and inanimate [pp. 575-576].
>
> [Greenacre refers to Spitz's work (1957) when she states:] Certainly the pervasive and powerful influence of vision is soon apparent when the infant begins to indicate choice through his head movements. The *no* makes a refusal through a direct turning of the head to the side to dispose of the undesired stimulating object by removing it from vision; whereas the *yes* through up and down movement permits it to remain in the range of focus and be affirmed again and again. . . . the contrast between the affirmative and the negative is determined in large measure by the bilaterality of the eyes [p. 576].

This concept may help to understand why Ann's expressions for "yes" and "no" were so poorly distinguishable when she first entered treatment. However, the child's developing sense of himself and of reality also depends on experiences with the other modalities of perception, especially hearing, touch, position change when in contact with the adult body, and certain aspects of taste and olfaction.

The blind child is vitally dependent on tactile and kinesthetic experiences to substitute and compensate for the absence of vision. In fact, Deutsch (1940) investigated the sense of reality in congenitally blind children through devising a test based on touch. He stated: "In order to test systematically how his lack of sight affects the sense of reality in the person born blind, we worked out a method which uses the sense of touch as the basis for testing the sense of reality." Touch is crucially important in providing the child with experiences that establish the differentiation of the self from the nonself. Through these tactile experiences ". . . are mediated any perception of differences in temperature, texture, moistness, and many other subtle changes in kinaesthetic vibratory sensations and pressures, differences which gradually build up to some sense of degrees of separateness or of aloneness" (Greenacre, 1960).

In our patient, the lack of vision and her mother's reaction to the child conspired to deprive Ann of the auxiliary ego she required for her development. Because of her affective withdrawal, the mother was unable to respond to the child's need for tactile, kinesthetic, and auditory experiences that would aid her in coping with the gap created by her blindness. At the time Ann entered treatment she regressively clung to her mother, but the depressed, frantic woman was frozen and wooden in her responses, feeling helpless and overwhelmed by her defective, blind offspring, a twin. The mother's aggression was only thinly disguised. When Ann began to give evidence of her adequacy as an alert and responsive child, the mother began to respond to the child with some warmth and appropriate attention. Before that, the mother's stiff compliance with the intellectual idea that a blind child should have opportunities to touch was experienced by Ann as an aggressive satisfaction which fixated the child's efforts at gratification from the constant human object at a dangerous sadomasochistic level. The libidinal attachment was largely aggressivized or alternately withdrawn onto herself in the autistic behavior which she demonstrated in the long periods in which she seemed to prefer to remain in her crib, away from the family.

Ann's anxiety, already sharply heightened by the real dangers of being blind, had become greater because her mother's depression minimized the protection and guidance the child required. Leta, the nurse, was not able to provide stimulation and hopeful expectations in the first two years of life because she was convinced that Ann was defective and could not be helped. She took care of the "outside" of the child but neglected the affective and psychic unfolding of the "inside" of Ann by her attitude that the blind child was hopelessly retarded. Leta's general attitude was directed toward isolating and infantilizing the child, although her sporadic cuddling, patting contacts were intensely remembered by Ann in the "Leta spank you" treatment episodes and the "comfort Rena" play.

In the initial phase of treatment, contact was first established through talking, since hearing was less conflicted and less anxiety producing than touching. After the therapist became familiar as a voice she began to touch Ann and to produce sounds and vibrations via the piano and voice. The vibrations formed a bridge to the touching experiences. Touching the child was more dramatic and effective in evoking responses and in establishing the therapist as a needed, guiding, and protecting love object. It was essential to diminish the child's anxiety before the other auxiliary ego functions provided by the therapist could be utilized.

It was only after the anxiety had been decreased in this way that the therapist was able to understand the child's dilemma. Ann's regression in the initial treatment sessions was rapid and frightening. Hearing was to some extent associated with anxiety because it had become the warning pathway for the danger of the unknown from which the blind child felt inadequately protected by her mother. Listening seemed to have become instinctualized in that auditory stimuli were often used to set off repetitive bouts of climactic sensuous excitement, as in the experiences of listening to the piano or the recall of listening to the rainfall. Later in the treatment it became clear that these eruptions of excited behavior also represented memories that were expressed as perceptual and motor behavior. We refer to these as sensorimotor memories, and will discuss them in greater detail below. The excitement associated with the rainfall was specifically related also to the erotic pleasure of urination. The erotization of listening was clearly referred to in Ann's discussion of her parents' "talks" in bed after everyone was asleep. One could speculate that listening became substituted for the voyeuristic impulses, and served both as a defense and as a trigger mechanism for instinctual discharge. It was not until the third year of treatment that one could observe Ann's use of verbalization for the expression of exhibitionistic impulses when Ann would provocatively say forbidden words to her mother in front of other people. With the protection of the therapist and other people, Ann could exhibitionistically and aggressively say "miaow" when the mother had effectively prohibited such verbal excitement at other times. Ann's favorite exhibitionistic word was "pooey," which was a derivative of her anal and urethral excitement.

In regard to the touching inhibition, Ann adhered physically to her mother in a diffuse anxious manner when first brought to treatment. Although she seemed to melt plastically into her mother's resigned and toneless body, she had developed a hand-touching inhibition by the time she was brought for treatment in her fourth year. This inhibition was specifically related to earlier intensely exciting episodes of touching her mother's body, especially below the waist. In retrospect, the mother disliked and discouraged this behavior, although she conveyed her excitement, as well as her disapproval, and the threat of withdrawing from Ann when this occurred. Ann's touching inhibition extended to her own body as well as to other human bodies, and also to soft inanimate objects. This inhibition excluded fisting her eyes when she was upset. It became clear that the tactile and kinesthetic modalities had been relatively understimulated in the first two years, but that being touched and touching came to be experienced as instinctualized climactic discharges. The inhibition was set in motion by the fear of losing contact with the mother if she touched her. The inhibition was reinforced by its association with castration anxiety. The castration anxiety was expressed as the fear of being overwhelmed from within by a mounting and uncontrollable instinctual tension and from without by unexpected dangers. Intense urethral-genital erotism was associated with the inner anxiety and the outer danger which were often not distinguishable. Ann's masturbation against the mother's knee was partly an effort to avoid touching herself, and was experienced as an aggressivized discharge that had as its climax a temper tantrum of clinging to the prohibiting mother. It is important to keep in mind that Ann's retarded development had limited her motor-discharge modalities and experiences which are so crucial for young children as a release from mounting tension and anxiety.

The fisting of the eyes is a well-known blindism. In Ann's case it represented, in part, a displacement of genital touching. But this is not sufficient to explain the phenomenon, which probably depends on a particular sensation of blind eyes, and which may represent a body language that expresses the child's anxiety as well as the defense against it. By rubbing the defective area she feels where she cannot see in order to cope with her anxiety. However, this is a speculation that will require more data than are now available.

Because of Ann's atypical development, it was difficult to detect the elaboration of her oedipal longings until the last year of her ongoing treatment when she was in her eighth year. There had been a great deal of play in which Ann was the mother as well as a baby, but the omission of the father was glaringly conspicuous. The father was referred to at times as a make-believe character, one who could be avoided or manipulated. It became evident that the father had responded to Ann as a pitiful, sorrowful child whom he sadly wanted to help. There was an absence of expectation and admiration for her feminine qualities. This sadness was too painful for Ann, and she warded it off by treating her father as a comic-strip character. The oedipal longings had been delayed not only by the necessity to deal with the anxiety caused by her blindness and the effects of her mother's depression, but also by the painfulness of her perception that father felt she was a helpless and hopeless creature. Also, her oedipal longings were distorted by a continued preoccupation with preoedipal conflicts, especially her efforts to cope with the fear of losing the depressed mother who could be kept in contact through provocative behavior. It is very likely that at the time the treatment began, the fixation at a sadomasochistic level in which the mother was experienced as a symbiotic object was facilitated by the distorted and undeveloped relationship to the father. He, too, could begin to respond to Ann with love and humor, and with a warm appreciation of her femininity, when her hopeless, helpless appearance and behavior became changed as a result of the treatment. In her eighth year, Ann's play with dolls and her fantasy play included the protective, loving father in the family, and she indirectly expressed envy of the mother who could go on trips with her husband.

Before discussing the failure of the early repressive functions of the ego, it will be necessary to comment briefly on the relative absence of the twinship influence and on the remarkable regression that occurred after the first year of life.

Ann's perceptions of being a twin were sharply curtailed by her blindness and the care she received. Because of the separation of the care of the twins at the hospital and at home, this limitation was heightened. The twins slept, ate, and were cared for separately. It was only after Ann could speak and understand verbal explanations in the sixth year of her life that the twin concept began to take shape. However, the impact on Ann of being a twin was revealed in her confusion of who took care of which twin, as well as in the fact that Ann had to share with her twin sister the available adult care and attention.

At the age of four months it became clear and definite that Ann was blind. Leta, the nurse, became convinced that Ann was damaged and unsalvageable. By the beginning of the second year, Ann's mother was concerned about Leta's attitude and behavior toward Ann, but the depressed mother could not mobilize herself to initiate a change until the twins were about two and a half years old. By the end of the first year, Leta gave up on Ann, except to treat her as a nice infant who would not mature. Simultaneously, she became extremely fond and possessive of Ann's twin sister. This, plus her pessimistic attitude toward Ann, led to the nurse's discharge when the twins were two and a half. The mother then employed daytime help to assist in the care of the children and the house.

In reconstructing this series of events it became clear that Ann's development after the first year was thwarted by Leta's encouragement of regression and later by the loss of Leta, as well as by her blindness and her mother's depression. Regression set in as the stimulation and assistance she required for her development and safety remained unavailable despite her progressing maturation. As Ann's developmental needs advanced, there was relatively less guidance and protection provided until a new balance was struck after she entered treatment.

In the second year of Ann's treatment when she was almost five years old it became evident that she suffered from the intrusion of painful and disorganizing sensorimotor memories from her earliest years. These memories are referred to as sensorimotor because one could observe and understand the memory mainly in her behavior. Then the therapist could verbalize and clarify the memory. A persistent example of this type of memory was demonstrated in the "Leta spank you" episodes, in which Ann would re-enact the memory of the sexualized excitement she experienced when Leta had patted and cuddled her in the first two years of life. Another early memory was clarified when Ann insisted that the doll had to be burped "just right" and groped to find a specific position for the doll on her shoulder which she finally achieved with relief. Usually these memories were of disturbing events, some of which were traumatic at the time they occurred (see p. 372f.), and some of which apparently became experienced as traumatic only later. In the latter group were the memories of Leta's departure, which had appeared to make little or no difference to the child when it occurred. Later, however, in memories of touching the mother and in the "Leta spank you" episodes, Ann expressed a distrust of adults that was based on a delayed reaction to the mother's withdrawal and to the trauma of Leta's departure. Ann's memories of Leta were intense, intrusive, and disorganizing. The same could be said of many experiences forgotten by the family, in which Ann had been hurt, frightened, or bewildered. These included references to the mother's absences, tantrums, and visits by neighbors and relatives.

Another illustration of Ann's "fabulous memory" (Mahler and Elkisch, 1953) is the following:

At the age of five and a half, two years after Ann began treatment, she asked, "When did I like pebbles?" This referred to an upsetting incident in her treatment at the age of three and a half when the therapist had carried her outdoors and put her down in a pebbly area hoping to encourage her to walk. For the next four years Ann refused or showed no interest in going outdoors while with the therapist, although the treatment room had an outdoor play area adjacent to it. (It had been decided to use the nursery school room and play yard as a space that would be well suited for the treatment of a blind child.) At the age of seven and a half, four years after the attempt to interest Ann in walking, the child accepted the suggestion to go outdoors in order to play out her notions of house training one of her animals. The associations to urination and defecation were not elaborated, but the closeness of the problem of control of the body in space, especially in walking about, and the control of the bladder and bowels was a repetitive association. This time she refused any assistance as she explored the pebbly area. For two sessions she gave no indication that she sensed anything familiar. The third time she came upon a large sandbox where the therapist had taken her on the way to the pebbles the first time. When the therapist identified the sandbox, Ann asked, after a pause, "Where are the stairs?" This referred to the steps up which Ann had been carried to the pebbly area four years earlier. When she was asked how she knew there were stairs near her, she replied, "At the pebbles." Because the stairs were easy for children to manage, the therapist had suggested that Ann try walking on them when she was three and a half, but because of the child's strenuous protest the therapist had carried her up the steps to the outdoor area.

There were innumerable examples of Ann's memories intruding into her play and into her relationship with current situations and people. It was not until we realized that much of the chaotic, repetitive regressed play and verbalizations represented memory traces that erupted without being filtered and organized by the ego that we could determine how to help the child use her treatment more effectively. Our formulation was that Ann's lack of vision and the relative understimulation of her other perceptual capacities had deprived her of the forerunners of repression normally available to the ego in the preoedipal period. We assumed that these forerunners consist of anticathexes available to the ego to stem and modify the eruptions of instinctual derivatives and primary-process thinking. Such anticathexes could be available from the primary autonomous ego energies or become available through the neutralization of instinctual energies.

Because of Ann's blindness, her primary autonomous ego functions were handicapped, especially in the area of forming psychic images that could be organized for selective remembering and forgetting. Because of the mother's depression and the nurse's attitude, object relations prior to treatment were fragmentary and arrested at the symbiotic level, interfering with the production of neutralized energies available for defense. The most conspicuously deficient defense activity appeared to be what we have termed the forerunners of repression. Ann's painful total recall with characteristics of primary-process thinking (condensation, concrete use of language,

loosely associated thinking, etc.) was characterized by the fragmentary quality of the psychic representations (see p. 366).

Following these formulations the therapist verbalized for Ann
the mental images evoked by her behavior and loose associations
that indicated early memories. These verbalizations were designed
to complete the images for Ann, and to pave the way to verbalize
and clarify the meaning of blindness to Ann. It was felt that until
Ann's blindness could be discussed, her inability to cope with the
absence of the visual component of the psychic representation would
continue to expose her to the trauma of the early memories, including the painful fragmentation of the object representations in the
first three years of her life.

As an example of how this was done, we report the following
illustration. In a session when Ann was five and a half, two years
after the death of the family dog and one year before the family's
second dog arrived, she began to giggle while drinking water;
letting it drool out of her mouth, she announced that she was "Billy
drinking water with wet whiskers." She wanted to know how he
"made the noise," apparently referring to the lapping sounds of a
dog drinking from a saucer. In selecting a suitable dish for the dog's
water in the play which ensued, Ann rejected those offered until one
was found which made the right sound as she held it under the running faucet. The rejected dishes were shallow saucers and the one
which she accepted was a deep heavy crockery bowl, quite like the
commercial variety of dog feeding dish. The therapist then verbalized a description of Billy drinking, of Ann's attempts to understand his noises and his blindness, and of the sad feelings that Billy
was dead. The reference to the blindness was one of the many preparations for the later verbalizations and interpretations of Ann's lack
of vision and its many implications.

When the child was four and five she could re-enact scenes from
her second and third years as they had actually happened. References
to punishments, tantrums, and her mother's absences in the second,
third, and fourth years were readily available in her memory. At the
age of six she had three sessions in which her blindness was the chief
topic of discussion and play, and a measure of its import became
apparent to her. Thereafter in treatment the subject of the blindness came up spontaneously every few months. Each time she turned
away from the subject as her anxiety became too painful. However,

each time that she faced her blindness in this way there was a marked advance in learning and in becoming more flexible at home and with her regular teacher. She wanted to know how the blindness started, why it did, and now long she would be blind. There were already intimations that Ann's resentment about her blindness would later be expressed in the treatment. After this she became physically and intellectually more active and revealed in a variety of ways that she was developing a clearer image of herself. However, she also began to ask questions about events of her earlier years in a way which suggested that she was no longer remembering them so vividly, and her facility for total recall was diminishing (see p. 379).

A study of the material pertaining to Ann's five years of treatment contact reveals a clear and consistent pattern of deepening fantasy, expanding knowledge, and increasing ability to deal with real life situations through playing them out. Ann's role in the play in the treatment sessions began with her as an audience of one listening to the therapist's simple monologue around the natural events of a child's life as she sat immobile and unresponsive. After becoming an increasingly active audience, she became a competent stage manager and later played multiple roles in cooperative play. In the later years of play Ann planned the sets, labeled the props, chose the dolls for character portrayal, and gave the cues for the lines in a highly organized dramatic production. The play itself emerged as she "wrote the script" in the process of bringing up the topics current in her life, e.g., "The baby is fussing. [What about?] She doesn't want the mother to go away," etc.

In this final section it is pertinent to discuss what the study of Ann and her treatment suggests about the importance of visual perception for ego development. In this cruel "experiment" of nature, visual perception was eliminated, and the depressed mother failed to provide the stimulus and aid for the development of compensatory perceptual capacities that later became available through the help of the treatment. In a sense Ann suffered from a discreet sensory deprivation as well as from a more general affective deprivation.

We are aided in our theoretical formulation by the views advanced by Rapaport and Gill (1959) and later extended by Goldberger and Holt (1961), who define sensory deprivation as ". . . one in which normal reality contact is subject to significant interference.

By the term 'reality contact' we mean perceptual contact with significant, structural aspects of the external world via the exteroceptors." This results in an interference and impairment of secondary-
process functioning, i.e., logical, reality-oriented thinking; and in a
reinforcement of primary-process functioning, i.e., the irrational,
unrealistic intrusions of drive derivatives. ". . . the functions of the
secondary process depend for their maintenance on continual contact
with reality, and the absence of reality contact facilitates a regression
to the primary process" (Goldberger and Holt, 1961, pp. 130-131).
From our treatment of Ann we can suggest that the development of
the functions of the secondary process and the ego's defense against
intrusions of primary-process drive derivatives into consciousness are
dependent on adequate and well-balanced perceptual contacts with
reality—the external world—via the exteroceptors. In Ann's development the absence of visual contact with reality and the relative affect
deprivation, including a lack of danger-free tactile and kinesthetic
experiences with the external world, combined to undermine the
development of the secondary process.

In sensory deprivation experiments, visual experiences are always
preponderant in sighted individuals (Solomon, 1961). Our work suggests that the capacity to form and use mental images and psychic
representations depends very heavily on visual experiences. When
these are absent the other perceptual experiences, especially the
auditory and tactile ones, are utilized to a greater degree. But the
absence of the visual component very likely signifies that psychic
representations are different in the blind person than in the sighted
one. Freud (1910) considered the visual apparatus essential for ego
function. The ego sees—and does not see, i.e., it selects and it
organizes. With blindness, one main device for dealing with stressful
experience is not available. Therefore, an essential process for defense—visual organization—is absent.

Freud (1920) introduced the concept of the protective barrier or
shield against stimuli which is a function of the ego. He stated (pp.
27-28): "In highly developed organisms the receptive cortical layer
of the former vesicle has long been withdrawn into the depths of the
interior of the body, though portions of it have been left behind on
the surface immediately beneath the general shield against stimuli.
These are the sense organs, which consist essentially of apparatus for

the reception of certain specific effects of stimulation, but which also include special arrangements for further protection against excessive amounts of stimulation and for excluding unsuitable kinds of stimuli." Bergman and Escalona (1949) have extended this concept in their study of hypersensitive children to include a shield against stimuli from outside (sensorium) or inside (organic needs).

Paradoxically, it is quite likely that the absence of vision weakens this protective shield against stimuli from the outside and inside. Without a great deal of compensatory perceptual experience the blind child lacks the expected protection of such a barrier. In a certain sense the blind child is a child with "unusual sensitivities" (Bergman and Escalona, 1949); or, as Provence (1955) has indicated, severe sensory defects such as blindness and deafness may predispose to the development of autistic symptoms.

In the autistic psychotic child the preoccupation with the inner world often serves to ward off the anxiety associated with an adaptation to human objects in the outer world. In the congenitally blind child, the lack of visual perception interferes with the child's ability to relate to the human objects in the outer world. In Ann's development, her mother's depression, the needs of her sighted twin sister, and the sporadic infantilizing attention of the nurse combined to accentuate the difficulty the child had in organizing and comprehending her perceptual experiences. Basic developmental experiences such as the recognition and differentiation of the love object, the distinguishing of the body boundaries, and the body's orientation in space were disorganized and were associated with danger and anxiety in a world that is set up for and takes for granted the warning and protecting function of vision. The danger and anxiety were heightened by the mother's inability to provide her with a substitute for the visual defense. This danger and anxiety resulted in an autistic withdrawal from the outer world. The withdrawal served to lessen the anxiety and to ward off physical dangers inherent in a sighted world for a blind child.

Ann's blindness and her early experiences with her mother interfered also with the development of a reliable psychic representation of the reassuring love object. The absence of a visual representation of the mother may seriously impair the capacity to form a useful memory of the mother if the mother is unable to provide other modes of libidinally cathected perceptual experiences, especially touching, to compensate for the absence of the visual experiences. Blindness and the mother's withdrawal interfered with Ann's capacity to be alone in an adaptive way as defined by Winnicott (1958).

The belief in a reliable and useful future, however difficult and conflictful, is dependent on sufficient early instinctual gratification. Being alone as an infant and small child in the presence of the mother is crucial. The blind child may be handicapped in achieving this basic experience in which vision plays a central role.

The blind child needs to develop the capacity to be alone as a stronger and more reliable resource than the sighted person. Other factors that might have interfered with this child's capacity to be alone were: being a twin who was kept in an incubator in the hospital for the first two months of life; the mother's depression; and the nurse's attitude and departure. Thus, another aim of the treatment was to promote the usefulness of the psychic representation of the therapist and to strengthen the positive relationship to the mother, father, and other important people.

At the beginning of treatment, Ann's object relations had a primitive narcissistic quality characterized by a poor definition of the boundary between herself and the object. The human object was used more for the climactic expression of aggressive outbursts than for libidinally soothing experiences. With treatment, neutralized energies became available for ego functions. Object relationships then could develop and be elaborated without direct instinctual discharge, thus enabling the child to engage for the first time in social relationships.

In a congenitally blind child perceptual recognition—or "perceptual identity" (Klein, 1959)—has a different development, and perhaps goal, than in a sighted child. Perceptual identity refers to the composite representation that a complex perceptual experience evokes in the intact individual. Each perceptual component will register itself, and the composite representation is a synthesis of these components. Normally, the visual percepts are essential for the completion of perceptual identity when auditory, tactile, kinesthetic, olfactory, and gustatory senses or memory traces are stimulated. In this sense the visual experience, and perhaps to some degree the auditory, is the main "confirming" perception that makes it possible to complete a perceptual identity. If the visual component has been present to begin with, this may facilitate the reaction to perceptual experiences as *familiar* at times when the visual component is absent.

Perceptual experiences, without visual components at any point in the past, are lacking a most important organizer so necessary for completing the perceptual identity of the sighted world. Therefore, for the blind person, a hierarchy of perceptual impressions is more difficult to develop. It is as though the filter is gross. Everything comes through without any visual organization to modify its passage, and thus the lack of a visual organizer may subject the child to an indiscriminate flooding of perceptual sensations. The lack of vision deprives an individual of the visual *coordinates* that contribute to the formation of a composite perceptual identity. This composite perceptual image enables the child to form memory images and later logical thoughts that are the hallmark of the secondary process.

Visual percepts are among the main sensory experiences which enable the sighted child to differentiate and balance inner and outer experiences, and to set up a repressing filter so necessary for the ego's discriminations of many perceptual differences, such as: inner-outer, before-after, me-you, here-there, and changing-not changing. Other senses also significantly contribute to these differentiations.

In the blind child, there is a blurring of the inner and outer discriminations because the registration of a perceptual stimulus may be incomplete and this imposes a difficulty in the development of an awareness of the perceptual experience. The blind child in this way is exposed to a greater number of sensory stimuli which may be registered in a fragmentary way by the receiving perceptual apparatus because of the lack of the visual organizing component. This tends to reinforce the fragmentary aspect of the perceptual experience.

When perceptual experiences can be transformed into mental images and representations, they can be differentiated and organized into thoughts, affects, and memory traces which can be remembered or repressed according to the dynamic and economic factors involved. Our hypothesis became: without vision from birth, the child has a considerable difficulty in transforming perceptual experiences into mental representations, and this in turn creates obstacles to the development of a capacity to organize and store such psychic representations—a capacity which is a necessary condition for the establishment of secondary-process thinking. Thus it follows that concept formation may be late in developing. Conversely, vision and developing visual capacities are influential in determining how experiences are remembered and how they are forgotten. As Ann's development proceeded, with the therapist serving as love object and auxiliary ego, Ann developed an infantile amnesia of which there had been little or no evidence at the age of five and a half to six.

In her eighth year, for the first time Ann said with puzzlement, "I don't remember things like that." It had become apparent that total recall was a terrifying experience in which there was little distance between the memory and impulsive behavior.

Summary

Ann's treatment enabled her to develop ego capacities necessary for repression, but this could not be fully accomplished until she was helped to establish better object relations and to be aware of her absence of vision. The awareness of her blindness was a painful and arduous achievement that required years of painstaking work. The treatment promoted the availability of neutralized energies through the therapist becoming a needed love object who was an ally of the child's ego. In this manner the treatment also enabled Ann to develop oedipal longings. Initially, the therapist made contact through an auditory and tactile pathway that established the therapist as an object associated with safety and with libidinal gratifications. Through this attachment the therapist was gradually permitted to provide leadership in organizing the perceptual experiences, especially those dependent upon a visual component. In blind children there is more anxiety because of a lack of visual warning involved in accidents. This danger factor disturbs ego consolidation. Such children need a protecting mother in order that hearing and touching can become useful as a protection.

Following the ideas set down by Freud (1915a, 1915b) in regard to the adaptive function of repression, especially the infantile repression, it occurred to us that Ann's painful memory represented a deficit of two of the ego capacities that are forerunners to the establishment of selective repression. These two forerunners are: (1) a stimulus barrier that permits a protective sensory filtering to prevent the child's exposure to an overwhelming amount of stimuli; and (2) the visual component of mental imagery. The eruption of fragmentary sensorimotor memories under the influence of the primary process occurred when deficits in the stimulus barrier and in the capacity to form a visual psychic image were combined with the understimulation and lack of protective guidance Ann received in the first three years of her life. This formulation could explain Ann's inability to erect repressive barriers as an adaptive mechanism available to her ego.

Through verbalization and interpretation Ann was helped to bind and transform instinctual energy and to contain the anxiety associated with the threatening outer world. As neutralized energies became available in this way the child could erect the anticathexes (Freud, 1915b) necessary for the establishment and maintenance of repression. The anticathexes facilitated the establishment of ego repressive activities, which in turn operated like the construction of a dam with transformers, valves, and spillways. These structural elaborations promoted a differentiated release of Ann's dammed-up impulses, permitting the mental energies to flow into the development of speech and logical thought, and the recognition of body boundaries.

The blind child is handicapped in his development, but this can be overcome by educational and therapeutic measures. Education of blind children tends to overexploit the speech development and the richness of the fantasy life. This may lead further to deficits in reality testing. Dorothy Burlingham (1941) has suggested that speech remains a foreign body, rather than an expression of inner life, for the blind since they lack visual images. Other sensory modalities should be invested, practiced, and elaborated in order to help with reality testing (Anna Freud, 1960).

In her autobiography written while she was a student at Radcliffe (1905), Helen Keller described the transformation from primary- to secondary-process functioning as she experienced it when language became available to her:

> I left the well-house eager to learn. Everything had a name, and each name gave birth to a new thought. As we returned to the house every object which I touched seemed to quiver with life.

That was because I saw everything with the strange, new sight that had come to me.

Ann's rebirth involved this acquisition of a "strange, new sight."

BIBLIOGRAPHY

Bergman, P. & Escalona, S. K. (1949), Unusual Sensitivities in Very Young Children. *This Annual,* III/IV.
Burlingham, D. (1941), Psychic Problems of the Blind. *Am. Imago,* II.
Deutsch, F. (1940), The Sense of Reality in Persons Born Blind. *J. Psychol.,* X.
Freud, A. (1960), Four Contributions to the Psychoanalytic Study of the Child. Lectures presented at New York.
Freud, S. (1910), The Psycho-Analytic View of Psychogenic Disturbance of Vision. *Standard Edition,* XI. London: Hogarth Press, 1957.
—— (1915a), Repression. *Standard Edition,* XIV. London: Hogarth Press, 1957.
—— (1915b), The Unconscious. *Standard Edition,* XIV. London: Hogarth Press, 1957.
—— (1920), Beyond the Pleasure Principle. *Standard Edition,* XVIII. London: Hogarth Press, 1955.
Goldberger, L. & Holt, R. R. (1961), Experimental Interference with Reality Contact: Individual Differences. In: *Sensory Deprivation,* ed. P. Solomon et al. Cambridge: Harvard University Press.
Greenacre, P. (1960), Considerations Regarding the Parent-Infant Relationship. *Int. J. Psa.,* XLI.
Keller, H. (1905), *The Story of My Life.* New York: Dell, 1961.
Klein, G. S. (1959), Consciousness in Psychoanalytic Theory: Some Implications for Current Research in Perceptions. *J. Am. Psa. Assn.,* VII.
Mahler, M. S. & Elkisch, P. (1953), Some Observations on Disturbances of the Ego in a Case of Infantile Psychosis. *This Annual,* VIII.
Provence, S. (1955), The Use of Developmental Tests in the Diagnosis of Autistic Disorders. In: *Proceedings of the Third Annual Psychiatric Institute.* Princeton: New Jersey Neuropsychiatric Institute.
Rapaport, D. & Gill, M. M. (1959), The Points of View and Assumptions of Metapsychology. *Int. J. Psa.,* XL.
Solomon, P. (1961), Discussion of "Effects of Drugs on Imagery Production in Sensory Deprivation," by W. F. McCourt et al. (Report). *New Engl. J. Med.,* CCLXV.
Spitz, R. A. (1957), *No and Yes.* New York: International Universities Press.
Winnicott, D. W. (1953), Transitional Objects and Transitional Phenomena. *Int. J. Psa.,* XXXIV.
—— (1958), The Capacity to Be Alone. *Int. J. Psa.,* XXXIX.

LEG AMPUTATION IN A FOUR-YEAR-OLD

Reactions of the Child, Her Family, and the Staff

EMMA N. PLANK, M.A. and CARLA HORWOOD, M.D.
(Cleveland)[1]

Ruth, four years and two months old, made a dramatic entrance into our hospital. She was brought to the emergency room with a high fever in a toxic, but alert condition. While being examined petechiae (small hemorrhages under the skin) broke out all over the child's body, and particularly severely over the lower extremities. She had a stiff neck, pain in the ankles and hips. The illness was diagnosed as meningococcemia (blood poisoning due to bacteria meningococcus). She was immediately started on sulfa drugs by intravenous medication. In spite of therapy, nine hours after her arrival on the Division for Contagious Diseases, the child had a temperature of 42°, blood pressure of 0/0, and seemed moribund. This condition lasted for about four hours, then the blood pressure slowly returned. When it appeared that this child had very little chance for survival a dramatic change for improvement began, which continued.

During the next few days the lesions on her legs and buttocks became larger and darker, and gangrene set in. The need to amputate seemed imminent. On the ninth hospital day it was still difficult to predict the fate of the legs, but it was decided to wait until gangrene or infection would force the issue.

During this whole period the child was fed by nasal tube or intravenously. Sixteen days after the onset of illness, arteriograms were done under general anesthesia to determine the extent of circu-

[1] From the Department of Pediatrics and Contagious Diseases, Cleveland Metropolitan General Hospital, and the Department of Pediatrics, School of Medicine, Western Reserve University.

Mrs. Plank is Director of Child Life and Education. Dr. Horwood is Playroom Supervisor in the Child Life and Education Program.

lation in her legs. Her left foot was definitely cold. The arteriograms fit the clinical observation of the line of demarcation of Ruth's circulation. It was decided to amputate the left leg just below the knee and to try to limit amputation on the right leg to the toes. The little girl was to be moved from the Contagious Division to the general children's ward and to wait there for the right moment for surgery. We give such detailed account of the medical picture to show what child, parents, and staff had gone through.

At this point the senior author was approached by the pediatric staff to enter the case. I was asked to take over the preparation of the child for the operation and to help the parents accept the tragic necessity, so that they too could help the child. This was an unusual request. The doctors usually are eager to do a great deal of the preparation themselves and to ask a medical social worker to help the family. In this case, though, it was felt that one central person should deal with both parents and child. I had been out of town when the case was discussed in grand rounds; no one wanted the specific responsibility for the preparation. The anxiety was understandable: most of the young doctors and the psychologist had little girls of Ruthie's age and attractiveness in their families. Also, the type of operation must have activated unconscious anxieties in these men. They found it most difficult to talk with the parents. At that time consultation with a child psychiatrist was not available to the staff either.

My first contact with Ruthie was typical of her at that time. She said: "Leave me alone, I don't want you!" I said that this was all right, and that I would stop by later; maybe she would like a visitor or some toys then.

I introduced myself to the mother as a person on the hospital team who would like to be available to her in talking over what was ahead. The mother immediately replied: "I don't want Ruthie to know anything before she goes up to surgery, we couldn't bear it." I replied how well I understood this wish, but that maybe, if Ruthie woke up after surgery with one leg and part of the other gone, she would be very angry with her parents that they had not prevented the doctors from doing it. Ruthie needed to know that the amputation was necessary to get her well and that the doctors and parents agreed and would help her before and after surgery. This argument convinced Mrs. A. She started to tell me a little about the child and herself prior to the illness.

Mrs. A. was an attractive young woman. She was in the second trimester of pregnancy. Ruthie was her only child so far. The mother had had two miscarriages between Ruth and the present pregnancy. She was not feeling too well right now and had suffered from chronic kidney trouble and a peptic ulcer. The father was a strong and tall skilled worker. The family had roots in this community, both sets of grandparents and a great-grandparent living in close proximity.

The mother described Ruthie as a very independent and willful child. She paid little attention to her mother's attempts to influence her eating or to correct her spells of anger. Mrs. A. avoided constant battling and let things go until Mr. A. got home; he set limits and the child obeyed him. Since the illness this had changed; the father was terribly upset, and the mother said he would never agree to have the little girl prepared for the amputation.

Ruthie's development had been quite uneventful. The mother nursed her for three months and weaned her from the bottle shortly after a year. The child walked early and was very skillful and daring in her motor activities. Toilet training was finished at two years with some struggle. The child was a picky eater but well developed.

After my first interview with the mother she suggested herself to bring the father in to see me, too. I met twice with both parents and Mrs. A. helped me to convince Mr. A. that Ruthie should know what was ahead.

Mrs. A. and I went with the little girl to the general children's ward on the day she was transferred. There she settled down without trouble. The staff decided to wait with specific preparations until final medical decisions were made. But both authors would see the child daily in the playroom and would through observing her at play and in relationship to them decide on how best to prepare her.

Once the first resistance was overcome the parents inundated me with questions: where exactly was the amputation going to be, what was the prosthesis going to be like, would Ruthie be able to ride a bicycle, what were the initial costs for the prosthesis and for its renewal and the like? Several interviews were scheduled for them to get as precise information as possible. They spoke daily about medical plans with the surgeon. The physiatrist explained all questions relating to the prosthesis and to Ruthie's training for ambulation.

Ruthie came from the Contagious Division to the Pediatric Ward three weeks after the onset of illness. The ulcers on her legs and buttocks were very large and painful and had to be treated daily. She could only move her legs from the hip. She saw the horrible black legs when bandages were changed. To reduce the contractions the physical therapist stretched Ruthie's legs daily. Meanwhile the doctors and we—the child care staff—worked on a day-to-day basis with child and family to await the most opportune time for the amputation. This period took about three weeks.

During this time, we got to know Ruthie well. Student nurses told us about the nursing part, we saw her daily for several hours in the playroom, and the family also informed us of changes in the child. We stayed in daily contact with the physical therapist. The observations in the playroom made by the junior author, who became the most important person in helping the child work through her anxieties about her illness, will show how we got our cues for preparing Ruthie and how the working through of Ruthie's feelings proceeded before and after the operation.

Our work with this child should be seen in its general framework. She was one of about fifteen to twenty children for whom we had the responsibility for a day program from 9:30 A.M. to 5 P.M. The playrooms are on the same floor as the treatment room and the children's ward, but definitely divorced from all treatment or nursing functions.

Since the head nurse is often too busy to elaborate on the explanation of procedures, the playroom staff has taken over the function of preparing children in detail mentally and emotionally for procedures and operations. Dr. Horwood reports:

I first met Ruth late in the afternoon of the transfer day. I introduced myself, picked up a doll of hers, and commented on how pretty it was, to which she sharply stated, "It's mine, don't touch it." I put it down and said we also had some things she might enjoy playing with, mentioning a few. She said she liked paints; I brought her some, set them up, and said I would be back to see her the next day.

In looking back, I realize that initially I was quite anxious about seeing Ruthie, because of the severity of her condition. In addition, I had not expected to find such an attractive little girl who at the same time was so very hostile. I feel that because of these factors I unconsciously maintained a certain emotional distance from Ruthie at the start. This gradually lessened as I worked with her, but disappeared completely only when she was no longer on the ward and I visited her in Physical Therapy.

During the first couple of weeks in the playroom, I tried to establish a relationship with Ruthie, help her play with other children, and at the same time to set clear, consistent limits in the playroom that no amount of whining would change. We decided to make no direct preparation for the amputation until medical plans were clearly established and eventually to prepare her only a few days before the day of operation.

There were constant, daily struggles with Ruth in regard to playroom routines; e.g., that she could not continuously go back and forth between divisions; that other children needed me too; that occasionally she had to wait for toys and not grab from others, etc. Through her anxiety she was unable to sustain any activity for more than a few minutes. Furthermore, she was very destructive toward other children and toys, and aroused much negative feeling from both staff and children. Few youngsters ever attempted to play with her. She persistently tried to monopolize a staff member (and often succeeded with new staff). As soon as an activity was started with another child, she immediately wanted to have the same thing.

During daily bandage changes and exposure to the sun lamp, there was constant crying and screaming. Treatments were given on the ward without the presence of playroom staff.

After I had known her for about ten days, I stayed with her while the dressing was being changed. The child could see the whole procedure and was well aware of the grotesque, black lower legs. The doctors, forgetting her presence, frequently alluded to the forthcoming operation, e.g., "We can save the knee"; "It's no good here."

I discussed this observation with Mrs. Plank the next morning. In view of the fact that the child had already heard so much from the doctors, which undoubtedly contributed to any fantasies that she had formed about her legs, we felt it would be wise to start to broach the reality of the plans for her now. Therefore, that day I went to her room before the playroom opened and said, "I know how sick you have been, Ruthie. Everything is almost well now except for one leg. The doctors will have to do something to help you walk again." To elucidate further, I added, "You know that when you touch your leg you don't feel anything?" She immediately changed the subject: "If you touch my TV set, it will break." No further mention was made of this the rest of the day by her or myself.

Two days later there was spontaneous play with the doctor set and dolls. She pointed to one doll, saying, "This one has sore legs. She doesn't want to see them." Several minutes later she referred to another doll: "This one can't stand." She asked for tape and wanted assistance with taping the doll's legs (usually binding the legs together). There was some talk in regard to one of the dolls having had an operation, but she was not interested in discussing it further.

During the next three days, at least once a day she would ask to play with the dolls and adhesive tape and when I would inquire how the dolls were, her answer would also be some version of "They have sore legs, just like I have." Around this time, I began to observe in her play how much interest she showed in being messy. For example, when given paint and paper, she never made a picture on the paper, but instead painted her hands, put her white, fluffy toy dog in the paint (having no desire to have it washed afterwards), got paint on her gown, etc. However, at this time, I had for the first time a glimpse of a rather charming and likable little girl who at times could relate to me without ordering me around.

Here we decided to take a cue from Ruthie's own play and to handle the preparation for surgery largely through the use of a doll. After finding out details about the prosthesis which Ruthie would get following the amputation, we constructed a special doll (later referred to as the prosthesis doll) which would undergo the same procedures as Ruthie. The amputation would be at the correct point, with the diseased part of the leg being blackened. The prosthesis would be of proportionate size, with a realistic leather attachment so that the child could manipulate it herself. It would be of similar color but more rigid and less lifelike than the doll's other leg, so that it would not look as if a leg had grown back. .

For raw material I used two dolls of the same size (14″). One had hard limbs and therefore felt quite different. A leg of this doll was to serve as the prosthesis for the other doll, whose lower leg I would amputate. We planned to save the introduction of the doll until the exact amputation point on Ruthie's leg was established.

Some days later Ruthie was extremely upset in the playroom, returning to her original whiney, destructive, demanding behavior. Later we found out that she had been in the Physical Therapy Division and while waiting for a long time to be seen, she had seen three leg amputees.

During the next week she was calmer again. Ruthie was now placed on a low cot where she seemed infinitely happier than in bed. One day on the ward, she was observed to be coloring black the legs of a doll in a picture book.

Surgery now definitely was going to be scheduled in two days. In a conference with the doctors, nurses, and social workers of the floor, it was decided that her doctor would tell her about the amputation in the presence of one or both of her parents. However, that afternoon, he learned from the parents that, contrary to previous plans, they had in their anxiety already told Ruthie about the amputation almost a week before.

The day before the operation, Ruthie was completely unable to concentrate, moving from play with the doll house to the tinker toys, to the playing cards, etc., in less than ten minutes. I therefore decided to start then to prepare her for the details of the surgery. I took her into a side room alone and began by saying, "I know that your parents and the doctors have told you about having an operation tomorrow." She replied, "No, they didn't." I then gave the standard preparation regarding the trip to the operating room and the anesthetic, and explained what would happen while she was asleep. Then we both went to get the prosthesis doll for the first time. I explained and showed her that one leg was black and sick and that the doll was not able to walk. She wanted to hold the doll herself and hold the black leg on. Then I showed her how the doctor would take part of the black leg off, so that later they could help her to walk with the artificial leg. At this point she said, "I don't want to walk." I said, "I can understand that you would feel that way now, but how nice it will be when you don't have to stay in a wheel chair and can walk and play like other girls."

She then asked, "She'll have another leg?" I said, "No, she will not grow one, but she will have a leg she and her mommy can put on just like the artificial leg that was on the doll. It is hard, but it looks like a real leg, and she will be able to learn to walk on it again." Then Ruthie, pointing to the doll's black leg, said, "Throw it away, it's no good." (This was repeated twice.)

Several minutes later, after a doctor had seen her again, and toe amputation on the other leg had also been confirmed, I mentioned that the doll's right toes were sick too, and she immediately said, "Cut them off, maybe you have to cut her foot off, too." I reassured her, "No, it's just the toes, the foot will get well by itself and she will have a special shoe which will match the shoe for the other leg." Later she said, "You be a doctor, I'll be the nurse, and we will tape her," which we did. Ruthie had listened and concentrated during this whole discussion. My anxiety had led me to put the artificial leg on quickly; she was very interested in taking it off, examining the stump, and putting tape on it. She then returned to the playroom and was able to play until lunchtime. When she went to nap later she tucked the doll in with her under the covers. During her physical therapy session in the afternoon she also took the doll with her and was reported to be putting the artificial leg on and off.

The next day Ruthie went to surgery in the early morning. After her return in the afternoon she frequently pulled back the covers, pointed to the leg stump, and said, "See," to various staff members. This was repeated in the next few days. Our first reaction was to try to cover the stump with the blanket, due to our own uneasiness. However, Ruthie tended to keep it purposely exposed, and after several days to take almost no note of it whatsoever.

The next two weeks went relatively smoothly in the playroom. Some of the other children now also came over to her bedside on the ward to talk to her. There was a gradual progression from bed, to cart, to wheel chair, and one day to a small wheel chair which she could happily propel herself. However, because of the need to straighten her legs, the physical therapist wanted her back in the larger wheelchair. This was very upsetting to Ruthie and caused a temporary setback in her ability to play, and again much insistence about being wheeled back to her room in the middle of the morning, etc.

Though less demanding in the playroom, on the ward she continued to order people about and very frequently got her way, particularly with student nurses and with her relatives. She fussed about food, and occasionally wet and soiled herself. Also, she seemed to be quite uncooperative with her physical therapist.

During this time Ruthie made several interesting remarks. To her physical therapist during a therapy session she said, "When will you buy me a new leg?" To one of the other workers in the playroom, "I can do this [touch the floor] with the good leg but not with my other leg." When one day I saw her holding the stump with her hands, I asked whether it hurt a little. She quickly replied, "But it's getting better, isn't it!" Several times she said, seemingly out of clear blue, "I don't want to walk," and I would talk to her about how difficult it was to wait. When other children asked Ruthie about what happened to her leg, without hesitation she would reply, "It was sick and the doctors took it off." Many people, both in the playroom and on the ward, noted that since the amputation there was more open masturbation. However, in the playroom she readily stopped when it was clearly stated that this was something that was not done in public.

Several bandage changes and a postoperative stump revision were necessary during these weeks. The first two changes were done under general anesthesia and caused no noticeable change in her behavior. However, about twelve days after the amputation she again went to surgery, this time without a familiar person, and another procedure was performed, with the child only under heavy sedation. Ruthie was extremely irritable and uncooperative upon her return and almost unmanageable when her mother visited. The child had seen her wound for the first time.

The relationship to me started to get stronger. I was sick and away from work for a couple of days. During my absence there were frequent questions about where I was and when I would be back. When I returned, Ruthie threw her arms around me, asked me where I had been, and said how much she had missed me. This was the first demonstration of any positive emotion for me.

Two days later, another bandage change was done in the morning under heavy sedation, but without anesthesia. She was not allowed to eat before the procedure and remained sleepy during the morning. At lunchtime she asked for her breakfast and was very angry when told that it had not been saved. She refused to eat her lunch and continued to scream for her breakfast. When her mother dropped in after lunch she was completely unable to handle the child. Finally she left with the threat that she would not come back if Ruthie did not behave better. After wetting her pants Ruthie refused to put on dry ones, and the nurses in desperation called Mrs. Plank to the ward. The details of the discussion between Ruthie and Mrs. Plank are interesting because this talk became a turning point in the child's behavior.

Mrs. Plank commiserated with her that she must be very hungry and wondered whether they could not get some food from the kitchen. The student nurse in charge of the child brought toast and milk, but this did not satisfy Ruthie either, and she continued furiously to insist on getting her own breakfast tray, which of course was not available. After a while, Mrs. Plank said that she was not going to stay any longer because Ruthie did not really want her to help, and she had many other things to do. However, if Ruthie would eat her toast now, Mrs. Plank would gladly wait for her and then take her to the playroom. At this point, Ruthie sat up in her bed and screamed: "You are not here to give orders, I am here to give orders," to which Mrs. Plank replied, "No, you don't give orders and I am not here to give orders either. I am here to help you and other children." Ruthie looked surprised and relieved, ate her toast, and was willing to come to the playroom.

There was a marked change in her behavior starting the next day. This pattern continued until the time of her discharge. She spent the next morning in the toddlers' room with me and Jeannie (a girl about her age suffering from a terminal illness) and Roy (a fifteen-month-old-baby). She played some with Roy, sang, and wanted to play school with me being the teacher. Her doll-house play with Jeannie was the first real cooperative play I had observed. Interestingly enough, the main play was dropping the mother down the doll-house stairs on her head. I decorated her wheel chair with her name, which greatly pleased her. In watching her play with dolls I could confirm the observation reported to me by some of the nurses that she always took their clothes off, actually with glee, and had no interest whatsoever in dressing the dolls again. Open masturbation was still present, but appeared to be greatly reduced.

Ruthie's destructiveness of toys and hostility toward other children continued, and their overtures toward her were rare. Nevertheless, one day, Herman (age nine) agreed to help her make play dough upon my suggestion. At one point he told her not to use the rolling pin until the dough was less sticky. Ruthie went ahead and took it regardless. Herman immediately grabbed it back from her, saying, "No, I told you to wait till later." Instead of her usual outburst upon the slightest frustration, Ruthie looked stunned and said nothing, apparently realizing that this sort of behavior would get her nowhere with Herman. This was a great step forward for this little girl.

A few days later, a split-thickness skin graft, taken from the abdomen, was applied in an operation under anesthesia for which it was necessary to apply fully covering casts to both legs. The next day in the playroom we were playing with some shells that a relative had brought her. Pointing to one where the outer part had been chipped off, she commented, "It has no skin." I was then able to discuss her skin graft with her.

Ruthie continued to become more cooperative, less demanding, more able to endure frustration (e.g., waiting while a staff member helped some other child), and more willing to do things by herself. About four weeks after the amputation she was able for the first time to continue an activity even while I was out of the room for a few minutes. After much encouragement, Ruthie was now even willing to wheel herself to and from the playroom.

At this time I introduced some authentic surgery equipment into the playroom: an intravenous setup, surgical drapes, caps and masks, a (dull) knife, and a mask for anesthesia. Here I followed the selection suggested by Florence Erickson (1958). Ruthie was immediately very interested, and she and Yolanda (age eight) performed multiple operations on the dolls, with Yolanda being a sort of head surgeon. Ruthie's operations involved almost exclusively the legs, and she invariably made the incision near or actually right where the vagina would be. This play was terminated only by the playroom's closing and commenced the first thing the next day. One day she mentioned to me that she might have an operation the next morning. I said that I was sorry that I could not tell her more about it because I had not been informed, to which she said, "It's alright, I know you'll tell me all about it afterwards."

The next day under heavy sedation the upper parts of the casts were removed and Ruthie was returned to the floor late that morning. She wanted to go to the playroom immediately. I was firm in stating that I knew she was tired, and she could stay in the playroom only as long as she was cooperative and not whining. Within half an hour she started refusing to put toys away, crying, whining, and we felt it best to return her to her cubicle. This was the last time that I observed such a marked regression to her original behavior.

During the next few weeks Ruthie's legs were healing well, and bandage changes were now done on the floor without sedation and with increasingly less protest. Though it was now possible to reason with her, there were a few last token outbursts in the playroom. We could observe one when the doctor came and proposed a bandage change so that Ruthie would be ready for a visit home at Thanksgiving. She screamed and resisted, but I could explain the necessity of the bandage change to her, adding, "Let's get it over with." At this she stopped crying, said, "Alright," and was willing to go with the doctor. She was home part of Thanksgiving Day with no noticeable change in her behavior upon returning.

Several days later after already having had two dressing changes during one day, when the doctor mentioned that he had to change the abdominal dressing also, she burst into tears. I suggested that we could change the dressing on the doll. She stopped crying, became very absorbed in taping the doll's abdomen, wanted to tape also the doll's legs, and finished by taping the legs together. Still, until the time of her discharge, she occasionally cried and screamed when the nurses took her for a bandage change directly from the ward.

Since the introduction of the surgery equipment she asked to play with it almost daily, being absorbed usually at least an hour and sometimes during the whole day's play periods. In addition to other procedures, all primarily on the legs, she frequently gave injections into the bottom of the doll's feet, taped the doll's legs together, and sometimes first handcuffed the doll's arms before performing an operation. She was also very interested in taking the tape off broken dolls to see what was underneath.

In surgery play I noticed her being most able to sustain cooperative activity with other children and to play in my absence. The first request by another child for her presence was from one of her daily surgical companions, Ernest (age ten). One day when the playroom opened, he said, "You'd better hurry up, Ruthie, if you want to play surgery."

Some of her other play was also noteworthy. She was pretending that a doll was her daughter and was sick in the hospital. I asked her how her daughter was getting along. She said, "She had meningitis, but she is getting better." The same day in the doll house she had the father carrying the little girl and placing her in bed. I asked what the matter was, and she again answered, "She has meningitis." This sort of play and verbalizations were repeated many times in the ensuing weeks. Around this time Ruthie became fond of a two-and-a-half-year-old boy. Once when she was playing with the doll house and he started to move some of the furniture in it, I told him that Ruthie was playing with it now and that he must wait until she was finished (something that I had said numerous times in comparable situations to Ruthie). However, to my surprise, she said, "It's alright, he can play with me." When a movie was shown several days later, she wanted him to be near her and to touch him. (Ruthie had been told before she fell ill that her mother expected a baby.)

Another child, Greg (age six and hospitalized for an infected severe burn on his leg), also interested Ruthie very much. He first came to our attention through his uncontrollable temper tantrums during and following procedures, such as having blood drawn or bandages changed. One morning we noticed that Ruthie stayed to watch these two boys have their blood drawn and tried to comfort them. At other times the relationship of these two children was highly ambivalent. Both had to endure very painful procedures. While Ruthie struggled to get adjusted to her amputation, Greg must have feared that his leg, too, could be cut off if he did not fight every interference. They both received, but also had to share, a great deal of my attention.

One day, when I was holding Greg, and sitting next to Ruthie, I commented to Greg about whether he would get new shoes for Christmas; he said, "Yeah, you get your feet cut off and then you get new shoes for Christmas." Ruthie could take even this in her stride. She made no comment and just went on playing. However, on the whole she and Greg became progressively more disruptive of each other's play, grabbing toys from each other, etc., and it was sometimes necessary to have them play in different rooms.

We still saw evidence of Ruthie's struggle with the loss of her leg. One day, a student nurse was painting a large Santa Claus on a window and the perspective happened to make one leg appear shorter than the other. Ruthie asked the student nurse, "Why is one leg shorter? Did they cut it off, or did you just forget to put it on?"

During this time Ruthie continued to feel progressively closer to me. Once I was getting the puppet stage down for her from a high shelf. It looked as if it could be falling. She stated confidently, "You wouldn't let anything hurt me, would you." Another day when I was late because my car would not start, she expressed concern before I came in. After I arrived she immediately came over to see me and said that she had worried about me, adding, "I could help you start next time." Another day she impulsively grabbed my arm as I was leaving, held it close to her saying, "I love you."

Ruthie made excellent progress medically. The size of the bandages had been decreased almost daily; by now there was none on her left leg stump, and only the right foot was covered. She started standing on her right leg in physical therapy, and tried crutches two days later. She was now spending most of the afternoon learning to ambulate and was eager to go for her exercises, acting very warmly and cooperatively toward her physiotherapist.

It was also remarkable how completely at home she appeared to be with the condition of her legs. For instance, I happened to walk into the treatment room during one of the bandage changes and must have looked slightly stunned, for she reassured me, "It's alright, you can stay with me and watch." Another time in the playroom she told me how soft the new skin felt that was growing back on her leg, and took a worker's finger to touch the skin. Furthermore, there continued to be no hesitation in answering the other children's questions about her legs.

Two incidents in the next few days shortly before her discharge illustrate that she was now able to handle herself in contrast to her initial behavior. When a nurse came in to get Ruthie for a bandage change, Ruthie said pleasantly, "Alright, but can you wait a minute because I have to put the toys away first." The following day, Greg and another boy were playing with marbles. Ruthie went over and took some of the marbles from them. Greg protested and I stepped in and said that Greg was already playing and she could join them if they gave permission. She was silent a minute, then meekly asked and was accepted. The three of them soon made a game of putting the marbles in and out of the can and laughing merrily.

This ends Dr. Horwood's notes.

Parallel with our work with Ruthie, but much less intensive, was our work with the parents. It developed in the following way. There was great relief after all details of the illness and the amputation were discussed over and over again. Time was in our favor as the parents had about five weeks to get used to the necessity of surgery. They were most cooperative in helping us with Ruthie's adjustment in the playroom. However, after the date for surgery was finally set, the anxiety of relatives started to confuse both the parents and the physicians. A well-to-do great-uncle wanted to take the child to another hospital to ask for at least one more medical opinion, though the gangrene was evident and shockingly convincing for both parents and child. Two specialists on the hospital staff spent hours with the great-uncle and the father to reiterate their medical plans for the child. In this critical period—a week end—the senior author did not talk to the parents. But she was on the ward before the child was taken to surgery. Both parents were with Ruthie when her bed was moved to the surgical floor. The mother joined the nurse who had taken care of Ruthie, but the father turned away and could not face the moment of parting. Only after the child had left did the mother break into tears. By that time the father had found himself and could support her.

The father may have felt shattered and useless at the thought that a strong man could not protect his little girl and helplessly had to accept the necessity for the amputation. He reassumed the role of the disciplinarian in the family after the wound started healing and appeared to push Ruthie into being a normal child.

Seven weeks after the amputation Ruthie returned home. She came back to the hospital three times a week for training in ambulation. As her mother's pregnancy progressed, the father brought Ruthie for her rehabilitation exercises. After her discharge from the hospital the physical therapist became Ruthie's closest contact. However, she continued to be very positive and warm toward both authors. Ambulation was interrupted by chicken pox which the child stood well at home. A month after discharge, Ruthie was a proficient crutch-walker. Less than five months after the operation, she was fitted with a left leg prosthesis.

After the operation, the regular contact with the family was switched to a medical social worker, who among other things helped the family with getting assistance from the Society for Crippled Children. Since the prosthesis will have to be changed periodically as the child grows, this contact is very important.

It is obvious that we were concerned with how Ruthie would cope with the arrival of the new baby. At the writing of this paper the little boy is three months old. Ruthie has shown some jealousy, occasionally demanded to be carried like the baby, but has taken his arrival in her stride.

On a home visit five months after Ruthie's discharge, the junior author was met by a confident, active little girl who warmly welcomed her, briefly showed her the new baby, and then demanded her full attention. Ruthie moved around the house with a noticeably abnormal gait, but with extreme agility—even climbing stairs. She wore regular oxford shoes. Her mother stated that she was learning to roller skate and to ride a bicycle, and that she played outdoors again.

These skills reflect the parents' ease and lack of need to overprotect her. They make great efforts to create a normal atmosphere for Ruthie to grow up in. Furthermore, Ruthie's mother could ask her if the stump hurt, in the natural tone of voice that would be used to ask if a child was tired. Ruthie has recently been registered in kindergarten for next Fall, and her mother reported that she had especially requested the principal to treat her just as any other girl.

During the visit the mother spontaneously said how much help she thought the special prosthesis doll had been for Ruthie to grow accustomed to the procedures that would have to take place. The mother also mentioned, though, that several times Ruthie had wondered whether a leg would grow out of her stump.

One other point in this case struck us as unusual—the tremendous reaction of the physicians to the amputation itself and to our role in the preparation for it. Some of the doctors had just started their service on the floor shortly before the time of amputation. Others had known the child since the beginning of her illness when death seemed almost unavoidable, and they reacted with renewed anxiety to this new crisis.

The intern, a warm, dedicated doctor, had done a very fine job in helping the parents accept the amputation, and he was the one who told the child. He was rather irritated, though, when we proceeded to give the child the prosthesis doll and discussed the impending operation with her again. Some of the newer nurses and doctors on the floor were actually hostile and angry about our continuing the preparation, and they found the doll "hideous" or "revolting." We needed the active support of the chief resident and the staff doctor in charge of the division to allow us to proceed according to our plan—something that had never been necessary before. Our good relationship was restored immediately when the child was on the way to recovery and when the staff's anxiety was dispelled as they saw the good results.

We will try to analyze what we attempted to do and what we think was achieved. When Ruthie entered the pediatric ward, our clear objective was to lay the ground work and then actually prepare her for the forthcoming leg amputation. We had to take into account her immediately preceding experience in the contagious ward of being critically ill and at one point very close to death, and of having continuously to undergo many frightening and painful procedures. We would be working with a child who had had great difficulty accepting authority even before her illness and who was bright and able to verbalize well. Greatly in our favor was the fact that her intelligent, conscientious parents were, after their early resistance, eager for help with the preparation.

Our general plan before surgery was threefold. First, we felt it essential that Ruthie form a strong, trusting relationship, primarily with one worker from the playroom. Arrangements would be made to bring her to the playroom as much as possible where she would be helped to feel at home. We would strive for consistency and security in the playroom environment and with personnel; we would attempt to be very conscientious in carrying through on plans and promises, but also on limitations which would not be changed by her demands. We would try to help her realize that only when her behavior became more positive would other children choose to play with her.

Second, we decided not to prepare for the amputation too far ahead of the actual operation. This meant that we would not talk about the legs except when she brought up the topic, and even then would introduce no new material.

Third, when time for preparation came, we would try to give as complete information as possible about the amputation. Our general theme in introducing this explanation would be, "Most everything is healing well except your one leg. The doctors will have to help this leg." Gradually we would move toward telling how the doctors would help.

Following the child's lead, we then switched from a direct approach to the use of the prosthesis doll as an adjunct to the preparation, thereby turning her passivity as a patient into activity in play and verbalization.

We do not think that any existing dolls (like the commercially available amputation dolls, where arms or legs can be pulled off) would have filled the needs of this child. Our problem was not to find an outlet for aggression and for atoning for it by restitution through pulling off a limb and sticking it on again, but to help the child to understand and integrate the fact that the useless leg had to be taken off, that nothing would grow back there, but that through the skill of the physiatrist the new artificial leg would take on the functions of the lost one.

Postoperatively, there were several things we had planned to help Ruthie with: verbalize what had happened during the operation, give continual reassurance that the artificial leg would come when the stump was sufficiently well healed; and prepare as completely as possible for any bandage changes, wound revisions, and skin grafts that would occur.

Feelings after the loss of the leg could be expressed in play with the surgery equipment. The word "play" seems inadequate—it was rather an intense, absorbed activity with the equipment, not an outlet for anger, but again an attempt to understand and to integrate. The aggression found its outlet in Ruthie's relation to people —parents, workers, and children—and with some playthings. It decreased proportionately as the leg began to heal and as she knew that she would walk again.

Our methods and goals were different from a treatment situation in a psychiatric setting. We had to work with this child not in individual interviews, but as part of a group program for many children. Though we hoped fervently to be able to help this little girl, we had responsibility for many other children with a great variety of medical and emotional problems, who needed us as well.

Since we function in a department of pediatrics, our work was geared to the needs immediately resulting from the illness and its management, but not to uncovering the child's deeper emotional problems. Eventually we would help her make the transition to returning home and being followed in physical therapy.

Ruthie could modify her original behavior sufficiently to allow herself to use our help. She seemed unusually well able to accept the amputation once it was performed, and afterwards became increasingly better able to cooperate with procedures as time went on. The by-product of this experience was that a warm, likable little girl emerged who could form positive trusting relationships with the unavoidably large number of people who had to care for her.

We found several details the same as Joyce Robertson (1956) described them in her report on her daughter's tonsillectomy: the need to get rid of the diseased organ (by throwing away the doll's black leg), and the open masturbation postoperatively.

We did not start out with a definite and detailed plan how to prepare this child, but were feeling our way. This was such an unusual case that we could not draw on previous experience.

The way we managed to help Ruthie through her illness may be applicable in other children's hospitals. However, one may have to deal quite differently with a child of different background, age, sex, or degree of verbal accessibility. We probably would develop other ways of preparation if the child were a boy or older, though we note that Pearson's Case 1 (1941), the only case of leg amputation on a child we found reported in the psychological literature, concerns a boy of ten whose emotional reaction to the impending operation was markedly similar to Ruthie's.[2] We feel that the manner in which we attempted to work with this girl—with understanding of the meaning of her behavior, though without choosing to work on a deeper level—worked out beneficially.

BIBLIOGRAPHY

Erickson, F. H. (1958), Play Interviews for Four-year-old Hospitalized Children. *Child Develpm. Mon.*, XXIII.
Hawkes, C. (1915), *Hitting the Dark Trail*. New York: Holt.
Pearson, G. H. J. (1941), Effect of Operative Procedures on the Emotional Life of the Child. *Am. J. Dis. Child.*, LXII.
Robertson, J. (1956), A Mother's Observation on the Tonsillectomy of Her Four-year-old Daughter. With Comments by Anna Freud. *This Annual*, XI.

[2] How a nine-year-old boy was "sickened to his heart's core" when he was not prepared for an amputation of the same type is forcefully described in Hawkes's autobiography (1915).

BEHAVIOR DISORDER AND EGO DEVELOPMENT IN A BRAIN-INJURED CHILD[1]

SHELDON R. RAPPAPORT, Ph.D. (Philadelphia)[2]

In surveying the literature dealing with the disorders of thought processes and behavior found in the brain-injured child and adult, three views are encountered. Each of these views recognizes the presence of behavioral and cognitive disturbances on the one hand and of damaged neural tissue on the other. They differ in what they regard as the genesis of the behavioral disturbance, and consequently in what they recommend for handling such patients.

The oldest and still most prevalent view attributes the observed thought disorder and behavioral deviations to irrevocably damaged neural structures (Hunt and Cofer, 1944; Klebanoff, Singer, Wilensky, 1954). Either impairment in the higher inhibitory cortical centers, or brain-stem lesions are held responsible for hyperactivity, impulsiveness, and hostile or destructive outbursts so commonly found in the brain-injured child (Blau, 1936; Kahn and Cohen, 1934; Strauss and Lehtinen, 1947; Timme, 1952); and their anxiety is also considered to be determined by the organic lesion (Bender, 1949).

The second view in general leaves a hiatus between the organic and the psychological factors, the implication being that the former are irreparable and can only be controlled by means of drugs and/or by delimitation of the environment to make it nonfrustrating. As for the psychological factors, this view advises guidance of the parents

[1] This paper is fondly dedicated to the late Dr. David Rapaport. He gave generously of his all-too-limited time so that through his helpful suggestions and editing this paper could take its present form. It is based on a case presented as part of Workshop 12, "Psychotherapy with the Brain-Damaged Child," at the 1960 American Orthopsychiatric Association Annual Meeting.

[2] Director, The Pathway School, Narberth, Pennsylvania, and Research Consultant, Children's Unit, Eastern Pennsylvania Psychiatric Institute, Philadelphia, Pennsylvania.

and treating the "accompanying neurotic problems" of the child (Bender, 1949; Bradley, 1955; Weil, 1958).

According to the third view, the total picture presented is the result of the *interaction* of functional and organic factors (Betlheim and Hartmann, 1924). Indeed, in restating Schilder's position, Rapaport (1951, pp. 660, 288f.) has suggested that organic damage and psychological disturbance may use the same mechanisms, though differing in intensity and extent. The mechanisms referred to are the ego functions. Whether symptoms are characteristic of brain damage, of psychological disturbance, or of both present simultaneously, they still involve the ego functions.

While Mahler (1952), Weil (1953), and others have greatly furthered our knowledge about ego dysfunction in the emotionally disturbed child, the study of the nature of ego functions in the brain-damaged child has been neglected. Perhaps that is primarily because historically the brain has been regarded as a highly vulnerable organ, irreparable when damaged. However, today we know that the brain is a much more resilient organ than it was previously thought to be. We also know that the cerebrum is—by and large—not composed of loci of specific intellectual functions (Hebb, 1949; Landis, 1949), and that the function of a damaged area can be taken over, to a large extent, by other areas. Contrary to previous belief, the minor cerebral hemisphere is also capable of accommodating training for a particular skill when the dominant hemisphere has been extirpated (Nielson, 1946), and children can still learn to speak after the speech areas of the dominant hemisphere are destroyed (Penfield and Roberts, 1959). Therefore it is worth while to study the brain-damaged child centering attention on his ego functions and avoiding the assumption that damage to neural tissue plays the paramount role in his behavior and thought disturbances.

The facts just cited do not mean that damaged neural tissue is of no importance at all. But they do mean that we have yet to learn exactly what role damaged neural tissue does play in the disabilities of brain-damaged children. In fact, there is still considerable disagreement as to what role damaged neural tissue plays in behavioral disturbance in general. Some writers, such as Bender (1947), believe that there is neuropathology underlying all behavioral and emotional disturbance. Investigators have also found abnormal EEG patterns both in children and adults who showed behavioral disturbance but no clinically demonstrable brain damage (Kennard, 1959; Silverman, 1944). The question remains whether or not there is, indeed, a neuropathological matrix, which at times is only manifested sub-clinically, underlying all behavioral disturbance, or whether, as suggested by Morrell's work with monkeys (Morrell and Jasper, 1956; Morrell, Roberts, Jasper, 1956), abnormal EEG patterns can be consequences of a psychological process. In the face of the complexity of such problems, it does not seem warranted to regard the impulsive and driven behavior of the brain-damaged child as solely the result of the damage to neural tissue. To approach the brain-damaged child from the standpoint of ego functioning permits us to study the interaction of neurologic and psychologic factors and provides the opportunity for treating him more efficaciously, as a whole person. As Hartmann (1952, p. 18) has stated, it is particularly the study of ego functions that might facilitate the meeting between the psychoanalytic and the neurophysiologic approaches.

The thesis of this paper is that behavioral disturbance, such as found in the case to be presented, (1) is not due solely to damaged brain tissue per se and therefore is not necessarily irreversible; (2) but is due to a considerable degree to the disturbance which that damage causes in the epigenesis of the ego; (3) the deviant ego maturation fostering a disturbed parent-child relationship that in turn inhibits proper ego development; and (4) the disturbance both in ego development and in the parent-child relationship can be alleviated by psychotherapy and adjunctive therapies.

Case Presentation

Kenny came from middle-class, second-generation American parents. His father was an assertive but jolly hale-fellow-well-met. His mother spoke in a high, whining, soft voice, which was in keeping with her general demeanor of sweetness and light. Both parents had rather strict, orthodox Jewish backgrounds. The father's family had struggled very hard, so that from an early age he had to make his way in the world by his own wits and aggressiveness. Working while in school he managed to receive a high-school education. After returning from service during World War II, he worked very hard to build his own business and succeeded in providing his family with the usual comforts and conveniences. The mother came from a family that was financially somewhat superior to her husband's. The family was able to go to the seashore for summer vacations and to finance her education at a teacher's college. While teaching, she continued her education and earned a master's degree. She described herself as having been a quiet, shy child who envied her older brother's outgoing nature and many friends. When her brother died, after she finished college, she was very depressed. She described her mother as having been a ravishing beauty whom everyone admired and respected and whom she adored. Her mother had opposed her marriage, feeling that her prospective husband was beneath her. In turn, the husband resented his mother-in-law, feeling that she was forever turning his wife against him. He also felt that his wife owed allegiance first to him and not to her mother. When his wife wanted him to do things for her recently widowed mother and he voiced his resentment, she would coldly pull away from him. She, in turn, resented his mother, a widow, though she, living at a great distance, visited only rarely. Although she never told her husband, she felt that her mother-in-law was a selfish woman; she would not help out when she came to visit and expected to be waited on. According to her report, the mother-in-law would lounge around all day only to put on a great show of industriousness and cooperation when her son came home from work.

Kenny's two-and-a-half-year-older brother was born with diabetes, and although the parents were distressed about this, they soon took it in their stride. Their relationships with him were good, and he made a good adjustment until Kenny's difficulties began to demand too much of their attention. Even then he showed only transitory emotional upsets, which were alleviated by counseling the parents on their handling of him.

Kenny's delivery (twelve hours of labor) was normal and spontaneous. He barely cried at birth and only whimpered when pinched. Because of an Rh incompatibility, he was given multiple transfusions of Rh negative blood. He slept a great deal and his activity level was low, but he did accept the bottle and sucked without falling asleep while feeding. Kernicterus and Rh negative erythroblastosis fetalis were diagnosed.

His mother began to take care of Kenny when he was brought home from the hospital at five weeks of age. Because he slept a great deal and was not responsive, he received little attention from his mother except at feeding time, when he was held and cuddled. At nine months of age he first began to smile in recognition of his mother and could still not support his head to any real degree. He showed no coordination of arm and hand movements until fourteen months of age, and no righting reflex until sixteen months of age. As Kenny's motor activity increased, it proved obviously athetotic.

Starting at five months of age, repeated EEG's were made. At first they were reported to be highly abnormal, with the basic frequency very slow, two to three per second, and the amplitude very high, reaching 300 microvolts. There were numerous plateau type waves and an occasional spike formation. Although the abnormality was described as quite diffuse, there were also apparently zones of hyperirritability in the right motor, occipital, and temporal regions. By seventeen months of age, the electroencephalographic tracings were considered to be within the upper limits of normal, both in rhythm and amplitude, and there were no abnormal wave forms indicative of cortical hyperirritability. After that, the physician in charge felt that no further EEG's were necessary.

Because Kenny did not respond consistently to the usual auditory stimuli in his environment, his hearing was repeatedly examined starting at five months of age. It was thought that he had a bilateral hearing impairment associated with the erythroblastosis and kernicterus, but just how extensive the hearing loss was could not be established at the time.

I first saw Kenny when he was eighteen months of age. Because his EEG's and gross neurologic tests by then had shown improvement, Kenny was brought to me in order to determine his intellectual status. He had just learned to sit alone without support, but as yet made no attempt to pull himself to a standing position. Unlike most youngsters of that age, he sat quietly on his mother's lap for almost an hour and a half. When he became restless, he was put on the floor, where he crawled around for a while. Soon tiring of that, he lay quietly. He showed a less than normal amount of interest in his surroundings. His mother reported that at home he also was quite passive and unresponsive. He smiled only upon tactile contact and caressing from his mother. She related that Kenny made sounds occasionally, but he made none during his two-hour visit with me.

On the Cattell Infant Scale (Cattell, 1947), Kenny obtained an M.A. of 9.8 months, and an I.Q. of 54. He succeeded on all items at the seven-month level and failed all items at the twelve- and thirteen-month levels. He was sufficiently interested in reaching for and examining articles presented to him (such as a shoestring, a bell) to be credited with most items at the eight-month level, and to be credited with such items as recovering a toy hidden under a handkerchief, at the ten-month level. He imitated my poking my finger into the hole of a peg board, at the ten-month level, and also imitated my placing a cube in a cup, at the eleven-month level. However, he had not been taught such simple responses as pat-a-cake or waving bye-bye, at the nine-month level. Kenny also showed a strong grasp and an overhand thumb and forefinger prehension, at the eleven-month level. However, he did not have the coordination to bang two objects together or to rattle a spoon in a cup, at the ten-month level.

On the Vineland Social Maturity Scale (Doll, 1947), Kenny received an S.Q. of 61. At the 0-to-1-year level, he was penalized because he could not stand alone or walk and still drank only from a bottle. At the one-year level, he was credited only with spontaneously starting to pull off his socks and with being able to be in the company of other children without creating antagonism. He still was fed completely by his mother. She held him while feeding him liquids in a bottle and baby foods with a spoon. She had never tried to get him to hold a utensil in his hand, or to eat junior foods or table foods, and she had never allowed him to sit alone in the high chair and eat the baby foods with his fingers. Kenny also had not been introduced to pencils, crayons, picture books, or educational toys for infants.

After seeing Kenny that first time, I had a conference with the mother in order to explain the test findings. I pointed out, for example, that his responses on the Cattell suggested that Kenny had enough interest and attention to learn simple acts, such as pat-a-cake; that he had sufficient muscle strength and prehension to hold a spoon or cup; and that he needed her stimulation in order to learn and to become more self-sufficient. I advised her to stimulate Kenny with activities that would be within his scope and would challenge him without undue frustration. My purpose was to provide Kenny with the pleasure of simple accomplishments, which in turn could serve as motivation for trying more difficult tasks. His accomplishments, I hoped, would also evoke in his mother the desire to give him more attention and to teach him more, which in turn would promote his development.

When I again saw Kenny and his mother, a year and a half later, she had been quite faithful in giving him more stimulation. After teaching him to use a cup, she had weaned him from the bottle (at twenty months); she had encouraged him to feed himself and to use a spoon, and to assist with the dressing process—e.g., taking off his own socks and trousers at bedtime—and she had taught him to play simple games, such as pat-a-cake. She had also started him in physiotherapy at a clinic for cerebral palsied children, at twenty-six months of age. The program was directed at "aiding him with head control, with balance, reciprocation, standing balance, and walking." He resisted the training and was never described as more than "fairly cooperative." Kenny had also had an audiometric test, which showed a 20 to 40 decibel loss at 200 cycles, a 55 decibel loss at 500 cycles, and an 85 decibel loss at 1000 cycles. He had been examined, too, at the cerebral palsy clinic in preparation for speech therapy. The findings were: "He drools. Chewing, sucking, and swallowing reflexes are not normal. Phonation is fairly good. Breathing is mildly irregular. The tongue is depressed at the radix and there is tension in the geniohyoid and mylohyoid muscles. He does not close his lips adequately but there is no particular athetoid involvement and this movement is possible. He should be approached primarily as a severely hard-of-hearing child with athetoid involvement." As a result of these findings, at three years and four months of age, Kenny was started on speech therapy designed for deaf children.

During the visit with me when he was three years of age, Kenny was sociable and showed interest in his surroundings. He was not shy and soon after entering the examining room he sought attention and affection from me. He enjoyed manipulating the various materials in the room, and he especially liked scribbling on paper with a pencil, a feat his mother had taught him. However, most of his behavior was without purpose and was not aimed at accomplishing a goal. For example, he handled the various toys in the room but did not play with them or try to make them do something. He usually would not respond to auditory instruction, and even though he watched what I was doing, he generally did not imitate my actions. Only when he was asked to perform a familiar task, one in which he had already achieved success many times over, did he immediately set out to do it. Those were also the only times he showed any sustained attention. At all other times he was hyperdistractible and pulled away from the task as soon as I asked him to perform it, as though it posed a threat to him. Because it would have reflected his inaccessibility rather than his intelligence, I gave him no intelligence test at that time (Rappaport, 1951, 1953). However, he did show an S.Q. of 51, as opposed to the previous S.Q. of 61. The drop was due to his having made no gain in communication or in locomotion, and what credit he received for the skills that his mother taught him was not sufficient to offset that.

My next contact with Kenny was five years later, at the age of eight. Many important events occurred during that period. Soon after he became three, the cerebral palsy clinic to which he went for physical and speech therapy started a school, and Kenny attended it for full-day sessions, five days a week. His program there was essentially the same as it had been at the cerebral palsy clinic: speech and physical therapies. Up until that time no attempt had been made to toilet train him. The school initiated toilet training and after several months succeeded in making him not soil while at school. He then retained his feces while at school and continued to soil at home. Along with being forced suddenly into bowel control when he entered the school, he was also separated from his mother for the first time. His crying and screaming when his mother left him were vocal verifications of his separation anxiety. The crying and screaming subsided only after he had been going to school for over two months. Kenny hated the school and even today shows his dislike of it by sticking out his tongue each time he passes the building. Despite the fact that this was a very disturbed period of his life, Kenny did learn to walk. He walked without support at three years and ten months of age, with an athetotic gait which is still present.

As I was to learn later (see footnote 4 below), the mother felt inadequate because she had not gotten Kenny to control his bowels at home as he had learned to do at school, and so she started an all-out campaign to *make* him achieve bowel control at home (at this time

Kenny was just about four years old). Even though she kept him on the toilet for periods as long as half an hour, he would do nothing. Instead he would defecate while alone at night and would smear his feces all over his crib and the adjacent wall. This was his "gift" to his mother each morning. At about the same time Kenny began to refuse to go to bed at night. Each time he would be put down, he would get up and go downstairs where his parents were. The father often gave him beatings to stop this. When this did not avail, the parents in their exasperation took to locking him in his room. This enraged him. He screamed, kicked, and beat on the door. As a result he got more severe beatings. Most nights he went to sleep only when overcome by complete exhaustion. The parents were then at their wit's end, and the father restrained Kenny by means of a jacket in his bed. Despite the jacket, Kenny could throw himself backward and bang his head against the headboard. He did this with such vehemence that the parents feared he would "kill himself." They therefore put a football helmet on him at night. The battle of the bed continued for a whole year. Then, although the parents do not know why, Kenny suddenly stopped fighting about going to bed; and the football helmet, the restraining jacket, and the locked door became things of the past. The smearing, however, continued for another six months, a total of a year and a half. It stopped when Kenny, at the age of five and a half, acquiesced to defecate in the toilet, both at home and at times even at school. Nocturnal bladder control was not established until Kenny was over eight years of age.[3]

Between four and five and a half years of age, Kenny's over-all behavior became increasingly disturbed. By five and a half, he flouted his mother's authority in most everyday situations, as though to compensate for his submitting to her in toilet training. He was willful and negativistic when asked to do something. He was also very demanding of his mother, and would have a temper tantrum if not given his way. Even when out in public with her, he would dart off in all directions at once, grabbing this, demanding that.

At six years of age, the school which he had attended closed and Kenny started going to a school for the deaf. This was his first experi-

[3] This came about when he began to emulate his father a great deal. The father showed his dislike of Kenny's bed wetting and expressed the hope that Kenny would be a big boy and stop the wetting.

ence in a formally structured classroom situation. He would not mind the teacher, and he disturbed the class by kicking and shoving other children and by running up and down the aisles. The more he was punished—whether by the beatings of his father, by being yelled at, locked in his room, or sent to the principal's office—the more hyperactivity and diffuse hostility he showed. Kenny had always been hyperdistractible, but his hyperdistractibility increased markedly in any situation that made demands on him, such as school did, making him even less manageable there. His mother had such great difficulties with him that she dreaded his being at home, so that each time the telephone rang she was afraid the school was calling to tell her to take Kenny home again. All her difficulties with Kenny brought her into a state of near-panic. She told her husband often that she was afraid she was going to have a nervous breakdown. Her only way of managing Kenny was to cajole or appease him at every turn. This was the state of affairs when I next saw Kenny. He was then almost eight years of age.

It should be mentioned here that when Kenny entered the school for the deaf he also changed speech therapists. During the thirty-two months spent with the first speech therapist, he uttered only occasional sounds which had any kind of inflection. With the second speech therapist, in eight months' time (after which apparently she gave up) he learned some basic pantomime, intended as an intermediary to speech. He also began uttering sounds that did have inflection and sounded like, as McGinnis, Kleffner, and Goldstein (1956) so aptly put it, "scribble speech." He managed to pronounce some words fairly clearly, such as *ar* for *arm,* and even an occasional word distinctly, such as *home.* But in both cases he could not retain the achievement for any length of time. At school he also received instruction in reading, by the method of associating pictures with the word symbol. Kenny was able to learn the meaning of single words, but only in individual instruction, not in a group. The group proved too distracting, and also too stimulating to aggression.

On psychological retest Kenny obtained an S.Q. of 64. This score would have been higher if he had not been penalized partly for his athetosis, which did not permit him to ride a bike and do many other things boys his age do, but primarily for his refusal to conform with such expectations as dressing himself and exercising caution. Under fear of punishment from the father, Kenny showed that he could dress, and in general could take care of himself. In everyday living, however, he would refuse to do so and would flout his mother's authority.

On a nonverbal test of intelligence (Arthur, 1947), Kenny achieved an I.Q. of 60, not significantly different from his previous one. During the testing he showed a fear of challenge, withdrawing from the task as soon as he met with difficulty. He also showed marked hyperdistractibility. For example, during the visual test of attention span, the edge of my gold cuff link was exposed. Although it made no glare and was unobtrusive, it was sufficient to distract him from the task to which he was attending at that moment quite well. But his attention could be regained fairly readily. Kenny also had a disturbance in the structuring of his percepts. For example, on the Healy Picture Completion Test II (a series of ten pictures showing a boy's day at school, from his getting dressed in the morning to his return home at evening), in which a square portion of each picture is cut out, and the subject is to pick from a wide variety of squares the appropriate square to fit each picture, Kenny was unable to select the appropriate square eight out of the ten times. But, when I covered everything except the elements immediately relevant to a particular cutout, Kenny did perceive what was going on in that picture and then was able to choose the appropriate missing square. By covering up everything else I helped him to perceive the essential details and relegate all other details to the background, thus structuring a percept without being lost in a mass of minutiae.

The psychological test findings as well as Kenny's fear of challenge, his hyperdistractibility, his disinhibition, and his "scribble speech" pointed to his suffering from a severe aphasia—which, in turn, was inextricably interrelated with his behavioral disturbance. It seemed clear that to help Kenny it would be necessary to overcome the aphasia, aid him in developing control over his impulses, and assist his parents in their relationships with him.

In a discussion with the parents, we agreed that I would see them once a week to help them cope with the home situations, I would see Kenny twice a week for psychotherapy, and Kenny would get speech therapy again.

The first step was to help the mother overcome her morbid fear of

Kenny, which prevented her from relating with him effectively and often immobilized her in her dealings with him. At first she was completely unable to admit her anger and resentment over Kenny's behavior. In her sweetness-and-light voice, and without one word of anger toward him, she would tell me about his kicking and hitting her in his temper tantrums, and would complain of being afraid to be with him and of not knowing how to cope with him. I pointed out to her repeatedly that his behavior was extremely hard to bear and that anyone would be angry about it. She gradually became able to tell me about how angry she was with Kenny. Even then it was still difficult to get her to describe exactly what Kenny did and how she handled any specific situation. It took four months before she could allow herself to describe in detail an entire "crisis" with Kenny. The more she became able to admit her anger toward Kenny and to take a look at her reactions to him, the less she had to appease him, and she started to manage him effectively.[4] In the process of helping

[4] The changes in the mother resulted without delving into the unconscious conflicts which, as it was revealed later, played a role in her relationship with Kenny. This is what happened:

Fourteen months after therapy with Kenny began, the maternal grandmother took care of Kenny and his brother while the parents went away for a week end. Kenny objected to his mother's leaving and gave his grandmother a bit of a hard time. The grandmother, who had a coronary condition, suffered a slight heart attack that week end. A couple of weeks later, she died of a coronary attack. The week after Kenny's mother got up from sitting in mourning, she suddenly became fed up with the children's bickering between themselves and ran out of the house on a cold, rainy morning, clad only in a raincoat pulled around her nightgown. That evening her husband found her, sitting in a deserted railroad station. As a result of that incident, I saw the mother a number of times over the next two and a half months. During this time she brought out memories of many instances in her childhood and adolescence in which she felt that she was left out and unwanted, whereas her brother was the center of attraction. She felt that she was always wrong. Even after she married, her mother disapproved of her choice of a husband; and when she had children, even they did not bring her praise and a sense of pride. Similarly, she mentioned the fact that the school had been able to toilet train Kenny when she had not been able to do so. She also felt bad that she had not been able to handle Kenny and had to tell me her mistakes so that I could tell her what to do. In general, the material she brought out, among other things, suggested unresolved hostility to her mother and brother, which, attended by guilt, caused her feelings of inadequacy. In turn, she projected her feelings about her bad, defective self onto Kenny. It is probable that this was one of the direct unconscious factors in her inability to tolerate her angry feelings toward him. But she became able to tolerate such feelings toward Kenny and to examine her own reactions to him without the uncovering of these unconscious factors. Even after she had brought out feelings of hostility and guilt in her sessions with me, she never connected this with her relation to Kenny. The cathartic relief afforded by these interviews apparently reinstated her established defenses and she did not want to probe any further into her unconscious.

her to reach this point, we worked out plans for handling the major situations that caused stress in everyday living. Limits were established and when Kenny would not conform to those limits, he was "bounced" (Redl and Wineman, 1951, p. 39) from the situation. In so doing he was not, however, restrained, locked in, or excluded for very long. By gesture it was indicated to him that he was acting like a baby and when he could act like a big boy again, he could rejoin the group.

As the father became aware of Kenny's aphasia and the frustrations which it imposed on the boy, he tolerated Kenny's negativism and aggression without feeling that such behavior was a personal threat to him both as a man and a father. He began to develop projects in which the boy could find gratification in building simple things while sharing his father's company. Kenny enjoyed these times with his father and eagerly looked forward to them.

As the months went by, the "bouncing" became less and less necessary and the gestures of "big boy" or "baby" were sufficient to aid Kenny in controlling his impulses. Kenny now spent more time with his father. He began "shaving" with him in the morning and imitated in many ways the father's activities and mannerisms.

Kenny's "identification" with his father brought another interesting change. To lead up to that change, from three years of age on, Kenny showed preoccupations with various objects. First, as he learned to scribble, he became overattached to pencils. Wherever he was, whenever he saw one, he would seize it and begin scribbling with it. When Kenny was taught at school how to brush his teeth, his fascination shifted from pencils to toothbrushes. Each time the family visited someone's house, Kenny would dash into the bathroom to use the toothbrushes there. Later the fascination shifted to keys. He would sneak into his parents' bedroom and make off with any or all of his father's keys. Some mornings his father would be furious because Kenny had made him late for work by running off with the ignition key. Along with his attraction to keys, he was enchanted by cars. Walking down a street, he had to touch each new car he saw. Whenever he saw a toy model of a car, he nagged his parents for it. When he became frustrated and angry, he would break whichever object fascinated him at that particular time. As Kenny identified increasingly with his father, his preoccupation with taking keys diminished. Instead, he was satisfied to have his own set of keys, "like Daddy's." He also came to tolerate seeing model cars without insisting that they be purchased for him, and he could walk past a new car on the street without touching it and merely gestured that it was new.

In my discussions with the parents, we also worked on Kenny's hyperdistractibility and his difficulty in foregoing immediate gratification of his wishes. The approaches I suggested to the parents were the same as I used in the therapy sessions. The hyperdistractibility was handled by helping him not to deviate from his intended goal. For example, he would indicate that he had to urinate and be on his way to the bathroom, only to be distracted by something and never get there. At such a time, he would be shown, through gesture, that first he should go to the bathroom and then he could pursue the other activity. After this type of external structuring went on for a number of months, Kenny himself proudly would gesture the sequence of activities to those around him, without being distracted. Still later, he was able to pursue a goal to completion even without gesturing.

Designating the sequence of activities also helped him to delay gratifying his wishes. For example, he was told that big boys do not just take; first they ask for what they want. That led into helping him accept the concept that part of growing up is knowing we just cannot have everything we want. It also led into helping him accept the fact that he had to earn many of the things he wanted, either by first showing big-boy responsibility, or by earning money in little jobs around the house.

Along with Kenny's other improvements, he also began showing an interest in learning to communicate. Within a year's time he learned and retained a good fund of gestures and even a few actual words.[5] His ability to write words increased noticeably. As his interest grew and as success came, he was able to concentrate on schoolwork quite well. He no longer showed hyperdistractibility and hyperactivity while in class.

Now let us turn to Kenny's behavior during his therapy sessions.

---

[5] Not being familiar with aphasic children, the speech therapist remained convinced during all the time she worked with Kenny that he was severely deaf. It was proven later that this was not the case. Aphasia, not hearing loss, was the primary cause of his not being able to speak. Had she been trained to work with aphasic children, Kenny's over-all progress would most likely have been substantially accelerated.

Therapy started when he was eight years and four months of age. For the first six months, I saw him twice a week, and for the next year and a half, once a week. In the beginning Kenny's behavior during these sessions was primarily destructive. His interest was confined to toy cars and trucks, which he would run back and forth vigorously, only to smash them suddenly underfoot. Without any sign of remorse or a glance at me, Kenny would indicate that the car or truck was broken, and he would throw it out. When given a new car he would be very pleased with its newness and shininess and would want to share his pleasure with me. When the car was no longer shiny he would polish it with his saliva and his sleeve, or put Scotch tape over its surface in order to pretend that it was new and shiny again. Then he would bring it to me to be admired. In short order he would nevertheless suddenly smash it. In his ambivalence toward the car, his using it as an object for his hostility always won out. When he was not being destructive, he showed a great deal of pleasure in being able to control the movements of the cars. He would back them up, make them turn sharply, make them speed around obstacles, and so on. All the while he would keep his eyes down on the level of the car so as to make his fantasy of driving the car more realistic.

That period of his play was also characterized by his wanting to take home with him whatever caught his fancy. When I would indicate it was time for us to stop, Kenny would seize an object and dash out with it. He might take a pad of paper, a paper clip, a railroad timetable, a car, or just about anything. During that same period of time he would crunch hard candy voraciously during his sessions.

I made no attempt initially to help Kenny curb either his acquisitive or destructive wishes, because I thought that he was enacting with me his wish for the giving, good parent who would not retaliate and whom he could incorporate. After several months he began looking at me with a sheepish smile when he smashed a car, and I communicated to Kenny through gestures that I knew how much he liked the new cars and was sorry he smashed them. A bit later I communicated that I would not let him smash the cars because he would feel bad afterwards and would have no shiny car until I had a chance to get a new one. Gradually Kenny began to inhibit his destructiveness and finally merely signaled his intention to destroy so that I

could intervene. He would smile happily then. His signaling his
intention to destroy and my intervention became a game that was
repeated many, many times. Through this game Kenny did gain
mastery over his destructive impulses, which seemed to have been a
defense against his fear of being "smashed and broken" by his father.
This type of play recalls Freud's statement (1920) about the ego gaining mastery through turning a passive situation in which one is overwhelmed into a situation of action and preparedness.

After such games had gone on for a while, Kenny turned to the
miniature life dolls. He would pull off their arms and legs, indicating
to me that I should cry in order to show that I was sorry. My crying
would at first send him into gales of laughter. Later he would ask
me to fix the dolls. He also began discovering minute defects in the
cars. For example, a speck of plastic had run over on the wheelbase
of one car, and this made it "broken." He would want me to "fix" it
for him. When I indicated that Kenny wished that the cars or dolls
were broken instead of himself, he vigorously denied it. As it happened, during that time Kenny had an accident with his bicycle. (He
had learned to ride a bicycle which had training wheels.) He lost
control of it, smashed into a wall, and broke his collarbone. When I
first saw him after the accident, he indicated through gestures that
the bone was broken and that the doctor, a very good man, had fixed
it for him. I indicated that he did not like to have the broken bone
and was glad to have it fixed. He agreed heartily. In the following
weeks I then had the opportunity to point out to him that *he* did
not like to feel broken, as he showed in his anger at not being able
to ride a bicycle without training wheels, at not being able to build
models as his brother did, at not being able to talk, and at having to
wear a hearing aid (which many times he had refused to wear when
he came into session). Because he did not want to feel that he was
broken, he would rather the car or doll be broken. Although Kenny
made no overt response to such interpretations, his play entered a
new phase.

Kenny brought in a book from school. In the book he showed
me a story about a child whose father was reading the newspaper and
fell asleep. The child sneaked up on the father and said, "Boo!"
This startled the father and he shook his finger at the child, saying,
"You naughty boy!" In playing out the story Kenny at first wanted

me to be the father. As I shook my finger at him, he would laugh. Later he reversed the roles. In this play Kenny used the role of the boy to assimilate the anxiety (Peller, 1954; Waelder, 1932) associated with his earlier hostility for which he had received more than ample punishment at the hand of his father. In the play, it was a relief to find that even though father was angry at him, nothing terrible resulted; i.e., he was not castrated. In playing the role of the father, Kenny employed, apparently for the first time, the defense of identification with the aggressor (A. Freud, 1936): Kenny did the admonishing instead of being the bad boy who got hurt by his father. That role also provided him with the gratification of not being defective, of being able to hear. In the months that followed, Kenny brought in many stories which gave him an opportunity to deny his feeling of being hurt or damaged, and which allowed him to identify with the aggressor.[6] His mother also reported that at home he would admonish her by calling her a baby when he had done something wrong, as though anticipating her admonition.

During those months I asked the mother to come and participate in the play also.[7] My purpose in doing so was to help her develop a better relationship with Kenny by understanding what he was struggling with at that particular time (his ways of handling his fears about his earlier beatings and his dread of being defective) so that she could help him with similar behavior at home. I also hoped that her participating in the play would aid in the fusion and neutralization of his aggressive energy, making it available for ego use (A. Freud, 1949, p. 41f.; Kris, 1950, p. 35). The opportunity for bringing the mother into the play occurred naturally. When Kenny began playing out the "naughty boy" story, he was so delighted that he wanted his mother to see him playing it and invited her in. At first she was tense and uneasy about participating, but as she understood his play as a means of working out his fears, she entered into it readily. Kenny, in turn, showed genuine affection toward his mother for participating

[6] Another reason for that type of play seemed to be that it furnished him with still another opportunity to deny his defectiveness through being able to read. Each time he brought in a new story, he would read it to me in his "scribble speech," pointing to each word. Later on, when he stopped bringing in that type of story, he delighted in showing me how well he did his homework. When he finished the homework, he would gesture how smart he was.

[7] For a discussion of the mother's entering into the therapeutic situation, see Schwartz (1950).

in the play, and his affection also carried over into the home. That seemed to contribute to his needing less and less external prohibition in order to maintain control over his impulses. He then also lost interest in the candy which was available to him in the office and showed less interest in taking things home with him on leaving.

Kenny's controls developed to the point where he was able to go to an amusement park without being overwhelmed and without dashing madly into all the enticing concessions. Instead, when he was interested in a concession, he would excitedly ask permission to go.

During that same period of time, Kenny also began showing re-action formations to his hostility. He showed pity for those who were sick or injured. Whereas previously he delighted in his mother's being ill, in his brother's being hurt, or in his brother's getting injections of insulin, Kenny no longer laughed gleefully in such situations but showed compassion. Similarly, if he stained his underpants, he was disgusted. He also began smelling his clothing, rejecting any that did not smell clean. In addition, he started taking some interest in keeping his belongings in a fairly orderly fashion.

After having worked with me for a year and a half, Kenny was able to spend the summer at an overnight camp for cerebral palsied children. While there he gained a few new motor skills, got along well with the other boys, and became quite popular. When he returned home, he showed only token hostility to his mother for having been separated from her. This was followed by a show of more than usual affection.

When Kenny returned from camp, he entered a stage of trying to show his prowess. Whereas previously he had displayed only vestigial indications of phallic aggressiveness—in his preoccupation with pencils, toothbrushes, keys, and cars, and in his coming out of his room and intruding on his parents instead of going to sleep at night —he now was intent on being big and strong, of flexing his muscles and performing feats of strength. He also began to show pride in his intellectual accomplishments at school. In both cases he wanted particularly to impress his mother with his feats and gain her praise through them. He also liked hugging her and noted that she had a bosom and men did not.

Therapy with Kenny and counseling his parents were terminated after twenty-five months in preparation for Kenny's going to the Aphasic Unit of the Central Institute for the Deaf, in St. Louis, in order to receive speech therapy. Even though I no longer see him for therapy, I have seen him on occasion as a "friend," and his parents have kept me posted on his progress.

I do not mean to give the impression that Kenny's growth was continuous or that it was a positively accelerated curve without peaks and valleys. It was not. During the two-year course of his development described above, he showed many discouraging, but temporary, setbacks. For about six months after he stopped therapy, he occasionally started to aim a hostile outburst at his mother but did not follow through. These abortive outbursts appeared to be triggered by situations in which he felt inadequate; i.e., he felt others were demonstrating their prowess or showing their adequacy, whereas he could not do likewise. Helping him to understand that he too could become proficient in many skills, if he only practiced them enough, aided in aborting the outbursts. For the past six months Kenny's controls have been as good as would be expected of a child of his age.

Kenny's sense of adequacy has been greatly enhanced and his controls stabilized by his learning to speak while at the Central Institute. Though he had a working vocabulary of less than six words at ten and a half years of age—after a total of six years of speech therapy—with the help of Central Institute's special methods (McGinnis, Kleffner, Goldstein, 1956), he learned in only five months' time to speak and to write seventy-five words and to put them together into sentences! This was accomplished without the use of a hearing aid, and without his having to learn gestures as an intermediary step to speech. As Kenny became able to say words at will, he showed a great eagerness to learn more words. Even though in the year he has been taught by Central Institute's methods he still does not have full command of speech, being able to talk has given him an obvious sense of accomplishment and pride, the equal of which he never showed when he learned to make gestures. Being able to speak has fostered in Kenny a greater sense of identity. This in turn has enabled him to internalize parental wishes more completely, so that he shows, for example, a sense of pride when he is cooperative and well mannered.

Discussion

During his first three years of life, Kenny did not walk or talk; he did not comprehend adequately; he did not show normal interest in or perception of his environment; and he was unusually passive and phlegmatic. These are signs that his ego apparatuses of motility, language, perception, and intention (Hartmann, 1939) had not matured in accord with the normal timetable. Unlike the average child, he therefore was not born with the intact ego apparatuses which serve as the primary guarantees of the organism's adaptation to its environment (Hartmann, 1939, 1952; Erikson, 1937, 1940).[8] The lack of intactness of these primary ego apparatuses in turn fostered a lack of responsiveness on the part of his mother, thus interfering with his first stage, the mutuality phase (Erikson, 1950, 1953) of ego development. Had Kenny been born a normally alert and responsive child, he would have stimulated in his mother the natural desire to interact with him more, thereby aiding his further ego development. If Kenny had been a normal baby, he would have been the wished-for extension of the mother, which would have further enhanced the likelihood of her providing him with the necessary stimulus nutriment (Rapaport, 1958a) for further ego growth. However, as is evident from her becoming able to maange Kenny effectively as she could admit her anger toward him, without resolving the unconscious roots of that anger (see footnote 4 above), the mother's unconscious conflicts played only a small, secondary role in her difficulties with him. Unlike the mothers described by Rank (1949; Rank and MacNaughton, 1950), Kenny's mother *was capable* of a giving relationship with her child, but the instrumentation of that capacity was obstructed by Kenny's not having the necessary ego intactness to stimulate it. Hence Kenny's ego development was impeded primarily by his not being equipped at birth with the primary givens that insure adaptation and only secondarily by his mother's unconscious reaction to his defectiveness. But both together contributed to his not developing a sense of being "all right," the basis for developing a sense of identity (Erikson, 1950).

8 For a discussion of Hartmann's and Erikson's concepts of the primary and secondary apparatuses of ego autonomy, see Rapaport (1956, 1958a, 1958b).

During his early years, one congenitally inadequate ego apparatus, the apparatus of motility, in particular would seem to have played the major role in impeding his development. Unlike other toddlers, Kenny did not experience the pure pleasure of functioning and of being able to master new functions. He did not experience the stature of "one who can walk"—as Erikson (1950) puts it—nor could he get parental confirmation of being such a one. This certainly interfered with the natural development of an early sense of self-esteem and the development of identity. The inadequacy of his motor apparatus was also a road block to an important avenue of developing other ego functions. At any given early age Kenny did not have the normal motor development required for exploring the environment and for differentiating between himself and the external world; nor did he have the fine coordination with which to get added information about the environment so as to test reality better and to widen his scope of interests and pleasures. Hence his inadequate motor apparatus interfered with his developing the ego functions of mastery, integration, reality testing, and control of impulses (Mittelmann, 1954, 1957).

It is interesting that the first time he mastered an object, when he learned to scribble with a pencil, he became preoccupied with it. It is as though he had to keep repeating the new-found gratifications of motor mastery and maternal praise. Because of his faulty motor and perceptual apparatuses, it seems as though Kenny had not learned to distinguish clearly between himself and his mother, and in hoarding the object and repeatedly deriving pleasure through it he was attempting to introject the good mother into himself. His seizing and hoarding the cherished objects only to break them and throw them away whenever frustrated would seem to reflect Kenny's ambivalence toward his mother (Hartmann, Kris, Loewenstein, 1946): breaking them representing projection of the bad mother. Later on, even at eight to nine years of age, he apparently did not yet have an adequately differentiated self-image, because whenever he could not have what he wanted or could not succeed in accomplishing what he was striving to do, he would hit or kick his mother.

His newly developing sense of ego identity was further interfered with just when he began to find increased gratification through his mother's teaching him motor skills: he was suddenly separated from her, he feared losing her love when he would not consent to be toilet trained, and he feared castration and abandonment (Mittelmann, 1954) when beaten and restrained because he would not consent to go to bed. Thus, at a time when he was really just starting the process of achieving a sense of identity, he suffered all these traumatic restrictions on his budding self-expressions. The behavioral disturbance which followed would seem more likely due to Kenny's attempt to preserve his embryonic ego identity than to any organic drivenness. As Erikson (1950, p. 212) has stated, just as an animal defends itself with astounding strength when attacked, so will a child when deprived of all the forms of expression which allow him to develop and to integrate the next step in his ego identity, for "in the social jungle of human existence there is no feeling of being alive without a sense of ego identity." Hence, by means of his disturbed behavior he was trying to ward off being swamped by external demands so that he could survive as a psychic entity. When his mother tried to force him to be toilet trained, his *refusal* to be toilet trained was carried over to his *refusal* to go to bed and to his *refusal* to comply with the teacher's (a mother substitute) requests—all being manifestations of the same retaliatory wish toward his mother for the threat which she posed (Fraiberg, 1950). His fighting at bedtime and his banging his head even when restrained were also attempts to ward off the same threat, the head banging probably also being a substitute for attacking his father (Mittelmann, 1954, 1957). When Kenny was able to give up refusing to go to bed and refusing to defecate in the toilet, he did. But in doing so he became increasingly hostile, negativistic, and demanding, which continued until he achieved a better sense of identity and a more adequate ego organization during therapy.

To summarize Kenny's problem, he was born with damaged ego apparatuses, without the intact function of which it is difficult to develop a sense of ego identity. In addition to the failure to develop a feeling of self-esteem at the usual time of life, when he did begin to find some gratification in achievement and in showing some beginning signs of phallic aggressiveness, he was so traumatized that he developed a fear of abandonment and castration. That served to reinforce and solidify his feeling of defectiveness. The behavioral disturbance which he developed as a means of protecting his budding identity was nonadaptive and only further impeded development.

In the initial stage of therapy, both through the changes brought about in the mother herself and through his relationship with me, Kenny was helped to work through his ambivalence toward his mother. His anal-sadistic wishes, as evidenced in his destroying cars and throwing them away and in his negativism toward his mother, waned. His oral-sadistic demandingness of his mother and his having to get everything he wanted also diminished. In time he was better able to see his mother as an individual and not as an omnipotent extension of himself. He began to obey her more and show affection toward her. Apparently he began to fuse his hostile and libidinal impulses, thereby binding and partially neutralizing his hostile impulses, so as to be able to form a libidinal attachment to her.

During that same period of time, the father was no longer punitive and spent considerable time with Kenny, teaching him various motor skills which were masculine in nature. Kenny delighted in these new achievements. He then began imitating his father, forming a motor identification (Mittelmann, 1954, p. 156f.) with him. As he did so, he no longer had to *be* the father, by incorporating partial objects which represented the father. Instead he was able to be *like* the father; viz., his not having to steal his father's keys, but being able to have keys like his father's.

Kenny also began working out in play, during the initial stage of therapy, his castration fear by turning the passive role into an active one. The nature of his destructiveness indicated that in the face of the trauma his beginning phallic aggressive wishes had regressed to an anal-sadistic level, but it was still primarily the castration fear he was dealing with. Hence, in his play *Kenny* did the smashing, at the same time showing his wish to be the father in his agile maneuvering of the cars. He attempted to work through the same fear in his pulling off the extremities of the dolls and wanting me to fix them; that is, make them not castrated, but whole.

Soon after therapy began, his mother, his father, and I, all related to him so as to supply his faulty ego apparatuses with the external structure they needed in order to develop. Whereas he did not have the ability for anticipation and delay, we supplied it for him by designating the sequence of activities. As he internalized that, he became less distractible and he was able to delay seeking gratification. Moreover, for the first time in his life, what was expected of him by his parents was communicated to him consistently and in a way which he comprehended.

As Kenny worked out his ambivalence to his mother and developed a healthier libidinal attachment to her, as he identified with his father, as he worked through his castration fear, and as he developed the means for anticipation and delay, as well as a clear and consistent idea of parental expectation, his ego controls grew steadily stronger. Hyperactivity and hyperdistractibility diminished, and he had sufficient neutralized energy available for concentrating in school and learning his work well.

In his next developmental step, Kenny employed the defense of identification with the aggressor, which paved the way for his internalizing parental demands and developing his superego (A. Freud, 1949, p. 124f.). With that he was able to control his impulses even under seductive circumstances, such as an amusement park. He then also manifested reaction formation against his anal-sadistic impulses: compassion, disgust with dirt, and neatness—substantial ego and superego achievements.

After these reaction formations were established Kenny displayed strong and widespread phallic aggressive wishes. It seems as though his libidinal development progressed only after his ego development had reached the stage at which it should have been normally when the libido reaches its phallic stage. We may speculate that he would have entered fully into the phallic stage if he had not suffered the traumata just as the phallic impulses were emerging, but in view of all the help his ego needed in order to develop, that seems doubtful.[9]

Even though Kenny's ego controls developed greatly during the two years of therapy, they were not truly stabilized until he overcame his aphasia. This is understandable in that overcoming it greatly enhanced his self-esteem and also contributed substantially to the consolidation of his ego. It is indeed doubtful whether Kenny would

[9] In Kenny, as in many other brain-damaged children, libidinal development seemed to be arrested along with ego development and to progress along with it. Although Kenny did show vestiges of phallic aggressiveness, the phallic impulses were not really evident until his ego was quite developed. This is in contrast to the psychogenically ego-disturbed child who appears to have a fragmented or disturbed ego development but whose libido shows evidence of all stages of psychosexual development. Even though the libidinal development is not integrated, it is there, in apparent contrast to many of the brain-damaged children I have seen. This apparent contrast presents an interesting problem for further research.

have had so severe a behavioral disturbance if he had been helped
to overcome his aphasia around four years of age. On the other hand,
if he had received only speech therapy appropriate for deaf children
—even though he did show a high-frequency hearing loss—and therefore had not overcome his aphasia, in all likelihood he would not
have achieved the ego intactness he now shows.

CONCLUSION

The damage to Kenny's brain tissue in itself did not cause an
irrevocable enslavement to his hostile impulses and ultimately did
not prevent his gaining autonomy from them. Control of his impulses was commensurate with his ego development, which was
brought about by psychoanalytically oriented psychotherapy in conjunction with the McGinnis method of speech therapy for aphasia
and techniques designed to structure his innately faulty primary ego
apparatuses.

Whether or not most brain-damaged children, or even most
aphasic children, would respond to similar handling could be determined only by further research. However, in a number of children
having congenital brain damage, which Kenny exemplifies, approaching their rehabilitation from the standpoint of ego psychology has
been fruitful.

Perhaps the time is nearing when those who have been concerned
with the brain-damaged child will enlarge their scope sufficiently to
view him from the framework of ego development. For example, the
symptoms which Myklebust (1954) recognizes as associated with the
aphasic child's *lack of organismic integrity* could be considerably
amplified and clarified if examined in terms of the concepts developed by Hartmann, Kris, Erikson, and Rapaport. Similarly, in
their new book, Strauss and Kephart (1954) emphasize the importance not only of considering all the possible effects of brain injury
on the total organism but also of considering the effect of the injury
"upon the development which is in process and the effect upon the
organism which will eventually result from the deviation of this
development" (p. 1). They trace the brain-damaged child's disturbances to dysfunctions of such basic processes as perception, language,
and concept formation. What they are discussing is the epigenesis of

the nervous system and its effect on the organism's later activities. Perhaps it is not a giant step from the epigenesis of the nervous system to Erikson's concepts of the epigenesis of the ego (1937, 1939, 1940, 1950), so that the damaged cognitive processes which they discuss could be viewed as the ego's primary apparatuses of autonomy. To combine their work, together with that of Hebb (1949), Piaget (1924, 1927a, 1927b, 1936, 1937), Richter (1941), Gottschalk (1956), and others, into the conceptual matrix of ego psychology would not only enhance our knowledge of the cognitive and behavioral distortions of the brain-damaged child, but would also further our knowledge of cognitive and behavioral structures in general.

SUMMARY

Kenny's congenital brain damage manifested itself in athetosis, aphasia, and faulty ego apparatuses in general. His faulty ego apparatuses, which resulted from the congenital brain damage, and environmental punishment and restriction, interacted to cause a hostile and impulsive behavioral disturbance. Hence, it was necessary to help him structure those faulty ego apparatuses and work through his emotional conflicts arising from the aforementioned traumata in order for him to develop adequate ego function and a sense of identity. That was achieved through the aid of psychotherapy and counseling the parents, conjoined with the McGinnis method of speech therapy for aphasia and techniques designed to provide external structure to his faulty primary ego apparatuses. In so doing, his hostile and impulsive behavioral disturbance was overcome.

BIBLIOGRAPHY

Arthur, G. (1947), A Point Scale of Performance Tests, Revised Form II. New York: Psychological Corporation.
Bender, L. (1947), Childhood Schizophrenia: Clinical Study of 100 Schizophrenic Children. *Am. J. Orthopsychiat.*, XVII.
—— (1949), Psychological Problems of Children with Organic Brain Disease. *Am. J. Orthopsychiat.*, XIX.
Betlheim, S. & Hartmann, H. (1924), On Parapraxes in the Korsakow Psychosis. In: *Organization and Pathology of Thought*, ed. D. Rapaport. New York: Columbia University Press, 1951.
Blau, A. (1936), Mental Changes Following Head Trauma in Children. *Arch. Neurol. Psychiat.*, XXXV.

Bradley, C. (1955), Organic Factors in the Psychopathology of Childhood. In: *Psychopathology of Childhood,* ed. P. H. Hoch & J. Zubin. New York: Grune & Stratton.

Cattell, P. (1947), *The Measurement of Intelligence of Infants and Young Children.* New York: Psychological Corporation.

Doll, E. A. (1947), *Vineland Social Maturity Scale, Manual of Instruction.* Philadelphia: Educational Test Bureau.

Erikson, E. H. (1937), Configuration in Play—Clinical Notes. *Psa. Quart.,* VI.

—— (1939), Observations on Sioux Education. *J. Psychol.,* VII.

—— (1940), Problems of Infancy and Early Childhood. *Cyclopedia of Medicine.* Philadelphia: Davis; also in: *Outline of Abnormal Psychology,* ed. G. Murphy & A. Bachrach. New York: Modern Library, 1954.

—— (1950), *Childhood and Society.* New York: Norton.

—— (1953), Growth and Crisis of the "Healthy Personality." In: *Personality in Nature, Society, and Culture,* ed. C. Kluckhohn & H. A. Murray. New York: Knopf.

Fraiberg, S. (1950), On the Sleep Disturbances of Early Childhood. *This Annual,* V.

Freud, A. (1936), *The Ego and the Mechanisms of Defense.* New York: International Universities Press, 1946.

—— (1949), Aggression in Relation to Emotional Development: Normal and Pathological.*This Anual,* III/IV.

—— (1952), The Mutual Influences in the Development of Ego and Id: Introduction to the Discussion. *This Annual,* VII.

Freud, S. (1920), *Beyond the Pleasure Principle.* London: Hogarth Press, 1922.

Gottschalk, L. (1956), The Relationship of Psychologic State and Epileptic Activity: Psychoanalytic Observations on an Epileptic Child. *This Annual,* XI.

Hartmann, H. (1939), *Ego Psychology and the Problem of Adaptation,* tr. D. Rapaport. New York: International Universities Press, 1958.

—— (1950), Comments on the Psychoanalytic Theory of the Ego. *This Annual,* V.

—— (1952), The Mutual Influences in the Development of Ego and Id. *This Annual,* VII.

—— & Kris, E., Loewenstein, R. M. (1946), Comments on the Formation of Psychic Structure, *This Annual,* II.

Hebb, D. O. (1949), *The Organization of Behavior.* New York: Wiley.

Hunt, J. McV. & Cofer, C. N. (1944), *Psychological Deficit.* In: *Personality and the Behavior Disorders,* II, ed. J. McV. Hunt. New York: Ronald Press.

Kahn, E. & Cohen, L. C. (1934), Organic Driveness: A Brain-stem Syndrome and an Experience. *New England J. Med.,* CCX.

Kennard, M. A. (1959), The Characteristics of Thought Disturbances As Related to Electroencephalographic Findings in Children and Adolescents. *Am. J. Psychiat.,* CXV.

Klebanoff, S. G., Singer, J. L., & Wilensky, H. (1954), Psychological Consequences of Brain Lesions and Ablations. *Psychol. Bull.,* LI.

Kris, E. (1950), Notes on the Development and on Some Current Problems of Psychoanalytic Child Psychology. *This Annual,* V.

Landis, C. (1949), Psychologic Changes Following Topectomy. In: *Selective Partial Ablation of the Frontal Cortex,* ed. F. A. Mettler. New York: Hoeber.

McGinnis, M., Kleffner, F. R., & Goldstein, R. (1956), Teaching Aphasic Children. *Volta Rev.,* LVIII.

Mahler, M. S. (1952), On Child Psychosis and Schizophrenia: Autistic and Symbiotic Infantile Psychoses. *This Annual,* VII.

Mittelmann, B. (1954), Motility in Infants, Children, and Adults: Patterning and Psychodynamics.*This Annual,* IX.

—— (1957), Motility in the Therapy of Children and Adults. *This Annual,* XII.

Morrell, F. & Jasper, H. H. (1956), Electrographic Studies of the Formation of Temporary Connections in the Brain. *EEG Clin. Neurophysiol.*, VIII.

—— & Roberts, L., Jasper, H. H. (1956), Effect of Focal Epileptogenic Lesions and Their Ablation upon Conditioned Electrical Responses of the Brain in the Monkey. *EGG Clin. Neurophysiol.*, VIII.

Myklebust, H. R. (1954), *Auditory Disorders in Children*. New York: Grune & Stratton.

Nielsen, J. M. (1946), *A Textbook of Clinical Neurology*. New York: Hoeber.

Peller, L. (1954), Libidinal Phases, Ego Development and Play. *This Annual*, IX.

Penfield, W. & Roberts, L. (1959), *Speech and Brain Mechanisms*. Princeton: Princeton University Press.

Piaget, J. (1924), *Judgment and Reasoning in the Child*. New York: Harcourt, Brace, 1928.

—— (1927a), *The Child's Conception of the World*. New York: Harcourt, Brace, 1929.

—— (1927b), *The Child's Conception of Physical Causality*. New York: Harcourt, Brace, 1930.

—— (1936), *The Origins of Intelligence in Children*. New York: International Universities Press, 1952.

—— (1937), *The Construction of Reality in the Child*. New York: Basic Books, 1954.

Rank, B. (1949), Adaptations of the Psychoanalytic Technique for the Treatment of Young Children with Atypical Development. *Am. J. Orthopsychiat.*, XIX.

—— & MacNaughton, D. (1950), A Clinical Contribution to Early Ego Development. *This Annual*, V.

Rapaport, D. (1951), tr. & ed., *Organization and Pathology of Thought*. New York: Columbia University Press.

—— (1956) Present-day Ego Psychology. Lecture, San Francisco Psychoanalytic Society.

—— (1958a), The Theory of Ego Autonomy: A Generalization. *Bull. Menninger Clin.*, XXII.

—— (1958b), A Historic Survey of Psychoanalytic Ego Psychology. Introduction to *Identity and the Life Cycle*, by E. H. Erikson [*Psychological Issues*, I (1)]. New York: International Universities Press, 1959.

Rappaport, S. R. (1951), The Role of Behavioral Accessibility in Intellectual Function of Psychotics. *J. Clin. Psychol.*, VII.

— (1953), Intellectual Deficit in Organics and Schizophrenics. *J. Consult. Psychol.*, XVII.

Redl, F. & Wineman, D. (1951), *Children Who Hate*. Glencoe, Ill.: Free Press.

—— —— (1952), *Controls From Within*. Glencoe Ill.: Free Press.

Richter, C. P. (1941), Biology of Drives. *Psychosom. Med.*, III.

Schwartz, H. (1950), The Mother in the Consulting Room. *This Annual*, V.

Silverman, D. (1944), The Electroencephalograph of Criminals. *Arch. Neurol. Psychiat.*, LII.

Strauss, A. A. & Kephart, N. C. (1954), *Psychopathology and Education of the Brain-injured Child*, II. New York: Grune & Stratton.

—— & Lehtinen, L. E. (1947), *Psychopathology and Education of the Brain-injured Child*. New York: Grune & Stratton.

Timme, A. R. (1952), What Has Neurology to Offer Child Guidance? *Neurology*, II.

Waelder, R. (1932). The Psychoanalytic Theory of Play. *Psa. Quart.*, II, 1933.

Weil, A. P. (1953), Certain Severe Disturbances of Ego Development in Childhood. *This Annual*, VIII.

—— (1958). Seminar held at the Institute of Philadelphia Association for Psychoanalysis.

THE DREAD OF ABANDONMENT

A Contribution to the Etiology of the Loss Complex and to Depression

GREGORY ROCHLIN, M.D. (Boston)[1]

The external and the inner influences which discernibly evoke despair prove to have a common denominator—the experience of loss. In a previous paper (1959), I attempted to show some of the significant effects of such a loss in various periods of psychological development. Why loss should have such a profound influence throughout life is the subject of this paper.

Loss refers here, in the psychoanalytic sense of the term, to object loss, a desired relationship to another person who had to be abandoned. The object[2] may represent or be substituted by some abstraction or may even be represented or substituted as a desired

[1] Assistant Clinical Professor, Psychiatry, Harvard Medical School. Director, Child Psychiatry Unit, Massachusetts Mental Health Center (Boston Psychopathic Hospital).

This paper was presented at the Tenth Anniversary Symposium, the Child Psychiatry Unit, Massachusetts Mental Health Center, Harvard Medical School. The symposium was devoted to "Psychoanalytic Studies in Object Loss and Depression."

[2] In the present context, person and object tend to be used synonymously. However, in the ontogenesis of a relationship there is a difference. The relationship to a person represents the most archaic form of an object choice, the chief libidinal investment being then narcissistic. The infant or young child, because of its immaturity, can make no other connection or cathexis. With time and maturity the relationship, although no less significant or less important, will change with alteration in the type of investment, i.e., from narcissistic to object libido. What has previously been a person becomes transformed into an object choice. Hence it is important to distinguish between relationship to a person and relationship to an object from the point of view of psychological development, which in turn is greatly influenced by the nature of the libidinal investment. In the case of the former, the relationship is on the basis of an indiscriminate need; in the case of the latter, the need is no less, but the experience is on the basis of choice. This leads to the probability that the person can readily be substituted because the young child's emotional life is governed essentially by need. The person is important only to the extent that the need is fulfilled. Object choice, however, is additionally governed by an emotional commitment whose significance goes far beyond a primitive need fulfillment.

mental image of oneself. The range of experience which relates object loss to narcissism begins in early infancy and extends throughout
old age. It is a lifelong human condition to experience loss as well as
to attempt restitution (Rochlin, 1959). Whatever the variation may
be, the dissolution of a relationship that was meaningful or of a
satisfying image of oneself that is foregone, for example, through an
illness in fact or in fantasy, invariably promotes the sense or experience of loss and brings with it a rather typical set of reactions. The
conditions which produce a narcissistic injury, or hurt self-esteem,
or circumstances where the person is devalued, produce the same
reactions and the same responses and conflicts seen in object loss in
which self-esteem has been affected. There are countless provocations
in life which will strain and temper the self-esteem of an individual
as he grows up and as he continues to live thereafter. These may
indeed to a large extent account for the constant variations in mood,
the momentary and fleeting despair and elation, which are a daily
commonplace (Rochlin, 1953a).

Vain people are especially prone to narcissistic injury. They are
often revealed to be most likely to suffer severely from a loss of self-
esteem when they experience object loss. The young child, ruled
primarily by self-interest, also reacts to object loss with heightened
narcissism but with a readiness to accept a substitute for the object
that is lost. Only later in psychic development as object libido has
been established, even though it may be incomplete, does the individual meet object loss in fact or fantasy with a lowering in self-
esteem and, under certain conditions, with emerging guilt. This
suggests that the critical difference between the adult's and the child's
reaction is in emotional development. Since the lowering of self-
esteem always depends upon "a criticizing faculty of the ego and the
ego as altered by identification," these reactions can become apparent
only when the more organized functions of the ego resulting from
identification evolve. This step also marks the development of the
superego (Freud, 1917). At this point the child holds the belief that
disappointment, frustration, and therefore the neglect it experiences
as a result of the loss signify its own worthlessness. The Mosaic
legend exemplifies how these old conflicts can be overcome. According to this belief, instead of being forsaken, one is chosen; instead
of being abandoned among the bulrushes, the emphasis is upon

being found. Restitution of the self is made by being given a noble station in place of ignominy. In all significant relationships, whether to an object or to some symbol of one, persistent unrequited wishes to be favored or to be chosen invariably appear. The need for such an advantage, invoked especially during crises of life, is nowhere more forcefully or more eloquently expressed than in a parable from Isaiah where man is revealed as idolatrous and base. The Lord inveighs against this promiscuity by declaring, "I *am* God and *there is* none else; I *am* God and there is none like Me" (Isaiah, 46 : 9). With His supreme powers as the Chosen One, He turns to man and addresses him, "Behold I have refined thee, but not with silver; I have chosen thee in the furnace of affliction" (Isaiah, 48 : 10). We can here discern that God asserts His own uniqueness and superiority. He is chosen. Then He makes His choice, that of idolatrous and base man, and in so doing He rectifies man. Both are thus elevated. God is given His due and man is redeemed. The variations on the theme of being a chosen person or a chosen people are countless. No child wants to believe it is not wanted, hence the prevalent childhood fantasy and wish of being chosen or favored. Most important is that the entire device operates to elevate an otherwise doubtful or precarious self-esteem.

The narcissism of early childhood is compelled by the constant force of reality to give way. The fantasies, the wishes, and the sense of omnipotence become increasingly weakened as reality contradicts them, frustrates and denies them. Self-esteem which appeared so strong is eroded and replaced by esteem for an object. As these changes occur, fears of loss or abandonment also tend to occur. In the eagerness to be chosen there is the danger of not being favored. Children at this time are concerned with a remarkably banal question, which is: "Who will love me when I am left?" Parenthetically, the assumption is that they may be left. And just as regularly the answer is: "No one may want you." Such a pernicious question is regularly associated with fears of not being loved and with being hated. Furthermore, there seems to be a substantial basis for such thoughts which are born of the familiarity with one's own everyday experiences of frustration, anger, disappointment, and hostility. Retrospectively, it is the child's view that there is no danger except if one is worthless because only what is no good is given up. To be angry and hateful is to be no good. These reactions and corresponding fantasies are part of the everyday mores of childhood. The burdensome exactions of such a life are lifted through wishing for the opposite: the belief that there will always be one who cares, or one who watches out. It is no marvel that man's intransient enigma, which extends beyond history, can be observed in his beliefs of being privileged, or belonging to a chosen people. Hence he who resigns himself to the Divine Will, renouncing the aggressive instincts and practicing pity, kindliness, and patience, will thereby achieve his salvation. Then there will no longer be the perhaps well-deserved persecutions for aggression and hostility that are both conscious and unconscious but instead enduring love for everyone. These ideas embody the world's great religions and its little beliefs.

Self-esteem, whether in fact or fantasy or legend, can rarely be supported or elevated in the absence of objects. The myth of the singular hero is a much later phenomenon in human development. Psychoanalytic studies of emotional development have shown that the formation of meaningful relationships is a principal psychic process of childhood. Such relationships become the prototypes of all subsequent relationships throughout life. When a central psychic process supports life from the outset and becomes a principal developmental process, it can hardly be seriously impaired without at the same time producing profound effects upon the individual.

Not only is the process of forming object relations itself of primary importance, but the object per se is also of central significance. Whatever threatens such an object invites an assault upon the process, the individual, and the object. The sources of such a threat may be from within the self or they may be from without. In either case, the ensuing conflicts are remarkably similar. The fact that the child is in the unique situation of depending upon an object for his relief from tension, and thus depends upon an object for maturation, brings the object immediately into close relation with the elemental problems of life and development. Without an object neither can proceed in an orderly fashion. Without a person the young child does not survive. Moreover, if deprived of adequate object relationships later, the child will show little emotional maturation or severely impaired development. This suggests that the object plays a special role which may insure not only life but growth and development as well. The need for a relationship to support life points to the help-lessness that is characteristic of man in childhood. The child cannot alone relieve his discomfort, nor can he reduce his tension without the fostering or nurturing care of an adult. Ego and libidinal de-velopment are, by definition, processes of maturation; although this development cannot entirely be attributed to an interaction of drives and environment, these processes cannot evolve in a reasonably plastic fashion unless there is an object outside the self. When this object is lost, there is a tendency to give up object cathexis and in-crease the narcissism; despite this tendency, however, even in the most narcissistic states objects are still sought, although in greatly modified or pathological forms. Objects seem, therefore, never to be entirely relinquished, and they endure even though the means to secure them may change beyond ordinary recognition, as, for ex-ample, through inanimate objects of early childhood or the common persecutory auditory hallucinations of psychotic adults in which the voices are recognizable as the parental figures (Modell, 1958; Freud, 1923).

The intrinsic role accorded the object in the course of human development suggests that Cannon's formulation (1929) of the prin-ciple of homeostasis has a special applicability. "Homeostasis . . . the living functions are extremely flexible and mobile, their equilibrium [is] being disturbed uninterruptedly but being re-established by the organism equally uninterruptedly. Homeostasis is, as a principle, at the root of all instinctual behavior." Taken a step further into the principle of mental functioning, Fechner's hypothesis, that every increase in mental tension is felt as displeasure and every decrease as pleasure, is expressed in Freud's earliest psychological studies with Breuer as the "principle of constancy" (see Freud, 1920, p. 9, n. 2). However, in man these characteristics of living and mental functions cannot be carried out independently as an operation of the organism. In whatever way this principle may apply to all organisms, its refer-ence to man has an additional consideration, which is that the prin-ciple of homeostasis and object need are indivisible. It shows that man cannot achieve the principle of constancy or the reduction of tension alone and without care. This may in part be true of other animals as well. The degree, however, to which it pertains in man indicates that the concept of homeostasis, the tendency of organisms to achieve this condition, is in man inseparable from an object relationship. Our entire conception of the organism striving toward constancy, however it may be applicable to man, must in this instance include an outside agent, an object, in order to approximate its aims. We know from common observation that the lack of an object is associated with discomfort. The younger the child, the greater is the dependence; and correspondingly the lack of an adequate relationship fosters discomfort. Hence the concept of homeostasis coupled with an object that provides care, and thereby reduces tension, suggests that even on the most elemental level a relationship to an object is indispensable to the principle of constancy and to existence. The most disrupted states of inconstancy and unsteadiness are observed in children who have been deprived of a relationship (Rochlin, 1953b). The lack of an object is throughout life associated with discomfort. This formulation does not suggest that discomfort always signifies the loss or deprivation of an object. It does, however, suggest that the loss of a meaningful object cannot be without discomfort.

A sense of abandonment does not always go back to the child's beginning, for such an assumption would imply that the child had, at the outset or soon thereafter, some preconceptions of object relationships. There is nothing to suggest that this is the case. There is much to support the observations that like many similar processes, this one evolves, develops, may become mature, and always prevails. It remains to us to show some of the early forms that the dread of abandonment takes; the later forms are altogether common enough to need no exposition here. A failure to provide for the neonate's pleasure would hardly mean abandonment to the baby. The infant requires care and it can sense neglect, as demonstrated by ample clinical instances and common-sense observations. However, it is not likely that the young infant conceives of frustrating experiences as anything other than a lack of pleasure. To explain this developmental step several writers have introduced into the mental life of the infant such concepts as good and bad objects; moreover, with the infant's further moralizing over them. Such ideas, although having a certain popularity, tend to pre-empt development itself. The absence of pleasure or the persistence of displeasure in turn play a critical part in activating the "constancy principle." It is this operation, in conjunction with a person or primitive object choice, which places the two into an inseparable association. The pleasure principle and an object cathected with narcissistic libido make a binding primitive connection for the child upon which all subsequent experience is built. There is no original sense of abandonment. It is necessary, rather, to understand the dread of abandonment as having its origins in these related forces—the child's need, the primitive object, and the activated constancy principle.

The simplest care of the infant introduces the object. The child's experience of care is immediately so comingled with pleasure and the relief of discomfort and tension that to forego it constitutes pain. In this way, perhaps, the pain-pleasure principle is introduced and with it, of course, inextricably bound, is an object. Here an archaic fundamental association is formed: primitive object relationship, homeostasis, and pleasure principle. This in turn suggests that object need and relief and the relationship of object loss to discomfort are imbedded deep and early in psychic development. At no point in later life is physiology more closely related to mental functioning or to an object than in infancy. The early psychological disorders associated with object relationship typically reveal themselves in developmental emotional retardation, in physical dysfunction of sleep, and in gastrointestinal-tract disorders. The latter are the most common forms of emotional somatic disorder found throughout later life. This correlation in early childhood may represent a prototype for the somatic effects that are commonly observed in adults who after object loss develop clinical depressions and insomnia, motor disturbances, and systemic disorders. Hypochondriacal complaints, characteristic in states of heightened narcissism, are in later life often associated with object loss, the prototype for which has been shown to exist in infancy. Clinical experience abounds in examples of the chaotic emotional states in which these aims of the activated constancy principle are wide of their mark when object relationships have been seriously impaired.

The tendency of all living tissue to right itself, to establish an equilibrium, led Freud to believe in the "dominance of the pleasure principle in mental life"; it also led to the hypothesis that the mental apparatus endeavors to keep the quantity of excitation present in it as low as possible, or at least constant. Although this thesis is often taken as axiomatic, it remains, I believe, an incomplete statement.

Man is in the unique position that the first principle of mental functioning, the relief from tension and the tendency to constancy, is directly associated with object relationship. Thus the need for an object may be said to enter into development of mental functioning in such a way that the relationship to another person is part of that functioning. In man, therefore, part of the principle of homeostasis should include an object without which its aims cannot be achieved. The tendency toward constancy, achievement of the pleasure principle, and the adherence to the reality principle cannot be gained by man alone. He can succeed in these aims only through the society of another person.

We can merely speculate how early in life there occurs the infant's dimmest recognition of its dependence upon an object for the relief of its discomfort from without and its frustration from within. A significant way in which this influence is expressed is that seen in the first phase of development in which being loved and cared for are most important or take precedence over loving. The person is indispensable. When loss occurs, self-interest is heightened, a withdrawal of interest from the frustrating object takes place as well, and a readiness for a substitution occurs.

The inseparable association of lost self-esteem with abandonment comes only as some maturity of the ego takes place. In the earliest years this significant association does not make its appearance; instead we see that abandonment seems to evoke an emphasis upon frustration, anger, and perhaps even hatred. When an object relationship is still regarded from the view of primarily relieving discomfort and satisfying need, and when love has but a small part to play, the aggressive instincts predominate. It is only in the phases of emotional development which have yet to come, when the libido will have evolved sufficiently and significantly from narcissistic to object libido, that the more familiar and distinct phenomena of mourning and depression can be seen to emerge with object loss. Depression is the psychology of disappointment not frustration. Psychoanalytic work with young children who have experienced object loss, in fact or fantasy, through separation, deprivation, or in whom adequate object relationship has failed to develop, has shown that the clinical picture is ruled by the infantile vicissitudes of aggression (Hartmann, Kris, Loewenstein, 1949; A. Freud, 1949; Rank, 1949; Mahler, 1955).

The commonplace equation of being left with being worthless does not depend upon the countless little circumstances of the facts of reality or of desertion and separation. These incidents in early life evoke aggression, frustration, and hostile responses in the very young child. Its tears and fury are directed toward the frustrating object. The devaluation of the self occurs later in development when the object itself is valued. These same incidents, occasions, or circumstances later representing abandonment evoke aggression and lead to sadism that turns on the self, a process which can be observed in masochistic attacks. By directing hostility to the self, the disappointing object may be spared. The tendency to direct the aggression against the self seems to come about when the object has assumed an importance beyond its nurturing functions. As the object begins to have more than intrinsic value, the self has correspondingly less. The implications are significant because as the narcissistic libido gives way to a measure of object libido, the fantasies of being left become equated with being worthless, or, in other words, a sense of worthlessness seems to occur only when the object that may be lost is worth while. The loss of a worthless object seems to evoke neither a sense of devaluation nor masochistic attacks.

Man is the only creature that knows its own death is its inevitable end, and he acquires this knowledge remarkably early in life. In addition, he learns it usually far in advance of its occurrence. He applies this knowledge not only to himself but also to the objects he has learned to depend upon. Far from adding to the stability of his world, this insight makes for even greater uncertainty. The more clearly the child learns these plentiful facts of the world, the more the uncertainty of the future is demonstrated. Ordinarily, all children learn these lessons very early and never forget them. It is all the more remarkable how little is currently written about the influence that such unique insight brings to bear. These illuminating ideas are viable in very young individuals, two to three years old, who still have only inadequately evolved sentiment, altruism, and pity. They are the "little sadists and animal tormentors" who fear they themselves may become objects of scorn and hurt (Freud, 1915, p. 296). And if we add to these convictions the awareness of dependence that a child has upon being cared for by an adult, the world of the child is more uncertain than it is stable. A substantial basis for the dread of abandonment seems to be well established by experiences in reality as well as by dreams and fantasies. Man begins life in utter social dependence. Aristotle, observing this, called him a political animal who does not live on his own but in a society. Childhood is full of a need for people and the fears of being left by them. There was never a child who did not need an adult, nor was there a child who did not fear losing an adult he had. It is axiomatic that this contention is the human condition. Freud (1937, p. 112) wrote that the weak and immature child's ego is permanently damaged by the strain of the child's efforts to ward off the dangers which are peculiar to that period of life; moreover, the child pays for the security of his parents' protection by the fear of losing his parents' care and love, which he tends to equate. Hence, whatever disrupts a relationship represents an exposure to danger and a sense of helplessness that should be warded off. This reaction continues throughout life. This "feeling [of helplessness] is not simply carried on from childhood days but is kept alive perpetually by the fear of what the superior power of fate will bring" (Freud, 1930, p. 21). If we couple this commonplace fear of what might happen with the further danger of being left or isolated to cope relatively alone with the demands of reality on the one hand and the no lesser inner forces of the instincts on the other, two great inseparable fears of man are joined: one, the fear of not surviving or death, and two, the dread of abandonment. There is substantial evidence that indicates how man deals with the fears of death and abandonment and the despair which is evoked.[3]

It is inevitable that such primordial conflicts which are actively conveyed throughout life should find rich expression or lead to and

[3] Vying against the comprehension of death, the durable knowledge that existence has its limits and that intolerable losses will be experienced, is the defense of denial. Before it enters into the service of some of man's highest aesthetic experiences, however, it is readily seen in the very young as a well-developed faculty which deals with unpleasant realities and in the fulfillment of wishes. It is thus perhaps the earliest defense to emerge in psychic development, and it is also the most persistent. The denial of one's own dying, death, or inevitable death together with certain other irreversible vicissitudes of life as a personal experience seems to be a normal state. But with the onset of an obsessional neurosis, or when an ego tries to spare itself anxiety, renounces the instincts, and turns from reality, the balance is shifted favoring pathological denial.

utilize certain early mental mechanisms. As I have indicated above, a frantic and inevitable substitution of the lost object takes place in the young child. In fact, if he cannot find such restitution in another person, inanimate objects are used, in part at least to govern or control and to represent those who escape him (Rochlin, 1953b). In the older child psychic development has carried him to the point where the significant relationships, the parental figures, are internalized objects of identification. He now holds them within himself, and they are a permanent part of himself. A loss of them or abandonment by them, in fact or in fantasy, is now apt to take a different course than at an earlier period. Before, when the figures were given up, the child does what was done to him. He abandons those whom he lost and takes up with others. Now that he is older he cannot relinquish these central figures as he previously might have done. The extent of the identification is also a measure of the tenacity with which they are held. The difference lies in the fact that with development narcissistic libido has been altered into object libido. The growing superego is not merely a "deposit left by the earliest object choices of the id," but a powerful institution that cannot be readily relinquished. Through it the object choices are retained. Hence, object losses and the dread of abandonment at this phase of development and throughout later life tend to direct the superego against the ego. The classical clinical examples are readily seen in the depressions which are characterized by "a cleavage between the criticizing faculty of the ego [superego] and the ego as altered by the identification" (Freud, 1917, p. 159). It seems that the wish to rid oneself of the loss by disengagement from the object, as one might once have done in early childhood, unfortunately raises the old antagonisms, frustrations, disappointments, and now guilt. This results in hostility and ambivalence to the objects. But the superego does not permit this abandonment, since to do so is dangerous and disloyal, and instead attacks the ego. Furthermore, the internalized figures which are permanently imbedded in the matrix of the character partly serve, among other functions, to insure against losses in reality as well as against hostility from within, whether conscious or unconscious. This appears at best to be only a partial solution, a fixation on the object in order never to be left alone or abandoned. The tendency to project and to transfer these internalized objects to outside ones seems to be in the service of maintaining an equilibrium by creating surrogates outside the self that represent the primary figures. Toward the same ends the mobile or labile libido of childhood becomes increasingly fixed in the process of maturation (Freud, 1937, p. 24). The importance of this finding seems to bear out that the fixation which takes place is in the development of object libido and in turn results in solidifying identification. In some measure this secures the primary figures against the vicissitudes that they are otherwise subjected to. Freud furnished the classical example from his own experience in which a child invents a game wherein the absent mother is represented by a reel tied to a string. The child, by throwing the reel so that it disappeared and pulling it back at will, encompassed and solved his problem, temporarily. Freud (1920) used this observation to illustrate an expression of the pleasure principle. In addition, this example shows that giving up an object which leaves the child is short lived, if it occurs at all, and only partial at that. The giving up is countered by a mechanism that holds the figure. Otherwise the game might have been simply to throw the reel; but to keep it tied and control its return are of central importance. The child cannot give up the object, and although through his game he seems to master his loss, he does so only by tying it to himself. There are countless illustrations of the same mechanisms not only in childhood but throughout life where figures who appear to be given up or lost are permanently bound to one.

There are many sources of verification for the assumption that severe loneliness cannot ordinarily be endured more than temporarily without leading to psychotic developments, if loneliness does not in fact occur as an intrinsic part of mental illness. One source of verification is found in the psychoses which develop in people undergoing an experience of enforced isolation; the other, in the psychosislike states ensuing from experimentally induced states of loneliness, and states involving sensory deprivation (Zilboorg, 1938). It appears that loneliness, isolation, or separation from others can be tolerated only temporarily without profound psychic changes taking place regardless of the phase of development or of the age at which they may occur. This points to the fact that the process of internalization of important objects, although serving a variety of ends, including that of not giving up objects, is an insufficient aim. The need to project and to transfer object relationships is equally indispensable. Two clinical conditions, depression and paranoia, illustrate some effects of destructive intentions toward important objects.

Freud (1913) showed that even those processes which yield a pathological product, e.g., a delusional formation, are "in reality an attempt at recovery, a process of reconstruction." Freud then quotes Goethe's Faust who, having uttered the curses that free him from the world, is immediately exhorted to remake it: this time "more splendid build it again, build it up in thy bosom" (p. 457). Restitution is a process toward recovering a balance. It may commonly be observed in restitution of an object by identification, or in the search for the idealized object as in Conrad's *Lord Jim*, described by Helene Deutsch (1959) as the defense against destruction of the object by projection.

In a footnote to "Ego Development and Certain Character Problems" (1936), Ives Hendrick wrote that there are certain economic gains in projection. The principal points that are of interest here are his comments that

> . . . there is less anxiety associated with the idea of being hated by the object, than with the idea that the object will retaliate the subject's unprojected hostility. That is to say, the experience of hostility, and therefore the associated anxiety, is less intense when it is referred to an external agency than when it is perceived as one's own primary impulse. This may be due to the fact that projection accomplishes a division of mental presentations of the hostile impulse; . . . projection is a successful defense as long as it is incomplete, and the hostility is experienced as though originating both in the ego and the other person. This is supported by the fact that when projection is most complete, the intense anxiety of paranoid panic occurs [p. 329, n. 2].

From the point of view of the considerations entertained here, a further conclusion may be drawn which is the inability of the ego to tolerate the destruction of an object without itself being significantly altered.

Hendrick states in effect that the primitive ego depends upon projection as one of its principal defenses when it experiences frustration and hatred in its conflict with a primary object. However, in the process of development the object is incorporated and becomes part of the self; and as destructive fantasies and wishes are attached to this internalized object, a danger to the self is thereby brought about. The object, it is feared, may retaliate. As part of the self is threatened, a part of the self may attack. Here is a danger that may not be gotten rid of. But the indispensable and now incorporated object is on the one hand a source of gratification and hence pleasure, and on the other hand disappointing, a source of discomfort and a menace. There seems to be no final resolution to this conflict. As further organization of the ego takes place with development, identification with the object occurs. The old enmity cannot be gratified—parenthetically, it would represent a destruction of the object which cannot be tolerated—there develops an identification. It represents the only possible partial solution. The identification becomes a substitute, an affectionate object choice which has succeeded the hostile aggressive attitude but it has not replaced it. The importance of the object has been reinforced and with that the preservation of the object has been further insured. This alteration in the character conserves the object (Freud, 1923, pp. 37, 50). An enforced peace with the id is thus partially achieved. In the metaphor of current affairs, coexistence rather than a permanent peace is made possible. The archaic conflict between the self and a significant, and therefore indispensable, object results in retribution to the self. The ego shows poor tolerance for supporting destructive wishes, especially when the identification with the object while heightened is at the same time threatened.

There are two generally well-known states of emotional disorder which best reveal how the ego is affected when hostile wishes, destructive impulses, and aggressive fantasies are directed toward a significant object. There is a wide variation of the symptomatology within each condition and between the two conditions. In respect to a loved object, they bear in principle a remarkable resemblance which has not been given enough attention and which has a special significance here. In all instances a previously loved object directs its criticism, reproaches, and hatred against the one who loved. And with this occurrence the loved object is lost. The important feature is that the love of the object that is perceived as lost, either in fact or in fantasy, is caused by the hostility which has replaced the love. Anger, hostility, and frustration, accorded archaic power, are always responded to as destructive by the mere fact of their existence. The affectionate object choice which previously succeeded the hostile aggressive attitude is now reversed. Coincident with this change the previously loved one, the persecutor, now demeans the self; this is expressed in "The lament of the paranoiac [which] . . . shows that at bottom the self-criticism of conscience is identical with, and based upon, self-observation" (Freud, 1914, p. 53). In the clinical depression the criticizing faculty of the ego is directed against the ego, "so that the latter could henceforth be criticized by a special mental faculty like an object, like the forsaken object" (Freud, 1917, p. 159). In other words, we see that hatred for a previously loved object results in a withdrawal of libido, heightened narcissism, a return of the repressed, unconsciously wished-for attacks by the object, and persecutory abuses directed at the self by one who was once loved. In these respects the two conditions, the paranoid and the depressed states, are indistinguishable. They both show in ways that leave no room for doubt that the attacks on the previously loved object result in assaults on self-esteem. Heightened narcissism notably turns to support the ego, while the superego has its sadistic aims satisfied. In this way, although the love object is rejected or reviled, it turns out nevertheless to be supported, while the ego is belittled and demeaned.

Whatever attacks upon a loved object take place, the relations between ego and superego appear to undergo typical changes. However, there is an important difference which occurs when the object choice and the self are of the same sex as is the case in paranoid conditions. The psychodynamic aspects of homosexuality need no elaboration here. But its importance lies in the fact that the narcissistic libido is heavily invested in identification with such an object—the ego ideal. In no other condition is the attack on an object more nearly an attack also upon the self as when the attack is directed toward a homosexual object. Aggressive wishes in such cases tend to destroy the ego ideal, that narcissistic aspect of the self that is most valued. This represents so serious a danger to the ego that it dissociates itself from such wishes toward a valued object and particularly toward one in its own image. Through repression narcissism is exaggerated, the ego disclaims its hostility and attributes it to the previously loved object and explains its own anger as a reaction to the hostile object that reviles and slanders the ego. It appears thus that the characteristics of the object are internalized. Although the defenses that the ego finds useful under these circumstances are primitive, they seem to be better understood as occurring in a highly organized ego that in the face of threatening conditions resorts to early developmental or immature forms as well as mature ones.

As Hendrick (1936) shows, panic ensues when the balance of relations between the ego and the object is shifted in favor of predominantly destructive wishes without retaliation, or when the abuses are directed solely toward the object. This is a very useful observation in the study of the self and its objects. The self is then, it appears, in the greatest danger from its own attacks often expressed as suicidal wishes and impulses. This suggests that to entertain destructive wishes toward a meaningful object cannot be endured. In the presence of such wishes the self must take the abuse even if only by way of projecting the source of hostility onto another. The object must be spared. Conservation of the object is an essential characteristic in all of these conditions, even though often contradicted in the manifest content. To these ends, it seems evident that just as internalization is essential, so is its opposite important: the externalization of the relationship. Were total internalization possible and then sufficient, it would on the one hand perhaps prove to be satisfying, but then on the other hand it would probably lead to isolation and would not serve but contradict the ends of social need. Hence, we take into ourselves the important figures not only to be like them but also to have them; then we set about finding their counterparts in others. In this way we retain in perpetuity the significant figures both within ourselves and in the world about us. In this way, the feelings of helplessness and the early conflicts in relation to objects and their inconstancy are not simply carried over from childhood but are kept viable throughout life. Those experiences which substantially contribute to form the sense of helplessness and dependence are probably among the earliest organized concepts in man's existence. They sink their roots very early into the matrix of psychic development, and the dread of abandonment by an object is an invariable outcome. Hence the fear and the act of abandonment have in common fantasies of being lost and losing, of destruction and of aggression toward objects, of grief and of death.

These timeless problems are not basically cultural. They merely find different expression socially and culturally. Moreover, in principle, the differences are not significant. Joseph Campbell (1960, p. 4) writes, "And why should it be that whenever men have looked for something solid on which to found their lives, they have chosen not the facts in which the world abounds, but the myths of immemorial imagination." The answer is to be found in the fact that reality offers little comfort even though the things of the world are most permanent. Men do not relate themselves to things primarily but to people, and to things only in so far as they represent people. The solidity of life evidently does not rest on *matériel*. It does depend upon relationships with other people; and however strong they may be, they are nevertheless realistically temporal. To mitigate the risk of loss there appears to be a need for insurance which will provide against catastrophe and which regularly brings man to the market place as a trafficker in myths and fantasies.

One of the most powerful, persistent, and timeless myths found everywhere serves to defend man against his deepest and earliest fears in relation to his objects. These defensive attempts have two aims which are never really separate but which might for the sake of convenience be described as if they were. One is to quell the fear of death by a continuity of life, and the second is not to have to abandon all that is cherished. The individual's early infantile wishes of omnipotence to exercise control give way to the weight of reality. But later in psychic development when Earth is bound to Heaven, life is thus linked to eternity. In this way the future may be foretold, its evil uncertainty is warded off, and the superior force of a precarious fate is mollified. In commonplace observation, the human condition of wishing to be together forever is a better way than single-handedly to defend oneself against the dreaded outer world, and so is that of combining with the rest of the human community and taking up together the attack on nature and fate (Freud, 1930, pp. 29-30). The paradisal existence tries to lift the oppressiveness of separation, loss, and death. A study of the "paradise myth" affords an excellent illustration. "We encounter the paradise myth all over the world in more or less complex forms . . . it has a certain number of characteristic elements, chiefly the idea of immortality. The entire religious history of man shows it" (Eliade, 1959, pp. 255, 267). In the paradise myth which rests entirely upon restitution, it is not left to the individual to work out his fate. His efforts being too puny, like the child's, it is left to the more superior beings and forces to take over. Death and abandonment are no longer separation but are, through myth, turned into just the opposite, a joining with others, with what is wished for, to be a chosen one or a chosen people. Thus is achieved not only immortality but also a continuum from this world to the next, to the happy garden where our first parents lived. This theme has countless variations which stretch from the present Christian era to prehistory.

It follows that the wish for another chance at life is expressed in the rebirth ritual, in the Resurrection, and is seen in the discovery of the Neanderthal skeletons interred with supplies for another life. The little Neanderthal child standing at the graveside would not experience the elementary idea (*Elementargedanke*) directly figured in mythology. Since it is rendered by way of local ethnic ideas or forms locally conditioned (*Völkergedanke*), we must take this process into account when looking for the general principle (Campbell, 1960, p. 130). We do not know what mythological ideas were incorporated in the remote Mousterian-Neanderthal Period of the Dordogne, but the discovery of an individual interred in a small natural depression oriented east and west, accompanied by shells, some Mousterian flints, the remains of a woolly rhinoceros, horse, reindeer and bison (Campbell, 1960, pp. 342, 354) suggests that the mystery of death had been encountered. In short, then, a prodigious continuum has been identified, deriving in time at least from the period of the Riss-Würm interglacial about 200,000 B.C. The daily task of dealing with death and the anxiety about an uncertain future had to be resolved by mastering a system of defenses against the importance of death, not the least of which is to develop a mythology of the continuity of life.

Throughout time and from first to last the conflicts of childhood are not simply delivered to adult life as recollections or associations of an uncertain and precarious past existence. They give a morphology to the foundation of a relationship to others, superior beings, the parental figures. As reality renders their proportions less colossal and their existence temporal, the conflicts remain. Further solutions are sought. First they are seen in the transference to others and then in the obeisance to the superior forces of the gods of man through whom his temporal nature is mitigated.

The profound effects of the experience of loss appear to have their roots in the dread of abandonment. This has its beginnings when the earliest relationship to a person activates the never-ending principle of constancy or homeostasis. In man, unlike all other creatures, the degree to which an object serves these ends makes him forever dependent for his comfort upon a society of which he is a part and which becomes part of himself. One of the most civilizing influences is another person. When he cannot realize this political existence in fact, he reconstitutes it in fantasy. In either case he does not allow himself to be alone.

In the child's emotional development in which the formation of meaningful relationships is the principal psychic process, there rests the matrix of the dread of abandonment. The childhood fantasies of omnipotence, immortality, and the tenacious concern with origins and kinships give way in adult life to formal myths. In these beliefs and in material accomplishments are found permanent defenses which help ameliorate both the inevitable experience of the dread of abandonment and the realization of external losses. In neither respect is there a stable solution but instead a constant modifying and developing of both material achievements and psychic defenses whose foundations reach into the earliest relations to the primary objects.

BIBLIOGRAPHY

Campbell, J. (1960), *The Masks of God: Primitive Mythology*. London: Secker & Warburg.

Cannon, W. B. (1929), *Bodily Changes in Pain, Hunger, Fear and Rage*. New York: Appleton.

Deutsch, H. (1959), The Character of Lord Jim, a Restitution Process. Presented at Edward Bibring Memorial Meeting of the Boston Psychoanalytic Society and Institute, Inc., April 14, 1959. *Bull. Philadelphia Assn. Psa.*, IX.

Eliade, M. (1959), The Yearning for Paradise in Primitive Tradition. Myth and Myth-Making. *Daedalus* [Spring].

Freud, A. (1949), Aggression in Relation to Emotional Development. *This Annual*, III/IV.

Freud, S. (1913), Psycho-Analytic Notes upon an Autobiographical Account of a Case of Paranoia. *Collected Papers*, III. London: Hogarth Press, 1948.

—— (1914), On Narcissism: An Introduction. *Collected Papers*, IV. London: Hogarth Press, 1948.

—— (1915), Thoughts for the Times on War and Death. *Collected Papers*, IV. London: Hogarth Press, 1948.

—— (1917), Mourning and Melancholia. *Collected Papers*, IV. London: Hogarth Press, 1948.

—— (1920), Beyond the Pleasure Principle. *Standard Edition*, XVIII. London: Hogarth Press, 1955.
—— (1923), *The Ego and the Id*. London: Hogarth Press, 1947.
—— (1930), *Civilization and Its Discontents*. London: Hogarth Press, 1946.
—— (1937), *An Outline of Psychoanalysis*. New York: Norton, 1949.
Hartmann, H., Kris, E., Loewenstein, R. M. (1949), Notes on the Theory of Aggression. *This Annual*, III/IV.
Hendrick, I. (1936), Ego Development and Certain Character Problems. *Psa. Quart.*, V.
Mahler, M. S. (1955), On Symbiotic Child Psychosis. *This Annual*, X.
Modell, A. A. (1958), The Theoretical Implications of Hallucinatory Experiences in Schizophrenia. *J. Am. Psa. Assn.*, VI.
Rank, B. (1949), Aggression. *This Annual*, III/IV.
Rochlin, G. (1953a), Disorder of Depression and Elation. *J. Am. Psa. Assn.*, I.
—— (1953b), Loss and Restitution. *This Annual*, VIII.
—— (1959), The Loss Complex. *J. Am. Psa. Assn.*, VII.
Zilboorg, G. (1938), Loneliness. *Atlantic Monthly*, CLXI.

REGRESSION AND RESTITUTION IN OBJECT LOSS

Clinical Observations[1]

ADELE E. SCHARL, M.D. (Boston)[2]

In the past ten years there has been an increasing interest in the effects of real trauma on the normal psychological development of children. Among such traumata, object loss is particularly crucial because of its special influence upon the development of object relationships and the child's subsequent defenses.

A few years ago I had the opportunity to study two young girls who had suffered a series of important object losses. In this paper I shall attempt to show how the loss of their father affected these sisters, and how their previous development and the nature of their object relationships led them to react to the same loss in quite different ways. The two girls, aged eight and five respectively, witnessed their father's violent death by decapitation in an automobile accident.

The two sisters were quite different, and so was their relationship with father before his death. The younger child, Nancy, was pretty, charming, and father's favorite. She was skilled at eliciting admiration from people around her. Her relationship to father was a narcissistic one in which to be admired and loved seemed to be her principal wish. She achieved much pleasure from the fact that she succeeded in her aim to charm and please. The older sister, Linda, on the other hand, seemed unable or unwilling to compete with Nancy in her seductive relationship to father. Linda appeared inde-

[1] This paper was presented at the Tenth Anniversary Symposium, the Child Psychiatry Unit, Massachusetts Mental Health Center, Harvard Medical School. The symposium was devoted to "Psychoanalytic Studies in Object Loss and Depression."

[2] Instructor, Psychiatry, Harvard Medical School. Staff Child Psychiatrist, Child Psychiatry Unit, Massachusetts Mental Health Center (Boston Psychopathic Hospital).

pendent, sullen, and dissatisfied. She would not tolerate being cuddled and pampered, activities which her sister adored. She behaved as if she did not care whether Nancy was loved by father or not.

After the father's death, a major change occurred in Linda. She never mentioned the tragic event, and her mother reported that Linda acted as if she was relieved by his death. This sullen, sulky child suddenly became efficient, cooperative, and cheerful. She helped around the house, cooked meals, and took care of her mother. Her schoolwork improved greatly. Previously lonely and isolated, she now acquired some friends for the first time; and except for constant vicious fighting with her younger sister, she became a perfect child. She was brought to the clinic because of mother's worry that Linda never mentioned the father's death, and continuously fought bitterly with her sister.

When I first saw Linda, six months after the tragedy, she was eight and a half years old. She appeared pale, frightened, and suspicious. She had great difficulty separating from her mother. She went back several times to kiss her good-by. In the playroom she was reticent and negativistic and instead of talking to me she repeatedly drew a man without a head, hanging from a tree. She left these pictures with me and rushed back to her mother. For several weeks, she chose stereotyped games such as basketball in order to avoid direct contact with me. In the course of these she addressed herself to a ping-pong ball, saying, "If you don't love me, I will kill you," and she then urged me to take an extra turn in order to win the game. When I felt that her relationship to me had improved, I ventured to say that she must miss her father, to which she replied that she much preferred animals to people. She then proceeded to talk about Rusty, a dog her father had given to the children. She and her sister fought frequently over him, with Linda saying that Nancy mistreated him and therefore had lost her rights to the dog, and that Linda should be the sole owner now. She reported that Nancy was a nuisance in every respect, that Nancy was destructive and could not be trusted with toys or animals. Should she discover that mother loved Nancy more, Linda would throw her sister in the reservoir.

When Linda in her first hour drew a decapitated man, she confessed her constant preoccupation with killing her father. Later when she talked to the ping-pong ball, she was telling me that she was filled with murderous feelings and therefore should not have a relationship with living people but only with inanimate objects. Linda's whole life seemed to be dominated by jealousy and the defenses against it. Whereas formerly she had used mainly reaction formation and denial, she now projected her own hostility and feelings of worthlessness onto Nancy. Having displaced her badness onto Nancy, Linda then had fantasies of throwing her into the reservoir.

At this point, she confessed further incidents involving animals. Her rat had just died. She herself had run over it with her bicycle. She maintained that she had no regrets because the rat had often bitten her fingers. She reported that she had killed her turtles by boring a hole into their backs with a fork. After her turtles were dead she gave them to Nancy and stated that this was all Nancy deserved. She did not miss the turtles because she had a new pet. As she was repeating these incidents she became very infantile, demanding, and whining. She seemed to me to have regressed to her younger sister's level. She later complained that mother did not love her and then corrected herself to say that she hated her mother. At the same time, she accused me of throwing her out of the office too soon. With these actions she seemed to be denying her losses by bringing them about herself and then pretending that she did not care for her pets (possessions). Moreover, in her attempts to cope with her own sense of worthlessness, she used, in addition to denial, other defenses: reversal ("Mother does not love me—I hate mother") and projection (I throw her out of the office).

In the following weeks, she insisted on playing games involving the disjointing of small toy animals. She assigned me to the job of disjointing, claiming that she could not bear to do it herself. It made her fingers feel too powerful and she feared that she would break the animals and destroy them. She continued to insist on her worthlessness when she wished to become a worm on a fishing rod to be devoured. She then hit herself on the head, saying she hated her head, and hammered quite vigorously on it. Openly she stated now that mother should not love her because she was so bad. She tolerated this self-hate for awhile, but would then turn this anger to her mother by asserting, "I hate mother." Immediately thereafter she said she hated me, blaming me that I was the one who disjointed animals. As time went by, she continued to play out some of her aggressive fantasies. For instance, each time she would take aim with a gun at the male puppet, she became the one who was hurt. She became accident prone at home as well as in the office, spoke of sprained legs, dislocated vertebra, and frequently cut and bruised herself. At the same time, she denied her own fear of death when she said that in an airplane crash everyone was killed except for mother because she was too tough to die. Mother and she herself were immune to death. Thus it became clear that she had fantasies of omnipotence through identification with her mother.

A year after her father's death, at a time when Linda was struggling intensely with feelings of worthlessness, she had a new severe trauma. Her uncle, father's brother, who had become a father to the girls, died suddenly of a heart attack, and in the same week her maternal grandfather died. Instead of mentioning these events, she brought two guinea pigs to her hour, again to show me how well she could take care of them. Nancy, she said, was the murderous one and would have killed them if Linda had not intervened. She asked me to keep one of them, but I told her that I trusted her good care. Two weeks later, Linda, looking pale and upset, said the male guinea pig had committed suicide by jumping out of his box. She felt it was her fault because she had put his box up too high and he had fallen out and hit his head. He died instantly. The guinea pig's wife, Linda said, died a few days later out of loneliness, but again, as with the turtles, Linda denied all feelings of loss about the guinea pigs. She hoped, she said, to replace them with new animals. She felt grown up because she did not cry.

As pets came and went, she continued to worry about her dog, her father's gift. She used less projection involving Nancy and consciously wondered whether she was to blame for her animals' deaths. Circumstances seemed to be against Linda's mastering these traumas. A new threat entered her life. It was discovered that she had a heart murmur. Again her attitude was of not being concerned.

In summary, as we have seen, Linda made repeated symbolic attempts to find replacements for the lost father. However, her efforts at restitution were only partially successful because of her guilt about her persistent fantasies of killing father and about her other unresolved wishes toward him. The wishes and the fantasies compelled her to give up each new object. Manifestly more striking was her increasing ability, through reaction formation and identification with each of the parents, to assume a new independent state, which in time allowed her again to have a less critical and more narcissistically satisfying picture of herself.

I shall now report part of the work with Nancy, whom I asked to have brought to the clinic. She was then five and a half years old. She was originally described by the mother as a perfect child who caused no problems. She was extremely upset about her father's death and said, "If Daddy is dead, life isn't worth living." On my first meeting with Nancy, in contrast to Linda, she separated from her mother very easily. She took my hand in a friendly fashion and declared that she liked to be with me very much and she was very happy that she could meet me. She repeated this statement several times during her first session. She was unusually friendly to everyone in the clinic, especially men, trying to get their attention in a rather seductive fashion, insisting on being introduced to all the workmen. On her return to her mother, she threw a kiss in her direction, exclaiming, "I love you. How nice of you to wait for me." Her narcissistic preoccupation became clear. She praised herself, saying that her paintings were beautiful, that she did well in school and also here. She feared it was unsafe to leave her pictures with me. She often commented on her charming hairdo and how nice her clothing was. She looked at herself admiringly in windows and in mirrors. She was constantly searching for compliments and wanted to know whom I liked better, her or her sister. She wondered whether I thought her sister was prettier. She enjoyed finger painting. She made a red house, saying it was a lipstick house in which she was the sole occupant. Smearing and messing with paint was most pleasurable to her. She painted my desk, the dolls, the floor with delight. She had great interest in the toilets, wanted to see them all, and tried them all out. Her elation at times was quite conspicuous, especially when she returned from week-end trips to New York where she had been temporarily left by her mother with her grandparents. Although she acknowledged that she had been neglected, she whistled, sang, and became hyperactive. Without sadness she said, "I wish mother would leave me with you and never come back because here I do things I like. She is no good anyhow."

In time, fantasies about her father were expressed. For example, while playing with the dolls, she said, "Daddy is away in New York returning by plane. There is no bed for him. His brother took his place," or, "Daddy is the sandman flying around the house putting everyone to sleep, but he himself disappears by the time morning comes." Clearly Nancy was unable to accept father's death and clung to the fantasy that he would return. Toward her uncle, a doctor, she formed the kind of close seductive relationship she formerly had had with her father. She declared, "Doctors can cure everything. Doctors never die." As she believed her father would return, so she believed her uncle, who replaced father, could never die. Then, as we remember, her uncle, without warning, succumbed to a heart attack and died, and within the same week the grandfather died too. I was struck in the first interview following these events by how very sad Nancy looked. She sat alone in the waiting room, appeared very small and frightened. She clung to me on the way down to the office and seemed to be terrified of people we met on our way down. She lay down on the floor and wanted to be undressed and fed. She was crying and clung to me like a baby. Instead of talking about her uncle, she talked about her worry about her tooth which had to come out. She then told me that she had the measles and her mother was with grandmother in New York. I asked, "How about your grandfather?" Nancy said, "He dropped dead and I don't know why, but my mother came back." She then admitted the death of her uncle and regressed further at this point. She could not do anything by herself, had to be treated like an infant. In the following weeks, I noticed what had not been apparent in Nancy before. She became increasingly destructive, shot puppets, wanted to shoot me, broke toys, smeared my office. She said her father had to die because he was the oldest. She was the youngest and therefore she was going to die last. In her destructiveness, very marked sibling rivalry was apparent: she wanted to destroy everything she suspected her sister left in my office.

In her regression, she formed a very close dependent relationship to me and said in our last session before vacation, as she brought me some apricots, "If I don't get back in the fall, I will kill myself because I love you so." Then she suddenly recalled being in the hospital the night after the accident in which father was killed. She remembered a crib which was too small for her. She thought she was a baby again and in fact wet her bed. I learned for the first time that she had not been asleep when the accident occurred, but actually remembered when the car turned around. As she recalled this, she became increasingly anxious. She stamped her foot, saying, "Don't ask me any questions. Stop it. Stop it." She shouted, covered her ears, and became hyperactive, messy, poured water and paint all over my desk and office. On her return in the fall, she continued her messy anal play, and regression could regularly be reproduced whenever I mentioned the accident. One day the loudspeaker paged a doctor whose name was identical with that of her uncle. Nancy turned pale, saying, "I had a relative by this name. He is in the skies now." She then became furious and shot at the loudspeaker and at the male puppet, saying, "I hate him. I am angry at him. I hate widows." Now her anger at the men who abandoned her and her inability to accept their deaths were both in evidence.

After her father's death, Nancy restored her lost objects seemingly with great ease. She related to people with her seductive charm. Her multiple losses of the men who gratified her narcissistic needs, however, confirmed her own feelings of worthlessness. Her narcissistic preoccupation changed into a picture of herself as an ugly little animal no one could love. Instead of attempting to seduce all men with her charm, she was frightened of them and tried to avoid them, as she regressed further into an anal state.

I shall conclude by presenting some material which came up when we were planning to terminate. I think it again shows how hard it was for Nancy with her narcissistic orientation to accept a loss, how in fantasy the actual loss was not accepted, and also how this little girl equated separation with death. When the last hour came, she continued her denial and asked me to collect chalk for her during the summer so that she could use it next year. She hoped that I would spend all my summer cleaning the blackboard after her, that I would not be successful, and that therefore no other child would ever be able to write on it. She asked me how I would like to die. She herself would like to suffer a great deal first. "Everybody dies some day," she said. When the time finally came to say good-by, she went to the bathroom and stated, "I'm always so dirty. I'm nothing but a dirty little thing," and then she left the office.

I had known for several months before termination that Nancy's mother was preparing to be remarried and that they would be leaving the city. I therefore was in a position to discuss termination with Nancy for a long time. I attempted to bring it up often, but Nancy ignored my remarks. She had to retain and not relinquish this view of herself as worthless and dirty, which expressed her rage and hostility at her mother for marrying and preferring a man, and at me for letting her go.

DISCUSSION

Psychoanalysts have been increasingly interested in the specific psychic phenomena associated with growth and development in the child. The role that trauma plays is therefore a matter of particular concern when factors of development are weighed. The cases described above illustrate with particular clarity that the same external event has a different traumatic impact on different individuals. The special significance depends on many factors—among them individual character differences, the previous life history, and the stage of psychosexual development at which the traumatic event occurs. The two cases cited illustrate that in addition to the sisters' individual differences, there were two central facts which affected each child in a different way: each had had a different relationship to their father when his death occurred; moreover, one was in the midst of her oedipal phase, while the older sister was in the latency period. Meiss (1952) described her observations which were made upon a fatherless child whose development showed the marked effects of the loss of the father upon the particular developmental phase in which the child was. Rochlin (1953) shows in considerable detail how the child integrates object loss in terms of the developing psychic economy.

In the older child, the effects of object loss more closely approximate those commonly observed in adults. In the younger child, however, regressive phenomena seem to be more prominent, probably because the defenses of the ego are still too inadequately developed. Intellectual and social achievements are sacrificed as regression sets in, and further development is often arrested as Anna Freud (1952) has shown. The extensive psychoanalytic literature provides many examples illustrating some of the effects of object loss occurring in various phases of psychic development (Bowlby, 1960; Bornstein, 1951; Deutsch, 1919, 1937; A. Freud, 1952; A. Freud and Burlingham, 1944; Rochlin, 1959). However, it appears that insufficient emphasis has been placed on the fact that in the younger children regression is more prominent than in older children. In the older child the defenses have become more elaborated, are less readily relinquished, and lend the ego a greater measure of adaptability. In the younger child there is still more narcissism, the pleasure ego and hence regression hold sway. Although some of the same dynamic effects can be observed even in the older child, who is also subject to regressive forces, he has the advantage of a more fully developed ego, strengthened identifications, more desexualized libidinal relationships, and a superego that is apt to be less critical. All these factors may cooperate to help the older child form better and more independent relationships than existed before the trauma.

Both children described here suffered a severe object loss, and both showed processes of regression and restitution. The older child, however, being in a later phase of psychic development, was able to support a constructive restitution of her loss. She did not succumb to regression to the same extent as her younger sister.

These two cases illustrate that object loss seriously affects the course of psychic development: in one instance, the trauma enhanced, in some respects even promoted it; and in the other, the trauma retarded emotional development and in certain aspects even led to a relinquishment of what had been achieved. The significant difference in the reactions to object loss appeared to result from the phase of psychic development at which the trauma occurred.

BIBLIOGRAPHY

Bornstein, B. (1951), On Latency. *This Annual*, VI.
Bowlby, J. (1960), Separation Anxiety. *Int. J. Psa.*, XLI.
Deutsch, H. (1919), A Two-Year-Old Boy's First Love Comes to Grief. In: *Dynamics of Psychopathology in Childhood*, ed. L. Jessner & E. Pavenstedt. New York: Grune & Stratton, 1959.
—— (1937), Absence of Grief. *Psa. Quart.*, VI.

Freud, A. (1952), The Mutual Influences in the Development of Ego and Id. *This Annual*, VII.
—— & Burlingham, D. (1944), *Infants Without Families*. New York: International Universities Press.
Meiss, M. (1952), The Oedipal Problem of a Fatherless Child. *This Annual*, VII.
Rochlin, G. (1953), Loss and Restitution. *This Annual*, VIII.
—— (1959), The Loss Complex. *J. Am. Psa. Assn.*, VII.

THE SIX-YEAR-OLD WHO BEGAN TO SEE

Emotional Sequelae of Operation for Congenital Bilateral Cataract

ALIZA SEGAL and FREDERICK H. STONE, M.B. (Jerusalem)[1]

In February, 1950, Brachah B., a six-year-old Yemenite girl, was referred to the Lasker Center of Hadassah, Jerusalem. The child had been born blind, on account of bilateral congenital cataract, and only some time after her fifth birthday, following a surgical operation at the Department of Ophthalmology, Hadassah Hospital, Jerusalem, did she begin to see. For her vision to be at all adequate, it was necessary that she wear spectacles, and this Brachah resolutely refused to do. It was in connection with this specific and apparently well-defined problem that our professional help was enlisted. This circumstance afforded us the unique opportunity of observing the reactions of the child, and of her mother, to the belated "gift" of sight.

CASE RECORD

Background Material and Initial Diagnostic Impressions

On the February 24, 1950, Brachah and her mother paid their first visit to the Lasker Center. Mrs. B. was a small, dark, very thin woman with a depressed and careworn expression. Her dress was tattered but meticulously clean. At her side was the child, bent double, almost on all fours, and clinging with hands and mouth to

[1] From the Lasker Mental Hygiene and Child Guidance Center of Hadassah, Jerusalem, Israel. Miss Segal, psychotherapist at the Center, conducted the child-therapy sessions. Dr. Stone is now Consultant in Child Psychiatry, Royal Hospital for Sick Children, Glasgow, and Honorary Clinical Lecturer in Child Psychiatry, University of Glasgow.

The authors wish to acknowledge the helpful criticism and encouragement of their colleagues at the Lasker Center, Jerusalem, and their indebtedness to Miss Anna Freud for her help in the preparation of this paper.

her mother's skirts. In this way, unwillingly, she shuffled along, part
led, part dragged by her mother. The girl was thin, fair-skinned,
light-haired, and blue-eyed, unusual coloring in a Yemenite. She
seemed frightened and unhappy, from time to time emitting a whining cry. Mrs. B. scolded her and gave her a smack; a moment later
the mother's apparent exasperation had changed to laughter, and
then again to affected indifference.

In subsequent casework interviews with the mother, we learned
that Mrs. B. was a widow and Brachah her only child. Mrs. B. was
married when she was about eight years old (child marriages are
accepted practice in Yemen) and the marriage was consummated
when she was fourteen. Brachah was born two or three years later.
The birth was normal and the child, a plump, healthy baby, was
breast fed without difficulty for eight months. Then Brachah's father
died, and shortly afterwards Mrs. B. fell ill with what she described
as a severe depression. She felt neither dead nor alive and did not
eat except when fed by force. Though she was vague about this, it
seemed that during this illness the baby was cared for by one of
Mrs. B.'s sisters. She told us that during her depression she had a
dream in which she saw a beautiful country where the sun shone
on wooded hills. This she knew to be Jerusalem and decided that
there she must go. Thereupon she recovered and set about making
preparations for the journey, selling all her belongings including the
most valuable possession of a Yemenite woman, her silver- and gold-
embroidered wedding gown. She and her child, along with her
mother, traveled by truck from her home in Saanah to Aden, a
journey lasting four to six weeks, where they waited about two years
before being brought by air transport to Israel.[2]

On arrival they were received in a Yemenite immigrants' camp,
but in order to see the fulfillment of her dream, Mrs. B. persuaded
the medical authorities to allow her to proceed to Jerusalem, ostensibly in order that Brachah might have her operation. Meanwhile
the grandmother was found to be suffering from tuberculosis and
was admitted to a sanatorium. Brachah and her mother were found
to be free from tuberculous disease. In Jerusalem, one of the social
workers of the Municipality who helped Mrs. B. with her initial

[2] For description of the Yemenite migration to Israel, see Barer (1952).

problems of housing and work arranged for Brachah to be sent to a regular school, being under the impression that the child was just spoiled and should be placed in an institution to be "improved." In a few days it transpired that Brachah could not see, and ophthalmic examination revealed bilateral cataract for which an operation was proposed and shortly afterwards performed.

As far as could be ascertained, Brachah was not prepared at all for admission to the hospital or for surgery, and during the first few days there she refused to eat until her mother visited four times a day to feed her. During these visits Brachah seemed to have been in good spirits, was pleased to see her mother, and ate well. At other times of the day she occasionally tried to get out of bed and go home. When the child returned home after the operation, the "real difficulties" began. She refused to be separated from her mother even for a moment, became destructive and very aggressive, hitting, biting, and kicking her mother and strangers alike. She refused to eat, spoke to no one except her mother, and would not play with other children. She refused to wear her newly prescribed spectacles. Day and night there was soiling and wetting, an exceptional occurrence because the child had been trained at an early age. Mrs. B. described how the child would sit on her bed and defecate, declaring that she was punishing her mother for sending her to the hospital. Not surprisingly Mrs. B. found this difficult behavior almost insupportable. She declared that life was not worth living and she wished she were dead. Her only solution, she felt, was to find employment. This would necessarily involve placing Brachah in an institution, which in any case was the only way the child "could be taught to be good." The question of placement was raised again and again, and was often openly threatened to the child herself.

This then was the situation when Mrs. B. first brought Brachah to the clinic. The psychologist found it quite impossible to test the child formally because of her intense fear. Most of the time Brachah clung to her mother and moaned, and when an attempt was made to remove her hat, she struggled and screamed. Mrs. B. tried to interest her in the play materials without success. Lifting a toy animal she explained to Brachah with appropriate gestures, "This one comes at night and sticks its horns into one's belly"; or "These come at night and eat one up"! It seemed that the mother really believed that wild

animals roamed the streets of Jerusalem at night, though she had
never seen them. Thus, she never ventured out of doors after night-
fall. Mother and child conversed in Yemenite or elementary Hebrew.
Though testing was not feasible, Brachah did not give the impression
of being intellectually retarded.

On the basis of the foregoing material a tentative diagnostic statement was formulated. Our information was not adequate to assess
Brachah's emotional state preceding hospitalization, but when first
seen the child seemed to be in a state of intense insecurity and to be
suffering from reactive depression with regressive features. These
were understood as the result of the hospitalization experience with
its attendant separation from her mother; in addition, the child was
making her first attempts to adjust to seeing. Her mother likewise
was very insecure and depressed, in part due to her recent transition
to a totally new and strange environment, and in part due to the
tremendous difficulties in handling Brachah. She seemed unable to
react intuitively to her child's needs, and ostensibly at any rate
desired to be rid of her. It was therefore decided to offer help in the
form of play therapy for Brachah, and casework interviews for her
mother. Our explicit and strictly limited therapeutic goals were to
help Brachah adjust to the necessity of wearing spectacles and to give
her mother some insight into the child's problems. A few months
were thought likely to suffice.

Therapy with Mother and Child

First Period: March–July, 1950.—During this phase of treatment
Brachah, accompanied by her mother, came to play-therapy sessions
four times a week; once a week the mother had individual interviews
with the psychiatric social worker. In the first sessions Mrs. B. wept
a great deal, complained bitterly about Brachah's obstinacy and
aggressive behavior and her intolerable wetting and soiling. The
latter entailed endless washing; moreover, Mrs. B. could not take the
child visiting; she was too ashamed. Not that Brachah consented even
to come for a walk, and bringing her to the clinic was an ordeal.
The child picked up every object she encountered in the street and
held it close to her eyes. When rays of light coming through the
window fell on Brachah's pillow, she hit them furiously. "It is too
much—the child must be placed in an institution." Mrs. B. felt she

must go to work and earn some money, instead of receiving public assistance. The reasons for the child's behavior were explained many times: how frightening the new experience of seeing must be, how upset she may have been by the separation from her mother during hospitalization. Mrs. B. should regard the money she received as payment for a job that only she could do—looking after Brachah during this difficult time. Mrs. B. expressed relief at being able to discuss her thoughts and feelings with the caseworker. In the fourth interview she reported, however, that she had been to visit a "wise man"[3] who told her that her child was afraid, and that she should change her name to Rachel. The evil spirit which possessed her would then be cast out with the old name. The mother carried out this advice forthwith, but regarded it as unimportant if others continued to call the child by her former name, as did the therapist.

At the end of the first month, some improvement was described. The child was less aggressive, could occupy herself in the home, and had begun to play with other children. Yet Mrs. B. admitted that she did beat her at times, not out of anger, but because her neighbors demanded that such disturbing behavior be punished. "Brachah certainly does it out of spite . . . or maybe she has no brains."

Mrs. B. spoke of her early life; of her good father whom she never knew, and of her stepfather who treated her mother so badly; of her dear husband who died. Sometimes she tried to tell Brachah about him, but the child showed little interest. She remarked that she would really like to have her mother come and stay with them, but she could never cope with Brachah and an ailing old woman.

In the month of July there was obvious deterioration in Mrs. B.'s condition, both physical and emotional. She felt poorly and complained of headaches. The caseworker took the initiative in accompanying her to a physician for a medical checkup. She was found to be very rundown, but no actual disease was detected, and a tonic was prescribed. There was evidence of a beginning depression. Mrs. B. had lost all interest in shopping, preparing food, or eating. She talked of wanting to die and going to heaven where "it is clean, and there is no eating—like the Day of Atonement." She would rather

3 "Wise man" (Hebrew: *Chacham*), a characteristic figure in Yemenite and other oriental Jewish communities, who is consulted on all manner of problems for which he prescribes traditional remedies.

spend her money on a wardrobe than on rations. "After all, if one is hungry one can tighten one's belt; but a wardrobe in the house is dignified." The mother's emotional state led us to consider referring her for psychiatric treatment, but it was decided that for a further trial period the casework interviews should continue, under psychiatric supervision.

During the first three play sessions Brachah clung tenaciously to her mother; indeed, no attempt at separation was made. By the fourth session the child already began to move away from her mother, who nevertheless remained for a considerable time in the therapy room. *It may be mentioned here that at no time during the entire treatment contact, in all twenty-seven months, did Brachah communicate verbally with the therapist,* though she did talk in her presence to her mother and later to other children, usually in whispers. It was characteristic of the first hours that Mrs. B. would enter, Brachah clinging to her, and immediately complain about her daughter's difficult behavior, Brachah listening the while with a malicious expression on her face. The child requested quite early that mother should not tell the therapist about her "naughty" behavior. At first, Brachah played mainly with dolls, feeling their shape carefully with her fingers, touching their faces, and searching for their eyes. Her sight without spectacles was very limited and she could see objects only by holding them close to her face. Every new object encountered, the child passed on to her mother, and indeed this continued almost to the end of treatment. Brachah and the therapist usually sat side by side at a little table, Mrs. B. facing them. At first the mother continually interrupted, either asking the Hebrew names for toys, etc., or actually insisting on playing with the same material as the child, for example, with plasticine or crayons, laughing as she quite obviously competed. Brachah was easily angered by these interruptions, and would hit her mother, who often smilingly accepted the child's beatings though eventually she became annoyed. Later on, the mother would at times lie down on a rug in a corner of the room and go to sleep, becoming very irritated when Brachah woke her to demonstrate a new toy. In such ways mother and child quite often came to blows. When Brachah wanted something, she would take the therapist's hand and indicate her wish. If understood correctly she would nod, otherwise shaking her head. If a toy pleased her, she kissed it; if it did not, she would throw it down or spit on the ground or at the therapist.

In the seventh hour Brachah was shown the spectacles but at once turned her head away and did not even want to touch them. She became interested, however, when the therapist demonstrated how she could look through the lenses without actually wearing the glasses, and this she soon learned to do herself and particularly enjoyed looking at pictures. Brachah was given a special place for her spectacles in a cupboard in which she subsequently placed them at the beginning of each session, and used them each time for a short while in the manner described. At first the child relied extensively upon her sense of touch, only gradually becoming interested to see what she had felt. For example, in the tenth hour she first used crayons and paper and laughed with enjoyment when she saw through the glasses the drawing of a man begun by the therapist and completed herself (Fig. 1). She then carefully followed the outline of her drawing by tracing it with a finger, as though to feel it. For some time thereafter Brachah completed at least one drawing at each visit, her strokes steadily becoming surer (Fig. 1-10).[4] During the fourth week of treatment Brachah was encouraged to wear her glasses, but all attempts invariably met with the same refusal. The child had now begun to express aggression in her play, even directly toward the therapist, and it was decided not to press the wearing of the glasses, but to adopt a permissive attitude for some time before making any demands.

The contents of several sessions at this stage seem worthy of recording in some detail.

Session 17 (beginning of fifth week).—This session started with the child playing by herself with plasticine. Whenever I praised what she had done, she destroyed it and began afresh. Then I began to work beside her, and Brachah looked on. I asked whether she would like to do the same and she nodded assent. We then worked simultaneously, finally joining our pieces of plasticine. Brachah enjoyed this, laughing loudly. When the plasticine was finished I

4 The originals of these drawings, reproduced in black and white, were colored. The first four, in which the subject was suggested by the therapist, were in blue crayon. Beginning with Fig. 4, a variety of colors were used, the latter as well as the subjects being the child's own choice.

FIG. 1. Human figure. No differentiation of head and trunk [28.3.50].

FIG. 2. Human figure. Arms projecting from head which is not connected to trunk; mouth and eyes (3 or 4) outside head outline; head and trunk constructed by rotary movement [10.4.50].

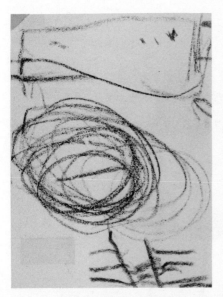

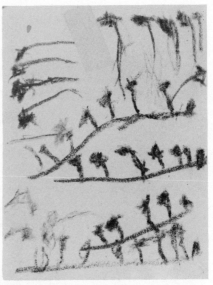

Fig. 3. Human figure. Facial features now within head outline [13.4.50].

Fig. 4.
Flowers. Repetitive design [23.4.50].

Fig. 5. Children; a house. All children bespectacled; each represents a friend, with name attached. Largest figure is herself. No differentiation of sexes [March, 1951].

489

FIG. 6. Flowers; houses [April, 1951].

FIG. 7A.   FIG. 7B.

Boy and girl. Clear differentiation of sexes by genitalia, hair, clothes [27.6.51].

FIG. 8. Garden Scene. Child without spectacles; neck differentiated [July, 1951].

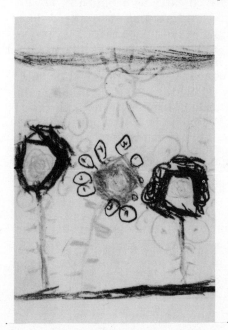

FIG. 9. Flowers [13.11.51].

FIG. 10. Girl. Teeth clearly represented; apparently still difficulty in uniting head and trunk [6.5.52].

491

proposed that we go to the bathroom to wash our hands; she made
no move. "Maybe you'd rather I brought in the soap and water?"
No reaction. I brought them in. Brachah turned and kicked me,
then followed me, kicking all the time. I said, "O.K., let's take
turns kicking, first you, then I." I put my foot out and encouraged
her to kick. She hesitated; then did so. I did likewise, and again
offered my foot. Brachah ran back and forth, laughing tensely. After
a short time I said, "Now let's stop." Brachah sat down on a chair
and began to cry. I brought over a ball and we sat pushing it back
and forth. "Good," I said, and she at once began to throw the ball
out of my reach enjoying immensely that I had to retrieve it each
time. Mrs. B. had meantime finished her interview with the psychiatric social worker in the adjacent room and when I told Brachah
we had finished, she refused to go to her mother, and eventually I
had to lead her by force. When Mrs. B. offered her hand Brachah
hit it. Mrs. B. turned to leave, pulling Brachah behind her. Only
when her mother had hit her lightly did she yield, but still pulling
in the opposite direction.

Session 18.—Today Brachah arrived carrying a bunch of flowers
which she had picked on her way to the clinic and we arranged them
in a vase. Spontaneously she began to draw pictures of flowers,
repeating the same pattern again and again (Fig. 4). Only when I
suggested another activity did she discontinue. We went over to the
sandbox and I gave her some colored cups. They were full of sand;
the moment she felt this, she threw them and went back to her chair.
Then we played with the ball, Brachah laughing with enjoyment
and taking her turn to retrieve it. When I told her to put the things
away she did so without any difficulty and held herself straight for
the first time. She took her drawings home with her and also accepted
my suggestion when I showed her how to fold them. Today I had
the feeling that she had found a positive relationship with me and
was also able to express it.

From this stage on, the relationship strengthened steadily. The
child was able to accept suggestions and really share her activities.
Bodily movements became freer, her posture erect, and she began
to move around the room with some confidence. She seemed to enjoy
it immensely at this stage if objects overturned or fell, or water was
spilled, but she avoided all contact with sand. Her play began to be
quite wild at times; indeed, having thoroughly familiarized herself
with the short flight of stairs leading down to the therapy room, she
began to jump from the top in a reckless and fearless manner, often

having to be restrained, as she could easily have injured herself. It was interesting to notice this child's very sensitive auditory perception and, in particular, her intolerance of silence. If the therapist remained silent for any length of time, Brachah would seize a stick and approach the therapist to hit her.[5]

At times Brachah would be faced with a situation which for her was completely new. She would stand completely still as if frozen with fear, giving the impression of listening and concentrating intently. If she was spoken to at such a moment, she first reacted aggressively and then quickly began to weep. Motor coordination was fairly good all along, but the "expression" of the child's body was one of fear, and she would relax only when she had "made sure" by touch. The moment something or someone strange appeared before her—or, for example, when the therapist stretched out her arm and the child seemed to find it hard to judge its distance from her—she would fold herself up as far as possible, holding her hands before her eyes as if to ward off something, and flexing the upper part of her body.

Session 22.—Mother has begun to make toys for Brachah. She made some rag dolls which Brachah brought to show to me.

When during doll play I gave her some shells to use as plates, I showed her that I had taken them from the sandbox; then she herself went to fetch some. This was the first time she approached the sandbox by herself. She picked out the shells, washed them in water, and later made a little garden in the sandbox.

Today Brachah separated without difficulty from her mother.

Session 23.—There is an obvious change in her behavior. The child is much more relaxed and able to give and take things from the therapist. It seems that she likes it when I touch her from time to time. Before, she always shrank back when I put my hand out. She moves freely in the room and dares to touch sand and water.

Session 24.—At the beginning of this session Brachah played with the doll family, gave them food, bathed and dried them, and put them to bed. Then she found the teddy bear in another corner of the room (she liked him from the first hour because of his soft fur), took

---

[5] Just as some children have anxiety attacks in bed at night when it becomes dark, so blind children react similarly when the accustomed noises of the day fade into silence. (Anna Freud, personal communication.)

the bear to the box with the small dolls under her arms, and put them all to sleep.

I then proposed that we play "hospital." Brachah brought the dolls over and I arranged a bed for each. I told the dolls that I was the eye doctor and that I would operate on them so that all of them could see well. Brachah helped me to bandage each doll. Then we fed them and put them on the pot. Brachah held them over the pot and after we finished with this I said that now they were all right and we would take off the bandages. She helped me with this too, and I said that their eyes were all right now and we would go to the doctor in the shop and buy glasses for them. I sat down at another table and she brought me the doll to have glasses put on. Then she brought them back to their bed and I told her that I would come and visit them and bring them flowers. I did so, and let the dolls bring the flowers very near their eyes. I then said to the dolls, "If you have your glasses on you do not have to put them so near your eyes." Then I exclaimed to each doll in turn: "Now I can see the flowers clearly from far away." Brachah listened very attentively with a smile on her face. From time to time she came near to have a better look at the dolls. She left in a very gay mood.

During the last few sessions I had mentioned the glasses from time to time, when it was hard for Brachah to distinguish things. In the *Session 25* I produced the glasses; she did not want to put them on, but knocked them down on the floor to break them. When I made a gesture to take them away, she tried to get them back.

Session 26.—I brought out the glasses; Brachah started to clean them and then together we looked at the picture books. At first she tried to cheat by peering round the lenses; after a short time she put them before her eyes and looked at the pictures from a greater distance. I put my arm around her, holding the glasses from one side. I told her stories while looking at the pictures. When I told her after a while to put the glasses away she did not at first move, but when I gave her the spectacle case she put them away. Afterwards she looked at her hand where she had a little scratch and I asked where she got it from. As an answer she started to hit, pinch, and scratch me, and also wanted to bite me. Then she threw over tables and chairs. I was standing and she was sitting. I asked whether she was angry with me, whether I had done something to her. She looked at me, got up, and started to kick. I said: "Let's kick the wall together," and we both started to do so. She stopped kicking me for a moment and when I stopped too, she tried to kick me again. She came over very quietly and stood beside me. I said that she could tell me if I did something wrong and that I liked her even if she did such things. She turned away, made faces as if she wanted to cry, and hit her own hands. I waited for a while. She went over to her mother who asked me what happened in such moments with Brachah, because at home she also started hitting without any provocation. I said that I could not tell because Brachah did not tell me what troubled her, but maybe she did not want to go home yet. Then I asked whether she wanted to give me her hand. She came nearer and again started to kick. I said that I would come with her without taking her hand.[6]

Session 27.—During this and the previous session Brachah spent part of the time playing in the sandbox. She became freer in using the sand, and at the end of her play she took a shovel and started to put the sand on the floor in little heaps. She enjoyed it very much and tried to test me out at the end by throwing it around. She also poured water on the little heaps. Only when she became very excited about this did I stop her play by proposing something constructive. Thereafter Brachah stopped soiling herself.

Session 28.—I had told Brachah last time that as from today we would put her glasses on. I sat at the table and asked her to sit down as well. She took her two dolls with her. When she saw that I really had brought the glasses, she wanted to get up. I told her that she could get up only after she had worn them. She got up; I put her back onto the chair. She started to hit me; I held her hands telling her that I would not allow her to hit me, but that I would not hold her if she stopped. She did so, but the moment I wanted to put the glasses on, the same sequence recurred. This was repeated again and again. I said that I would have to hold her hands and put the glasses on by force, and did so. She closed her eyes and did not want to look. After a minute I told her that was enough for one day, but that from now on we would put them on for a short time every day.

Session 29.—Brachah began by playing with the small dolls. I gave her water to bathe them and told her that she might play with the dolls while wearing her glasses. She resisted again at first and I had to put them on by force. She adjusted her scarf (which she wore day and night as do most Yemenite women) and then put down the glasses. I said that maybe she did not need the scarf, and took it off. She wanted it back. I told her first to put the glasses on. She let

---

6 The significance of the aggressive outbursts toward the therapist in this interview and in the seventeenth were not clearly understood at the time. It seems probable now that soap and water were closely associated with the sounds and smell of the hospital. Again, here, the child associated the spectacles with trauma; they may have amounted to castrating instruments. In both instances this is almost certainly a negative mother transference.

me do so. I gave her the scarf, she put it on and the glasses down. This she repeated several times, laughingly. Then I told her very seriously that I would not give it back to her if she did not leave on the glasses, and held it back for a little while. She began to hit and throw blocks. Then she started to weep. I said that there was no reason to weep, because I would give the scarf back to her if she kept the glasses on. She dried her eyes. I put the glasses on and gave her back the scarf. She again touched the glasses and I said: "Brachah, you know what I said before." She did not take them off but started to hit herself. I began to play with the dolls, she looked at me and the dolls, but from time to time she hit herself. Then I rolled a wheel toward her. She wanted to catch it, but after she made a movement toward it she hit herself. I took the teddy bear and said: "Look who is coming." She turned around and smiled and received him with open arms and hugged him. When I let the other dolls come, she received all of them. I took the carriage and proposed to put the dolls in and go for a walk. She cooperated although I took a very active part. Thus we played until the end of the hour. When I told her that time was up, she touched the glasses but did not remove them. I then told her that she could now give them to me. She did so and put the dolls away in a hurry. She was relaxed when we left and when we went out together I hugged her, to which she responded with a smile.

Summer-Autumn, 1950.—It was felt at this stage that in the autumn Brachah might begin to attend kindergarten, and so the summer vacation period, when treatment was interrupted, was used to discuss the situation with the child's future headmaster and kindergarten teacher. In October, Brachah paid her first visit to kindergarten, and for the first week the therapist accompanied her and her mother. For two days Brachah was very fearful, suspecting all new places of being hospitals where she might be left. However, she was quickly reassured at seeing the other children play and then return home afterwards. She rapidly became familiar with the new surroundings and seemed likely to adjust. Her mother meanwhile found a job as a charwoman in the school building! The therapist limited her contacts to a weekly visit to the kindergarten, and soon Brachah was talking and playing with the other children and becoming interested in listening to stories, but she never addressed a word to any adult except her mother. It was decided that the therapist's visits should gradually be discontinued to allow the child to form a relationship with the kindergartner. This was clearly an error of judgment. Brachah again refused to wear her glasses, became very aggressive toward the other children, and rejected all her teacher's approaches. An unfortunate incident about the same time probably also contributed to the deterioration. The physician paid his routine visit for health inspection purposes on a day when the teacher herself was absent, and Brachah was submitted to the physical examination by force. It was therefore decided to resume regular treatment at the clinic, and that the therapist should work with both mother and child. From then on, the mother was seen once a week, Brachah twice.

December, 1950-January, 1951.—When Mrs. B. returned after the long interruption she seemed dejected, careworn, and run down. All her early feelings about Brachah were voiced again. The child was too difficult and should be sent somewhere. She herself wanted to die. She was afraid she would die. She had no appetite and could not sleep. In spite of this severe depression Mrs. B. continued to work without a break. She began to take sedatives, but stopped when she developed a severe generalized urticarial eruption—probably a sensitization rash. Attempts to find a convalescent home which would accept mother and child together were fruitless. The child herself came rather unwillingly to her therapy sessions, and reacted to her mother's complaining about her by hitting her and tearing her dress. The therapist stated that she could not allow her to hit in this way. Brachah smiled, lifted her hand, and then stopped. She was soon interested again in the dolls and the paints. For the next three months Mrs. B. came to her own sessions regularly, but she did not bring Brachah, complaining that it was too difficult to bring her.

The therapeutic difficulties of working with a silent child are obvious, but no less difficult was the task of finding a common therapeutic language with a mother whose conceptual processes function on what by Western standards is a very primitive level, who must convey her thoughts and feelings in a foreign tongue, who fluctuates between outright rejection of and intense identification with her child, often openly competing with her for the therapist's love and interest, who believes in magic and superstition and yet is capable at times of apparently effortless insight. Clearly the stresses, emotional and economic, with which she struggled were extreme, and the available community resources meager, yet we were by now convinced, in the face of intense opposition by the welfare and education authorities, that any plan involving separation of Brachah from her mother would be detrimental to both, if in fact it was not doomed to sabotage by the mother in spite of her protestations. Mrs. B.'s periods of depression and lethargy were a recurrent feature, and it was only by direct confrontation that she could be jolted into wakefulness, allowing her a little more understanding of her own and Brachah's behavior.

For example, on one occasion when Mrs. B. was particularly depressed and unwilling to bring Brachah again for treatment, the therapist stated that she well realized how hard it was for her but that she also had the impression that she did not want us to help her.

Mrs. B.: How can you say such a thing? What do you mean?
T.:   You are trying to show me that you cannot be helped, and so Brachah must be sent away. You come here regularly but provoke Brachah to be bad.
Mrs. B.: Please explain what you mean.
T.:   One day last week when my session with Brachah was ending, the child wanted to go with you and sought your hand. You hid your hands and Brachah became angry and began to tear your dress. Only when I took your hand and put it into hers did you go with her.
Mrs. B.: [laughing] How can you say such a thing?
T.:   I saw it happen, and though I am sure you did not do it on purpose, that is what you did. We all do things like that sometimes. . . . I hear only bad things about Brachah from you, but I am sure there are also good things to tell. If we are angry with someone, we only see the bad things, but you can be angry with her and at the same time worried about her because you love her.
Mrs. B.: I must think about that during the week [long silence]. I will bring her . . . but how could you have thought such a thing about me.

Mrs. B. left in a cheerful mood! The following week she again appeared alone. It was explained that Brachah must be brought, otherwise she herself cannot be seen. Then for the first time Mrs. B. expressed her anger about treatment being interrupted when Brachah went to kindergarten. From then on she brought the child regularly.

Some of the most revealing glimpses of the mother's emotional life were obtained from her dreams which she related quite frequently, and with complete spontaneity. When it was remarked, for example, how great an undertaking her journey from Aden must have been, Mrs. B. described the following dream: It was some time after her husband's death. She and her relatives were living in her parents' home in Saanah. Everyone was called to the table to eat, except herself. She said nothing, but felt her heart beating, and reflected sadly on what would become of the child. How would she manage to feed her? If only she had a tent of her own. At this point she wakened feeling frightened, looked around her room, and said to herself, "What do I have to worry about? Thank God I am in my own room with strong walls which do not let in the rain. I am alone. I am in Jerusalem."

Mother and daughter slept in the same bed, and Mrs. B. described how the child insisted that her mother hold her in her arms throughout the night, complaining at once if she even turned in her sleep. The worker commented that it seemed as if Brachah feared mother would leave her. To this Mrs. B. responded, "You know, the other night, we were in our room, and I wanted to call the child. She was not there. I went outside to search, calling her, but she was nowhere to be found. I was very frightened and thought I had lost her, and then I realized she was lying beside me." It was not clear to the therapist if all this had really happened and she asked. Mrs. B. laughed and explained that it was only a dream. Still, it had upset her very much. "You know," remarked the therapist, "that Brachah must be feeling like that at times?" and the mother's sly smile confirmed that she had been correctly understood. This incident clearly revealed the mother's identification with her child.

Spring, 1951-Spring, 1952.—In the spring of 1951 it was arranged that Brachah should begin to attend school the following term, an achievement necessitating much preparatory work with the headmaster, and, of course, the child herself was prepared for this in her therapy sessions over a period of some months. Before the start of the school year, the therapist accompanied Brachah and her mother to the school to introduce them to the place and to the new teacher, who easily established contact with the child. Brachah quickly lost her initial fear and was soon exploring the classroom and participating in a game. Mrs. B. arranged for the child to undergo the routine medical examinations which were all carried through without any special difficulty, and Brachah was formally accepted by the education authorities.

As Mrs. B. was obliged to leave home very early in the morning to go to work, she arranged for some of Brachah's classmates to collect her later and accompany her to school, having prepared all the necessary school items, lunch packet, and so forth, in advance. During the first few weeks at school, Brachah was rather aggressive, but settled down quite quickly, and began to participate to some extent in the class activities. During "break," however, she almost always remained in the classroom because she was afraid the bigger children might hit her. It upset her also to discover that she could not run as fast as the others. "Why do they say I am blind?" she asked her mother. "I can see now. But why can't I run well?" Sometimes Brachah would threaten that she would not go to school and Mrs. B. would explain how pleasant it was to learn. "One day you will know more than your mother and have a profession." On one occasion the child exclaimed that when she grew up she would marry and have children, that she would always do what her children asked, and would never leave them alone. In fact, she only went to school because mother was working and she did not want to stay at home alone. "And," she added, "I like to be with children." Each day after school Brachah talked incessantly, telling her mother everything she had been taught. One day on her way to the Lasker Center, chattering to her mother as they walked, she halted at the corner of the road, and exclaimed: "Now I close my mouth till we come out." Her teacher, to whom she likewise never spoke, was not surprisingly quite doubtful whether the child was understanding or absorbing anything at all. In fact, she learned a great deal.

Her attendance was regular for some months till one day she witnessed the giving of routine injections of typhoid vaccine to some of the children, and from then on persuasion was often needed for her to go. She later told her mother how she feared that the clinic or the school was another kind of hospital where she might be left. When Mrs. B. went shopping in town, Brachah preferred to stay at home—in case her mother might decide to leave her somewhere.

Everything connected with hospitals seemed to hold terror for the child. Once, the doctor was called to examine her at home because of some minor illness. She refused to let him touch her, and threw a temper tantrum, yet a visit to the dentist was accomplished without difficulty. For a long time Brachah was afraid of going to the lavatory.

By the spring of 1952 Brachah had been attending school for six months. Her participation in the class program was largely passive; for example, she loved to listen to stories, but she was no longer aggressive, and played regularly with groups of children, both in and out of school. She wore her spectacles all day, at home and at school. About the same time her mother reported that she was now sleeping in her own bed.

Following two missed appointments in the month of February the therapist paid a home visit and found Brachah alone, just finishing dressing herself. The therapist explained that she had come to see why she had not been coming. Brachah at once opened a drawer and began to show her toys. Then one of her friends came in and explained that Brachah was not at school because it was raining and she feared she might catch a cold. Brachah then produced the fancy-dress costume she had worn for the festival of Purim and dressed herself in it before the mirror. Then the two girls with much laughing and giggling danced and sang Purim songs. Brachah wore her glasses all the time and when moving about seemed to rely extensively on her vision. When Mrs. B. next came to the clinic, she said that Brachah had described every detail of the visit.

In the last month of treatment, Brachah devoted the sessions almost entirely to writing practice, or drawing with pencil and crayon. A representative selection of her drawings covering almost the entire period of treatment are reproduced.

Technical Considerations.—It may be helpful at this point to interpose a few words on therapeutic technique, to explain what the therapist tried to achieve and the methods she sought to employ. From the foregoing account, elements are discernible of classical procedures of play therapy and casework. Both mother and child were given the opportunity of forming a positive relationship with the therapist at their own pace. The initial attitude was a permissive one within the framework of the mutually recognized limits of place, time, and behavior. Yet, great flexibility was allowed. Mrs. B. was present at many of Brachah's sessions, though her inter- ference by acting out was gently but firmly limited. For a time, other children accompanied Brachah to the clinic and even partici- pated in the play, a phase which rapidly closed of its own accord. Regular contacts were maintained with external agencies, the social welfare department, kindergarten, school, medical clinics, and so forth, and the therapist often acted as a supportive intermediary in introducing mother and child to new situations. As confidence in the therapist grew, both mother and child were able to express or indicate their hostile feelings. The traumatic episodes in the lives of each were played out as, for example, Brachah's hospitalization experience, or Mrs. B.'s loss of her father and later her husband— the recital and understanding of her dreams amounting to an abreac- tion equivalent. Yet with the progress of treatment all this was seen by the therapist as subordinate in importance to the task of helping Mrs. B. to understand and respond to her new and difficult daughter, that is, of handling the disequilibrated relationship between mother and child. Moreover, it became clearer that this could be achieved largely by means which depended not upon the use of abstract concepts, meaningless for the mother and certainly for Brachah, but by "demonstration in action." An example from each will serve. It will be recalled how the therapist permitted and even encouraged Brachah to demonstrate her anger by kicking. Talking about angry feelings was meaningless until they had been acted upon. In actual fact, the method was at the time used *faute de mieux* because of the child's refusal to talk, its significance becoming apparent only later. As a procedure with a child of six, this is not so unusual. This could hardly be said of an incident such as that in which Mrs. B. hid her hand from Brachah, to which the therapist reacted by placing the child's hand in the mother's. Here the symbolic representation of rejection (hand withdrawal) was at the time neither commented upon nor interpreted, but demonstrated in its effect, viz., the rapid calm- ing of the enraged Brachah. Later this "therapeutic intervention" was an eminently suitable topic to work through with the mother, on a completely concrete level. Only then could the unconscious motivation be discussed. While it has been stressed that Mrs. B. often showed remarkable insight into her identification with Brachah, thereby achieving great understanding of the child's feelings, the underlying motivation of much of her behavior toward the child was unconscious. What is unusual here is, of course, not the mechanism but the way it was handled in therapy. Mrs. B.'s resolute participation in the child's therapy sessions, which might have been regarded as an interference, was here utilized as a therapeutic tool. Facets of the disturbed mother-child relationship were being played out in action and responded to by the therapist. Again and again, what began as a complaint by the mother about the child's behavior was discussed with her in Brachah's presence. It was hoped that Mrs. B. could be given understanding of the reason for the child's behavior and her own part in contributing to and influencing it.

In the early stages the mother developed a very dependent relationship toward the therapist as regards not only her child but her total life situation; so much so that in her struggle toward independence she was loath to admit any success in her handling of the child. The possible reasons for the child's fear of the toilet were discussed at length, and then for weeks gave way to other topics. Suddenly Mrs. B. with coy smiles would announce that for some time that particular difficulty had been overcome. Now, of course, there were others!

The Ending Phase.—It can readily be appreciated how difficult a decision it was to end intensive therapeutic work. It need hardly be said that our strictly limited therapeutic goals as initially defined had long been abandoned. That Brachah wore her spectacles and that her mother had acquired considerable understanding of the child's needs were now viewed as almost incidental achievements. On the other hand, we could not pretend that the outlook for the future was a particularly happy one. The possibility of Brachah developing toward happy, independent adulthood was remote. Clearly, she would always need a protected environment, emotional and economic. Her mother, on whom the greater part of the burden would inevitably fall, had but limited personal resources.

In the final therapeutic hours, a problem which Mrs. B. raised several times was the future of her own mother, whose tuberculosis had in the meantime been "cured," and who was now living in an old-age home. Mrs. B. was in perpetual conflict about whether and when to visit the grandmother and appealed to the therapist for guidance. She did in fact visit at irregular intervals, at times taking Brachah along with her. The grandmother expressed her wish to come and live with her daughter, and Mrs. B., who felt that she could not shoulder the additional load of a frail and helpless old lady, finally found the courage to refuse. But the decision gave her much guilt and pain. Mrs. B. of her own accord also discussed with Brachah the child's refusal to talk to strange adults to which it seems the child replied that she did not speak for fear of being laughed at, and promised that she would begin to speak "next year."

This, then, was the general picture in the closing phase. The child, though by no means easy to handle, had overcome the severe regression following hospitalization, was attending school fairly regularly and participating to some extent, had found friends, and had gone some way toward "adjusting to seeing." Her mother had become able to use her own initiative in handling successive problems, could prepare the child for coming experiences, and brought her successes to the therapist for discussion and approval. There was no mention of her placing Brachah in an institution—indeed, she remarked to a friend that she could not believe she had ever contemplated doing so—and she felt she could continue on her own to help and care for her child.

Subsequent Developments.—After a year, a follow-up home visit was made and it seemed that progress was being maintained. Some months later, however, Mrs. B. reported a definite deterioration. Brachah suddenly and for no obvious reason refused to go to school, stopped wearing her glasses, and would eat only in the evening when her mother was there to feed her. In the month of March, 1954, compulsive features appeared in the form of repeating hand washing, and a constant desire to have the furniture arranged in certain ways. Gradually she began to withdraw into herself and sat alone in a corner of the room, becoming very aggressive if approached. She was then admitted to the Government Mental Hospital, Talbieh, Jerusalem, where the clinical picture was considered characteristic of schizophrenia. Mrs. B. had been visiting her daughter four times a day to feed her and to her alone does the child speak. (This was the situation in June, 1954.)

Discussion

Very little has been written on the subject of acquired vision in persons blind from birth and still less on the psychological aspects. The earliest references to acquired vision from both scientific and lay sources were reviewed by von Senden (1932) whose monograph was largely concerned with the function of the visual and other special senses during the postoperative phase. These studies as well as the experimental work of Riesen (1947), who reared chimpanzees in total darkness till the age of sixteen months, were submitted by Hebb (1949) as contributory evidence toward his neuropsychological theory of human behavior. There are interesting clinical case histories by Miner (1905) who records the progress of a young woman operated successfully for bilateral cataract at the age of twenty-two years, and by Fischer (1888) who gives one of the few accounts of a blind-born child operated at the age of eight years. In each instance, however, the follow-up study covers but a short period of time. All these authors are agreed that the patients, after their operation, have the greatest difficulty in recognizing familiar objects without the customary use of touch, smell, and senses other than visual. Familiar persons, for example, are for a long time recognized by their voices. There is an initial period of delight in the new faculty, and special pleasure in colors, followed invariably, according to Senden, by a period of resistance to learning. Particularly difficult is the recognition of shapes and patterns.

Though it has long been known that considerable emotional upset may follow operations for acquired cataract, and especially in elderly patients with senile cataract (Linn et al., 1953), this aspect has received almost no attention in congenital cases. It is probably true that nowadays in countries with developed medical services, cataract is recognized and treated during infancy with no striking psychological aftereffects, although it is doubtful whether this has received specific study. The present case has therefore been described in some detail because it is an interesting and unusual clinical record. On the basis of the slender evidence available it would be unwise to draw any general conclusions, especially because the record is unavoidably deficient in one essential. No adequate description of the child is available prior to the operation for cataract. The mother's account of the child's development and behavior throughout infancy and early childhood must be regarded as very tenuous evidence indeed. Thus it is not certain that Brachah until the age of five was normal in all respects other than being blind.

Further, while the sequence of events strongly suggests a causal relationship between the operation and the onset of severe symptoms, it may be asked what exactly constituted the specific traumatic event? Was it the unprecedented separation of the child from her mother, the actual experience of the hospital and surgical procedure, the impact of vision as such, or a combination of these? It is clear, however, that an unusually strong bond existed between mother and child, partly because her blindness made Brachah extremely dependent on her mother, and this bond was almost certainly further strengthened by the fact that the child was fatherless from an early age. This same factor probably operated in another way, by causing the mother to bind the child to her, thereby deriving comfort in her loss. At all events, it is clear that this woman who suffered from recurring bouts of intense depression, as a result of one of which she was quite unable to cope with the ordinary daily demands of life including the care of her baby, did not have a constant healthy relationship to her daughter. It is interesting to recall that the mother lost her own father in infancy, and that shortly afterward she herself suffered as a result of separation from her mother and stepfather. It is a matter of conjecture how much this "reliving of generations" distorted the relationship between Mrs. B. and Brachah, and to what extent this was reinforced—and this includes the critical hospitalization period—by Mrs. B.'s clear conflict over her inability to have her mother, now elderly and ailing, come to live with her. It may be questioned whether Brachah's final stage of selective mutism, withdrawal, and food refusal, while unquestionably a state of severe regression, is to be regarded as schizophrenia. To return, however, to the clinical picture in the early phase, while regression is commonly seen following separation of children from their parents, it is seldom that a child expresses in such an unequivocal way her anal sadism. Brachah defecated on her bed to punish her mother for sending her away. In her refusal to eat, to be separated from her mother, to speak to strangers, in her hitting, biting, soiling, and wetting, one can perceive elements of regression, fear, and a desire to punish. Possibly the spectacles themselves were regarded fearfully as the instruments which had hurt her eyes. It must be remembered that the hospital experience may have been particularly terrifying for this blind child who, dependent to such a large extent on hearing, was exposed to unfamiliar sounds and an almost unknown language. Perhaps her silence toward the therapist—it has emerged how closely she associated the child guidance clinic with hospital—was a personal and refined form of retaliation. Again one may conjecture that whenever Mrs. B. suffered from depression she herself became silent toward her child, so that for Brachah to be silent may have been equated with withdrawal of interest and love.

It is difficult not to attribute some aspects of the child's behavior to the unaccustomed impact of visual stimuli. Her doubled-up posture and the "warding-off" position of her hands seem to suggest a defensive attitude, as if she experienced an attacking force; particularly striking is the way she hit the sun's rays falling on her pillow. Those who are familiar with children blind from birth or an early age are wont to say that these children do not seem "to mind" their blindness. In this connection it has been described how patients centrally blinded as a result of head injuries appear to become particularly distressed when their vision begins to return. The crouching posture adopted by this child when first seen suggests perhaps that her postural reflex mechanism which had presumably become established by the interaction of nuchal, kinesthetic, and vestibular systems was disorganized by the belated functioning of the visual component.

The child's pictures were thought to be of sufficient interest to be worth producing, yet we would be chary of drawing conclusions. One can observe clearly enough her increasing skill, for example, in drawing the human figure. But how is one to interpret the first primitive attempt (Fig. 1)? It is not so different from the product of many a two-and-a-half to three-year-old. At the time this was drawn the child had markedly regressed in behavior. Was this a significant factor, or was the specific difficulty already mentioned, of shape and form recognition and therefore of pictorial representation, of great importance? There was great difficulty in relating the eyes to the face, and the head to the trunk. An understanding of this would require some knowledge of body-image formation in the blind, which the writers do not possess. For an indefinite period extending over months all faces were bespectacled. Was this connected in some way with the relating of the form of external objects to the subject's own body image, or was there an emotional motivation, a desire to have all children like herself? It is not clear how important cultural conditioning was. The drawings of many Yemenite children are recognized as Yemenite by being curiously and specifically stylized, as, for example, in the representation of the genitalia which are often more symbolic than realistic. Yet, presumably, in the visual sphere this factor could begin to operate only after the child was able to see. The kind of repetitive drawing shown in Figure 4 was typical of a phase, and might be interpreted either as a compulsive activity, or developmentally as a desire to enjoy a newly acquired skill by repetition.

In retrospect, there is scope for self-criticism. Clearly the depth and ramifications of the clinical problem were at first underestimated. As regards the technique of therapy, it is obvious that in spite of good resolutions the pace was unduly forced, and of equal importance there was inconsistent fluctuation between educational and analytic principles. Perhaps as great a difficulty as any was the cultural gulf between therapist and patient, an oft-neglected aspect of countertransference, and in this case exemplified by the therapist's nonacceptance of the "wise-man's" injunction to give the child a new name. He, it would seem, regarded the acquisition of sight at this age as tantamount to rebirth, and in this was perhaps wiser than ourselves.

This record, though a rarity, reinforces the opinion that congenital cataract should be treated as early as is surgically practicable. When the diagnosis is made in later childhood and operation undertaken, it would be wise, facilities permitting, for a psychotherapist to establish rapport with the parents and the child beforehand, and to cooperate throughout with the surgeon, and especially in the immediate preoperative and postoperative phases.

BIBLIOGRAPHY

Barer, S., ed. (1952), *Magic Carpet*. London: Sacker & Warburg.
Fischer, E. (1888), Bericht über ein achtjähriges Kind, angeborener Katarakt und dessen Verhalten während der ersten drei Wochen nach wiedererlangtem Sehen. *Klin. Monatsbl. Augenh.* (Stuttgart), XXVI.

Hebb, D. O. (1949), *The Organization of Behavior*. New York: Wiley.

Linn, J., Kahn, R. L., et al. (1953), Patterns of Behavior Disturbance Following Cataract Extraction. *Am. J. Psychiat.*, CX.

Miner, J. B. (1905), A Case of Vision Acquired in Adult Life. *University of Iowa Studies*, IV.

Riesen, A. H. (1947), Development of Visual Perception in Man and Chimpanzee. *Science*, CVII.

von Senden, M. (1932), *Raum- und Gestaltauffassung bei operierten Blindgeborenen vor und nach der Operation*. Leipzig: Barth.

A STUDY OF LOSS REACTIONS IN A SEVEN-YEAR-OLD[1]

BENJAMIN SHAMBAUGH, M.D. (Boston)[2]

The reactions of a child to an event of such great importance as the loss of a parent, if studied psychologically, can be seen to include responses which in an adult might seem alarming or could suggest severe pre-existing pathology. Yet, considering the relative weakness of a child's ego in comparison to that of an adult, and the child's great and real dependence on the object who is lost, one should not be surprised at the severe and prolonged reaction to such a trauma. One should anticipate, even in a normal child, that every defense is mobilized to ward off its impact, and that every new object relationship as it develops will be influenced by the fact that an earlier one was lost. The severity and extent of the normal child's reactions to loss can probably be accurately assessed only through depth-psychologic investigation, just as the importance of an early loss for an adult can be gauged only in his analysis. This is true because of the child's ability to mask, through massive but not necessarily pathologic denial, from adults the vicissitudes of his inner life. For in the child I shall discuss, and doubtless in many other instances, the major changes which were taking place were not at all apparent to the casual observer or even to his family. His family were able to note only that his behavior had become "more difficult," and that he was more of a "pest" than before.

The child, whose treatment will, I think, demonstrate the major impact of a loss, was a seven-and-a-half-year-old boy whose mother died during the time I was studying him. I had seen the boy, Henry,

[1] This paper was presented at the Tenth Anniversary Symposium, the Child Psychiatry Unit, Massachusetts Mental Health Center, Harvard Medical School. The symposium was devoted to "Psychoanalytic Studies in Object Loss and Depression."

[2] Instructor, Psychiatry, Harvard Medical School. Staff Child Psychiatry, Child Psychiatry Unit, Massachusetts Mental Health Center (Boston Psychopathic Hospital).

over a five-month period of time before his mother died and continued to see him for over two years subsequently. I shall present material showing the nature of his immediate reactions, the upheaval in his object relationships, and then the vicissitudes of these important object relationships (to his sister, his father, and to his new stepmother) during the remaining time I knew him. This investigation was part of a project investigating loss in children carried out in the Children's Unit of the Massachusetts Mental Health Center (Boston Psychopathic Hospital).

Henry was a handsome, active, slightly built, black-haired boy with an intelligent look. He was talkative, friendly, and open, and did not impress one as being an unusual boy for his age. In other circumstances therapy would not have been recommended for him, but his father and the clinic knew Henry's mother was dying of cancer. Henry was aware of his mother's illness and of the operations on her breast, but not of their severity. It was in fact the father's concern over the future of his child and not the child's present adjustment which brought Henry to the clinic's attention.

During this initial five-month time, Henry, in his weekly interviews, played freely with games, trucks, and soldiers. He was interested in constructing things and hoped to become a fireman or a policeman, occupations in which his father (who was a salesman) had formerly been involved. Henry was rather easygoing and irresponsible about his schoolwork, which was poor, in spite of constant prodding from his mother. His father, characteristically, was not so concerned about Henry's schooling.

Henry spoke little to me of his family. He seemed to be fond of his sister Dorothy, age four, though he clearly felt irritation when he saw her being pampered by his father. Henry's father was a narcissistic and infantile man in his late thirties. He tended to be emotional, and was either seductively overindulgent of Henry or angrily intolerant of his active behavior. He was not consistent, and felt at a loss in managing his children during his wife's illness. However, Henry loved and admired his father, boasted of his father's big car, and was never critical of him. After each interview, he ran to his father's arms.

Doubtless, Henry's relationship to his mother during this time was influenced by the operations she had had and by her increasing invalidism. She was a somewhat cold, stern woman, who demanded good behavior and performance. Henry avoided, whenever possible, referring to his mother's illness. He denied its severity and would often say to me, "She is nearly well now." "She will be out of bed soon." Ambivalence in his feelings for her were apparent quite early. He would be quite angry at her demands of him to do better in school and would provoke her; on the other hand, he certainly felt she ought to be obeyed. As she became more ill, his anger toward her became altogether suppressed in the interviews. This, then, is a very brief description of the state of Henry's relationships which underwent a crisis when his mother died.

This initial period of observation was brought to an end by Henry's refusal to come to the clinic. His mother, as her illness progressed, openly voiced her dislike of her children attending the clinic, saying, "Henry should do his homework and not go to the clinic and play." As her feelings in this respect became more insistent, Henry made them his own and voiced them himself. His guilt about coming to the clinic, which was only slightly relieved by bringing his homework in, made it seem unwise to insist on his continuing. He would, I thought, have been too much at odds with his dying mother. My work with Henry was therefore interrupted for seven months, and was resumed very shortly after his mother's death.

When I started to see Henry again, I was struck by his affect. He did not look like a boy who had suffered a loss. Instead, he came to his first interviews as if he were full of energy. He was hyperactive and gay, sometimes even to the point of euphoria. He said he was glad to come back, laughed, told me jokes he had heard at school, recited puns, and remarked on all the amusing and interesting things which had happened at school. He was inclined to boast about his exploits at school which caused his friends to admire him. He showed me magic tricks and new games he had invented. He was very restless and distractible, playing each game only for a few moments before leaving it in a hyperactive manner to find some new diversion. Sounds in the street or in the hall of the clinic would immediately divert him from the activity he had just been occupied with and induce him to look out into the hall and out the window to see what was going on. He would pick up puppets, start a puppet play, and break it off at once. He would choose to paint, and after making a few strokes he would throw the paper away.

In this period, he did not mention his home or the tragedy. There seemed to be suppression not only of affect about his mother's death but of the event itself. Whenever this suppression was threatened, Henry reacted at once with anxiety and anger. For instance, once he mentioned that there had been a newspaper article referring to his mother's death, and he said angrily, "Why did they have to write about it?" And, "It was none of their business." When I once alluded to his mother's death, he reacted to me with similar anger and ran from the office. Later he characterized his attitude to the loss, and told me how he would like most to think of it: "When she died at the hospital, I waved and said good-by and forgot it." Still later, when he spoke of her, it was without any of the earlier ambivalence. He said no one could make up for her. She had been perfect. It was she who had taken him to circuses and bought him candy.

His fantasy play during these early weeks, in so far as his attention span allowed it to be expressed, was altered. He still played with trucks and soldiers, but now the theme was of a family who was moving from one house to another. Such fantasy would start only to be dissolved with violent and destructive play. The family would be making plans to move when the moving van would be demolished. Then the house would be blown up and everybody killed. Two or three times the play was as follows. A family lived in a house; somebody was sick; an ambulance came; then the house was burned down and the ambulance would blow up. Invariably, as soon as destruction came into the play, Henry became extremely anxious, broke it off, and sought distraction. In time, the play became somewhat repetitive. There was a boy in the family. The boy became destructive. In an attempt to control himself, the boy became Superman. Then Superman grew violent and was also uncontrolled. He then made various efforts to control Superman but without success. In these ways, uncontrollable anger at his loss was expressed.

Very evident, too, during these early weeks, was Henry's tendency to regress to marked oral and dependent demands. He wanted from me many things during each interview. He wanted candy, Cokes, ice cream, or milk. Sometimes he would bring in money with which to buy these things, and at other times he would harass me until I bought them for him. His demands were insatiable and he was never content. He wanted new toys in each session. He would ask to draw and I would give him a pad of paper. He would use one sheet after another, never producing a drawing, but would tear the paper up, throw it away, and demand a new pad. His attitude verbally expressed in each interview was that he was always gypped. He felt gypped in games when I happened to win. There was also an increase in magical thinking, and he brought in rabbits' feet to guarantee winning at games. He would cheat blandly and seemingly without guilt. He could deny himself nothing. During one interview, he went to the blackboard and drew a picture which showed two or three people standing around a table. Each person had a wide-open mouth and Henry said they were all hungry and never had enough.

Another reaction characteristic of these early weeks was a marked increase of narcissism. This was expressed in Henry's frequently recurring fantasies of independence and maturity. Henry spoke of plans to take care of himself, to prepare his own meals, to get his own clothes. He spoke of getting a job and earning his own money, so that he would not need his father for support. Sometimes his fantasies were more grandiose and he thought of becoming a television star, world-famous and very rich. He belittled his father as a supporter and said he did not need him. He denied he needed me or that I could do anything for him. But nevertheless, as he increasingly expressed that he had no need of me, he made innumerable demands to be given things and to be fed. He developed fantasies of omnipotence and invulnerability. On one occasion, his sister became sick and he stated that he could never become sick. Other people could get colds or pneumonia or perhaps die, but he was immune.

Summarizing the salient features of Henry's immediate reaction to his mother's death, we see an alteration of affect with something like euphoria replacing an expected sadness; violent fantasies; regression to orality; and narcissistic fantasies of self-sufficiency and independence from objects. In addition, there was a marked change in his object relationships. These changes were apparent in all of his relationships. I shall first review that to his sister.

At first, Dorothy seemed to have very little importance for Henry, as indeed he was insisting he needed no one. But soon, as he was showing an increase in oral demands, jealousy of his sister quickly became more pronounced. He was angry when he saw her with food or with drink from her own doctor. He thought this unfair and felt gypped. She, too, was being seen at the clinic. On a couple of occasions, she burst into my office and once managed to sit on my lap. Henry demanded that I throw her out and in anger ran from the office himself, furious with his sister and me. Soon, however, Henry found a new use, a defensive one, for his sister. She seemed to express for him the affects he could not tolerate in himself. He often spoke of how sad Dorothy was, of how much she missed her mother. He told me of her rage when she was being teased at school by children who would say, "Your mother's dead. Your mother's dead." He showed me how she attacked the children who tormented her. One then could see how, in the following weeks, Henry continued to use his sister as a foil for warding off impulses. As he was slowly giving up his regressive orality, saying he no longer needed candy or Cokes, he criticized his sister for still needing them. He took to calling her a baby and made fun of her. He ridiculed her when she cried. This attitude of belittling disapproval of his sister seemed to continue for a long time—for the time he was trying to master his own oral impulses. But gradually one became aware of the fact that a change in his criticism of her was developing. He started to say it was not so bad that she was given candy because she was so small and young. He pitied her. He laughed in an understanding way about her babyishness. Then he himself began to indulge her. He became warm and close to her. He said he would look out for his sister and thought of buying her candy. He could be seen walking up and down the hall of the clinic with his arm around her, consoling her. In a word, there came times when he treated her as a loved child would be treated by a parent, as, in fact, his father could be seen to treat him at the end of each interview.

The vicissitudes of Henry's object relations were further complicated by a new event. After his mother's death Henry had for seven months lived with his father, sister, and a succession of housekeepers. Then, with little warning, he heard that he was to have a new mother, and four months later his father remarried. With the stepmother in the home, Henry's relationship to his sister at once became strained again, with many feelings of rivalry. He gave up indulging Dorothy and resented her relationship with his step-

mother. His view of his sister changed again when his stepmother
took to her bed, stating she was sick.

I should say a word about Henry's stepmother. It soon became
clear that she was a childish woman; younger than her husband,
previously unmarried, she had hoped to acquire a family ready-made.
She did not foresee, and did not seem prepared to accept, the responsibility with which these two, now difficult children presented her.
She intensely resented any reminder of the woman she replaced. She
reacted to her troubles at times by threatening to leave, and at other
times by claiming to be sick and keeping to her bed. When this
happened, Henry vented his rage on his sister and blamed her for
making his stepmother sick.

In Henry's relationship to his sister, then, we see that in the
first months after his mother's death, he used her to express the grief
and anger which he could not tolerate himself. She became a vehicle
for expressing his own unacceptable affects as well as the target of his
projected sense of guilt and blame. As he increasingly identified
himself with some aspects of both parents, he began to treat her as a
parent would a child, as his father treated him, as he would like to
be treated—no doubt also by the mother he had lost.

It is easier to follow Henry's changing relationship to his father
because Henry used his father less defensively than he did his
sister. Immediately after the loss of his mother, his clinging dependence on his father was marked. At the end of each interview he
would attach himself to his father who would address him in baby
talk. At the same time, however, as Henry regressed to orality and
developed fantasies of exaggerated independence, he openly belittled
his father and denied that he needed him.

Then, during the months which followed and before his stepmother appeared on the scene, he increasingly seemed to identify
himself with the self-indulgent and irresponsible aspects of his
father's character. For instance, he showed no concern over his falter-
ing schoolwork. Instead, he spoke repeatedly of certain new fantasies.
He thought he would go with his father alone to Florida and lie
in the sun. He would not go to school, his father would not work,
and there would be no responsibilities. Or his father would buy a
ranch in Texas with ponies. He would ride all day with his father
and would worry about none of the things about which his mother

had been concerned. Sometimes during this period, he played out another version of this fantasy. There was a family living in a house. The family consisted of a boy, a father, and a housekeeper, or, "a mother housekeeper" as she was once called. In this play, boy and father threw mother housekeeper out or locked her in a closet. She was no good and they hated her. (This, in fact, mirrored Henry's general reaction to the real housekeepers whom his father brought home.) Following the ejection of the play housekeeper, the boy would be alone with the father, and they would then always share the same bed. Henry, then, not allowing housekeepers to replace his mother, was tempted to take his dead mother's place himself and form a homosexual relationship with his father. It was during this period that in the interviews Henry wished for a close physical contact with me in spite of the obvious anxiety which this desire caused him.

This warm, anxiety-laden, homosexually colored relationship to his father changed dramatically after Henry learned that he was to have a new mother. The fantasy play just mentioned was given up at once. He renounced his wish to go to Florida with his father and now made fun of his father for having had these plans, which he re- garded as silly. Fantasies of an openly oedipal nature appeared. I shall refer to them in greater detail later when I discuss his relation- ship to his stepmother. But in a word, he claimed a particular relationship to his stepmother and felt he was his father's rival.

Finally, when his stepmother took to her bed, Henry was tempted to revert to an earlier attitude: women were no good; he wished his father had not remarried; it would have been better to have gone to Florida with him and lie in the sun.

In Henry's relationship to his father, we see that following mother's death he became increasingly dependent on his father. He began to hate women and developed fantasies in which he took their place in relation to father. This attempted homosexual solution was abruptly brought to an end when his stepmother appeared on the scene. Now he showed signs of a more frankly oedipal constella- tion, with a concomitant decrease in his anxiety.

Finally, one could follow Henry's changing relationship to women during the time that I knew him. The women who were important to him were, of course, his mother, the housekeepers, and then his stepmother.

As mentioned earlier, Henry's relationship with his mother had been a close and ambivalent one. As he became aware of her progressively serious sickness he suppressed and rejected the angry aspect of his ambivalence. He made efforts to be good; and to please her, he stopped coming to the clinic. After her death, for a great many months, explicit thoughts of his mother seemed almost to have disappeared. Instead, he spoke with continuous abuse, criticism, and anger about the housekeepers. He hated to have them try to take care of him; he resented their very presence, and wanted them to be thrown out. As he had earlier expressed only positive feelings toward his mother, he now expressed only hostility toward the succession of unfortunate housekeepers who had replaced her.

We thus see that with the loss of his mother there occurred a further split in his ambivalent feelings. While negative feelings were directed to the housekeepers, his tender longings for his real mother were revealed only in fantasies involving his relationship with his father. It was therefore particularly striking to observe the eagerness with which he initially accepted his future stepmother. Her presence clearly freed him from the anxiety which attended his homosexual orientation. He arrived at the office very pleased and told me how nice she was, what a perfect mother she would be, and how much she would love him. He maintained that it was he who had proposed to her for his father and she had accepted his proposal. He had convinced her to marry his father. He quickly referred to her as his mother and no longer as his new mother. He shared secrets with her which he could not share with me or with his father.

This carefree "honeymoon," characterized by solely positive feelings toward her, lasted through his father's engagement and for a brief time after the marriage. Gradually, however, reality intruded. His stepmother soon became disillusioned with her family, and felt unable to cope with the children. She began to complain, to have angry outbursts, and from time to time openly voiced thoughts of leaving the family. At other times, she took to her bed claiming she was sick. On these occasions Henry quickly became anxious. He started to blame his sister and then himself, telling me he had been bad at home, had spoken too loudly, or had slammed a door. The self-blame appeared intermittently but nevertheless did lead to his making efforts to be good as he had formerly tried to be good to his dying mother. He told me once he could never really love his stepmother until he was sure she would not go away. As his anxiety over her threatened departure mounted, he was again tempted to renounce her and to wish he had remained alone with his father.

Increasingly, Henry projected blame for his stepmother's illness onto his sister and was furious with her, telling me that what he hated most about the whole situation was to have stepmother go to father and to complain about him. If stepmother complained only to Henry himself, she would not leave the home, but if his parents fought about him, father might kick her out. Either sister or father, then—but not he—would be the cause of stepmother's leaving.

In one interview during this time Henry was as hyperactive, distractible, and restless as he had been following his mother's death. Then he told me that his stepmother was again very sick and in bed. Suddenly he held his hand to his chest, said he had a terrible pain, that he was having a heart attack. When I wondered what he was thinking, he told me that he had just remembered his mother's operation on her chest. Then he became sad and serious and stated that he ought not to come to the clinic and talk and play any longer; instead, he should be at home doing his homework, because his grades were poor. This was certainly the first mention of worry over school that I had heard for many months. His dead mother's injunctions had suddenly come to life again.

During the next few interviews, Henry began for the first time openly to compare his real mother and stepmother. He thought of ways in which they were different; they dressed differently; his first mother liked old furniture, while his stepmother liked modern furniture.

After a time, another series of events occurred in the home which forced Henry to come to terms with the memories of his first mother and the relationship to his stepmother. His stepmother, in her preoccupation with obliterating all traces in the home of the woman she had supplanted, resolved to throw out all the old furniture and have the apartment redecorated. Henry was delighted. He was again hyperactive, euphoric, and joked. He said it was good to get rid of the old furniture. Everything must be new, and the old must be forgotten. Once more he seemed to be waving good-by to his mother and forgetting her. But in the next interviews, he was anxious and sad, and then he mentioned some glass animals. These he regarded as extremely valuable gifts from his real mother. He said they were worth $200. He treasured them. He was afraid his stepmother would throw them out with the furniture. He said he had locked them up where his stepmother could not find them, and she had no right to know of them. He seemed preoccupied and suddenly again referred to his schoolwork, saying that it was poor, that he ought to work harder, and that he should stay at home doing homework rather than come to the clinic and play.

In the next few weeks, as plans were materializing for the apartment to be refurnished, Henry seemed to solve for himself the obvious conflict which he felt between the memory of his mother and the realities of his stepmother. He agreed with his stepmother that the whole apartment should be changed over, but she must agree with him that he could keep his glass animals forever.

DISCUSSION

It is clear that for this eight-year-old boy the loss of his mother seriously disrupted for a time his remaining object relationships. For a while his reaction centered upon regression to orality, anger, and fantasies of violence. The intense anxiety which accompanied this reaction led to his using his surviving objects, especially his sister, primarily for defensive purposes. Her significance as the recipient of his projected grief and anger became paramount.

Later, one might have thought that his passive homosexual orientation to his father could have blocked an acceptance of a relationship to his stepmother. However, this was not the case. Defensively, again, he seemed first of all to use her presence to relieve himself of homosexual anxiety. This was certainly one important reason why he so quickly established a relationship with her. His relationship with her was in fact smooth and seemed idyllic until she threatened to leave him. His anticipated loss of her at once brought to light his ambivalence to her. Again he attempted to suppress his anger toward her, as he had toward his dying mother in the hope of keeping her. Then, as his fear of losing his stepmother increased, he was tempted to give her up and to reunite himself, through identification, with his dead mother. This, I think, ushered in his problem of conflicting loyalties between mother and step-mother. He tried to solve this with a minimum of guilt by keeping them both—his stepmother through her new furniture and his dead mother through her glass animals.

Since Freud (1917) described the normal and the abnormal adult response to loss, much more attention has been paid in psychoanalytic literature to depression than to its normal counterpart—mourning. Freud's characterization of mourning (a painful affect, a loss of interest in the world, an inability to adopt new objects of love, a hypercathexis and gradual withdrawal of libido from all memories of the lost object) remains the classical scientific description, and pertains to adults. Lindemann (1944) described a number of varia-tions from the standard picture of grieving in adults, among them the common occurrence of an inability normally to grieve but with-out the development of melancholia. H. Deutsch (1937) described situations where a normal process of mourning, in adults who experi-ence a loss, does not occur if for some reason the ego lacks strength or is overburdened with other tasks. She suggests that there may be an analogous situation in children, whose ego may not have the resources to undertake the work of grieving. The process of mourn-ing as seen in adults apparently differs from that seen in children. Rochlin, especially in his paper "The Loss Complex" (1959), ex-presses the view that whatever a child's reaction to loss may be, it does not include depression as seen in adults, and his material sug-gests that an adult type of mourning is not common. Bowlby (1960), in a recent article, however, states that the young child's reaction to loss is more similar to the grief of adults.

Three factors, at least, separate a young child subject to an important loss from a bereaved adult: his real state of dependency on adults, his not yet fully incorporated superego, and his relatively undeveloped ego. In regard to the first point, Henry indeed with-drew libidinal investment from his remaining objects with an increase in narcissism to the extent of developing megalomanic fan-tasies of independence, yet his real condition of dependency rein-forced by regression counteracted this tendency, and his demands for dependent gratification were greatly increased.

Henry's superego, as it appeared before his mother's death, was clearly derived from identification with her. Unlike an adult, in whom one would expect a reinforcement of this identification following loss, when Henry's mother died his superego identification with her seemed to disappear. His superego was still strongly dependent for its maintenance on the presence of the object from which it was derived. Then, in his attitude to work, to school, and to his responsibilities, his superego took on characteristics identical to those of his most important remaining object, his father. Only much later, when the threat of losing his stepmother reminded him of his first loss, did his long-forgotten, stern and demanding superego identification with his mother reappear for a time.

The process of mourning requires for its purposes a relatively strong ego unburdened by too many other tasks. Henry's childish ego lacked the strength to harbor consciously the image of the lost object and gradually to decathect its memories. Instead, his reaction to loss seemed to consist in an effort to free his ego from this burden, to deny the painful affect, and to distract itself from any conscious consideration of what he had lost. Rather than coping with the burden of grief work, his ego had to deal with the burden of regression and anxiety.

In conclusion, this case illustrates the profound effect which an important loss—the death of his mother—had on this normal early latency boy: it produced a crisis in his life and in his object relationships, it severely burdened the resources of his ego, and it interrupted his normal development which could be resumed only after a considerable length of time. He did not mourn as an adult might mourn but reacted in ways consistent with his childish condition.

BIBLIOGRAPHY

Bowlby, J. (1960), Grief and Mourning in Infancy and Early Childhood. *This Annual*, XV.
Deutsch, H. (1937), Absence of Grief. *Psa. Quart.*, VI.
Freud, S. (1917), Mourning and Melancholia. *Standard Edition*, XIV. London: Hogarth Press, 1955.
Lindemann, E. (1944), Symptomatology and Management of Acute Grief. *Am. J. Psychiat.*, CI.
Rochlin, G. (1959), The Loss Complex. *J. Am. Psa. Assn.*, VII.

MOURNING AND THE BIRTH OF
A DEFECTIVE CHILD[1]

ALBERT J. SOLNIT, M.D. and MARY H. STARK, M.S.S.
(New Haven)[2]

The study of human crisis permits the extension of our understanding of psychological health and illness and how they overlap. These opportunities become especially fruitful when the observer is also the person offering professional assistance to those whose crisis requires them to seek help.

However, these professional people require a comprehensive theory of human development to clarify and organize their observations and to make possible formulations that lead to a useful course of action. Psychoanalysis is such a theory of human psychology. In recent years the health care professions have had opportunities to integrate insights from this theory into the care of the child and his family in many different crisis situations (Bowlby et al., 1952; Burlingham and A. Freud, 1942; A. Freud, 1953; Jackson, 1942; Lindemann, 1944; MacKeith, 1953; James Robertson, 1953, 1958; Joyce Robertson, 1956; Solnit, 1960; Solnit and Green, 1959; Solnit and Stark, 1959; Spence, 1946, 1947). When a defective child is born, the pediatrician and his colleagues can make observations of the family's reactions to this catastrophic event. These observations may indicate the factors that shape the family's trauma or that lead to the family's adaptive responses.

The material on which this study is based has been collected

[1] Supported by the Children's Bureau, U.S. Department of Health, Education and Welfare; the Connecticut Department of Health; and the Grant Foundation.

[2] From Yale University School of Medicine, Department of Pediatrics and Child Study Center.

We wish to acknowledge with warm appreciation the helpful suggestions and criticisms of Berta Bornstein, Ira Gabrielson, Sally Provence, and Milton J. E. Senn.

Certain aspects of this paper were presented at the Annual Meeting of the American Orthopsychiatric Association in New York, March 25, 1961.

from pediatric, psychiatric, and casework contacts with mothers and their defective children. The theoretical approach to our work is founded on the psychoanalytic explanation of the process of mourning as applied to the mother's reactions to the birth of a defective child (Freud, 1917, 1923; Bibring, 1959, 1961; Janis, 1958a, 1958b). Freud's contributions to the understanding of narcissism and its vicissitudes (1914) are essential for the study of object loss—in our case, the loss of the longed-for healthy child.

The psychological preparation for a new child during pregnancy normally involves the wish for a perfect child and the fear of a damaged child. It is very likely that there is always some discrepancy between the mother's wishes and the actual child; to work out this discrepancy becomes one of the developmental tasks of motherhood that are involved in the establishment of a healthy mother-child relationship. However, when the discrepancy is too great, as in the birth of a defective child, or where the mother's wishes are too unrealistic, a trauma may occur.

The study of pregnancy—what Ernst Kris (1955) termed a normal illness—reveals a loosening up of defenses and the more direct, and at times more threatening, access to unconscious representations, wishes, and scars (fixations). In a normal pregnancy, labor, and delivery, there are psychological rearrangements and achievements necessary for the developmental advances leading to early motherhood (Benedek, 1959; Deutsch, 1945). These changes, often subtle, appear gradually over a period of time, and are best seen in the interacting development of mutuality of mother and child (Erikson, 1950). The mother's anticipation of the baby, especially of the first, is in many ways like adolescent turmoil because the adult psychic structure is gradually prepared for the birth of a new individual and the crystallization of a new unfolding within the self.

The image of the *expected baby* is a composite of representations of the self and of the love objects (mother, husband, father, and siblings). The composite representation includes the image of the expected child which has been conveyed to the expectant mother by her own mother. Each of these kaleidoscopic shifting impressions summon up for recollection and emotional review older issues, conflicts, and fears. This anticipatory process is part of the normal preparation for motherhood. As a preparation it repeats and solves again certain of the basic conflicts and identifications that the expectant mother had with her own mother.

However, this preparatory and adaptive process is abruptly interrupted by the birth of a defective or retarded child. Although the mother's reactions to her defective child are to a significant extent shaped by the type and degree of defect, they also are greatly influenced by her own past experiences with parents and siblings as well as by other significant life events. Conflicts in the woman's relationship to her own mother and in regard to her own femininity are often reawakened during the psychological work of the pregnancy (Bibring, 1959, 1961). The vicissitudes of this psychological preparation (Janis, 1958b) are outside the scope of this presentation, but an awareness of these preparatory developments in the mother will heighten the understanding of the impact of the disappointment, feeling of helplessness, and sense of failure that the individual woman experiences when the child she bears is obviously blighted.

There are many aspects of the diagnosis and treatment of defective children and their families which it will not be possible to encompass in this paper. However, the thesis of this paper will be of little value if one does not at the same time take into account specific factors, such as familial disease, previous trauma to the mother, family constellation, the genesis of the retardation, and the severity and characteristic of the defect. It will be noted that "defective" and "retarded" are used interchangeably in this paper, simply indicating that all of the children referred to are retarded and that the defect is more or less apparent.

In an experiment created by nature, the birth of a defective or deviant child, one can observe more directly the "sudden" loss of the baby that was expected; and the "sudden" birth of a feared, threatening, and anger-evoking child. The course of motherhood, a developmental process, is influenced by the characteristics of the baby, first by his appearance and gradually by his responses. Significant deviations, such as gross retardation or obvious congenital defects, may limit or interrupt the mother's developing capacity to accept the new child who is totally dependent upon her.

In a recent article, "Is Grief a Disease?" George L. Engel (1961) has drawn attention to the importance of the mourning process in human development. Borrowing from Freud's (1917) and Lindemann's (1944) work, Engel describes mourning in terms that are useful for this presentation. "Grief is the characteristic response to the loss of a valued object, be it a loved person, a cherished possession, a job, status, home, country, an ideal, a part of the body, etc. Uncomplicated grief runs a consistent course, modified mainly by the abruptness of the loss, the nature of the preparation for the event, and the significance for the survivor of the lost object."

In the mother's mourning reaction to the loss of the healthy child, her wishes for and expectations of the desired child are crushed by the birth of the defective child. Her anxious fears of having a damaged child are realized. These disappointed, highly charged longings for the normal child may be recalled, intensely felt, and gradually discharged in order to reduce the impact of the loss of the expected loved child. This process, which requires time and repetition, can liberate the mother's feelings and interests for a more realistic adaptation. The mourning process makes it possible to progress from the initial phase of numbness and disbelief; to the dawning awareness of the disappointment and feeling of loss with the accompanying affective and physical symptoms; to the last phase of the grief reaction in which intense re-experiencing of the memories and expectations gradually reduce the hypercathexis of the wish for the idealized child.

In childbearing, the simultaneous loss of one child—the expected and narcissistically invested one—and adaptation to the deviant or defective child makes a demand that is very likely to be overwhelming. There is no time for working through the loss of the desired child before there is the demand to invest the new and handicapped child as a love object.

It is as though the work of preparing for the new child has suddenly become useless. Established libidinal pathways and attachments are abruptly terminated, and at the same time a demand for new libidinal cathexes is made.[3] The unexpected aspect of the birth at a time of physiological and psychological depletion is an essential factor in the traumatizing effect of the experience.

Thus, at the time the mother is prepared to be nurtured by the satisfaction of her creative experience, and to begin nurturing her

[3] To some extent a similar situation occurs when there is the unexpected birth of twins or of a premature child.

child, her adaptive capacities are sapped because she has failed to create what she intended, and feels damaged by the "new" child— the defective organism to whom she has given birth. Just as pregnancy itself is a normal crisis in which there is no turning back, so defect or retardation is a condition which cannot be undone. The irretrievable nature of the retardation adds to the mother's trapped feeling—she has failed to achieve what she has so laboriously prepared herself to create or produce. Fathers, too, will have similar or related reactions. For the purpose of this discussion, and because the mother's vulnerability is much greater, we limit our primary considerations to the mother.

Although each situation has to be individually analyzed for the highly specific considerations essential for planning and treatment, in our experience there are two extreme reaction patterns that delimit the continuum of the pathological reactions to the birth of a defective child. The manifest reaction and the underlying feelings should be differentiated. At the one extreme is the guilt feeling leading to the mother's manifest dedication of herself unremittingly and exclusively to the welfare of the retarded child. At the other extreme is the parents' manifest intolerance of the child and the almost irresistible impulse to deny their relationship to the child. The underlying narcissistic injury is intolerable. The following example illustrates the first extreme.

Jimmy, the first-born child of a young couple, was severely retarded. His mother was unable to care for her second child, Danny, who was normal, because of her "devotion" to Jimmy. Her inability to accept the reality of the retarded child began when she left her pediatrician who had advised institutionalization shortly after Jimmy's birth. It became necessary for the paternal grandmother to live with them in order to organize their household and to care for Danny shortly after he was born. The father's dissatisfaction with this plan finally resulted in a request for consultation in regard to long-term planning for Jimmy.

At the other extreme, Arnold's mother had apparently accepted the interpretation of slow development in her son soon after a difficult birth. During his first year, the parents arranged for Arnold to be placed in a foster home because they felt unable to care for him. From the many medical recommendations sought, the parents favored that one which said institutionalization at a training school would be advisable. Arnold was only slightly retarded and made good strides in his development at the foster home, eliminating the need for a training school. The parents said they could accept Arnold only if it could be guaranteed that he would be "perfectly normal." Otherwise, they feared he would "damage" their family life. Their move to another locale, which made it impractical for them to see Arnold, was to some extent determined by the father's occupation, but it also represented their effort to strengthen the denial of their relationship to their son in order to avoid the intolerable narcissistic injury evoked by their contacts with him.

There are elements of both denial and guilt involved in the reactions of parents to the birth of a retarded or defective child. However, the defenses represent the modes of warding off depression, guilt, and feelings of narcissistic injury. The defenses are selected from the interaction of the individual's characteristic patterns of defense and influenced by the predominance of the painful affect evoked by the birth of a defective child. By taking into account the parents' feelings of loss, defeat, and resentment about their defective child, and their individual ways of coping with their feelings, the interpretation of the child's diagnosis and its implications can be made more effective.

When the mother wards off her feelings of grief by establishing a guilty, depressed attachment to the retarded child she may fail to relate adequately to other members of the family because she feels she must give her life to the care of the damaged child. Conversely, the mother may identify with her defective child. In identifying with her defective offspring, the mother feels narcissistically wounded. This narcissistic injury is often intolerable, because the mother feels painfully defective as she is caring for her retarded child. The mother's withdrawal then becomes a denial of the needs of this child, which the following example illustrates.

Sally, two years of age, the second of two girls, had been examined by two doctors. When she was eight months old, a substitute for her doctor (the family doctor was ill) told the mother that Sally was a Mongol and "there would be trouble later on." This mother, aged twenty-nine, worried about the above statement for nearly a year. Her husband thought she was foolish to worry. Both parents knew Sally's development was delayed, but the father thought she would "catch up" in time. Finally, the mother was able to ask her family doctor about Sally. She had hoped that since he had not mentioned it, perhaps it was not so. He told her that he had been concerned about Sally since birth and agreed with the diagnosis of Mongolism. He said he had not brought it to her attention because nothing could be done about it. He pointed out the fact that her eyes were far apart. He agreed to arrange a consultation for Sally with a specialist in child development.

The mother told the social worker, who worked with the consultant, that she thought Mongolism was a strange disease, and she blamed herself for Sally's condition. As a child, the mother's poor vision required her to attend a sight-saving class in school. She associated the doctor's comment about Sally's eyes with her own visual defect. She also blamed herself for marrying a man twenty years her senior; she had read that older parents tend to produce retarded children.

Because of her painful feelings of inadequacy the mother had found herself withdrawing from Sally and spending more time with her seven-year-old daughter who provided evidence of her mother's adequacy. Sally was kept in a crib a good part of the day.

As this mother was given a descriptive picture of the extent of Sally's retardation (her motor development and adaptive behavior was about that of an eighteen-month-old child) and some suggestions regarding the everyday care of her child, she began to realize that Sally's future was not so hopeless. When she could talk about her disappointment and fears for Sally's future, her own poor vision, her marriage, etc., she felt less guilty. Her pent-up energies were then released to be used constructively for both of her little girls. She devoted more time to Sally, provided her with suitable toys, and began to explore nursery school opportunities that would be available when she was older.

The lack of opportunity to discuss the child's diagnosis can create a situation in which the parents feel overwhelmed and unable to gauge the reality of their child's retarded development. Denial then serves to ward off the anxiety and depression. The following vignette illustrates such a situation.

Susan, a first child, was born abroad when her father was in Service. The baby was born in the seventh month of the mother's pregnancy, weighing 3 lbs., 4 oz. Three convulsions occurred on the second day of her life. Because of her prematurity, she remained in the hospital for eight weeks. No definite diagnosis was discussed with the parents. This was a difficult time for the parents because Susan was in a critical condition and fed poorly. When Susan was brought home she continued to be a source of anxiety to the parents because she failed to thrive. By eight months, she was not rolling over, and she was returned to the hospital for further studies. The parents said they would never forget the words of the physician at the time of her second hospital discharge: "You might as well put her in an institution and let her die in peace." The harshness of such words added greatly to the suffering already experienced by the parents and interfered with the mother's recognition of the reality and with her mourning reaction. The mother blamed herself for not seeking out her obstetrician a week before delivery when she was having some abdominal pains. She reasoned, if she had gone to him then, her child would not have been retarded. The thought of institutionalization caused her to cringe with anger.

It was not until there was ample opportunity to review their hopes and to discuss their fears for Susan that the parents were able to utilize a thorough evaluation and interpretation of the child's development in a continuing relationship with the pediatrician and social worker. One might say that interpretation began with what was the parents' reality, their state of grief, and then under the guidance of a skillful pediatrician they were prepared to deal with the reality of their child's condition.

In many instances the initial diagnosis has been made accurately and with adequate consultation, and has been presented to the parents in a simple, straight-forward manner, taking into account their fears and questions. However, several months later the physician is surprised to hear from a colleague or neighboring clinic that his patient is "shopping" and has presented a distorted picture of the situation. Upon reviewing this very common complication of interpretation, we have been able to demonstrate in many instances that the parents' distortion was an unwitting one that stemmed from two main sources: (1) the inability to tolerate their painful reaction to the reality of the diagnosis or to accept the first diagnosis; and (2) the lack of what might be termed follow-up. Once the physician has conveyed the initial diagnosis to the parents there is a tendency to think the interpretation of mental retardation is completed when it has only begun. The main reason for this misconception by the physician is that he has not understood the repetitive aspect of the mourning process in the mother's reaction. If the therapist has not sensed or understood the need that parents have to grieve about their tragic "loss," he will feel ineffectual and reproached by the parents when they indicate their need for repeated opportunities to review and to re-examine the past in the current "loss."

Interpretation is a continuing process which utilizes interviews with the professional person to establish a sense of confidence and trust that will promote the parents' gradual understanding of the child's defect. In this atmosphere of trust and confidence the parents are enabled to express their critical and fearful questions to the pediatrician; and the physician can describe what is known and what is not known about the retarded child in a manner that increases the parents' understanding. This understanding refers to objective and subjective components—to the comprehension of the child's condition, and to the realization by the parents of their inner reactions of disappointment, resentment, humiliation, and loneliness. Many of the subjective reactions will be experienced as repetitions of previous losses or disappointments. The pediatrician, nurse, and social worker should not make interpretations of unconscious feelings or thoughts; or attempt to make connections for the patient between past experiences of loss and the current subjective responses to the birth of the retarded child. The psychiatrist who otherwise may interpret unconscious conflicts also may avoid such interpretations because of the narcissistic involvement during the mourning period.

The medical personnel should clarify the reality of the child's condition as the parent is able to bring up each one of his questions and fears. This clarification which strengthens the reality-testing capacity of the parents will indirectly reduce the distortions responsible for unrealistic connections between past and present. In this way the dynamic interpretation of the reality aids the working through of the mourning process as one of the major avenues to the mastery of the traumatic experience.

Ideally, the parents, especially the mother, will experience what Freud (1917) described: "Each single one of the memories and situations of expectancy which demonstrate the libido's attachment to the lost object is met by the verdict of reality." It is the physician or social worker's responsibility to facilitate this process, which is gradual, repetitive, and which requires that the "verdict of reality" be offered in a useful manner. This implies that at every stage of translating the defective child's condition to the parents, the language, sequence of thoughts, and focus of the interpretation will take into account other important factors involved in the parents' reactions. These factors would include the stage of the mother's development, her current situation, and the ways in which her past experiences, cultural and personal, influence her adaptation.

As we have indicated earlier, there are many aspects of working with the parents of retarded children that we are not considering in this presentation. One aspect is the mother's relative neglect of the other children if her attachment to the retarded child is abnormally intense. Another aspect that needs to be emphasized is how often the normal child reacts with fear, depression, and guilt when he has a retarded sibling. There are many measures that can be taken to help the normal sibling of a retarded child which cannot be discussed in this paper.

It becomes clear that the unexpected advent of a retarded child can have a traumatizing effect on the development of the mother and on the interactions and elaborations of family relationships. The ghost of the desired, expected healthy child continues to interfere with the family's adaptation to the defective child if the mourning process becomes fixed as the sustained atmosphere of the family.

DISCUSSION

Interpretation of mental retardation to parents should be synchronized to the mourning reaction. In this presentation, interpretation refers to a dynamic continuing process of successive translations and clarifications, rather than to a single definitive explanation. Such interpretations are communications that facilitate the recognition of reality and promote one's adaptation to the demands of reality. The effectiveness of these communications depends upon a relationship with the interpreter that will enable the parent to express highly charged feelings and to remember the past as it relates to the present. What are referred to as interpretations for the mother with the abnormal child are also the principles upon which are based the explanations and anticipatory guidance of the mother with the normal child.

Coping with the outer reality of a child with a congenital defect and the inner reality of feeling the loss of a desired, normal child requires a great deal of mental work. Such psychic work is slow and emotionally painful, and it proceeds through the gradual and repeated discharge of intense feelings and memories. These mental and emotional reactions enable the parent to recognize and adapt to the reality, the retarded child.

The mother's reaction to a dead child is different from her reaction to the birth of a defective child (Provence, 1961), though certain aspects of these differing mourning reactions are similar. In both situations there are: feelings of loss; intense longings for the desired child; resentment of the cruel blow that life's experience has dealt; and the guilt that the dead or defective child may evoke by representing the consequences of unacceptable feelings or thoughts. The main difference between the two reactions is the persistent effect on the mother of the living defective child who realistically requires care and attention. The daily impact of the retarded child on the mother is unrelenting. Attempts to withdraw libido from the "lost," normal child are disrupted by the demands to cathect the living, blighted child. When the defective baby dies, the libido can initially be withdrawn and then become available for new attachments without the daily corrosive reminder of failure. Probably, the process of mourning cannot be as effective when the retarded child survives.

When a person is mourning, their ability to recognize, evaluate, and adapt to reality is often significantly impaired. It is for this reason that the physician often turns to the father or grandparents in the planning for the newborn defective child. Sometimes immediate planning may require this. However, from the point of view of the mother's development and the child's care, it is essential to gauge the mother's mourning reaction in order to know how and when to help her to take an active role in planning for her child's care. The continuation of mourning into a persistent, depressed, self-reproachful state may be encouraged if the mother's mourning reaction is not understood, and if the care of the child as well as the planning are carried out without her active participation. Obviously the mother needs a great deal of support and time in order to deal with her feelings of failure. The father, too, will require such aid.

The gradual investment of feeling for the child who was born cannot be hurried and will proceed along a realistic line if the mother's capacities to think, feel, and talk about her disappointment, sense of failure, and feelings of helplessness are not impaired by the atmosphere of the hospital and the attitudes of her physicians and nurses. Surely the medical personnel's feelings of helplessness and defeat in regard to the retarded child are among the important reasons that parents may fail to receive understanding support. A common obstacle to the mother's adaptation is the urgency that the physician may feel in developing a plan because of his fear that procrastination may damage the mother. One sees the exaggerated effect of the physician's anxiety in those situations in which there is the conviction that the defective child should not be seen by the mother, but should be rushed away to an institution so the mother will not form a guilt-laden attachment to the child. This attitude reflects a misunderstanding about: the precision of the prognosis; what constitutes the mother's preparation for and reaction to the newborn child; and the physician's own reaction to the situation of his patient being defective. A correct understanding of the crisis will lead to a conservative attitude toward prognosticating; an expectation that the mother will need time and help to deal with her own reactions to having a defective child; and the awareness of the physician's own feeling of helplessness and resentment that his work has failed to produce a normal child.

Often this behavior of the medical personnel to the birth of a defective child mirrors the mother's psychological state. By wishing to send the child to an institution before the mother sees the child, they are reacting partly to their own feelings of helplessness and failure; and partly they are dramatizing the loss of the normal child that the mother feels. Perhaps there is the unconscious notion that if the defective child is sent away before being seen by the mother she will have a better chance to regain the lost, normal or idealized child. It is equally wrong to insist that a mother and father see a malformed child when they wish to avoid it and express their strong opposition to the experience.

The physicians and nurses can invest the deviant child realistically for the mother. This provides her with an opportunity to take an active role in planning for her child; to increase her self-esteem through the evidence that she can feed and care for the child; and to receive the satisfaction of those reactions that the retarded child demonstrates in response to the mothering care.

If the defective baby is a second or third child, and the older children are normal, the impact may be somewhat less though it follows the same pattern of mourning. If the retardation defect is not evident at birth but only gradually becomes apparent to mother and physician in the first year or two, the mourning reaction is less acute, but its structure is very similar. That is, there may be a nagging fear that the child's development is lagging and a gradual awareness of the child's inability to respond. In this more gradually developing situation the difficulty in recognizing, identifying, and adapting to the reality of the child's retarded development may be drawn out over a long period of time. However, the gradualness of the recognition may also strengthen the denial of the reality, leading to the more tortuous and chronic mourning reaction. In a sense the parents may become fixated between the recognition of the deviation of their child and the denial of its implications. For example, the parents may steadfastly deny the child's defect or slow development, but continue to seek special help to enable their child to overcome his difficulties. In a recent discussion, Helen L. Beck (1959) stated: "The parents who come to a mental retardation clinic are as a rule quite aware of the fact that they have a problem. They may, however, deny its nature."

In order to facilitate the work of the mourning process, the mother needs: physical rest; an opportunity to review her thoughts and feelings about the wished-for child; a realistic interpretation and investment of the feared, unwanted child by doctors and nurses; and an active role in planning for and caring for the newborn child as she is able. These are the measures through which the mother can minimize or overcome the trauma of giving birth to a retarded child. The physician, nurse, and social worker will take into account these dynamic psychological reactions of the mother in order that their use of the interpretative process becomes an essential aid to the mother in mastering this crisis in her development.

Summary

Our work in psychoanalysis, child development, pediatrics, and social work has reflected a continuing interest in the mutuality of theory and clinical work. The present paper arose from our observations that the theory of the mourning process was essential in order to understand the depressed reactions of certain mothers to the birth of their children. Although this could be observed most clearly and dramatically when a defective child was born, it was apparent to a lesser degree in the birth of children who were not overtly or significantly abnormal. One mother's depressed mourning reaction occurred when a son was born. In later years she said that it took her three months to resign herself to the loss of a daughter and to accept her son.

Another interest served by this paper is the opportunity for the application of insights from the study of human behavior to the care of the child in a family. The critical application by pediatric colleagues of suggestions and explanations resulting from this study has sharpened the analysts's clinical work and theoretical deductions. Observing and theorizing are reciprocal activities. While the pediatrician can make certain observations that are not available to the analyst, the former needs a general theory of human behavior to help him organize and comprehend his observations. Certain of the theoretical and clinical formulations in psychoanalysis suggest applications in a nonanalytic setting. Often these are guides to be used in child rearing or in the prevention of trauma when a child is physically ill. The pediatrician is in a position to apply many of these insights and to raise questions that stem from his clinical experiences. In a recent symposium on psychosomatic aspects of pediatrics, Anna Freud (1961) said: "I can only say that if I were a pediatrician I would start a fight for the pediatrician's influence from the start."

In our investigation of the grief reaction of mothers who have given birth to defective children, we were able to demonstrate that the physician's awareness of the mourning process enabled him to provide effective therapeutic help to the mother and her child. Additionally, the physician's awareness then extended to the concept that a mother's depressed reaction to the birth of a normal child might reflect her feeling of loss because of a significant discrepancy between her expected or wished-for image of the child and the actual normal child.

BIBLIOGRAPHY

Beck, H. L. (1959), Counselling Parents of Retarded Children. *Children*, VI.

Benedek, T. (1959), Parenthood As a Developmental Phase. *J. Am. Psa. Assn.*, VII.

Bibring, G. L. (1959), Some Considerations of the Psychological Processes in Pregnancy. *This Annual*, XIV.

—— (1961), A Study of the Psychological Processes in Pregnancy and of the Earliest Mother-Child Relationships. I: Some Propositions and Comments. *This Annual*, XVI.

Bowlby, J., Robertson, J., & Rosenbluth, D. (1952), A Two-Year-Old Goes to Hospital. *This Annual*, VII.

Burlingham, D. & Freud, A. (1942), *Young Children in Wartime*. London: Allen & Unwin.

Deutsch, H. (1945), *The Psychology of Women*, II. New York: Grune & Stratton.

Engel, G. L. (1961), Is Grief a Disease? A Challenge for Medical Research. *Psychosom. Med.*, XXIII.

Erikson, E. H. (1950), *Childhood and Society*. New York: Norton.

Freud, A. (1953), Film Review: A Two-Year-Old Goes to Hospital. *Int. J. Psa.*, XXXIV.

—— (1961), In: *Psychosomatic Aspects of Pediatrics*, ed. R. MacKeith & J. Sandler. London: Pergamon Press.

Freud, S. (1914), On Narcissism: An Introduction. *Standard Edition*, XIV. London: Hogarth Press, 1957.

—— (1917), Mourning and Melancholia. *Standard Edition*, XIV. London: Hogarth Press, 1957.

—— (1923), *The Ego and the Id*. London: Hogarth Press, 1927.

Jackson, E. B. (1942), Treatment of the Young Child in the Hospital. *Am. J. Orthopsychiat.*, XII.

Janis, I. L. (1958a), *Psychological Stress*. New York: Wiley.

—— (1958b), Emotional Inoculation: Theory and Research on Effects of Preparatory Communications. In: *Psychoanalysis and the Social Sciences*, V. New York: International Universities Press.

Kris, E. (1955), Personal communication.

Lindemann, E. (1944), Symptomatology and Management of Acute Grief. *Am. J. Psychiat.*, CI.

MacKeith, R. (1953), Children in Hospital: Preparation for Operation. *Lancet*, II.

Provence, S. (1961), Personal communication.

Robertson, James (1953), Film: *A Two-Year-Old Goes to Hospital*. London: Tavistock Clinic; New York: New York University Library.

—— (1958), *Young Children in Hospital*. New York: Basic Books.

Robertson, Joyce (1956), A Mother's Observations on the Tonsillectomy of Her Four-Year-Old Daughter. With Comments by Anna Freud. *This Annual*, XI.

Spence, J. C. (1946), *The Purpose of the Family: A Guide to the Care of Children*. London: Epworth Press.

—— (1947), Care of Children in Hospital. *Brit. Med. J.*, I.

Solnit, A. J. (1960), Hospitalization: An Aid to Physical and Psychological Health in Childhood. *A.M.A. J. Dis. Child.*, XCIX.

—— & Green, M. (1959), Psychologic Considerations in the Management of Deaths on Pediatric Hospital Services. I: The Doctor and the Child's Family. *Pediatrics*, XXIV.

—— & Stark, M. (1959), Pediatric Management of School Learning Problems of Underachievement. *New Eng. J. Med.*, CCLXI.

TERMINATION OF TREATMENT AS A LOSS[1]

HELEN D. WALLACH, M.D. (Boston)[2]

The therapy of an eight-year-old boy, Billy, provided an opportunity to study the termination of treatment as an experience of object loss. This boy's reactions illustrate in a particularly vivid manner phenomena which occur with less intensity during the termination of many cases because his mother's early death had made Billy especially vulnerable to the loss of a woman with whom he had a relationship.

His reaction to the loss of his female therapist was the more intense, since termination was not then therapeutically indicated, but necessitated when the therapist left the clinic. The early loss of his mother had not yet been adequately worked through. This unfortunate circumstance, the premature termination, gave ample evidence that this child experienced current losses as a recapitulation of his earlier traumatic experiences. Loss had so distorted his identification, his oedipal conflicts, and particularly both his castration fears and wishes, and expectation of loss had become so much a part of his character, that only prolonged therapy or analysis might have altered this basic constellation.

Billy was seen regularly once a week for ten months and twice a week for another ten months in psychoanalytically oriented play therapy. The loss of the therapist became a major reality during the last three months of therapy.

Billy was originally brought to the clinic at age six by his stepmother and father. They had many complaints. The chief ones were his hostile behavior to his little half brother, whom he would laugh-

[1] This paper was presented at the Tenth Anniversary Symposium, the Child Psychiatry Unit, Massachusetts Mental Health Center, Harvard Medical School. The symposium was devoted to "Psychoanalytic Studies in Object Loss and Depression."

[2] Physician, Massachusetts Mental Health Center (Boston Psychopathic Hospital), Child Psychiatry Unit. Assistant in Psychiatry, Harvard Medical School.

ingly push down, and secretive stealing of his stepmother's stockings and panties, at first from the trash can, and later from her bureau, until in desperation she began giving him her discarded clothes. He wore these under his own clothes because he liked the way they felt. He sometimes said he wanted to be a girl. The parents feared that he would become a homosexual, yet they also complained that he had been caught kissing a little girl under the porch, and that he had put his hand under his mother's skirt to touch her stockings.

Billy's history was a succession of losses. His mother had died when he was twenty-two months old, but she had already been lost to him in his ninth month when she suffered a respiratory and circulatory arrest during an operation and became decerebrate, a writhing, grunting, totally disoriented creature. Billy had been taken to see her at the hospital in the hope that she would recognize him, and after her death he visited her grave. From his ninth month until he was four, Billy lived with his father in his paternal grand-parents' home, and his grandmother became his substitute mother. The loss of the second mother figure, the grandmother, followed the remarriage of his father when Billy was four years old. Four months later Billy had a tonsillectomy, and five months after this illness the first rival was born, a boy. Billy was not openly jealous. Rather, he cried and sulked, particularly when his stepmother paid attention to Billy. Seven months after the first rival came a seven-month prema-ture boy who died a week after birth. When told of the baby's death, Billy smiled, but at night he cried and screamed, and a month later he developed abdominal pain and had an appendectomy.

Two more boys were born, one when Billy was six years nine months old, just before he started treatment at our clinic, and one when he was seven years eleven months old and had already been in treatment for a year. Thus, Billy had three living half brothers.

Billy was perfectly aware of his past. His rationalized view was that he was much luckier than his brothers, having had three mothers instead of just one. He said that his first mother was the best, almost as good as Mary, God's wife. She was so tiny when she died that he could not remember her name. She was in Heaven caring for the baby angels, but she could not see him. Only God could see down from Heaven. His next mother was his grandmother, and then his daddy married his mummy now.

In this complicated history one can see a steady progression of object loss; the grandmother partially compensated for the loss of the mother and then was lost herself. The stepmother replaced the grandmother and then was lost to the siblings, becoming further and further removed as each sibling was born, leaving the child to increasing rage and increasing symptomatology.

Billy was a strutting, stocky little boy with a rather angry, blustering manner. He did not initially appear effeminate in any way. In treatment he showed marked sadism, voyeurism, exhibitionism, and intense sexual curiosity, all increased at any implied loss of me. Such sexual concerns were often accompanied by a smirking, salacious manner. In Billy's angry view, something from outside was always interrupting our relationship: vacations, illness, other children. He could not accept his fantasies that his own murderous impulses drove me away, but constantly projected them onto external events. There was a persistent fantasy that if he changed in some way, he might prevent the threatened loss. The major way of changing was for him to become a girl, although there were variations.

The illustrative examples I am citing follow the course of treatment. Early, Billy asked what other children came to see me about and what they did, claiming angrily that he did not care if they came anyhow. He then ordered me to take out the soldiers, the doctor kit, and the red paint; laughing savagely, he painted the soldiers with stinging painful medicine, and said, "I know this is hurting, but it will make you better." He threw clay at me, simultaneously asking how much time he had left; then he sat down on the little chair saying he wanted to be a baby, but immediately moved to the big chair saying he wanted to be a big boy. He obviously considered my interest in other children a potential loss. His natural sibling rivalry having been intensified and made more desperate by this expectation of loss, he reacted to this in his own highly characteristic way with increased sadism and a frantic shifting of identifications from baby to adult.

Several months after the beginning of treatment, Billy brought an armful of candy and ice cream with him, and then stood at the window shouting at the children outside to beat it, and saying he would beat them up. When I restrained him from running out to do so, implying that this behavior did not please me, he suddenly became very obsequious and conciliatory to the children and threw all his sweets out to them. He anxiously begged me to tell him how much time he still had with me and pleaded with me to count out the seconds of the last minute so he would not miss anything. In the following sessions, Billy went to the candy and ice-cream machines to get food. One day he chose cheese and crackers, and asked me which lever to pull, and I by mistake told him the wrong one. He was both furious and frantic. He ran desperately through the halls asking everyone he met for more money without waiting to receive it. In a rage he demanded to be told whether other children received food from me. For a month thereafter he did not cease to abuse me for my mistake. One day when he was still talking bitterly of "the food you didn't get for me," he suddenly stopped and, in a most suggestive and seductive voice, invited me to lie down on the desk so that he could examine me. When I refused, he wanted to put on a pair of my overshoes; and then as if by accident, he fell to the floor trying to look under my skirt. He pleaded and begged in a girlish voice and then threatened that he would not come back if I did not let him look.

For Billy, to be orally deprived by a woman was equivalent to losing her, and he defended himself by identifying with her, a genitally deprived individual. He had to confirm whether I was such a creature, and tremendous anxiety accompanied his exploration.

When we discussed the summer vacation, he at first became subdued. Without warning, he fell off his chair into the doll house, banging his genitals so that he cried out in pain. He furiously accused me of not having warned him that he was falling. A moment later he had cut his finger on the desk drawer and said that he might die of an infection. He announced that he, too, was going away on a vacation, and he did indeed run away from home the next day for a few hours. When I saw him after this incident, he was angry and said that he did not want to see me. He talked of people who died and went away and never came back. He ran out into the hall several times saying that he was angry because I wanted to see him, not because I was going away. He shot at me with a toy gun, and then played checkers, captured my men and said he would keep them forever. He demanded to know the names of all the children who came to see me and if I gave them food.

In the final session before we stopped for the summer, when I acknowledged his distress about my going away and his fear of my never coming back, he told me a dream he had had the night before. Billy and his father go to look for his little half brother John who is badly hurt and has been sent to the cemetery. (Billy knew the difference between cemetery and hospital, but in the dream they were condensed.) They arrive at a house at the edge of the cemetery and are standing on the porch with the man who owns it, when some terrifying dummies come out the door. Billy and his father try to keep the dummies back, but the house owner says that if they hurt them John will never come back or get well. Dummies (who, I think, represent a sadistic, dead mother figure, perhaps a condensation of the two words "dead mummy") take Billy and father into the house and give them many painful needles. When they are at last released, they look for John in the cemetery, but they find him at home in bed getting better. Billy and I then talked of his feeling that I would go forever like a dead person, and he then wanted to know what girls I saw in the office and what girls the other doctors saw. He apparently felt that he would be replaced by a girl. Certainly his fantasy was that someone else, probably a girl, would be favored over him and that he would be abandoned unless he changed. I told Billy that I liked girls, and also boys, and I liked him, Billy, a boy. He said in amazement, "You mean you'd like me even if I were in rags?"

On resumption of treatment in September, Billy continued to be very concerned with my leaving him for other children, preferring them to him. He defended himself as before by identifying with me, but a new aspect of this conflict-ridden solution arose, namely, the struggle against the feminine identification with its threat of castration. For Billy this everyday struggle of the male child was distorted because feminine identification was so important for him. It was his chief means of preserving the female object which in his fantasy was always about to be snatched from him.

Soon after my return, the following sequence of play occurred over a two-month period. He asked if there were new toys for him; finding there were none, he took out the doctor kit and put the nurse's hat on himself. Then he removed it and put it on me, trying to touch me, smirking to himself. He complained that the doctor kit was not the same as last time, implying that another child had tampered with it. He angrily said he would be the doctor, not the nurse. A week later, when I had to cancel an appointment, he responded in the following session by increased interest in the doctor game. He assumed that I had been ill when I was absent. He played with two dolls calling them boys aged eight and five. The eight-year-old (Billy's age) had broken a leg falling from a tree. The leg would have to be operated on and maybe removed. While examining the leg, Billy also surreptitiously examined the genital area. In the next moment he began to boast how strong he was and how he could lift the big office chair. He announced also that the ward nurses were his girl friends. Here in sequence is his fantasy that I was ill, that is, lost, and the question of whether or not the boy should have his leg amputated, representing feminine identification. There was a loud protest from Billy's masculine side in his boasts of strength and male prowess with the nurses.

For some time we discussed the fact that small boys could not marry big ladies, when Billy announced that at school he really had a girl friend of his own who was seven years old. This rather forced male identification did not last. It fell under the pressure of what Billy considered another deprivation by me: Billy received a Christmas present from me, an airplane model, which he did not like. After rejecting the gift, he played the doctor game. This time the older doll was a boy; and the younger, a girl. The boy had appendicitis which he had gotten by doing something his mother had forbidden: putting a bee in his mouth and swallowing it. At this point in the game, the sex of the doll changed abruptly. *She* must have her stomach cut open with a stinging painful heat machine, and she might die. When she was bandaged up, Billy pointed to the two holes in the Bandaid and said, "She does not like those." He planned a second operation to repair the holes, and also the "third hole," pointing to the umbilicus. He then ignored the doctor game for a week, spending his time playing with a teen-age girl doll in an effeminate way, saying how pretty she was, undressing her carefully with much attention to the underclothes. About ten days after the "holes" game, Billy returned to the theme. The two dolls were this time both boys. Billy cured the holes by an operation and while doing so, he became very silly and excited. He fell on the floor several times, landing the last time with his hands on my feet, trying to look under my skirt. In the following hour he looked at the picture of an airplane, calling the rows of windows holes and said, "You know what? There are guns hidden inside those holes!" Next he had a puppet show in which the little boy Dick wanted to date the baby girl. The girl went to change her clothes, and returned changed into a grown woman, the mother. Dick asked the father if he could kiss the mother, and the father shouted, "No! Kissing is bad! It will give you germs and make you sick!" Father slapped Dick.

Here two major determinants to his feminine identification are evident: his oedipal conflicts and fears, as well as his fantasies of abandonment by a mother figure.

Treatment stopped when I took a leave of absence from the clinic. For Billy, termination represented a new real loss of a mother figure after a relationship of two years, but before the early loss was adequately dealt with. During our work on termination, which covered three months, Billy regressed at first and denied the impending loss by hyperactivity, eating, and getting things instead of losing me. The more infantile oral regression was soon limited by ego and superego with such remarks as, "See, I can stop myself eating so much," and, "I only need four candies today." Projection was even more prominent than during therapy, for it was always some other child who was to blame for his rejection.

I told Billy about stopping treatment three months ahead; his immediate reaction was to ignore me. However, he began to gorge on candy, and asked to borrow games from the next office as if there were not enough in mine. In the same hour he played hide and seek, and tried to hide in my coat, saying he liked it because it was black. He became overactive, leaping about the office, jumping from the desk to the chair. He did not hurt himself as he had before the previous summer vacation, and showed his awareness of this increase in ego strength by saying, "I could have fallen off that chair, but I didn't."

In the first session following the announcement of termination, when I asked him about his first mother, he told me, "She is dead. Dead is your body goes to sleep, and you go to Heaven or Hell. My mother is in Heaven being a mother to the baby angels. Lucky me, I have three mothers and my brothers have only one."

In the second session he was very quiet, ate candy continuously, and asked to be read to. He told me that on his way over he had imagined that I would not be at the clinic, but he had planned to come anyway to make sure. He said that he had needed half a bag of candy last time and he certainly needed that much again, but he did not know why.

In the next three weeks, Billy showed a wide variety of attempts to deal with the impending loss. He became more openly hostile and directly rejecting of me with an "I don't care" attitude. He was demanding and then would attempt to control his demands. He tried to bribe me with gifts, implying that he could provide not only for himself but also for me. About six weeks after I had told him we were stopping, he said he did not want to come at all and wanted to play with his friends at home instead.

The struggle with feminine identification became more intense. Billy arrived one day saying that he had broken his toe by picking at it, which he was not supposed to do. His toe was swollen, he said, clearly lying, and might be infected, and he might die. He tried to sit very close, to touch me, and then became angry. He had left some candy on my desk the last time for the girls who came to see me, he said. Where was it? An hour following the toe confession, he chose a girl's comic book, *Daisy Duck's Diary*, to read. Then he shifted, and said that he had an eight-and-a-half-year-old girl friend who liked him very much. He began to be openly angry, teasing, and tried to use the desk phone instead of the toy phone. Then he lay down on the desk provocatively on his back, as if inviting *me* to examine *him*. The next moment he jumped up, dropped his candies on the floor, and crawled about picking them up, and trying to look under my skirt.

The next session after this, he arrived, limping ostentatiously, and asked me to read to him. He sat down in my chair facing me and, while I read, he played with a pair of scissors, blatantly opening and shutting it along his leg and then over his genitals. Next he pretended to cut off his finger. When I remarked that he was trying to cut himself and I thought he was doing so because he felt he was bad, he became very angry. I said I thought he was angry with me because I would stop seeing him and when this was said, he nodded very seriously and put down the scissors. The conflict is very clear here: his defense against loss is a feminine identification. The feminine identification raises the terrible conflict over castration. This is not a conflict peculiar to Billy, but his past history and his ways of dealing with it make the solution much more difficult than for other children. Loss and the defenses against it affect and distort the normal processes of development. Billy was at this time eight and a half years old, yet his oedipal struggles were by no means settled.

In the final hour, Billy was flighty and overtalkative. He told me of the many activities in store for him over the summer: camp, Arts Festival, a school trip to the Hood's milk factory, a big part in a church play—there were so many things to do. When I pointed out to him that he was trying to forget that he would not see me, he became sober and said he would like to call up for a hundred appointments. He angrily rejected the book I gave him as a farewell gift, explaining, "It should have been a gun!" and ignored me, saying sadly, "I guess I don't have anything to say to you, and you don't have anything to say to me." He buried his nose in a comic book, but when the time was almost up, he suddenly returned to the rejected gift book and for the first time read aloud to me, with care and tenderness, glancing up to be sure that I heard him correctly. This was an imitation of me who had so often read aloud to him.

DISCUSSION

In looking back over this material, one can see that the termination represents a revival of old conflicts. There is certainly a new urgency and intensity, but the life of this child was so dominated by the constant fantasied threat of abandonment that the new real loss mainly served to strengthen the fantasy. Billy, compared to the case described by Rochlin (1953), also had a very early loss, at nine months, but this loss was immediately replaced by a tender grandmother and the father. Billy's second loss, of the grandmother, did not occur until the oedipal phase, at four years. In Rochlin's case the loss was early and without adequate replacement. It may well be that Billy's first loss determined his primitive, superficially fetishistic behavior with the stockings and panties, as an attempt to immobilize a part of the mother, just as Rochlin's little patient did with the fur coat. The early loss also may well have given an intensity to Billy's sadism which one would otherwise not see. Billy's ego development proceeded because the original mother was replaced by grandmother and father, although confusion of sexual identification was increased by father's maternal activities from nine months to four years: Billy had two objects, while Rochlin's patient had none.

When Billy lost his grandmother during the oedipal period, his reaction more closely followed the familiar dynamics described in "Mourning and Melancholia" (Freud, 1915): the shadow of the object falls on the ego. Billy's developing sexual identification was profoundly affected by the loss of this female object. His identification, not fully established as in an adult, was not simply altered from a fixed condition, but its whole development was severely distorted and compromised. Billy's transvestism and fetishism represent a condensation of a primitive attempt to immobilize the mother object, and a more developed identification with the grandmother.

As Lewin notes in *Psychoanalysis of Elation* (1950, p. 63):

> The growing child's ego is more nearly a pleasure ego than is an adult's, and it is due to the child analysts, particularly to Anna Freud (1936), that we possess some insight into the mechanism of denial. The child, not stringently bound to the reality principle, plays and imagines, and its moods and feelings are determined to a greater or less degree by its games and fantasies. It easily denies realities that surround it, and denial as a defense mechanism plays a role in its normal life as well as in the childhood neuroses. According to Anna Freud, the prominent conflicts in the child are between the instincts and the external world, and its ego finds little difficulty in accepting an altered view of the latter.

Lewin is describing the dynamics of mania here. When we consider that Billy was flighty and overtalkative in his last session, gloating over and listing the many delights in store for him over the summer, we see this denial at work, but in addition we see a turning from reality (the loss of the therapist) to narcissistic pleasure. It is similar to the child's dream, "Herman eaten up all the cherries" (Freud, 1900), but it is happening in Billy's waking life. Narcissistic libido replaces object libido in increasing degree, in this boy who already showed a partial failure in the transforming of narcissistic libido into object libido. Further regression to narcissism occurred under the stress of the new object loss.

In examining termination of treatment, which is always an experience of loss, we see the universal developmental conflicts of childhood, and their vicissitudes, in this case complicated by the early tragic experience. For Billy, feminine identification was a defense that was only partially successful, since it was in direct conflict with the more normal aspects of his character structure and his masculine striving.

BIBLIOGRAPHY

Freud, A. (1936), *The Ego and Mechanisms of Defence*. New York: International Universities Press, 1946.
Freud, S. (1900), *The Interpretation of Dreams*. New York: Macmillan, 1931.
—— (1917), Mourning and Melancholia. *Collected Papers*, IV. London: Hogarth Press, 1925.
—— (1928), Fetishism. *Int. J. Psa.*, IX.
Lewin, B. (1950), *The Psychoanalysis of Elation*. New York: Norton.
Rochlin, G. (1953), Loss and Restitution. *This Annual*, VIII.

CONSIDERATIONS OF THE DEVELOPMENT AND TREATMENT OF AUTISTIC CHILDHOOD PSYCHOSIS[1]

I. HYMAN WEILAND, M.D. and ROBERT RUDNIK, PH.D.
(Philadelphia)[2]

The difficulties in obtaining significant and long-term gains in reality testing and in relatedness to others, through psychotherapeutic treatment of autistic children, are well documented by many authors (Bender, 1956; Darr and Worden, 1951; Despert and Sherwin, 1958), and there is a striking repetition of similar themes in the many treatment proposals. For example, in 1947, Barbara Betz said of the treatment of childhood schizophrenia, "It is the task of the therapist to assume the initiative in negotiating a significant contact by some tactical approach near to the patient's particular receptive channels." She described her role with the schizophrenic child as a participation in his idiosyncratic activities to as great a degree as the child would permit, for the purpose of allowing or fostering greater satisfaction of the child's needs. Prall et al. (1958) elaborated some of Betz's formulations and suggested that the therapist participate in those autoerotic gratifications of the child which the child would permit. Thereby they could develop a symbioticlike relationship with the child. Later, Augusta Alpert (1960) described a similar technique, the essence of which is the establishment of an *"exclusive, need-satisfying* relationship between the special teacher (*therapist*) and the child."

The aforementioned as well as many other reports (Despert,

[1] This study is in part supported by the National Institutes of Mental Health research grant No. M-3890 (CI). The authors wish to thank I. Arthur Mirsky, M.D., for many invaluable suggestions during the preparation of this paper.

[2] Dr. Weiland is Assistant Director, Children's Unit, Eastern Pennsylvania Psychiatric Institute. Dr. Rudnik was formerly Supervising Psychologist at Eastern Pennsylvania Psychiatric Institute.

1947; Escalona, 1948; Gurevitz, 1952) describe "breaking through the autistic barrier" (Betz, 1947) by inducing the child to accept a relationship with a therapist which can be used for the apparent gratification of some of the child's needs. The essence of this relationship is the recognition by the child that the therapist can be the bearer of desirable gratification. The child will tolerate and may even seek out certain interactions with the therapist or others who can perform the same functions. This type of reaction, however, cannot be regarded as a "real" object relationship since it does not involve full awareness of the person as such but represents a toleration of the therapist's presence for need satisfaction. This relationship is similar to the parallel play of preschool children, but it serves quite different functions. It also bears some similarity to the symbiotic relationship of very young infants and of children with symbiotic psychosis, but it does not have the quality of frantic urgency, nor does it have the quality of clinging stickiness. Therefore it is preferable to categorize this relationship as parallel playlike or symbioticlike behavior. We are not aware of any reports of major progress beyond this type of relationship, nor have we found any comprehensive suggestions for advancing treatment beyond this point other than those of a few investigators such as Ekstein and Wallerstein (1956), who offer specific modification of more formal psychotherapy. Their recommendations and similar ones seem more appropriate for the less severely ill, psychotic child than for the children of whom Betz, Prall, and Alpert speak—even when this latter group of children have improved to the point of a parallel playlike relatedness.

We, too, face the same dilemma of not being able to progress beyond this parallel playlike relationship with most of our patients.[3] Some may develop more or less normal object relationships, but others still continue to use people in the same way that they use implements, relating only to that part of the human being which

[3] The patients who form the basis of our observations are more than thirty children who have been in residential treatment at Eastern Pennsylvania Psychiatric Institute for from one to four years. Their symptomatology is characterized by severe disturbances in object relationship, reality testing, and other important ego functions. Many of the children are nonverbal or have limited use of speech which is essentially noncommunicative in function. The diagnoses are autistic, symbiotic, or mixed psychosis, but elements of autism exist in all. Many are rather typical examples of primary infantile autism.

is an essential object for the attainment of their particular needs (i.e., they may place the hand of the examiner on an object which is desired while not attending to the rest of the examiner).

Even after a need-satisfying relationship has been achieved, the child often shows little interest in playing with his therapist or teacher merely for the sake of playing; he remains interested in the person only as a means to gratification of specific needs. DeMyer (1960), by means of operant conditioning techniques, has shown that autistic children can be trained to respond to mechanical vending machines as a means of gratifying some of their needs; her description of the relationship of these children to their favorite machines sounds quite similar to the parallel playlike relationship with people which we have described above.

Examination of the "child-care plans" and "progress summaries" of our clinic reveals frequent comments to the effect that the child is only able to *accept* interaction and that *it is the responsibility of the staff* to pursue the child to make use of his acceptance. Seldom is there any indication in the records that a child developed a strong interest and need for interaction; instead the child is usually described as having developed a stereotyped pattern of interaction-seeking and of interpersonal response. In other words, he has learned a pattern of behavior with an adult (or child) and seeks the particular activity rather than seek after the other individual for a variety of interactions (as one would expect a nonpsychotic child to do).

Illustrative is the case of Danny, a nine-year-old psychotic boy, who, for example, regularly greets various staff members with questions designed to reassure himself about certain painful incidents. This questioning is repetitious and accounts for almost all of his spontaneous contacts with some people; with other individuals he has another stereotyped set of overtures and questions.

Rather than achieving a primary object relatedness, the psychotic child seems to have evolved pseudo object relatedness in which the driving forces toward need satisfaction do not flexibly capitalize on the possibilities inherent in the therapist as a social being.[4] Thus the child seems to maintain his fixation around an omnipotent, autistic frame of reference.

[4] We do not mean to say that the child may not differentiate between certain individuals—in somewhat the same way as he differentiates between inanimate objects.

We might summarize our conclusions thus far by saying that some autistic children respond to "corrective object relationship therapy" (Alpert, 1960) by progressing to a working object relationship with the therapist out of which further gains can be made; many others fail to respond at all. A third group exhibits some changes but only develops a limited, pseudo object relationship. In our experience this has proved the largest group.

Mahler (1952), Mahler et al. (1949), Rank (1955), and others predicate the psychogenesis of childhood psychosis on early infantile experiences which have led to the expectation that object relationships are so dangerous[5] that the child regresses to or becomes fixated at primitive levels of functioning—autism or symbiosis. It is postulated that the expectation of murderous attack or of symbiotic engulfment by a psychotogenic mother[6] results in a failure to progress beyond autism and in panicky attempts to escape from symbiosis into autism or in fear of loss of the object with a resultant regression to symbiosis. These children avoid certain types of behavior with people and modify other responses more in relation to their expectations of reality than on the basis of the reality of the experience offered by the current object. Significantly, these children may be quite aware of their objects, although they misinterpret their actions and intentions.

If the resolution of conflict is to be effected by more or less formal psychotherapy or by the corrective effect of the therapy described above, it could be anticipated that progress should continue at a more rapid pace once the break-through is made. This does seem to be the case with some children who may progress to a more or less normal personality development. Most autistic children, however, do not respond in such a satisfactory manner.

Our patients who progress to, but not beyond, "pseudo object

[5] The terms object and object relationship will be used throughout in the commonly accepted sense of human beings for the former and interpersonal relationships for the latter.

[6] The implication is often made that the mother or her psychopathology is responsible for the development of the psychosis. We do not believe that this has been demonstrated conclusively, but there is considerable evidence to indicate that her personality is intimately involved in the disturbance of the child. For the present purposes it is sufficient to say that the patient acts as if his mother is the source of his psychotic fears, and he attributes the potentiality of the same responses onto other humans.

relationship" often seem to have other features in common, such as a relative absence of active defense against relatedness, even before treatment.[7] In spite of this he still is unable to recognize and make use of people as a separate class of objects. This occurs even if the child appears to be aware of the existence of the human object along with (but not distinguished from) other, nonhuman objects.

Illustrative is Morton, a nine-year-old autistic child, who paid no attention to his therapist as long as he was happily spinning any object. When the therapist offered a "better" object for spinning, Morton became interested only to get the new toy. If the therapist interfered with Morton's activity, Morton would brush the therapist away or would quietly turn away. When Morton became enraged, either in response to the therapist's persistent intervention or to unknown factors, he indiscriminately attacked the therapist, the furniture in the room, the walls, or his own person. This child appears to use the examiner as a tool. He appears to be almost unaware of the existence of other human beings as a separate class of objects, and he seems to have no information on specialized ways of dealing with his fellow human beings.

Another demonstration of the existence of this type of autistic child is seen in the following excerpts from diagnostic interviews. Jack, a seven-year-old psychotic boy, screamed, tore at his clothing, tried to crawl through the window, and showed every manifestation of anxiety when the examiner approached within a few feet. When left to himself, he would sit withdrawn, ignoring the examiner, or he would engage himself in manipulating and mouthing objects.

Another psychotic child, Nelson, aged five, would sit withdrawn, mouthing objects so long as he was left alone. He also paid little attention to the examiner and continued to ignore the examiner when the latter came near him, or even when he picked the child up. Nevertheless he gave evidence of an awareness of the change in his position in relation to the objects of his interest. He also permitted

[7] These and the following observations arose out of empirical observations of development in a clinical program, therefore they were not subject to rigid control, as is the case in most investigations growing out of a service program. However, it is the consensus among clinicians that children who have a history of clear-cut traumatic relationships with significant persons and who subsequently retreat from and defend against relating to people have a better prognosis than those who have never related to human beings adequately.

and enjoyed tickling games, which Jack rejected with anxiety. When Jack desired something he tended to ignore the possibility of the examiner offering assistance, whereas Nelson would "use" the adult's hand as a tool. Jack's interviewer was physically attacked when Jack wanted candy, but Jack rejected the possibility of soliciting the examiner's assistance, even when this was offered him. If the adult obstructed the approach to a desired object, Jack would retreat or would attack the examiner or would persist in attempts to get around the examiner, while Nelson would pull at the part of the examiner which was directly in his way and tended to be oblivious to the person of the adult. Thus Jack appears to be actively defending himself against relatedness, while Nelson seems unaware of humans as a separate class of objects.

In contrast to the above formulation, it can be postulated that the apparent unawareness of human beings as a separate class of objects is only the ultimate autistic defense against a relationship with the feared object. It is quite possible that both hypotheses may need to be called on to explain the state of affairs in various children.

Morton and Nelson, both of whom developed symbioticlike responsiveness in corrective object relationship therapy, demonstrated another unusual response. Morton's first therapist was unable to induce him to do more than accept the therapist as a bearer of objects that Morton could spin, for two years. Morton's second therapist had the same experience for approximately one year. Then, in desperation and in order to force some reaction from Morton, the therapist decided to interfere actively with all of Morton's autistic activities. It was in this situation where the only source of gratification and the major source of frustration during the interview was the therapist, that Morton first began to relate actively. Nelson, who had equal difficulties relating, was able to relate when his therapist refused to allow him to gratify himself. The observation that such a combination of gratification and frustration could foster better relationship with people was frequently reported in casual observation of the daily life of the child, but we have only recently begun to explore this phenomenon more systematically.[8]

Our experience to date suggests that some autistic children can

[8] See Appendix for a description of the results of an experiment with this therapy in one nonverbal child.

be induced to relate more actively to human beings in a situation which contains elements both of frustration and gratification arising from a single source. It would appear that there is something in almost all gratification arising from one source that makes the individual significantly more important to the child, or that the pain of the frustration forces his attentions onto the therapist or both.

It is pertinent to consider an explanation for (1) the apparent difference in the various groups of psychotic children; (2) the fact that the one group of even more disturbed children may respond as well as the other groups, and sometimes more readily, to a more simplified means of treatment; and (3) the observation that the more disturbed group seems to remain more fixated at this new level of response rather than progressing to greater therapeutic benefits.

The etiology of the syndrome of the special group of autistic children who form a pseudo object relationship is suggested by three major observations that have been noted above, viz.: (1) these children seem unaware of and do not defend themselves against contact with human beings; (2) they respond to "corrective object relationship" therapy by the development of behavior which has much in common with a conditioned response (pseudo-parallel play); (3) they can be induced to take cognizance of the therapist when the latter becomes the source of all gratifications in the immediate environment, and when he inhibits the patient from gratifying himself autistically. Further, these children seldom showed regression from a previously achieved level of function but were described as "always" odd—"never" interested in people except when they needed something. The lifelong history of failure to develop adequate means to deal with other human beings rather than a history of developmental progression followed by arrest or regression places the onset of the disorder in very early infancy.[9] Further, the absence of relatedness rather than an active defense against relatedness suggests that these children suffer from a failure to develop an important ego function rather than only from an avoidance of the use of a learned pattern of behavior. This failure may be due to an absence of the experiences crucial to the development of the function or to an elevation of threshold in regard to these experiences or to both.

[9] The ability to make the first social responses to human beings presumably develops somewhere between three to five months.

An explanation for these phenomena may be sought for in the concepts of imprinting[10] (Hess, 1959; Harlow, 1959a; Lorenz, 1937) and of the "critical period." Scott and Marston (1950), Blauwelt (1956), and others have demonstrated that there are specific periods in the infancy of various mammals, more or less species-specific, which are optimum for the development of certain interindividual and social responses. If appropriate experiences are not offered the infant at this critical period, the responses may not be able to be elicited at all or only in modified form. It may be postulated that the human infant must be exposed to certain experiences at crucial times in his life in order to develop those functions which are referred to as object relatedness.[11] Blauwelt's (1956) observations on the sucking reflex in human neonates and Spitz's studies (1950; Spitz and Wolf, 1949), together with the observations noted herein suggest that similar conditions for the development of certain ego functions are necessary in the human infant. Thus it may be postulated that appropriate conditions must exist in infancy to allow for the formation of at least two types of childhood psychosis. In one the symptoms may develop primarily as a defense against essentially traumatic and overwhelming experience with painful, primary objects. In the second group of psychotic children the symptoms may be related to a lack of exposure or an absence of crucial experiences at some "critical period" and a consequent failure to be "imprinted" on human beings with appropriate responses. Just which parameters of developmental experiences are significant to developing object relationships are not known. Since major disturbances in this function are relatively uncommon, natural-life studies have not been too fruitful. The objections to experimental studies with infants are obvious. On the other hand, Harlow's (1959b) studies of the development of affectional responses in the monkey give detailed descriptions of the sorts of experiences which seem to be important in the

---

[10] We are not prepared to discuss whether imprinting is a special form of learning dependent on the release of certain innate potentials by specific releasor mechanisms, as the above authors believe, or whether, as Moltz (1960) suggests in his thorough critique, imprinting is more related to conditioning, though influenced by the special circumstances in which it occurs.

[11] Expressed in psychoanalytic terminology, imprinting may be equated with primary object cathexis in which the primary object is invested, setting the pattern for subsequent relationships with this and with like objects.

development of functions in this subhuman primate which are similar to the functions which we call object relatedness.

That autistic children may be more capable of recognizing and dealing with (relating to) their therapists when the therapist actively interferes with the child's attempts to gratify himself (autoerotically) and when the therapist becomes the sole source of gratification is an active replication of that situation which obtains during normal infancy. In this latter instance, however, the autoerotic gratification is limited not by intervention by an outside force but by the immature state of the infant. All that can be stated at the present time is that some activity attendant to the gratification of the infant when he is in a helpless condition is possibly related to the development of the social response in man as it is in lower primates. It matters little whether this experience is referred to as imprinting or is attributed to certain experiences which occur in the human infant at a time when he is most helpless and dependent. The only essential hypothesis is that some experiences are critical in that they serve to introduce the infant to his first human objects and, perhaps, determine his subsequent behavior to them.

In accordance with the preceding considerations are Freud's (1914) observations which led him to suggest that certain libidinal responses develop in anaclitic relationship to the life instincts. It is conceivable that the behavioral responses under discussion as well as other social and interpersonal responses are similarly anaclitic to life instincts. The first three months of life are a very needful period for the infant, but it is probable that in the first three months the capacity to recognize the objects and to recognize the need for them has not adequately developed. From the third to the eighth month, or thereabouts, of his life, the parental object remains needed by the infant, and it is at this time that he has developed those perceptual capacities which would enable him to "recognize" the object. If the child does not undergo the appropriate experiences at the critical period, or if his constitution is so crippled that he cannot make use of the particular experiences which are assumed to engender object relatedness, we can anticipate that he may not become aware of, and deal with, human beings. Such children would not be expected to develop defenses against the object, because they would be unable to recognize humans as such and accordingly could not develop appropriate techniques of relating.

The child who defends himself actively against involvement with human beings because of his fear of them as potentially dangerous could respond to the kind of treatment described by Betz (1947), Prall et al. (1958), and Alpert (1960) only if it offers a therapeutically corrective life experience. Otherwise, the more the teacher or therapist participated in activities with the child, the more anxiety would be induced. The child's transference expectations of human beings would color the relationship with the same fearful anticipation with which he greets all human beings in life. On the other hand, the group of children who have not achieved the capacity to relate to others would not develop the same degree of basic suspicion and mistrust of human beings and therefore should be capable of learning to accept need satisfaction equally well either from people or mechanical objects. Since the development of this acceptance of need satisfaction from human beings does not occur in the framework of the intensive, needful situation of the infant, the object relationship is very tenuous, and differs significantly from that of the normal child in that it is based primarily on direct need gratification. By the time the autistic child enters therapy he has learned to provide most of his limited needs for himself and has little motivation to relate to the therapist who is not sufficiently meaningful and cannot become so under the conditions of corrective object relationship treatment.

The fact that the children comprising the group that have developed no awareness of others cannot progress in therapy beyond the establishment of a "pseudo object relationship" is attributable to the possibility that the child has merely learned how to accept into his life experiences another means of gratifying needs without the necessity of recognizing humans as a separate class of objects. The inclusion of a new function has not broadened the child's ego but has only added an additional means of gratification to the already existing functions.

These various considerations offer two possible approaches to the treatment of autistic children who have not developed the capacity to relate to others. If it is postulated that an intensely needful life experience is necessary for the development of object relationship, and that it cannot be re-created after some "critical period," then the only solution is to help the psychotic child make the best possible adjustment to as nearly a normal life situation as can be developed. This may be accomplished by teaching him as many experiences as possible in which satisfactions incidentally include human beings. Thus, in accord with DeMyer's (1960) experiences with operant conditioning of psychotic children, the autistic child may be conditioned to a large variety of experiences with others, in order that he may be able to move about in the environment, pseudo self-sufficiently (and, with increasing age, learn more formal skills), without essentially changing from his autistic orientation. In extension of this form of treatment the child may be conditioned not only to use another person for the satisfaction of those needs which he originally gratified autistically, but he may also be exposed to special techniques such as speech therapy and other similar experiences which could relate valuable, socially desirable forms of activities to the need-satisfying pattern of the child.

A more favorable prognosis might be anticipated if it could be assumed that the conditions necessary to facilitate the process of "imprinting" or primary object cathexis can be re-created beyond infancy, under special circumstances.

Observations of autistic children and of neonates suggest that the essence of cathecting the primary object is determined by the helplessness of the infant, coupled with the ability to recognize the source of his gratification as well as by the fact that the gratification arises primarily from one source (the mother). That this extremely needful and dependent condition can be re-created later in life is suggested by the hypnotizability of humans; even more extreme degrees of dependence in which the patient approaches the conditions of infancy are observed in traumatically brain-injured patients, who gradually learn at first primitive and then more complicated functions. In order to develop the impetus for a change in the child's orientation to other persons it is essential to induce an intense sense of helpless dependence, similar to that assumed to be present in normal infants at the time of "imprinting" on humans. Although electroshock or insulin coma can induce a state of extreme dependency, the effects are quite transitory. Such operations, however, as well as psychopharmacological aids may play some role in the over-all program.

In the ideal therapeutic program, the total environment of the child should be organized to allow all of his gratifications to be offered by some single person who could erect such barriers as to make it impossible for the child to achieve these gratifications by himself (autistically). Practical aspects, however, preclude the avail-ability of a single person who could tolerate the intense, intimate interaction. Consequently, it would be necessary to organize the child's care around one or two persons per shift. These persons, in turn, could maintain a constant observation of the child restricted to a relatively small area. Gratification without asking for the assist-ance of his specific worker(s) would not be permitted, while with-drawal would be obstructed by the persistent efforts of the worker. The child would be offered certain activities or objects which were known to be of high desirability to him. These would be given, however, only if the youngster specifically asked the worker for them.

The proposed therapy is similar to the technique that is used by Mildred MacGinnes (1960) in her speech therapy of aphasic children. Apparently she is very forceful in her persistent demands that the child speak in order to obtain a gratifying response from her. Some observers (Brutten, 1960) believe that MacGinnes may be dealing with autistic children in some instances, and that her tech-niques are applicable to autistic children.[12]

It is important to note that the above procedure could be ex-pected to be effective only after an initial period during which the child has learned that gratification can come from the worker. It is quite possible that MacGinnes also holds out the offer of gratifica-tion in order to stimulate the child to accept her demands. Accord-ingly, the techniques of Alpert, Betz, or Prall et al. could be applied until the symbioticlike relationship has been established, and then the therapeutic program could gradually be transferred to the type described herein. Such a therapeutic program could be approached by one or two teams of therapists who would spend three to four forty-five- to ninety-minute periods of the day with the child for at

---

12 Unfortunately Dr. MacGinnes has not published detailed descriptions of her work, and details of her technique come mainly from speech therapists whom she has trained or from those who have observed her.

least five days a week. Two or three of these sessions would occur during mealtimes, and the remainder should be oriented about activities of special significance to the child. These and other practical problems are now being evaluated in several pilot studies in progress at Eastern Pennsylvania Psychiatric Institute.

SUMMARY

An evaluation of the therapeutic progress of autistic children exposed to various therapeutic procedures made it apparent that all procedures result in the development of a pseudo object type of relationship by many patients. Progress beyond such a state is rarely attained. Therapeutic and other observations on autistic children raised the possibility that such children consist of two distinct groups. The development of the syndrome of one group is attributed to severe traumatic experiences during the period at which object relationships are just "learned"; the object relationship thereby attains the potential of danger. A second group is composed of children who have failed to experience those particular operations at some "critical period" essential to the organization of behavior that characterizes object relatedness. On the basis of these observations and interpretations, modifications in therapeutic techniques are proposed.

APPENDIX

Since writing the above we have applied the proposed treatment modifications in a more controlled manner to one child. We selected Nelson as an autistic child who had developed a symbioticlike relationship with the child-care staff following three years of psychotherapy but who had never developed a meaningful relationship with any person and who, at the age of eight, had not achieved the use of speech. Because of limitations in time and personnel we used volunteers from the child-care staff. Space limitations restricted us to the use of the "normal" ward environment. The child-care staff were asked, instead of cuddling Nelson, singing to him, etc., as usual, to spend as much time as he would tolerate offering his favorite toy (a ball) on the one condition that Nelson would ask for it by saying the word. No other change was to be made in the child-care plan and no additional time was to be spent with Nelson beyond that which had been customary in the past. We found that Nelson could tolerate brief periods of frustration several times during a shift, and the workers would show Nelson the ball at these times but not give it to him, indicating that he must say "ball" in order to obtain it. Within twelve weeks Nelson first said "ball" and shortly thereafter he frequently began to request the ball from the staff even when it was not offered. At this time we decided to repeat the procedure with doughnuts, a favorite of Nelson's. Within eleven days he had added this word to his "vocabulary." Within another week he began adding an average of one or two words a day, and by the end of this week Nelson had taken the lead and was eagerly learning words to communicate his wants to the child-care worker. At the present writing, Nelson has use of several dozen nouns and verbs to indicate his desires to the staff and eagerly plays games of identifying objects as a pleasurable activity in itself. He even enjoys singing simple songs.

We present this brief case report as an indication that the procedures described can be carried out, but we do not lay claim to any proof of our hypotheses from it. Our working assumption was that Nelson was enabled to learn to talk as the result of his needs being aroused by the "teasing" behavior of the workers who permitted gratification only when addressed appropriately. Although this is somewhat different from our earlier suggestions, it does make use of the same general principles of establishing a situation wherein the human being is the only possible source of gratification and must be reckoned with as capable of severely frustrating the subject. Whether a similar response could have been obtained by the use of a device for operant conditioning (using the word as the response) or not, we cannot say. It is also too early to tell whether Nelson's relationship to the staff is such that it will be more than a further extension of the symbioticlike relationship which we had developed before, or whether Nelson can begin now to make use of a more normal relationship with people. Nelson's pleasureful use of naming objects with and for the child-care staff certainly suggests that the act of naming, and perhaps also the relationship with adults, have achieved a special significance.

BIBLIOGRAPHY

Alpert, A. (1960), Reversibility of Pathological Fixations Associated with Maternal Deprivation in Infancy. *This Annual*, XIV.

Bender, L. (1956), Schizophrenia in Childhood. Its Recognition, Description and Treatment. *Am. J. Orthopsychiat.*, XXVI.

Betz, B. (1947), Study of Tactics for Resolving the Autistic Barrier in the Psychotherapy of the Schizophrenic Personality. *Am. J. Psychiat.*, CIV.

Blauwelt, H. (1956), Further Studies on Maternal-Neonate Interrelationships. In: *Group Processes* [Transactions of the Third Conference], ed. B. Schaffner. New York: Josiah Macy, Jr. Foundation.

Brutten, M. (1960), Personal communication.

Darr, G. C. & Worden, F. G. (1951), A Case Report Twenty-eight Years After an Infantile Autistic Disorder. *Am. J. Orthopsychiat.*, XXI.

DeMyer, M. (1960), Personal communication.

Despert, J. L. (1947), Psychotherapy in Child Schizophrenia. *Am. J. Psychiat.*, CIV.

—— & Sherwin, A. C. (1958), Further Examination of Diagnostic Criteria in Schizophrenic Illness and Psychoses of Infancy and Early Childhood. *Am. J. Psychiat.*, CXIV.

Ekstein, R., & Wallerstein, J. (1956), Observations on the Psychotherapy of Borderline and Psychotic Children. *This Annual*, XI.

Escalona, S. (1948), Some Considerations Regarding Psychotherapy with Psychotic Children. *Bull. Menninger Clin.*, XII.

Freud, S. (1914), On Narcissism. *Collected Papers*, IV. London: Hogarth Press, 1925.

Gurevitz, S. (1952), Treatment of a Schizophrenic Child Through Activation of Neurotic Symptoms. *Quart. J. Child Behav.*, IV.

Harlow, H. (1959a), Love in Infant Monkeys. *Sci. Amer.*, CC.

—— (1959b), Social Capacity of Primates. *Human Biol.*, XXXI.

Hess, E. (1959), Imprinting. *Science*, CXXX.

Lorenz, K. Z. (1937), The Companion in the Birds' World. *Auk*, LIV.

MacGinnes, M. (1960), Personal communication with mutual colleague of one of the authors.

Mahler, M. S. (1952), On Child Psychosis and Schizophrenia. Autistic and Symbiotic Infantile Psychoses. *This Annual*, VII.

—— & Ross, J. R. Jr., DeFries, Z. (1949), Clinical Studies in Benign and Malignant Cases of Childhood Psychosis (Schizophrenic-like). *Am. J. Orthopsychiat.*, XIX.

Moltz, H. (1960), Imprinting: Empirical Basis and Theoretical Significance. *Psychol. Bull.*, LIV.

Prall, R. C., Weiland, I. H., & Levy, E. (1958). Contributions to the Technique of Psychotherapy with Nonverbal, Autistic Children. Presented at the Meeting of the American Psychiatric Association, San Francisco.

Rank, B. (1955), Intensive Study ond Treatment of Preschool Children Who Show Marked Personality Deviations, or "Atypical Development," and Their Parents. In: *Emotional Problems of Early Childhood*, ed. G. Caplan. New York: Basic Books.

Scott, J. P. & Marston, M. (1950), Critical Periods Affecting the Development of Normal and Maladjustive Social Behavior of Puppies. *J. Gen. Psychol.*, LXXVII.

Spitz, R. (1950), Relevancy of Direct Infant Observation. *This Annual*, V.

—— & Wolf, K. (1949), Autoerotism. Some Empirical Findings and Hypotheses on Three Erotic Manifestations in the First Year of Life. *This Annual*, III/IV.

CONTENTS OF PREVIOUS VOLUMES

CONTENTS OF PREVIOUS VOLUMES

VOLUME III/IV, 1949

VOLUME V, 1950

VOLUME VI, 1951

VOLUME IX, 1954

VOLUME X, 1955

VOLUME XII, 1957

VOLUME XIII, 1958

VOLUME XIV, 1959

VOLUME XV, 1960